Volume 1 Topics 1–4

Authors

Robert Q. Berry, III
Associate Professor of
Mathematics Education,
Department of Curriculum,
Instruction and Special
Education, University of
Virginia, Charlottesville,
Virginia

Zachary Champagne
Assistant in Research
Florida Center for Research
in Science, Technology,
Engineering, and
Mathematics (FCR-STEM)
Jacksonville, Florida

Eric Milou
Professor of Mathematics
Rowan University,
Glassboro, New Jersey

Jane F. Schielack
Professor Emerita
Department of Mathematics
Texas A&M University
College Station, Texas

Jonathan A. Wray
Mathematics Instructional
Facilitator, Howard County
Public Schools, Ellicott City,
Maryland

Randall I. Charles
Professor Emeritus
Department of Mathematics
San Jose State University
San Jose, California

Francis (Skip) Fennell
L. Stanley Bowlsbey Professor
of Education and Graduate
and Professional Studies,
McDaniel College
Westminster, Maryland

Glenview, Illinois   Boston, Massachusetts   Chandler, Arizona   New York, New York

Mathematician Reviewers

Gary Lippman, Ph.D.
Professor Emeritus
Mathematics and Computer Science
California State University, East Bay
Hayward, California

Karen Edwards, Ph.D.
Mathematics Lecturer
Arlington, MA

This work is solely for the use of school instructors and administrators for the purpose of teaching courses and assessing student learning. Unauthorized dissemination, publication or sale of the work, in whole or in part (including posting on the internet) will destroy the integrity of the work and is strictly prohibited.

Copyright © 2017 by Pearson Education, Inc. or its affiliates. All Rights Reserved. Printed in the United States of America. This publication is protected by copyright, and permission should be obtained from the publisher prior to any prohibited reproduction, storage in a retrieval system, or transmission in any form or by any means, electronic, mechanical, photocopying, recording, or otherwise. For information regarding permissions, request forms from the appropriate contacts within the Pearson Education Global Rights & Permissions Department. Please visit www.pearsoned.com/permissions/.

PEARSON, ALWAYS LEARNING, SCOTT FORESMAN, PEARSON SCOTT FORESMAN, and **enVision**math are exclusive trademarks owned by Pearson Education, Inc. or its affiliates in the U.S. and/or other countries.

Unless otherwise indicated herein, any third-party trademarks that may appear in this work are the property of their respective owners and any references to third-party trademarks, logos or other trade dress are for demonstrative or descriptive purposes only. Such references are not intended to imply any sponsorship, endorsement, authorization, or promotion of Pearson's products by the owners of such marks, or any relationship between the owner and Pearson Education, Inc. or its affiliates, authors, licensees or distributors.

ExamView® is a registered trademark of eInstruction Corporation. Used under license.

PEARSON

ISBN-13: 978-0-328-90886-8
ISBN-10:   0-328-90886-X

1 16

DIGITAL RESOURCES

Digital

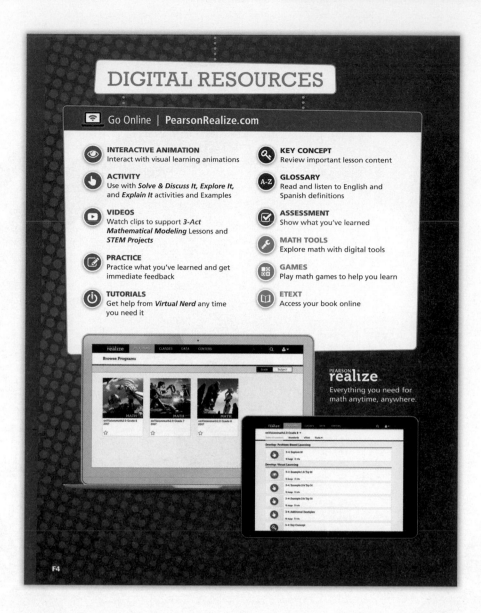

Additional Digital Resources

ETEXT

Teacher's Edition eText includes all pages from the Teacher's Edition plus access to printable resources and the digital glossary.

VIDEOS

Professional Development Videos include a **Topic Overview Video** that is presented by the authors and provides important information about the topic. **Listen and Look For Lesson Videos** provide helpful information for teaching particular lessons.

ACTIVITY

Today's Challenge for each topic is a set of 5 problems on separate screens that use the same data. They can be projected in class or assigned electronically to individuals. A Teacher's Guide with a page for each problem is available online.

ASSESSMENT

Online assessments are auto scored and include: Beginning-of-Year Assessment, Lesson Quizzes, Mid-Topic Assessments, Topic Assessments, Cumulative/Benchmark Assessments, and End-of-Year Assessment.

All print resources are also available online as eText pages or PDF files at PearsonRealize.com.

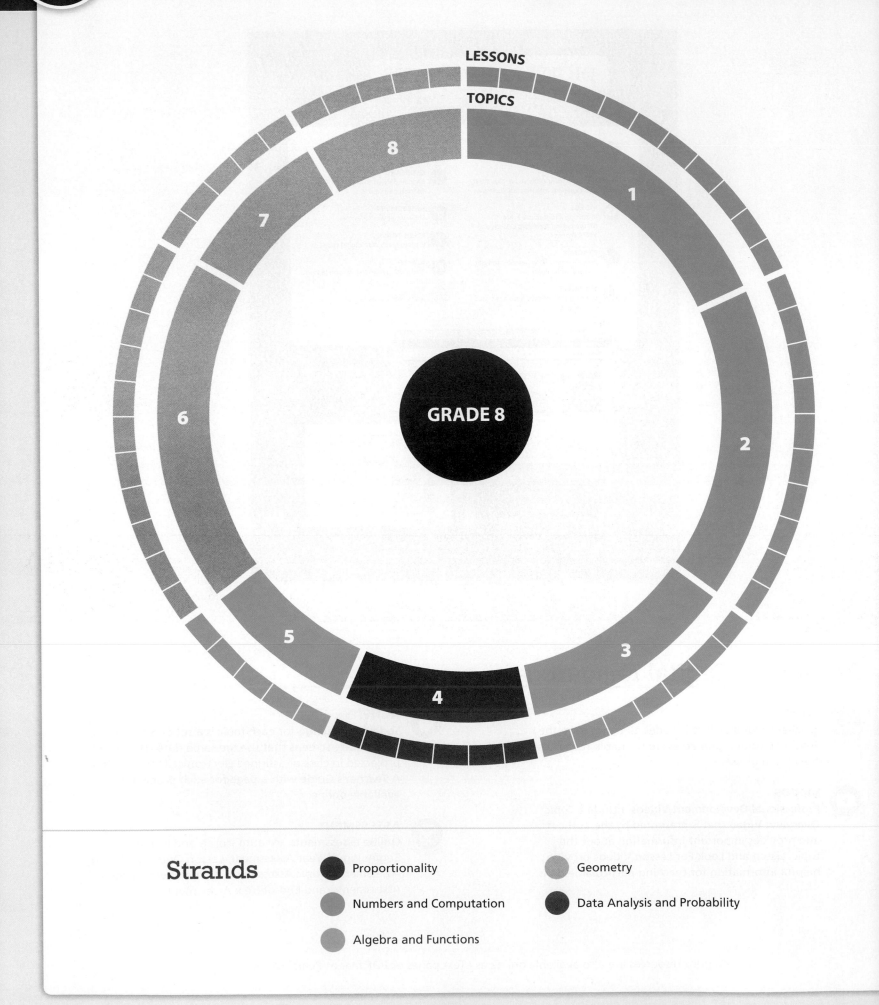

LESSONS

TOPICS

GRADE 8

Strands

Proportionality

Numbers and Computation

Algebra and Functions

Geometry

Data Analysis and Probability

**FOCUS
COHERENCE
RIGOR**

Content is developed with focus, coherence, and rigor. The attention to rigor reflects the balances of conceptual understanding, procedural skill and fluency, and applications. See each Topic Overview.

TOPICS

FOCUS ON

1 Real Numbers

In Topic 1, students explore irrational numbers and work with radicals and integer exponents.

2 Analyze and Solve Linear Equations

In Topic 2, students analyze, write, and solve linear equations.

3 Use Functions to Model Relationships

In Topic 3, students define, evaluate, and compare fuctions. They also use functions to model linear relationships.

4 Investigate Bivariate Data

In Topic 4, students explore bivariate data and investigate patterns of association.

5 Analyze and Solve Systems of Linear Equations

In Topics 5, students analyze and solve systems of linear equations.

6 Congruence and Similarity

In Topic 6, students explore concepts of congruence and similarity.

7 Understand and Apply the Pythagorean Theorem

In Topic 7, students explore and apply the Pythagorean Theorem.

8 Solve Problems Involving Surface Area and Volume

In Topic 8, students solve problems involving surface area and volume of cylinders, cones, and spheres.

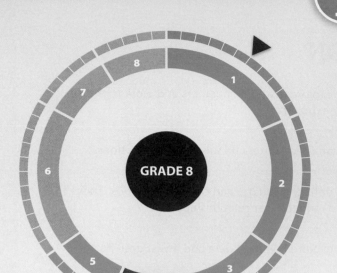

GRADE 8

In Topic 1, students explore irrational numbers and work with radicals and integer exponents.

TOPIC 1 OVERVIEW

TOPIC
1

Real Numbers

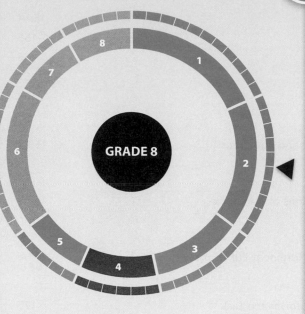

GRADE 8

n Topic 2, students analyze, write, and solve linear equations.

TOPIC 2 OVERVIEW

Analyze and Solve Linear Equations

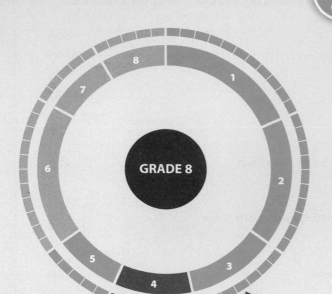

GRADE 8

In **Topic 3**, students define, evaluate, and compare fuctions. They also use functions to model linear relationships.

TOPIC 3 OVERVIEW

Investigate Bivariate Data

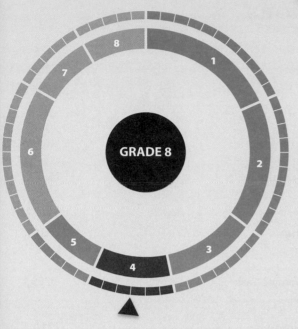

GRADE 8

In Topic 4, students explore bivariate data and investigate patterns of association.

TOPIC 4 OVERVIEW

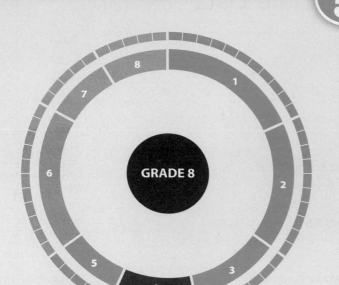

GRADE 8

TOPIC 5 | Analyze and Solve Systems of Linear Equations

In Topic 5, students analyze and solve systems of linear equations.

TOPIC 5 OVERVIEW

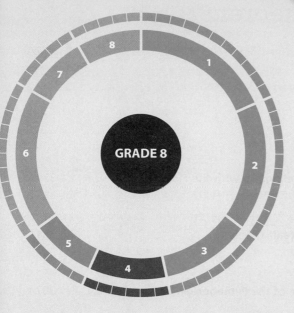

In **Topic 6**, students explore concepts of congruence and similarity.

TOPIC 6 OVERVIEW

TOPIC 6 Congruence and Similarity

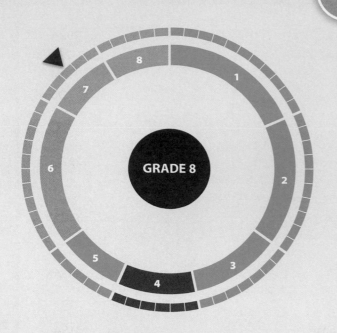

GRADE 8

In Topic 7, students explore and apply the Pythagorean Theorem.

TOPIC 7 OVERVIEW

TOPIC 7

Understand and Apply the Pythagorean Theorem

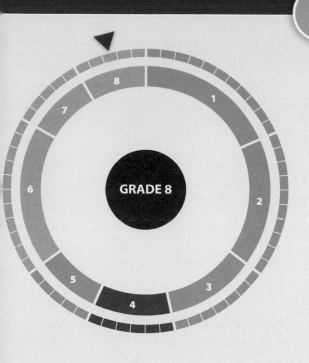

GRADE 8

n **Topic 8**, students solve problems involving surface
area and volume of cylinders, cones, and spheres.

TOPIC 8 OVERVIEW

Notes

Math Practices and Problem Solving Handbook

INTRODUCTION

Introducing the Handbook

This handbook can be used at the beginning of the year and at any teachable moment. Explain to students that the handbook will help them become good math thinkers and good math problem solvers.

The Math Practices are involved in all aspects of mathematics.

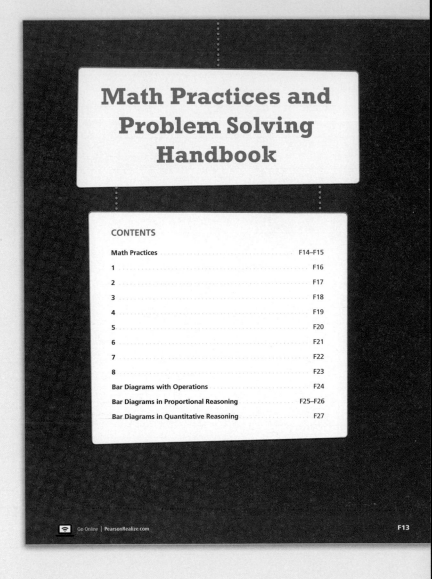

Math Practices and Problem Solving Handbook

CONTENTS

Go Online | PearsonRealize.com

F13

Math Practices

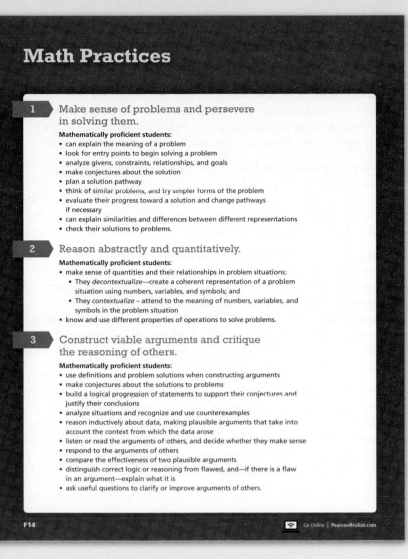

1 Make sense of problems and persevere in solving them.

Mathematically proficient students:
- can explain the meaning of a problem
- look for entry points to begin solving a problem
- analyze givens, constraints, relationships, and goals
- make conjectures about the solution
- plan a solution pathway
- think of similar problems, and try simpler forms of the problem
- evaluate their progress toward a solution and change pathways if necessary
- can explain similarities and differences between different representations
- check their solutions to problems.

2 Reason abstractly and quantitatively.

Mathematically proficient students:
- make sense of quantities and their relationships in problem situations:
  - They *decontextualize*—create a coherent representation of a problem situation using numbers, variables, and symbols; and
  - They *contextualize* – attend to the meaning of numbers, variables, and symbols in the problem situation
- know and use different properties of operations to solve problems.

3 Construct viable arguments and critique the reasoning of others.

Mathematically proficient students:
- use definitions and problem solutions when constructing arguments
- make conjectures about the solutions to problems
- build a logical progression of statements to support their conjectures and justify their conclusions
- analyze situations and recognize and use counterexamples
- reason inductively about data, making plausible arguments that take into account the context from which the data arose
- listen or read the arguments of others, and decide whether they make sense
- respond to the arguments of others
- compare the effectiveness of two plausible arguments
- distinguish correct logic or reasoning from flawed, and—if there is a flaw in an argument—explain what it is
- ask useful questions to clarify or improve arguments of others.

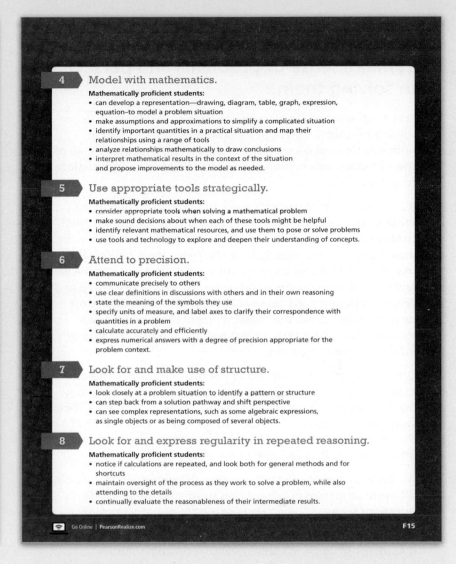

4 Model with mathematics.

Mathematically proficient students:
- can develop a representation—drawing, diagram, table, graph, expression, equation–to model a problem situation
- make assumptions and approximations to simplify a complicated situation
- identify important quantities in a practical situation and map their relationships using a range of tools
- analyze relationships mathematically to draw conclusions
- interpret mathematical results in the context of the situation and propose improvements to the model as needed.

5 Use appropriate tools strategically.

Mathematically proficient students:
- consider appropriate tools when solving a mathematical problem
- make sound decisions about when each of these tools might be helpful
- identify relevant mathematical resources, and use them to pose or solve problems
- use tools and technology to explore and deepen their understanding of concepts.

6 Attend to precision.

Mathematically proficient students:
- communicate precisely to others
- use clear definitions in discussions with others and in their own reasoning
- state the meaning of the symbols they use
- specify units of measure, and label axes to clarify their correspondence with quantities in a problem
- calculate accurately and efficiently
- express numerical answers with a degree of precision appropriate for the problem context.

7 Look for and make use of structure.

Mathematically proficient students:
- look closely at a problem situation to identify a pattern or structure
- can step back from a solution pathway and shift perspective
- can see complex representations, such as some algebraic expressions, as single objects or as being composed of several objects.

8 Look for and express regularity in repeated reasoning.

Mathematically proficient students:
- notice if calculations are repeated, and look both for general methods and for shortcuts
- maintain oversight of the process as they work to solve a problem, while also attending to the details
- continually evaluate the reasonableness of their intermediate results.

Introducing the Math Practices

Use pages F14–F23 to review with students the Math Practices. These practices represent the habits of mind, processes, and dispositions that proficient math thinkers have and use. Encourage students to refer back to these pages any time during the year.

Use the descriptions for each practice and the following rubric to evaluate a student's overall proficiency with the Math Practices.

Math Practices Proficiency Rubric	
4	**Exemplary** The student exhibits all of the behaviors.
3	**Proficient** The student exhibits most of the behaviors.
2	**Emerging** The student exhibits about half of the behaviors.
1	**Needs Improvement** The student exhibits less than half of the behaviors.

Math Practices and Problem Solving Handbook

Math Practices

Building Students' Proficiency with
1. Make sense of problems and persevere in solving them.

This math practice captures the essence of mathematics—solving problems, that is, REAL problems, where solution pathways are not given; not word problems that provide all of the necessary information needed to carry out the calculations to get an answer.

It is important that students work to understand and make sense of problems on their own, even if they sometimes need to struggle to do so. This productive struggle helps them build important thinking strategies. It also helps them understand that math isn't about carrying out operations to determine an answer, but about understanding the challenge presented and finding different ways to work through the challenge. Most rewarding for all are the "aha" moments that occur when students begin to make connections and see the structure of math through these tasks.

Once students have understood the task, encourage them to make guesses, or conjectures, about the solution before they begin to plan their solution pathway. These questions can help students think about the expected solution: *"What do you think the solution will be?"* or *"Do you expect the solution to be greater or less than [a value in the problem]?"*

As students identify a solution pathway, push them to consider different strategies or approaches to solving the task. Ask questions such as, *"Could you use a different sequence of operations?"* or *"What other representation could you use?"*

If students struggle to come up with workable solution pathways, help them to focus by asking, *"Can you think of another problem you solved that is like this one?"*

Remind students to monitor their progress towards a solution. Have them refer back to the conjecture they made before they began their solution strategy to check for the reasonableness of their work.

Building Students' Proficiency with
2. Reason abstractly and quantitatively.

When students reason abstractly and quantitatively, they are able to translate a problem situation from words to numeric or algebraic representations, and after solving, translate the numeric or algebraic solutions back to the problem situation.

Reasoning abstractly and quantitatively also means students can represent the problem situation appropriately, taking into consideration the meaning of the quantities or values, the units used or called for, and the properties of the operations needed to determine the solution.

Help students internalize the connection between the problem situation represented with words or images and the mathematical representation using numbers or algebraic symbols. These questions can help students make these connections: *"What do the numbers in the problem represent?"* *"How do the numbers relate?"* *"Which numbers and operations will you use to represent the problem mathematically?"* *"What unit will you need to use in the solution?"*

Once students have worked out a solution to the problem, help them connect the numeric solution back to the problem by asking questions such as: *"What do the numbers in the solution mean?"* *"How do you know your solution makes sense?"* *"What adjustment to the numeric solution do you need to make so that the solution makes sense?"*

1 ▶ Make sense of problems and persevere in solving them.

2 ▶ Reason abstractly and quantitatively.

Nori, her friend, and her mother bought a baseball game ticket package. The package includes good seats, lunch, and a chance to get autographs from players. The total cost for the three of them is $375. They each paid a $50 deposit. Write an equation that shows how much each of them still owes.

Nori finds out that if 6 people buy the ticket package it only costs $684. Each person still needs to pay a $50 deposit. How does that change the equation? Does each person pay less if 6 people go?

How can I represent this problem situation using numbers, variables, and symbols? I can use the equation I wrote before and change the number of people and the total cost of the ticket package.

What do the numbers, variables, and symbols in the expression or equation mean/represent in the problem situation? $6(p + 50)$ represents the total cost of the package, where p is each person's share.

What am I asked to find? An equation that shows how much each of them still owes.

What are the quantities and variables? How do they relate? The cost of the ticket package and the deposit amount are their expenses.

The amount of the deposits is subtracted from the price of the ticket package.

What can I do if I get stuck? I can start subtracting each $50 deposit to find out how much all 3 still owe.

What is a good plan for solving the problem? Define a variable for the unknown and use the quantities I know to write an equation that relates these quantities.

Other questions to consider:
- Have I solved a similar problem before?
- What information is necessary and unnecessary?
- How can I check that my answer makes sense?
- How is my solution pathway the same as or different from my classmate's?

3-Person Ticket Package
$3(p + 50) = 375$
$3p + 150 = 375$
$3p + 150 - 150 = 375 - 150$
$3p = 225$
$p = 75$

6-Person Ticket Package
$6(p + 50) = 684$
$6p + 300 = 684$
$6p + 300 - 300 = 684 - 300$
$6p = 384$
$p = 64$

The 6-person plan is less expensive per person.

Practice 1 Behaviors

Listen and look for the following behaviors to monitor students' ongoing development of proficiency with this math practice.

- **explain** the meaning of a problem
- **look** for entry points to begin solving a problem
- **analyze** givens, constraints, relationships, and goals
- **make** conjectures about the solution
- **plan** a solution pathway
- **think** of similar problems, and try simpler forms of the problem
- **evaluate** their progress toward a solution, and change pathways if necessary
- **can** explain similarities and differences between different representations
- **check** their solutions to problems

Practice 2 Behaviors

Listen and look for the following behaviors to monitor students' ongoing development of proficiency with this math practice.

- **make** sense of quantities and their relationships in problem situations
- **create** a coherent representation of a problem situation using numbers, variables, and symbols; and
- **attend** to the meaning of numbers, variables, and symbols in the problem situation
- **know** and use different properties of operations to solve problems

Math Practices and Problem Solving Handbook

Math Practices

Building Students' Proficiency with
3. Construct viable arguments and critique the reasoning of others.

Constructing mathematical arguments and critiquing the arguments of others is foundational to the field of mathematics, to the surprise of many students who tend to view the foundation of mathematics to be computation and calculation. When students construct arguments and critique reasoning, they engage in mathematical discourse, and engaging in this discourse provides opportunities for students not just to internalize mathematical vocabulary but also to deepen their understanding of concepts as they defend a solution or explain their arguments.

Mathematical discourse is richest when students are presented with high-interest tasks, whether they be real-world or mathematical, tasks with multiple solution pathways allowing for a lively exchange of ideas and arguments. The *Solve & Discuss It, Explore It*, and *Explain It* offer students such high-interest tasks and are ripe with opportunities to engage students in mathematical discourse. Creating an environment in which engaging in mathematical discourse is valued, where everyone's thinking and reasoning is public and open to comment is essential.

Before students begin work on a task, ask, *"What do you think the solution will be?" "Why do you think that will be the solution?"* Asking these questions before students begin to formulate their solution pathways helps them to frame the solution pathway in a logical progression of steps and to verify the accuracy of conjectures they have made.

As students share their solutions, encourage them to share their thinking and ask others in the class to respond to the thinking of their classmates. Ask *"How did you get your answer?" "Why do you think your solution is accurate?" "What mathematical arguments can you construct to show that your solution is correct?"* If students struggle to answer these questions, break them down into smaller steps, asking for example, *"What operations did you use? Why did you use those operations? What in the problem suggested you should use these operations?"*

During the sharing, regularly ask students to respond to a classmate's solution. Ask, for example, *"Do you agree with [Jamie]'s solution?" "Did you use the same or a similar solution pathway?" "How is your solution pathway different?"* If a student's solution is different, ask, *"What makes you think your solution pathway (and solution) is correct and [Michael]'s is not?"*

Building Students' Proficiency with
4. Model with mathematics.

Too often students question the worth of concepts they learn in the math classroom. What they are not realizing is that the math they are learning is integral to nearly every field of work and study through mathematical modeling. Mathematical models are the foundation to computer games and sports, probability and gaming, engineering and businesses. Making sure students see the worth and applicability of the mathematics they are learning — at every level of their academic studies — is the goal of this standard.

Providing students with opportunities to "apply the mathematics they know to solve problems arising in everyday life" requires more than just using real-world contexts to frame a computation exercise. Rather, students need tasks that require that they make sense of the situation, and then construct a model to represent the situation. The model can take many forms: a table, a diagram, a graph, or an equation; what is important is that students make a connection between the problem situation and the mathematical model, as well as the larger connection between so many real-world situations and mathematical modeling.

The *Explore It* tasks are designed to provide students opportunities to build mathematical models to match a problem situation.

If students struggle to build a model for a given task, these questions may help: *"What assumptions can you make about the problem situation?" "What is the structure of the problem situation?" "What does a diagram of the situation look like?"*

As students share their models for the *Explore It* tasks, be sure to have them explain not just their models, but also their assumptions that structured their model.

3 ▸ Construct viable arguments and critique the reasoning of others.

4 ▸ Model with mathematics.

Math Practices and Problem Solving Handbook

Michael's class is conducting an experiment by tossing a coin. The table below shows the results of the last 9 tosses.

Tails has come up 5 times in a row. That means the next toss will land heads up.

Michael

Coin Toss

Trial	1	2	3	4	5	6	7	8	9	10
Result	H	T	H	H	H	T	T	T	T	T

What assumptions can I make when constructing an argument? A coin can land on heads or tails, so there are two equally likely outcomes.

What questions can I ask to understand other people's thinking? Why does Michael think that the results of the last 5 tosses will affect the outcome of the next coin toss?

What flaw, if any, do I note in his thinking? He thinks that the outcomes of the previous tosses will affect the outcome of the current toss.

How can I justify my conclusions? I can make a diagram to show the possible outcomes.

Other questions to consider:
• How can I determine the accuracy (truth) of my conjectures?
• What arguments can I present to defend my conjectures?
• What conjectures can I make about the solution to the problem?
• Which argument do I find more plausible?

In the next experiment, the class decided to toss two coins at the same time. They wanted to decide whether it is more likely that both coins will show the same side, heads-heads or tails-tails, or more likely that the coins will show one heads and one tails.

Can I use a drawing, diagram, table, graph, or equation to model the problem? A tree diagram can show the possible outcomes.

1st Toss   H   T
2nd Toss H   T   H   T

Possible Outcomes: HH, HT, TH, TT

Other questions to consider:
• What representation can I use to show the relationship among quantities or variables?
• How can I make my model better if it doesn't work?
• What assumptions can I make about the problem situation to simplify the problem?
• Does my solution or prediction make sense?
• Is there something I have not considered or forgotten?

Math Practices and Problem Solving Handbook

Practice 3 Behaviors

Listen and look for the following behaviors to monitor students' ongoing development of proficiency with this math practice.

• **use** definitions and previously established results in constructing arguments
• **make** conjectures about the solutions to problems
• **build** a logical progression of statements to support their conjectures and justify their conclusions
• **analyze** situations and recognize and use counterexamples
• **reason** inductively about data, making plausible arguments that take into account the context from which the data arose
• **respond** to the arguments of others
• **compare** the effectiveness of two plausible arguments
• **distinguish** correct logic or reasoning from flawed, and—if there is a flaw in an argument—explain what it is
• **listen** or read the arguments of others, decide whether they make sense
• **ask** useful questions to clarify or improve arguments of others

Practice 4 Behaviors

Listen and look for the following behaviors to monitor students' ongoing development of proficiency with this math practice.

• **apply** the mathematics they know to solve problems arising in everyday life
• **make** assumptions and approximations to simplify a complicated situation
• **identify** important quantities in a practical situation and map their relationships using a range of tools
• **analyze** relationships mathematically to draw conclusions
• **interpret** their mathematical results in the context of the situation and propose improvements to the model as needed

Building Students' Proficiency with
5. Use appropriate tools strategically.

This standard is less about giving students different tools to use, and more about having students make decisions about strategies to solve problems. By middle school, students should have wide experiences with using different tools to solve problems. The focus can begin to shift to having students determine which of the different tools would be more useful for them to solve a given problem, and especially *why* that tool is most useful.

As students begin to work on a problem ask them which tool they plan to use and why they have selected that tool. Push them to think about other tools that they could also use and to explain why they decided on the one they chose. Ask questions such as *"Why did you decide on this tool? What other tools were you considering? How is this tool more useful in this situation that the others?"* These conversations help to inform teachers on students' understanding of different tools while also encouraging students to articulate, and often, clarify for themselves the usefulness of different tools.

These different physical tools also help students build mental models that students will be able to draw on throughout their academic career.

Building Students' Proficiency with
6. Attend to precision.

While this standard does include "calculate accurately and efficiently," this is not the primary focus. Rather, the essence of this standard is on precision of language, whether that language is verbal or written text, mathematical symbols, units of quantities, or graphs and diagrams.

To help students gain proficiency with this standard, model for them precise mathematical language and encourage (or require!) them to do the same. As students explain their thinking or defend their solutions using less than precise language, rephrase their explanations so they become accustomed to hearing the expected level of precision. Remind students as needed and as appropriate to state units for their solutions.

Precision in communication takes time to develop, so set reasonable expectations for students. Target a few key terms to focus on while working on particular topics. Remember that the focus is on integrating these key terms into students' working vocabulary, not on having students memorize definitions.

Math Practices and Problem Solving Handbook

5 Use appropriate tools strategically.

6 Attend to precision.

The Golden Company uses signs in the shape of golden rectangles to advertise its products. In a golden rectangle the length of the longer side is about 1.618 times longer than the shorter side. Draw rectangles to scale to create templates of possible small, medium, and large advertising signs.

What tool – objects, technology, or paper and pencil – can I use to help solve the problem? I can use paper and pencil, a ruler, a protractor, and a calculator. I can also use technical drawing software.

How can technology help me with a solution strategy? Technical drawing software can help to make the templates more precise and help me develop a variety of templates more efficiently.

Is my work precise/exact enough? I am using the appropriate tools to make sure that the dimensions of the templates are precise.

Have I calculated accurately? I draw the the shorter side and then multiply that dimension by 1.618 to determine the length of the longer side.

Other questions to consider:
• Can I use different tools? Which ones?
• What other resources can I use to help me reach and understand my solution?

Other questions to consider:
• Have I stated the meaning of the variables and symbols I am using?
• Have I specified the units of measure I am using?
• Is my work precise/exact enough?
• Did I provide carefully formulated explanations?

Practice 5 Behaviors

Listen and look for the following behaviors to monitor students' ongoing development of proficiency with this math practice.

• **consider** the available tools when solving a mathematical problem
• **make** sound decisions about when each of the available tools might be helpful
• **identify** relevant external mathematical resources, and use them to pose or solve problems
• **use** technological tools to explore and deepen their understanding of concepts

Practice 6 Behaviors

Listen and look for the following behaviors to monitor students' ongoing development of proficiency with this math practice.

• **communicate** precisely to others
• **use** clear definitions in discussions with others and in their own reasoning
• **state** the meaning of the symbols they choose
• **specify** units of measure, and label axes to clarify the correspondence with quantities in a problem
• **calculate** accurately and efficiently
• **express** numerical answers with a degree of precision appropriate for the problem context

Math Practices and Problem Solving Handbook

Math Practices

Building Students' Proficiency with
7. Look for and make use of structure.

Many mathematicians define mathematics as the study of structure and patterns; the study of "what ifs?". That is, mathematicians create a set of rules and then explore the results of following these rules. As they explore these results, they look for patterns in behavior. (This is especially true when people build and use mathematical models!) Helping students see mathematics in this way (rather than a series of operations and calculations) is at the heart of this standard, and in many ways, all eight of the standards.

Helping students develop proficiency with this standard means asking them to step back from their calculations to describe what they notice. A regular question to ask students — or even a mantra — is *"What do you notice about the solution or the solution pathway?"* If students struggle at first seeing patterns, ask specific questions, such as, *"What do you notice about the product of a whole number and a fraction? How can we make sense of that?"*

As students become more adept at finding patterns, help them make use of these patterns by asking those "What if?" questions. For example, when solving distance-speed-time problems, have students consider the change to travel time if the speed changes by asking questions such as *"What if the average speed was 10 miles per hour faster? 10 miles per hour slower?"* If students struggle, scaffold the questioning by asking questions such as *"If the average speed is 10 miles per hour faster, will it take more or less time to travel the same distance? Why do you think so?"*

Encourage students to try different solutions pathways or strategies to the same problem and then have them analyze the different solution pathways, focusing on the similarities and differences. From there, have students describe patterns that they notice.

Building Students' Proficiency with
8. Look for and express regularity in repeated reasoning.

This standard is the natural and logical next step from MP.7. This standard has students make use of the patterns they have noticed to generalize a situation, that is "look for regularity in repeating reasoning." Continuing the example of the distance-speed-time relationship cited in MP.7, students would notice that the greater the speed the less time needed to go a fixed distance. From that pattern, students could make a generalization that the speed correlates negatively to the time of travel.

Having students make conjectures before they begin to solve problems helps to develop their thinking in terms of regularity. Ask them to think about problems they solved previously that are similar to the one they are solving. Ask questions such as *"Can you think of a problem you solved that is similar to this one? What was the solution? How is this problem similar to that one? How might it be different? What does that tell you about the solution to this problem?"*

This thinking structure encourages students to focus on the solution pathway rather than just the solution, which is key for proficient math thinkers.

7 **Look for and make use of structure.**

8 **Look for and express regularity in repeated reasoning.**

Math Practices and Problem Solving Handbook

Stuart is studying cell division. The table below shows the number of cells after a certain number of divisions. He wants to make a chart that shows drawings of the cell divisions through 10 divisions. Is it reasonable to draw this?

Cell Division

Division	Initial Cell	2	3	4	5	6	7
Number of Cells	1	2	4	8	16	32	64

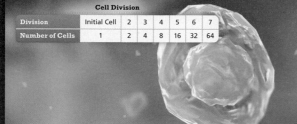

Cell Division

Math Practices and Problem Solving Handbook

Can I see a pattern or structure in the problem or solution strategy?
I see that 1 cell becomes 2 cells and 2 cells become 4 cells, and so on.

How can I use the pattern or structure I see to help me solve the problem?
I can write an expression that will show the number of cells after each division.

Other questions to consider:
• Are there attributes in common that help me?
• What patterns in numbers can I see and describe?
• How can I see expressions or equations in different ways?

Do I notice any repeated calculations or steps? Yes; the number of cells after each cell division is the previous number of cells multiplied by 2.

Are there general methods that I can use to solve the problem? I want to show 10 divisions, so I would have to draw 2^{10}, or 1,024 cells. If I try to draw this number of cells on my chart, I could have a really hard time making them fit.

Other questions to consider:
• What can I generalize from one problem to another?
• Can I derive an expression or equation from generalized examples or repeated observations?
• How reasonable are the results that I am getting?

Practice 7 Behaviors

Listen and look for the following behaviors to monitor students' ongoing development of proficiency with this math practice.

• **look** closely at a problem situation to look for a pattern or structure

• **can** step back for an overview and shift perspective

• **can** see complicated things, such as some algebraic expressions, as single objects or as being composed of several objects

Practice 8 Behaviors

Listen and look for the following behaviors to monitor students' ongoing development of proficiency with this math practice.

• **notice** if calculations are repeated, and look both for general methods and for shortcuts

• **maintain** oversight of the process as they work to solve a problem, while also attending to the details

• **evaluate** the reasonableness of their intermediate results

Math Practices and Problem Solving Handbook

BAR DIAGRAMS

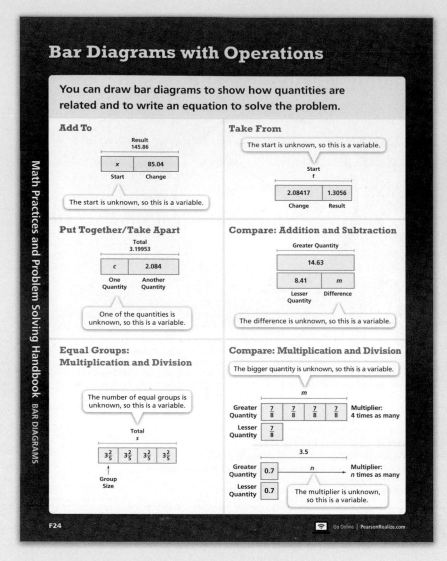

Bar Diagrams with Operations

You can draw bar diagrams to show how quantities are related and to write an equation to solve the problem.

Add To

Result 145.86

x	85.04
Start	Change

The start is unknown, so this is a variable.

Take From

The start is unknown, so this is a variable.

Start
t

2.08417	1.3056
Change	Result

Put Together/Take Apart

Total 3.19953

c	2.084
One Quantity	Another Quantity

One of the quantities is unknown, so this is a variable.

Compare: Addition and Subtraction

Greater Quantity

14.63

8.41	m
Lesser Quantity	Difference

The difference is unknown, so this is a variable.

Equal Groups: Multiplication and Division

The number of equal groups is unknown, so this is a variable.

Total
s

$3\frac{2}{5}$	$3\frac{2}{5}$	$3\frac{2}{5}$	$3\frac{2}{5}$

↑ Group Size

Compare: Multiplication and Division

The bigger quantity is unknown, so this is a variable.

m

Greater Quantity | $\frac{7}{8}$ | $\frac{7}{8}$ | $\frac{7}{8}$ | $\frac{7}{8}$ | Multiplier: 4 times as many

Lesser Quantity | $\frac{7}{8}$ |

3.5

Greater Quantity | 0.7 → n | Multiplier: n times as many

Lesser Quantity | 0.7 | The multiplier is unknown, so this is a variable.

F24

Go Online | PearsonRealize.com

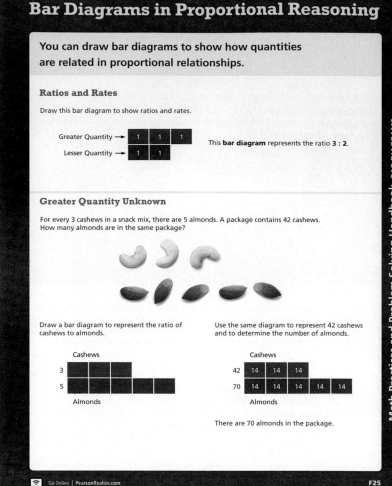

Bar Diagrams in Proportional Reasoning

You can draw bar diagrams to show how quantities are related in proportional relationships.

Ratios and Rates

Draw this bar diagram to show ratios and rates.

Greater Quantity → | 1 | 1 | 1 |

Lesser Quantity → | 1 | 1 |

This **bar diagram** represents the ratio **3 : 2**.

Greater Quantity Unknown

For every 3 cashews in a snack mix, there are 5 almonds. A package contains 42 cashews. How many almonds are in the same package?

Draw a bar diagram to represent the ratio of cashews to almonds.

Cashews
3
5
Almonds

Use the same diagram to represent 42 cashews and to determine the number of almonds.

Cashews
42 | 14 | 14 | 14
70 | 14 | 14 | 14 | 14 | 14
Almonds

There are 70 almonds in the package.

Go Online | PearsonRealize.com

F25

Bar Diagrams with Operations

If students have not had experience using bar diagrams to represent quantities and operations, spend some time introducing them to the bar diagrams with operations.

Encourage students to use bar diagrams to represent problems such as the ones below. Have students identify which situation the problem represents and the appropriate bar diagram to represent the situation.

Drew mixed topsoil and compost to create a soil mixture for growing vegetables. One planter contains 10.25 pounds of the soil mixture, which includes 3.8 pounds of compost. How much topsoil is in the planter?

Trevor baked 4 loaves of bread for a bake sale. The recipe for one loaf of bread calls for 6½ cups of flour. How many cups of flour did Trevor use in all?

Bar Diagrams in Proportional Reasoning

In middle grades, the study of mathematics shifts from a focus on arithmetic operations to proportional relationships and reasoning leading to a study of linearity and function. To help students gain both conceptual understand and procedural fluency, encourage them to use bar diagrams — familiar diagrams — to these new concepts.

The ratio of girls to boys in Millie's class is 4:3. Of the 21 students in Millie's class, how many are girls? How many are boys?

Jorge ran 3 miles in 42 minutes. Assuming he ran at a constant speed, how long did it take for him to run one mile?

A 6-bar box of one kind of protein bars costs $9.75 and a 12-bar case of another kind of protein bars costs $19.25. How do the prices of the protein bars compare?

Bar Diagrams in Proportional Reasoning

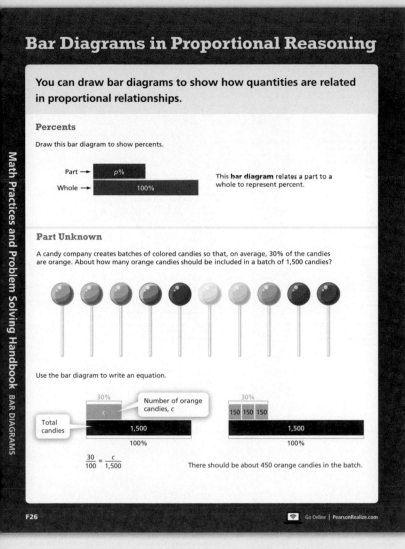

You can draw bar diagrams to show how quantities are related in proportional relationships.

Percents

Draw this bar diagram to show percents.

Part → $p\%$

Whole → 100%

This **bar diagram** relates a part to a whole to represent percent.

Part Unknown

A candy company creates batches of colored candies so that, on average, 30% of the candies are orange. About how many orange candies should be included in a batch of 1,500 candies?

Use the bar diagram to write an equation.

30%
Number of orange candies, c
Total candies
1,500
100%

30%
150 150 150
1,500
100%

$\dfrac{30}{100} = \dfrac{c}{1,500}$

There should be about 450 orange candies in the batch.

Bar Diagrams in Quantitative Reasoning

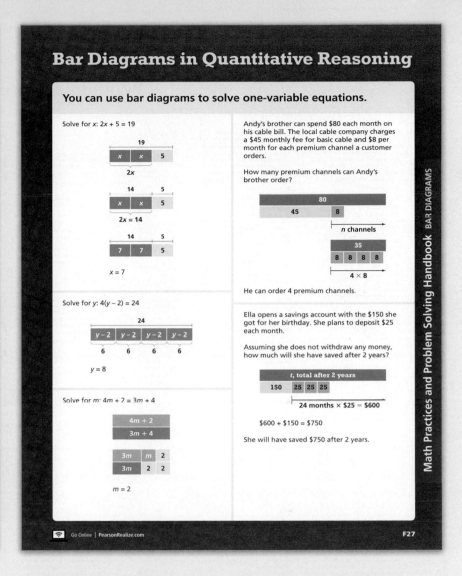

You can use bar diagrams to solve one-variable equations.

Solve for x: $2x + 5 = 19$

19
x x 5
$2x$

14 5
x x 5
$2x = 14$

14 5
7 7 5

$x = 7$

Solve for y: $4(y - 2) = 24$

24
$y - 2$ $y - 2$ $y - 2$ $y - 2$
6 6 6 6

$y = 8$

Solve for m: $4m + 2 = 3m + 4$

$4m + 2$
$3m + 4$

$3m$ m 2
$3m$ 2 2

$m = 2$

Andy's brother can spend $80 each month on his cable bill. The local cable company charges a $45 monthly fee for basic cable and $8 per month for each premium channel a customer orders.

How many premium channels can Andy's brother order?

80
45 8
← n channels →

35
8 8 8 8
← 4×8 →

He can order 4 premium channels.

Ella opens a savings account with the $150 she got for her birthday. She plans to deposit $25 each month.

Assuming she does not withdraw any money, how much will she have saved after 2 years?

t, total after 2 years
150 25 25 25
← 24 months × $25 = $600 →

$600 + $150 = $750

She will have saved $750 after 2 years.

Bar Diagrams in Proportional Reasoning

Introduce percent and parts unknown bar diagrams and have students practice creating bar diagrams for these problems:

Drew mixed topsoil and compost to create a soil mixture for growing vegetables. One planter contains 10.25 pounds of the soil mixture, which includes 3.8 pounds of compost. What percent of the soil mixture is the compost?

Bar Diagrams in Quantitative Reasoning

In middle grades, the study of mathematics shifts from a focus on arithmetic operations to proportional relationships and reasoning leading to a study of linearity and function. To help students gain both conceptual understand and procedural fluency, encourage them to use bar diagrams — familiar diagrams — to these new concepts.

Selena opens a savings account with an initial deposit of $50.50. She deposits an additional $10 each week. In how many weeks will Selena have saved $150?

A swimming pool contains 5,000 gallons of water and is being drained at a rate of 75 gallons per minute. Another pool is being filled at a rate of 17 gallons per minute. After how many minutes will the pools contain the same amount of water?

Assess

BEGINNING-OF-YEAR ASSESSMENT

Available Online

Beginning-of-Year Assessment

Grade **8**
Beginning-of-Year
Assessment

1. Andrew has one book that is $2\frac{3}{7}$ inches thick and a second book that is 3.56 inches thick. If he stacks the books, about how tall will the stack be? Round to the nearest hundredth.
- Ⓐ 5.93 inches
- Ⓑ 5.98 inches
- ● 5.99 inches
- Ⓓ 6 inches

2. Jeremiah makes a recipe that calls for $1\frac{1}{2}$ cups of flour and $\frac{3}{4}$ stick of butter. If Jeremiah uses 3 sticks of butter, how many cups of flour will he need?
- Ⓐ 2 cups
- Ⓑ $3\frac{3}{8}$ cups
- Ⓒ $4\frac{1}{2}$ cups
- ● 6 cups

3. What is the volume of the triangular prism?

3.2 cm
5.4 cm
6 cm

- Ⓐ 8.64 cm³
- Ⓑ 17.28 cm³
- ● 51.84 cm³
- Ⓓ 103.68 cm³

4. Rebekah bought g gallons of paint for $12.85 per gallon and b brushes for $4.79 each. Which expression can be used to determine the total amount Rebekah spent on paint and brushes?
- ● $4.79b + 12.85g$
- Ⓑ $4.79g + 12.85b$
- Ⓒ $12.85b + 4.79b$
- Ⓓ $12.85g - 4.79b$

5. At a wedding reception, an equal number of guests were seated at 12 round tables. The 13 people in the wedding party were seated at a rectangular table. There were 121 people at the reception altogether. Which equation could you use to find the number of guests, n, seated at each round table?
- Ⓐ $12 + 13n = 121$
- ● $12n + 13 = 121$
- Ⓒ $121 = 12n - 13$
- Ⓓ $121 = 13n - 12$

6. The world record for the greatest temperature range recorded in one day occurred in Browning, Montana, in 1916. The temperature fell from 44°F to −56°F. What was the temperature change that day?
- ● −100°F
- Ⓑ −12°F
- Ⓒ 12°F
- Ⓓ 100°F

Beginning-of-Year Assessment **1 of 6**   Copyright © Pearson Education, Inc., or its affiliates. All Rights Reserved. 8

---

7. A 12-section game wheel has a 25% probability that the pointer will land on green. What is the likelihood that the pointer will land on green?
- Ⓐ It is certain the pointer will land on green.
- Ⓑ It is neither likely nor unlikely the pointer will land on green.
- Ⓒ It is likely the pointer will land on green.
- ● It is unlikely the pointer will land on green.

8. How many triangles can be formed from two given angle measures and the length of their included side?
- Ⓐ None
- ● One
- Ⓒ Two
- Ⓓ Infinite number

9. A national survey of middle-school students asks which subject is most challenging. Which of these samples is a representative sample?
- Ⓐ 372 sixth-graders in a certain town
- Ⓑ 972 seventh-graders in a certain county
- Ⓒ 619 eighth-graders in different states
- ● 400 students from various states, representing different grades, 6–8

10. The manager of a food court estimates that he needs 7 pretzels for every 20 people who attend a hockey game. What constant of proportionality relates the number of pretzels to people?
- ● 0.35
- Ⓑ 2.86
- Ⓒ 35
- Ⓓ 140

11. A fishing derby was held over the Fourth of July weekend. What is the percent change in fish caught from Saturday to Sunday?

Sandy Pond Fishing Derby

Friday Saturday Sunday

- Ⓐ 20% increase
- Ⓑ 10% increase
- ● 20% decrease
- Ⓓ 10% decrease

12. Which expression is equivalent to $\frac{1}{2}x + (-7) - 2\frac{1}{4}x - (-2)$?
- ● $-1\frac{3}{4}x - 5$
- Ⓑ $1\frac{3}{4}x - 9$
- Ⓒ $3\frac{3}{4}x - 9$
- Ⓓ $3\frac{3}{4}x - 7$

Beginning-of-Year Assessment **2 of 6**   Copyright © Pearson Education, Inc., or its affiliates. All Rights Reserved. 8

---

13. Solve the equation below for x.
$$-\frac{1}{3}(3x - 4) = 11$$
- Ⓐ $-13\frac{2}{3}$
- Ⓑ $-8\frac{1}{3}$
- ● -6
- Ⓓ 6

14. Use the table from a random survey about the preferred service for streaming movies. Out of 750 people, how many would you expect to prefer Company B?

Service	Number of People
Company A	75
Company B	32
Company C	18

- ● 192
- Ⓑ 240
- Ⓒ 510
- Ⓓ 558

15. A bag holds 12 red marbles, 11 green marbles, 17 blue marbles, and 5 yellow marbles. What is the probability that you will **NOT** choose a blue marble?
- Ⓐ $\frac{4}{5}$
- Ⓑ $\frac{11}{45}$
- Ⓒ $\frac{17}{45}$
- ● $\frac{28}{45}$

16. What is the value of x?

$(5x)°$
15°

- Ⓐ 15
- Ⓑ 21
- Ⓒ 26
- ● 105

17. Find the quotient: $-\frac{10}{9} \div \left(-\frac{5}{7}\right)$.
- Ⓐ $-\frac{70}{95}$
- Ⓑ $-\frac{14}{19}$
- Ⓒ $\frac{14}{19}$
- ● $\frac{70}{95}$

18. What is the constant of proportionality shown on the graph?

- Ⓐ 0.80
- ● 1.25
- Ⓒ 4
- Ⓓ 5

Beginning-of-Year Assessment **3 of 6**   Copyright © Pearson Education, Inc., or its affiliates. All Rights Reserved. 8

---

19. Sonya buys four pairs of shoes on sale for buy one, get one 50% off. The sales tax is 6.5%. If the original price for each pair of shoes was $35, how much does Sonya pay for the four pairs altogether?
- Ⓐ $74.55
- Ⓑ $105.00
- ● $111.83
- Ⓓ $149.10

20. A gardener is installing fence around his garden. Let x represent the width of the garden, in feet. The perimeter of the garden is $8x + 8$. Which expression represents the length of the garden?
- Ⓐ $2x + 2$
- Ⓑ $3x + 4$
- Ⓒ $6x + 8$
- Ⓓ $8x + 8 - 2x$

21. Solve the inequality $-7x > 21$. What is the graph of the solution?
- ● ⟵ −5 −4 −3 −2 −1
- Ⓑ −5 −4 −3 −2 −1
- Ⓒ −5 −4 −3 −2 −1
- Ⓓ −5 −4 −3 −2 −1

22. Which is the interquartile range for the city that has the greater variability in temperature?

City A

0 10 20 30 40 50 60 70 80 90 100
Degrees Fahrenheit

City B

0 10 20 30 40 50 60 70 80 90 100
Degrees Fahrenheit

- Ⓐ 10
- Ⓑ 20
- Ⓒ 30
- ● 40

23. Kayla rolls two number cubes numbered 1 to 6. What is the probability that the sum of the numbers rolled will be 5?
- Ⓐ $\frac{1}{9}$
- Ⓑ $\frac{1}{9}$
- Ⓒ $\frac{1}{8}$
- Ⓓ ●

24. A cosmetics company tested a new lotion. Of the 2,500 people tested, 15 had an allergic reaction. What percent of the people tested had an allergic reaction to the new lotion?
- Ⓐ 0.006%
- Ⓑ 0.06%
- ● 0.6%
- Ⓓ 6%

Beginning-of-Year Assessment **4 of 6**   Copyright © Pearson Education, Inc., or its affiliates. All Rights Reserved. 8

---

25. Major League Baseball's fastest recorded pitch is 105 miles per hour. The distance between the pitcher's mound and home plate is 60 feet, 6 inches. How long did it take the ball to travel from the pitcher to the batter?
- ● About 0.4 second
- Ⓑ About 0.7 second
- Ⓒ About 4 seconds
- Ⓓ About 7 seconds

26. Maria needs to buy cat food. At Save Rite, cat food costs $5.25 for 3 cans. Spend Less offers cat food at $7.50 for 5 cans. Maria buys 15 cans from the store with the lowest price. How much did she pay?
- Ⓐ $8.57
- Ⓑ $10.00
- ● $22.50
- Ⓓ $26.25

27. Malik borrowed $8,000 to buy a new boat. He will pay off the loan after 4 years by paying back the principal plus 6.5% simple interest. How much will Malik pay back altogether?
- Ⓐ $520
- Ⓑ $2,080
- Ⓒ $8,000
- ● $10,080

28. Find the sum.
$(-7b + 8c) - (12a + 14) + (5a + 5b)$
- Ⓐ $-7a + 12b + 8c + 14$
- ● $-7a - 2b + 8c - 14$
- Ⓒ $17a - 2b + 8c + 14$
- Ⓓ $17a - 2b + 8c - 14$

29. A store sells three varieties of cheese—cheddar, Gouda, and Swiss. Each variety of cheese is available in two different styles—shredded or sliced. How many possible outcomes for the variety and style of cheese are there?
- Ⓐ 2
- Ⓑ 3
- Ⓒ 5
- ● 6

30. The low temperatures in two cities are being compared. In City 1, the range in temperature is 20°F and the IQR is 7°F. In City 2, the range in temperature is 15°F and the IQR is 7°F. What might you conclude about the cities based on the ranges and interquartile ranges?
- Ⓐ The weather patterns in City 1 and City 2 are equally consistent.
- ● The weather pattern in City 2 is more consistent than the weather pattern in City 1.
- Ⓒ The weather pattern in City 1 is more consistent than the weather pattern in City 2.
- Ⓓ There is not enough information to make a conclusion.

Beginning-of-Year Assessment **5 of 6**   Copyright © Pearson Education, Inc., or its affiliates. All Rights Reserved. 8

---

31. For Spirit Day, each 8th-grade homeroom designs a unique two-color T-shirt. They get to choose from the colors red (R), blue (B), green (G), violet (V), and orange (O). Each T-shirt is a solid color with a different color used for the student's name. What is the probability that a homeroom will have a T-shirt with a combination of blue and violet?
- ● $P(B \text{ and } V) = 10\%$
- Ⓑ $P(B \text{ and } V) = 20\%$
- Ⓒ $P(B \text{ and } V) = 30\%$
- Ⓓ $P(B \text{ and } V) = 40\%$

32. What are the dimensions of the vertical cross section shown on this right rectangular prism?

4 in.
5 in.
12 in.

- Ⓐ 5 in. × 12 in.
- Ⓑ 4 in. × 12 in.
- ● 5 in. × 4 in.
- Ⓓ 12 in. × 5 in.

33. Which inequality represents the following situation: $\frac{2}{3}$ times 5 less than a number is no more than 27?
- Ⓐ $\frac{2}{3}(x - 5) \geq 27$
- Ⓑ $\frac{2}{3}x - 5 \leq 27$
- Ⓒ $\frac{2}{3}(5 - x) \geq 27$
- ● $\frac{2}{3}(x - 5) \leq 27$

34. Charlie bought a car for 5% off the selling price of $7,200. The sales tax for his state is 3.4%. How much is the sales tax?
- Ⓐ $232.56
- ● $244.80
- Ⓒ $257.04
- Ⓓ $347.76

35. The circumference of a circle is 6π inches. What is the area of the circle?

$A = \pi r^2$

- Ⓐ 3π in.²
- ● 9π in.²
- Ⓒ 12π in.²
- Ⓓ 36π in.²

36. A company owns two manufacturing plants with daily production levels of $8x + 17$ widgets and $5x - 7$ widgets, where x represents a minimum quantity. How many more items does the first plant produce daily than the second plant?
- Ⓐ $13x + 10$ widgets
- Ⓑ $3x + 10$ widgets
- ● $3x + 24$ widgets
- Ⓓ $13x - 10$ widgets

Beginning-of-Year Assessment **6 of 6**   Copyright © Pearson Education, Inc., or its affiliates. All Rights Reserved. 8

Item Analysis for Diagnosis and Intervention

Item	MDIS
1	M24, L56, L77
2	M27, M35
3	N45, N56
4	K6
5	K27
6	L74
7	N86
8	N8
9	N82
10	M32
11	M46, N69
12	K18
13	K11, K29
14	M31
15	N86
16	N3
17	L50, L79
18	M32, K50, K52

Item	MDIS
19	M43, M44
20	K4, N37
21	K38
22	N75
23	N87
24	M27, M38
25	N33
26	M29
27	M48
28	K4, K8, K20
29	N87
30	N75
31	N87
32	N17
33	K37
34	M44
35	N47
36	K4, K20

You may opt to have students take the Beginning-of-Year Assessment online at PearsonRealize.com. The online assessment is auto-scored, with differentiated intervention automatically assigned to students based on their scores.

Real Numbers

Math Background Focus

Rational and Irrational Numbers

- **Understanding Rational Numbers** In Lesson 1-1, students write repeating decimals as fractions. This lesson develops the procedural skills that students need to write equivalent equations by multiplying by a power of 10 to move the nonrepeating decimal to the left of the decimal point in order to solve a problem involving writing a repeating decimal as a fraction.

- **Understanding Irrational Numbers** In Lesson 1-2, students classify numbers as either rational or irrational. Students understand that an irrational number is a decimal that does not repeat or terminate. Students learn to recognize perfect squares and identify that the square root of a whole number that is not a perfect square is an irrational number.

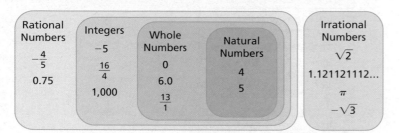

The number 0.24758326… is irrational because the decimal expansion is nonrepeating and nonterminating.

- **Comparing and Ordering Rational and Irrational Numbers** In Lesson 1-3, students compare and order rational and irrational numbers. Students learn to approximate the value of a square root by using perfect squares and decimal approximations. Plotting each approximation on a number line helps the students compare and order rational and irrational numbers.

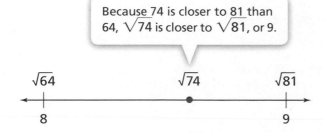

Because 74 is closer to 81 than 64, $\sqrt{74}$ is closer to $\sqrt{81}$, or 9.

Square Roots and Cube Roots

- **Evaluate Square Roots and Cube Roots** In Lesson 1-4, students learn how to evaluate perfect squares and perfect cubes and solve problems using perfect squares and perfect cubes. Students build fluency with square roots and cube roots by classifying a whole number as a perfect square, a perfect cube, both, or neither.

The symbol $\sqrt[3]{}$ means the cube root of a number.

$$\sqrt[3]{216} = \sqrt[3]{6 \cdot 6 \cdot 6}$$
$$= \sqrt[3]{6^3}$$
$$= 6$$

Taking the cube root and cubing a number are inverse operations.

- **Solve Equations Using Square Roots and Cube Roots** In Lesson 1-5, students solve equations involving square roots and cube roots. Students extend this knowledge to solve real-world problems using square roots and cube roots.

Kyle has a large, cube-shaped terrarium for his iguana. He wants to cover the opening with a square screen. What are the dimensions, s, for the screen?

$$V = s^3$$
$$343 = s^3$$
$$\sqrt[3]{343} = \sqrt[3]{s^3}$$
$$7 = s$$

> The value of s is not $\pm\sqrt[3]{343}$ because $(-7)^3 = -7 \times -7 \times -7$ $= -343$.

Each edge of the terrarium is 7 feet, so the dimensions of the screen are 7 feet by 7 feet.

$V = 343 \text{ ft}^3$

Integer Exponents and Scientific Notation

- **Use Properties of Integer Exponents** In Lesson 1-6, students use properties of integer exponents to simplify exponential expressions. Students learn to multiply and divide exponential expressions with the same base, to multiply exponential expressions with different bases, and to find the power of a power.
- **More Properties of Integers Exponents** In Lesson 1-7, students learn the Zero Exponent Property and Negative Exponent Property and use these properties to simplify expressions and to solve problems.
- **Use Powers of 10 to Estimate Quantities** In Lesson 1-8, students learn to estimate and compare very small and very large quantities by rounding and then using powers of 10.
- **Understanding Scientific Notation** In Lesson 1-9, students write very large numbers and very small numbers in scientific notation. Students extend their knowledge and understanding of scientific notation to convert numbers from scientific notation to standard form and from standard form to scientific notation.

The genetic information of almost every living thing is stored in a tiny strand called DNA. Human DNA is 3 nanometers, or 3×10^{-9}, meter long. Write the length in standard form.

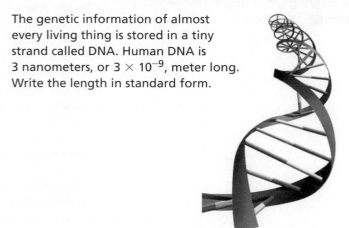

- **Operations with Numbers in Scientific Notation** In Lesson 1-10, students use the Product of Powers Property and the Quotient of Powers Property to multiply and divide numbers written in scientific notation. Students learn that to add and subtract numbers in scientific notation, the powers of 10 must have the same exponent.

Math Background Coherence

Students learn best when concepts are connected throughout the curriculum. This coherence is achieved within topics, across topics, across domains, and across grade levels.

Look Back

How does Topic 1 connect to what students learned earlier?

Grade 7

- **Rational Numbers and Integers** In Grade 7, students learned about rational numbers and integers. They performed integer operations in Topic 1.
- **Rewriting an Expression** Seventh graders learned that writing an expression in different forms can help when solving problems. Students will apply this skill when working with integer exponents and scientific notation.

Topic 1

How is content connected within Topic 1?

- **Rational and Irrational Numbers** In Lesson 1-1, students make the connection that repeating decimals are rational numbers because they can be written as fractions. In Lesson 1-2, students explore irrational numbers and recognize perfect squares. They learn that real numbers are either rational or irrational. Lesson 1-3 provides opportunities for students to compare and order rational and irrational numbers.
- **Square Roots and Cube Roots** In Lesson 1-4, students evaluate square roots and cube roots. In Lesson 1-5, students extend this knowledge by solving equations using square roots and cube roots.
- **Integer Exponents and Scientific Notation** In Lesson 1-6, students multiply and divide exponential expressions with the same base and multiply exponential expressions with different bases. In Lesson 1-7, students use additional properties of exponents, such as the Zero Exponent Property and the Negative Exponent Property, to simplify exponential expressions.

A billboard has the given dimensions.

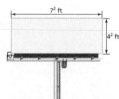

Using exponents, write two equivalent expressions for the area of the rectangle.

Lesson 1-8 helps students use powers of ten to estimate and compare very large and very small quantities. In Lesson 1-9, students write very large and very small numbers in scientific notation, and then convert numbers that are in scientific notation to standard form and numbers that are in standard form to scientific notation. The topic ends with Lesson 1-10, where students use properties of exponents to perform operations with numbers written in scientific notation.

Look Ahead

How does Topic 1 connect to what students will learn later?

Later in Grade 8

- **Surface Area** In Topic 8, students will use what they have learned about squares, square roots, and the irrational number π to calculate the surface area of solids.
- **Volume of Cones and Cylinders** When studying volume of a cone or cylinder, students will use what they know about squares, square roots, and the irrational number π to calculate the volume or find the length of the radius.
- **Volume of Spheres** Students will use their knowledge about cubes, cube roots, and the irrational number π to calculate the volume of a sphere or find the length of its radius.

Grade 9

- **Rational and Irrational Number Properties** In Grade 9, students will explain why the sum or product of two rational numbers is rational. They will also justify why the sum of a rational number and an irrational number is irrational. In addition, they will recognize that the product of a nonzero rational number and an irrational number is irrational.
- **Rational Exponents** In Grade 9, students will connect their understanding of rational numbers and integer exponents to learn about rational exponents. They will write and evaluate expressions involving radical and rational exponents using the properties of exponents.

Math Background Rigor

A rigorous curriculum emphasizes conceptual understanding, procedural skill and fluency, and applications.

Conceptual Understanding

- **Understand Rational and Irrational Numbers** Students build on their understanding of real numbers in order to classify numbers as rational or irrational. Students understand that repeating and terminating decimals can be represented as an equivalent rational number in fraction form.

- **Identify Perfect Squares and Perfect Cubes** Students understand the relationship between squares, square roots, cubes, and cube roots. Students recognize that irrational numbers do not have an exact decimal representation and can be approximated. Students learn that irrational square roots can be approximated by using perfect squares and decimal approximations.

- **Understand the Purpose of Scientific Notation** Learning how to estimate very small and very large quantities using powers of ten is a critical step in learning how to compare these quantities. Recognizing how to write very small and very large numbers in scientific notation makes it possible to add, subtract, multiply, and divide these numbers using less effort.

- **Recognize Integer Exponent Relationships** Students understand that any nonzero number raised to the power of zero is equal to one. Students use patterns to predict and understand integer exponent relationships.

Exponent Form	Simplified Form
3^4	81
3^3	27
3^2	9
3^1	3
3^0	?

$\div 3$
$\div 3$
$\div 3$
$\div 3$

- **Represent Integer Exponent Properties** Students learn properties of exponents and use these properties to add, subtract, multiply, and divide exponential expressions.

Procedural Skill and Fluency

- **Convert Repeating Decimals to Fractions** In Lesson 1-1, students change repeating decimals to fractions using equivalent equations.

- **Compare and Order Rational and Irrational Numbers** In Lesson 1-3, students use their understanding of perfect squares and decimal approximations to compare and order real numbers on the number line.

- **Find or Approximate a Square Root Using Perfect Squares** In Lesson 1-3, students approximate a square root by using perfect squares to estimate between which two perfect squares the number lies.

- **Solve Equations Involving Squares and Cubes** In Lesson 1-4, students evaluate perfect squares and perfect cubes. In Lesson 1-5, they use this knowledge to solve equations that have square roots and cube roots.

- **Simplify and Evaluate Expressions with Integer Exponents** In Lesson 1-6, students use their understanding of the properties of integers to simplify exponential expressions. In Lesson 1-7, students learn how to use additional properties, such as the Zero Exponent Property and Negative Exponent Property, to generate equivalent exponential expressions. In Lesson 1-8, students use powers of ten to estimate and compare very large and very small quantities.

- **Write Numbers in Scientific Notation and Standard Form** In Lesson 1-9, students write very small and very large numbers in scientific notation, and then write these numbers in both standard form and scientific notation.

- **Use Scientific Notation to Add, Subtract, Multiply, and Divide** In Lesson 1-10, students use scientific notation to solve problems involving the four basic operations.

Applications

- **Use a Number Line to Represent Real Numbers** In Lesson 1-3, decimal approximations can be plotted on a number line to help the students compare and order rational and irrational numbers.

- **Use Area of a Square to Find Length of Side** In Lesson 1-4, students find the side length of a square, given the area and their knowledge of perfect squares and square roots.

- **Use Volume of a Cube to Find Length of Edge** In Lesson 1-4, students find the edge length of a cube, given the volume and their knowledge of perfect cubes and cube roots.

Math Practices

The math practices and processes describe the behaviors and thinking habits that mathematically proficient students demonstrate when actively engaged in mathematics work. Opportunities for engagement in the practices and to develop expertise with these important behaviors and thinking habits exist throughout the topic and program. Here we focus on mathematical reasoning and explaining.

As students work with rational and irrational numbers, squares, cubes, square and cube roots, integer exponents, and scientific notation, look for these behaviors to assess and identify students who demonstrate proficiency with mathematical reasoning and explaining.

Math Practices Within Topic 1 Lessons	
Reason abstractly and quantitatively.	**Look for and make use of structure.**
Mathematically proficient students:	Mathematically proficient students:
• Make sense of rational and irrational numbers and compare and order them.	• Change repeating decimals to fractions using equations.
• Approximate a square root by using perfect squares and decimal approximations.	• Classify numbers as irrational or rational. • Recognize numbers as perfect squares or perfect cubes.
• Solve word problems using perfect squares and perfect cubes.	• Recognize patterns in exponential expressions, such as same bases or different bases, and use the properties of exponents to simplify these expressions.
• Use properties of integer exponents to simplify and evaluate exponential expressions.	• Analyze very large and very small quantities, and estimate these quantities using powers of 10.
• Represent very small or very large quantities using scientific notation.	• Represent very large and very small numbers using scientific notation.

Help students become more proficient with mathematical reasoning and explanation.

If students do not confidently identify, classify, compare, and order real numbers; recognize perfect squares and perfect cubes; and understand the properties of exponents, use these questioning strategies to help them develop their analyzing and reasoning skills as they solve problems throughout the topic.

Q: Why might it be easier to compare and order fractions on the number line by writing them in decimal form?

Q: How does knowing that $\sqrt{16} = 4$ and $\sqrt{9} = 3$ help you to estimate the value of $\sqrt{15}$?

Q: What is a real-world situation that might require you to find the cube root of a number?

Q: Why does it make sense that $2^{-1} = \frac{1}{2}$?

Q: Why is it important to look at the powers of 10 when adding numbers in scientific notation?

Q: Is 0.12112111211112... a repeating decimal? Explain.

Q: What are the steps to convert $0.\overline{71}$ to a fraction?

Q: What properties of exponents could you use to explain why $5^0 = 1$?

Q: Why is it helpful to estimate very large or very small quantities using a power of 10 when comparing?

Q: Is $(5^4)^3 = 5^7$? Explain.

Topic Readiness Assessment

Assess

Name _____

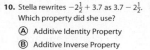

Topic **1**
Readiness Assessment

1. Which decimal is terminating?
Ⓐ $0.\overline{12}$
Ⓑ $0.4444...$
Ⓒ $0.5\overline{6}$
● 0.7878

2. Find the product.
$(-10) \cdot (-10) \cdot (-10)$
Ⓐ $-10,000$
● $-1,000$
Ⓒ $1,000$
Ⓓ $10,000$

3. The perimeter of the square kitchen floor measures 48 feet. What is the area of the kitchen floor?
Ⓐ 32 feet
Ⓑ 96 square feet
● 144 square feet
Ⓓ 144 cubic feet

4. Which number line below is correct?

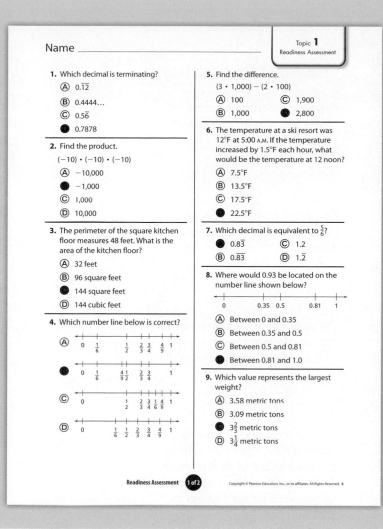

5. Find the difference.
$(3 \cdot 1,000) - (2 \cdot 100)$
Ⓐ 100 Ⓒ 1,900
Ⓑ 1,000 ● 2,800

6. The temperature at a ski resort was 12°F at 5:00 A.M. If the temperature increased by 1.5°F each hour, what would be the temperature at 12 noon?
Ⓐ 7.5°F
Ⓑ 13.5°F
Ⓒ 17.5°F
● 22.5°F

7. Which decimal is equivalent to $\frac{5}{6}$?
● $0.8\overline{3}$ Ⓒ 1.2
Ⓑ $0.\overline{83}$ Ⓓ $1.\overline{2}$

8. Where would 0.93 be located on the number line shown below?

Ⓐ Between 0 and 0.35
Ⓑ Between 0.35 and 0.5
Ⓒ Between 0.5 and 0.81
● Between 0.81 and 1.0

9. Which value represents the largest weight?
Ⓐ 3.58 metric tons
Ⓑ 3.09 metric tons
● $3\frac{2}{3}$ metric tons
Ⓓ $3\frac{1}{4}$ metric tons

10. Stella rewrites $-2\frac{1}{2} + 3.7$ as $3.7 - 2\frac{1}{2}$. Which property did she use?
Ⓐ Additive Identity Property
Ⓑ Additive Inverse Property
● Commutative Property
Ⓓ Distributive Property

11. What is the volume of the cube?

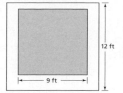

Ⓐ 21 cm^3
Ⓑ 49 cm^3
Ⓒ 147 cm^3
● 343 cm^3

12. Why is $-3\frac{1}{8}$ a rational number?
Ⓐ It is rational because all negative numbers are rational.
Ⓑ It is rational because all integers are rational.
Ⓒ It is rational because it can be expressed as a repeating decimal.
● It is rational because it can be expressed as a terminating decimal.

13. Which decimal is equivalent to $1\frac{5}{8}$?
Ⓐ 1.58 ● 1.625
Ⓑ $1.\overline{58}$ Ⓓ $1.\overline{625}$

14. Marlena places a square rug on her living room floor, which is also a square. What area of her floor is **NOT** covered by the rug?

(square rug diagram: 12 ft, 9 ft)

Ⓐ 9 ft^2 ● 63 ft^2
Ⓑ 12 ft^2 Ⓓ 81 ft^2

15. The water level in a swimming pool decreases from 60 inches to 58.25 inches in one week. Assuming that the water level changes at a constant rate, how much did the water level decrease each day?
● 0.25 in. Ⓒ 1.25 in.
Ⓑ 0.35 in. Ⓓ 1.75 in.

16. Which set of numbers below is in the correct order from least to greatest?
Ⓐ $-2.5 < 2\frac{3}{4} < -2\frac{1}{5} < 2.1$
Ⓑ $-2\frac{1}{5} < 2\frac{3}{4} < 2.1 < -2.5$
● $-2.5 < -2\frac{1}{5} < 2.1 < 2\frac{3}{4}$
Ⓓ $2.1 < -2\frac{1}{5} < -2.5 < 2\frac{3}{4}$

Readiness Assessment ● 1 of 2 Copyright © Pearson Education, Inc., or its affiliates. All Rights Reserved. 8

Readiness Assessment ● 2 of 2 Copyright © Pearson Education, Inc., or its affiliates. All Rights Reserved. 8

Assess students' understanding of prerequisite concepts and skills using the Topic Readiness Assessment found at PearsonRealize.com.

 You may opt to have students take the Topic Readiness Assessment online.

 Item Analysis for Diagnosis and Remediation

Item	DOK	MDIS
1	1	L80
2	2	L76
3	3	N37–N41
4	1	M7, M13, L73
5	2	L24, K8, K9
6	3	L56

Item	DOK	MDIS
7	2	M16, M22, M24
8	1	M17
9	2	M26, M22
10	1	K12
11	2	N52
12	3	L80
13	2	M24
14	3	N41
15	3	M28
16	1	M26

Topic Planner

Real Numbers

Lesson	Vocabulary	Objective	Essential Understanding
1-1 Rational Numbers as Decimals	none	• Locate repeating decimals on a number line. • Write repeating decimals as fractions.	Repeating decimals can be represented as an equivalent rational number.
1-2 Understand Irrational Numbers	irrational number, perfect square, square root	• Classify a number as rational or irrational. • Understand the concepts of square roots and perfect squares.	Every real number is either a rational number or an irrational number.
1-3 Compare and Order Real Numbers	none	• Approximate square roots by using perfect squares. • Compare and order rational and irrational numbers.	Rational and irrational numbers can be compared and ordered using decimal approximations.
1-4 Evaluate Square Roots and Cube Roots	cube root, perfect cube	• Evaluate square roots and cube roots to solve problems. • Evaluate perfect squares and perfect cubes.	To find the square root of a number, find the factor whose square is equal to that number. To find a cube root, find the factor whose cube is equal to that number.
1-5 Solve Equations Using Square Roots and Cube Roots	none	• Solve equations involving perfect squares or cubes. • Solve equations involving imperfect squares or cubes.	Solve equations with squares by taking the square root of each side of the equation. Solve equations with cubes by taking the cube root of each side of the equation.

Lesson Resources

Digital

Student's Edition

Additional Practice workbook

Print

Teaching Resources
- Reteach to Build Understanding
- Additional Vocabulary Support
- Build Mathematical Literacy
- Enrichment

Assessment Resources
- Lesson Quiz

Digital

Digital Lesson Courseware
- Today's Challenge
- Visual Learning Animation Plus
- Key Concept
- Additional Examples
- 3-Act Mathematical Modeling
- Online Practice powered by MathXL for School

- Virtual Nerd Video Tutorials
- Animated Glossary
- Digital Math Tools
- Online Math Games

Lesson Support for Teachers
- Listen and Look For PD Lesson Video

The suggested pacing for each lesson is 2 days for a 45-minute math class and 1 day for a 90-minute class.

PearsonRealize.com

Digital

Lesson	Vocabulary	Objective	Essential Understanding
1-6 Use Properties of Integer Exponents	Power of Products Property, Product of Powers Property, Quotient of Powers Property	• Multiply and divide expressions with integer exponents. • Find the power of a power.	The properties of exponents are used to simplify expressions by adding, subtracting, multiplying, or dividing either the base or the exponents.
1-7 More Properties of Integer Exponents	Negative Exponent Property, Zero Exponent Property	• Simplify exponential expressions using the Zero Exponent Property and the Negative Exponent Property.	Any nonzero number raised to the power of zero is equal to 1. Any nonzero number raised to a negative power is equal to its multiplicative reciprocal.
1-8 Use Powers of 10 to Estimate Quantities	none	• Estimate and compare very large and very small quantities using powers of 10.	An estimate of a very small or very large quantity can be written as a single digit times a power of ten.
1-9 Understand Scientific Notation	scientific notation	• Write very large and very small numbers in scientific notation. • Convert scientific notation to standard form.	Scientific notation is an efficient way to write very small or very large numbers.
3-Act Mathematical Modeling: Hard-Working Organs	none	• Use mathematical modeling to represent a problem situation and to propose a solution. • Test and verify the appropriateness of math models.	Many real-world problem situations can be represented with a mathematical model, but that model may not represent a real-world situation exactly.
1-10 Operations with Numbers in Scientific Notation	none	• Add, subtract, multiply, and divide numbers in scientific notation.	Operating with numbers in scientific notation is an efficient way to add, subtract, multiply, and divide very large or very small numbers.

Topic Resources

Digital

Print

Student's Edition
- Review What You Know
- Build Literacy in Mathematics
- Mid-Topic Checkpoint and Performance Task
- Topic Review
- Fluency Practice Activity
- STEM Project

Assessment Resources
- Topic Readiness Assessment
- Mid-Topic Assessment
- Topic Assessment
- Topic Performance Task

Digital

Topic Support for Students
- Math Practice Animations
- STEM Project
- 3-Act Mathematical Modeling Lesson

Topic Support for Teachers
- Topic Overview Video
- ExamView Test Generator

Topic Opener

Investigate Real Numbers

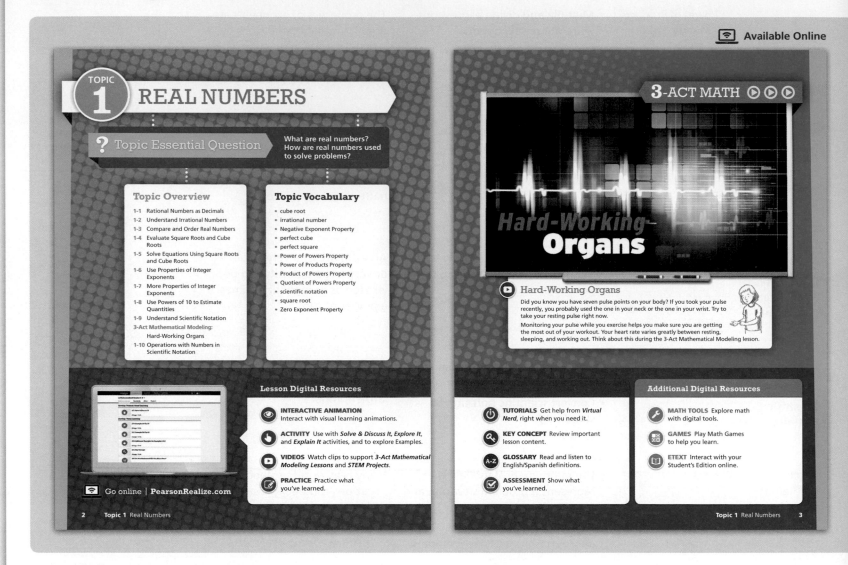

Topic Essential Question

What are real numbers? How are real numbers used to solve problems?

Revisit the Topic Essential Question throughout the topic. See the Teacher's Edition for the Topic Review for notes about answering the question.

3-Act Mathematical Modeling

Have students read about the Mathematics Modeling lesson for this topic. You can use the preview for this lesson to get students interested in learning the content of this topic.

The Mathematical Modeling in 3 Acts lesson appears after Lesson 1–9.

Going, Going, Gone?

Project Overview

In this project, students will represent the depletion rate of a natural resource in a table and a graph. They will explore other natural resources and describe their uses, depletion rates, and impact on the environment. Students will write a story focused on the sustainability of a natural resource.

What's the Math?

Students use real numbers to represent the availability and depletion rates of the natural resources they explore. They use rational numbers, rational number approximations, and operations with rational numbers to determine how much natural resource with be left after a given period of time.

What's the Science?

Students gather data about the depletion of natural resources, including the use of natural resources to make synthetic materials. They explore the impacts, positive and negative, that the use of these resources has on Earth's systems and on society.

What's the Engineering and Technology?

Students recognize the ways in which engineers use natural resources to form new materials, and therefore, new technologies. Students will construct an argument, in story form, for how they can impact the sustainability of a natural resource.

Introduce the Project

Present the project by having students discuss what they know about natural resources. The questioning below can be used to guide the discussion.

Q: What are some examples of natural resources? [Sample answers: Air, water, oil, land, minerals, light, fossil fuels]

Q: What are some examples of ways we use natural resources in every day life? [Sample answer: Drink water, use cell phones, use computers, take vitamins, take medicine]

Q: What is the difference between a renewable resource and a nonrenewable resource? [Sample answer: A renewable resource can be replaced. A nonrenewable resource cannot be replaced once it is used.]

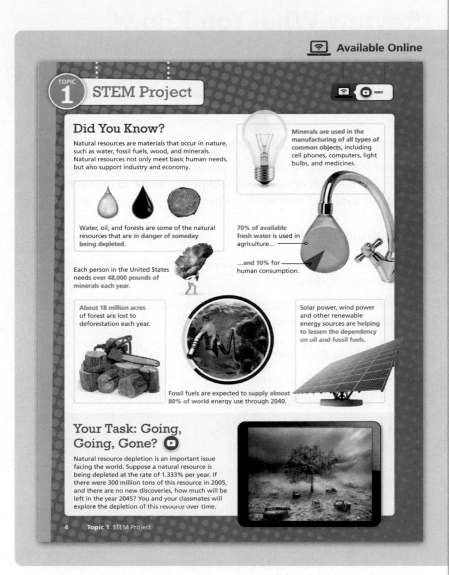

Q: Why is it important to understand the rate at which our natural resources are being depleted? [Sample answers: It is important to know how quickly we are using up the resources so that we can plan for ways to slow the depletion.]

You can launch this project any time during Topic 1.

Show the Topic 1 STEM video to generate interest in the project.

Teacher resources that provide students with project details and support are available at PearsonRealize.com.

TOPIC 1

Get Ready!

PearsonRealize.com

A-Z
Glossary

Review What You Know!

Assign the Review What You Know to activate prior knowledge and practice the prerequisite skills needed for success in this topic.

Encourage students to work independently or with a partner. Use these questioning strategies to help them get started.

Terminating and Repeating Decimals

Q: What is a repeating decimal? [Sample answer: A decimal number that has either a single digit or a block of digits that repeats over and over again forever.]

Multiplying Integers

Q: When you multiply two negative integers, what is the sign of the product? [Positive]

Q: When you multiply a positive and a negative integer, what is the sign of the product? [Negative]

Simplifying Expressions

Q: How do you know in which order to perform the operations? [You apply the Order of Operations to simplify expressions.]

 ### Item Analysis for Diagnosis and Remediation

Item	MDIS
1	M17
2	M17
3	L70
4	M1, M2, M4
5–10	M17
11–16	L76
17–22	L74, L75, L76

Vocabulary Review

You may choose to strengthen vocabulary with the following activity.

Have students create vocabulary flash cards. Ask them to write each term on one side of an index card and draw an example on the other side. You may choose to have students present their vocabulary cards to a partner.

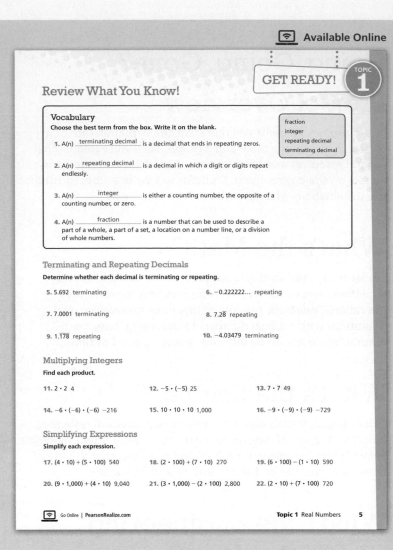

Available Online

GET READY!

TOPIC 1

Review What You Know!

Vocabulary
Choose the best term from the box. Write it on the blank.

> fraction
> integer
> repeating decimal
> terminating decimal

1. A(n) __terminating decimal__ is a decimal that ends in repeating zeros.

2. A(n) __repeating decimal__ is a decimal in which a digit or digits repeat endlessly.

3. A(n) __integer__ is either a counting number, the opposite of a counting number, or zero.

4. A(n) __fraction__ is a number that can be used to describe a part of a whole, a part of a set, a location on a number line, or a division of whole numbers.

Terminating and Repeating Decimals
Determine whether each decimal is terminating or repeating.

5. 5.692 terminating

6. −0.222222... repeating

7. 7.0001 terminating

8. 7.2$\overline{8}$ repeating

9. 1.1$\overline{78}$ repeating

10. −4.03479 terminating

Multiplying Integers
Find each product.

11. $2 \cdot 2$ 4

12. $-5 \cdot (-5)$ 25

13. $7 \cdot 7$ 49

14. $-6 \cdot (-6) \cdot (-6)$ −216

15. $10 \cdot 10 \cdot 10$ 1,000

16. $-9 \cdot (-9) \cdot (-9)$ −729

Simplifying Expressions
Simplify each expression.

17. $(4 \cdot 10) + (5 \cdot 100)$ 540

18. $(2 \cdot 100) + (7 \cdot 10)$ 270

19. $(6 \cdot 100) - (1 \cdot 10)$ 590

20. $(9 \cdot 1,000) + (4 \cdot 10)$ 9,040

21. $(3 \cdot 1,000) - (2 \cdot 100)$ 2,800

22. $(2 \cdot 10) + (7 \cdot 100)$ 720

Go Online | PearsonRealize.com

Topic 1 Real Numbers   5

Build Vocabulary

Pre-reading Strategy: Graphic Organizer

Use the graphic organizer to help you understand new vocabulary terms.

Q: Why is it helpful to show examples for each term along with its definition? [Sample answer: The example can help you understand what the definition means, and thinking of the example can help you remember the definition.]

Encourage students to pay careful attention to text features and visuals, as these frequently communicate key ideas about the vocabulary terms.

Q: What text features help you identify new vocabulary terms in each lesson? [Sample answer: Highlighted bold terms, Examples, and Key Concept boxes]

As students progress through the topic, encourage them to identify new terms and add additional details and examples to their graphic organizers to clarify their understanding of the new vocabulary.

Extension for All Readers

Challenge students to use their completed graphic organizers to write a brief summary of the new vocabulary terms they will learn in this topic. Help students to develop strong mathematical communication skills by encouraging them to include one or more examples using precise mathematical notation.

Available Online

Build Vocabulary

Use the graphic organizer to help you understand new vocabulary terms.

Term	Definition	Example
cube root	Sample answer: The cube root of a number, n, is a number whose cube equals n.	Sample answer: The number 5 is the cube root of 125 because $5 \cdot 5 \cdot 5 = 125$.
irrational number	Sample answer: A number that cannot be written in the form $\frac{a}{b}$, where a and b are integers and $b \neq 0$	Sample answer: $\sqrt{7}$
perfect cube	Sample answer: The cube of an integer	Sample answer: The number 64 is a perfect cube because $64 = 4^3$.
perfect square	Sample answer: A number that is the square of an integer	Sample answer: The number 49 is a perfect square because $49 = 7^2$.
scientific notation	Sample answer: A number written as the product of two factors, one greater than or equal to 1 and less than 10, and the other a power of 10	Sample answer: $7,120,000,000 = 7.12 \times 10^9$
square root	Sample answer: A number that, when multiplied by itself, equals the original number.	Sample answer: The number 9 is the square root of 81 because $9 \cdot 9 = 81$.

6   **Topic 1** Real Numbers   Go Online | PearsonRealize.com

Lesson 1-1

Rational Numbers as Decimals

Video Activity

Lesson Overview

FOCUS

Objective

Students will be able to:

✔ write repeating decimals as fractions.

Essential Understanding

Repeating decimals can be represented as an equivalent rational number in fraction form.

COHERENCE

In Grade 7, students:

- learned strategies to write rational numbers as decimals.
- understood that decimals either terminate or repeat.

In this lesson, students:

- understand that every number has a decimal form.
- convert repeating decimals into fractions.

Later in this topic, students will:

- compare and order rational and irrational numbers.

RIGOR

This lesson emphasizes a blend of **conceptual understanding** and **procedural skills and fluency**.

- Students extend their understanding of converting fractions to decimals to converting repeating decimals to fractions.
- Students analyze patterns of repeating decimals and relate it to multiplying by a power of 10 to move repeating digits to the left of the decimal point.

Math Anytime

Today's Challenge

Use the Topic 1 problems any time during this topic.

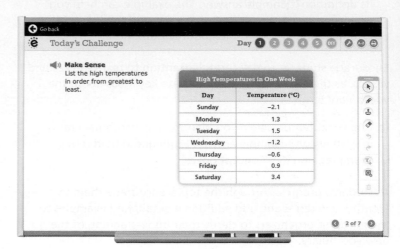

Watch the **Listen and Look For Video** for strategies and habits of mind to look for as students complete work on this lesson.

✓ Mathematics Overview

In this lesson, students will write repeating decimals as fractions. Students will use patterns as they develop the procedural skills needed to write equivalent equations by multiplying by a power of 10 to move the nonrepeating decimal to the left of the decimal point.

Applying Math Practices

Reason Abstractly and Quantitatively

Students will expand their knowledge about rational numbers and the relationship between decimals and fractions. They will decide which method to use to find fraction forms of repeating decimals.

Look for Relationships

Students will have opportunities to look for relationships in equations. They will identify and subtract repeating parts of decimals to solve for an unknown variable. Students will multiply equations by powers of 10 in order to simplify a problem and subtract the equations to eliminate the repeating decimal portion.

STEP 1 | Develop: Problem-Based Learning

15-20 min

Activity

Solve & Discuss It!

Reasoning As students work through the *Solve & Discuss It*, listen and look for a variety of strategies where students compare decimals and fractions to find the correct bolt size.

Before [WHOLE CLASS]

TP **1 Implement Tasks that Promote Reasoning and Problem Solving**

Q: How is the size of the wrench related to how the bolts are sized? [The wrench size is labeled in decimal form, and each bolt's size is labeled in fraction form.]

2 Build Understanding

Q: How can decimals and fractions be compared? [Sample answer: Decimals and fractions can be compared when written in the same form.]

Q: How do the labeled measurements describe the size of the wrench and the sizes of the bolts? [Sample answer: The measurement on the wrench describes the size of the opening of the wrench. The measurement on each bolt describes the length across the head of the bolt.]

During [SMALL GROUP]

TP **3 Support Productive Struggle in Learning Mathematics**

Q: How could you compare the size of the wrench to the different-sized bolts? [Sample answer: You could convert the bolt sizes from fractions to decimals, and then compare the different-sized bolts to the size of the wrench.]

Q: What other approach you could use to solve this problem? [Sample answer: You could convert the wrench size to a fraction, and then compare it to the different-size bolts.]

After [WHOLE CLASS]

TP **4 Facilitate Meaningful Mathematical Discourse**

Ask students to share their solutions. If needed, project Keisha's and Micah's work and ask:

Q: How did Keisha solve the problem? How does this compare with Micah's solution? [Sample answer: Keisha divided the fractions to find their decimal value. Micah used place value to write the decimal as a fraction.]

Q: What process did Micah use to write the size of the wrench as a fraction? [Sample answer: Micah first wrote the decimal as a fraction. He then found an equivalent fraction that matched the size of one of the bolts.]

5 Transition to Visual Learning

Q: How could you use a number line to estimate the answer? [Sample answer: Draw a number line from 0 to 1 in increments of $\frac{1}{10}$. Plot the sizes of the wrench and the bolts. The bolt that matches the wrench is the $\frac{3}{16}$-inch bolt.]

6 Extension for Early Finishers

Q: If the wrench was labeled 0.125 inch, what size bolt would fit? [$\frac{1}{8}$ in.]

Analyze Student Work

[Available Online]

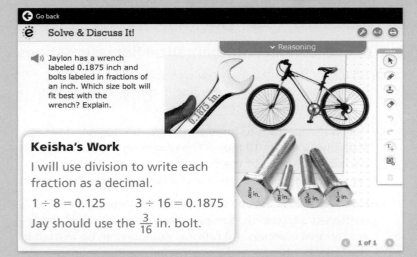

Go back

Solve & Discuss It!

⌄ Reasoning

Jaylon has a wrench labeled 0.1875 inch and bolts labeled in fractions of an inch. Which size bolt will fit best with the wrench? Explain.

Keisha's Work

I will use division to write each fraction as a decimal.

$1 \div 8 = 0.125$ $3 \div 16 = 0.1875$

Jay should use the $\frac{3}{16}$ in. bolt.

1 of 1

Keisha used division to write each fraction in decimal form.

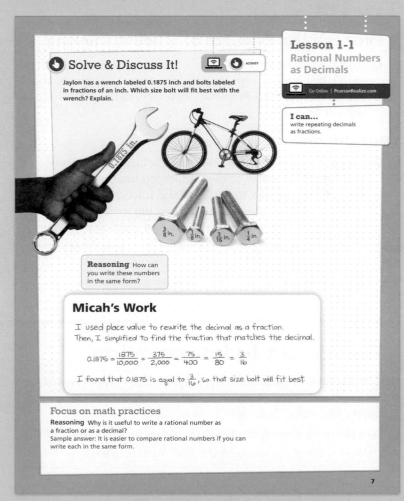

Solve & Discuss It!

Lesson 1-1
Rational Numbers as Decimals

Jaylon has a wrench labeled 0.1875 inch and bolts labeled in fractions of an inch. Which size bolt will fit best with the wrench? Explain.

Go Online | PearsonRealize.com

I can...
write repeating decimals as fractions.

Reasoning How can you write these numbers in the same form?

Micah's Work

I used place value to rewrite the decimal as a fraction. Then, I simplified to find the fraction that matches the decimal.

$0.1875 = \frac{1875}{10,000} = \frac{375}{2,000} = \frac{75}{400} = \frac{15}{80} = \frac{3}{16}$

I found that 0.1875 is equal to $\frac{3}{16}$, so that size bolt will fit best.

Focus on math practices

Reasoning Why is it useful to write a rational number as a fraction or as a decimal?
Sample answer: It is easier to compare rational numbers if you can write each in the same form.

7

Micah used place value to write the decimal as a fraction.

STEP **2** | Develop: Visual Learning

Visual Learning   Assess

ETP Establish Mathematics Goals to Focus Learning

Engage students in a discussion about the *Essential Question*. Make sure they understand that decimals can be written as fractions.

 EXAMPLE **1** ⊙ **Write Repeating Decimals as Fractions**

ETP Use and Connect Mathematical Representations

Q: How does the number line help to solve the problem? [Sample answer: The number line is used to estimate the fraction of the games the Sluggers won.]

Q: Why is it important to multiply $0.\overline{5}$ by 10? [Sample answer: Multiplying $0.\overline{5}$ by 10 moves the repeating digit of the decimal to the left of the decimal point. This allows the repeating parts of the decimals to cancel when subtracted.]

Q: How can you determine if a repeating decimal can be written as a fraction? [Sample answer: Repeating decimals are rational numbers. All rational numbers can be written in the form $\frac{a}{b}$, where a and b are integers, and $b \neq 0$.]

 Try It!

ETP Elicit and Use Evidence of Student Thinking

Q: How do you know that 0.444… means that 4 is a repeating digit? [Sample answer: In math, the three dots means that the number continues in the same way, so the repeating 4 will continue.]

Convince Me!

Q: Suppose that in the first line of the solution, x was set equal to $0.\overline{44}$. What power of ten would you multiply by in the second step? Would this change the fraction of games the team won? [Sample answer: You would multiply by 10^2, or 100, on each side of the equation. The fraction of games would still be $\frac{44}{99} = \frac{4}{9}$.]

Available Online

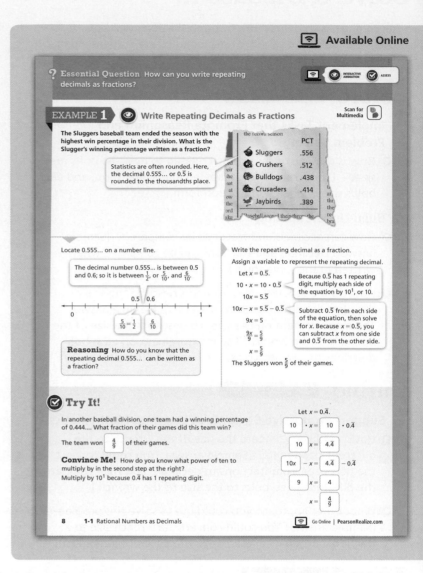

 Students can access the *Visual Learning Animation Plus* by using the **BouncePages app** to scan this page. Students can download the app for free in their mobile devices' app store.

 Response to Intervention

USE WITH EXAMPLE 3 Students may need to review place values to help determine which power of 10 to multiply a decimal by to eliminate repeating decimals.

• Have students identify place values of the first repeating digit.

   Q: What is the place value of the first repeating digit?

   $1.\overline{3}$ [3 is in the tenths place.]

   6.345555… [5 is in the thousandths place.]

• Remind students what happens to the decimal point when multiplied by a multiple of 10.

   Q: What is 2.5628 × 100? Explain how the decimal point moves. [256.28; multiplying by 100 moves the decimal point two places to the right.]

🏆 **Enrichment**

USE WITH EXAMPLE 2 Challenge advanced students to work through different variations of repeating decimals with nonrepeating digits.

• Have students identify repeating patterns.

   Q: What are the repeating digits in 2.4203203…? [203]

   Q: How can you find the equations to subtract when a repeating decimal has nonrepeating digits? [Sample answer: Multiply the repeating decimal by a power of 10 to move the nonrepeating digits to the left of the decimal point. This forms one equation. Then multiply the first equation by another power of 10 to move the repeating digits to the left of the decimal point. This is the second equation. Subtract the first equation from the second equation.]

EXAMPLE 2 — Write Repeating Decimals with Nonrepeating Digits as Fractions

ETP **Pose Purposeful Questions**

Q: When solving this problem, 10^1 was used to multiply the repeating decimal. Can other powers of 10 be used to solve? Explain. [Yes; Sample answer: Multiply by 1,000; $1{,}000x - 10x = 266.\overline{6} - 2.\overline{6}$, $990x = 264$, $x = \frac{264}{990} = \frac{24}{90}$.]

Try It!

ETP **Elicit and Use Evidence of Student Thinking**

Q: What is the first step when planning to solve this problem? [Sample answer: Identify the repeating digit(s) in the decimal]

EXAMPLE 3 — Write Decimals with Multiple Repeating Digits as Fractions

ETP **Pose Purposeful Questions**

Q: Why does this example show multiplying an equation by 100 instead of 10? [Sample answer: The decimal has two repeating digits, so multiply the equation by 100, instead of 10.]

Try It!

ETP **Elicit and Use Evidence of Student Thinking**

Q: What is an example of a repeating decimal where the equation used to convert the decimal to a fraction needs to be multiplied by 10,000? Explain. [Sample answer: 0.348934893489… You would multiply by 10,000 because there are four repeating digits.]

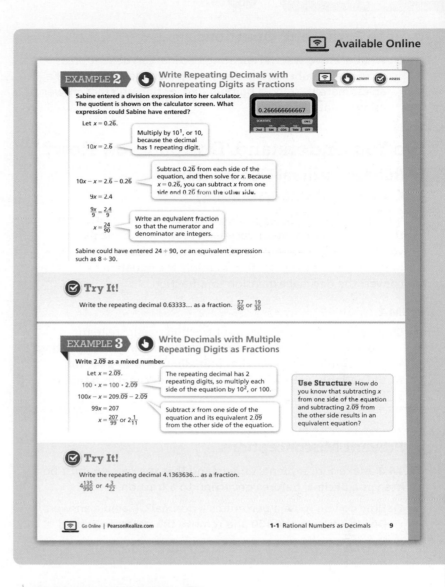

Available Online

EXAMPLE 2 — Write Repeating Decimals with Nonrepeating Digits as Fractions

Sabine entered a division expression into her calculator. The quotient is shown on the calculator screen. What expression could Sabine have entered?

0.266666666667

Let $x = 0.2\overline{6}$.

$10x = 2.\overline{6}$

Multiply by 10^1, or 10, because the decimal has 1 repeating digit.

$10x - x = 2.\overline{6} - 0.2\overline{6}$

Subtract $0.2\overline{6}$ from each side of the equation, and then solve for x. Because $x = 0.2\overline{6}$, you can subtract x from one side and $0.2\overline{6}$ from the other side.

$9x = 2.4$

$\frac{9x}{9} = \frac{2.4}{9}$

$x = \frac{24}{90}$

Write an equivalent fraction so that the numerator and denominator are integers.

Sabine could have entered $24 \div 90$, or an equivalent expression such as $8 \div 30$.

Try It!

Write the repeating decimal 0.63333… as a fraction. $\frac{57}{90}$ or $\frac{19}{30}$

EXAMPLE 3 — Write Decimals with Multiple Repeating Digits as Fractions

Write $2.\overline{09}$ as a mixed number.

Let $x = 2.\overline{09}$.

$100 \cdot x = 100 \cdot 2.\overline{09}$

The repeating decimal has 2 repeating digits, so multiply each side of the equation by 10^2, or 100.

$100x = 209.\overline{09} - 2.\overline{09}$

$99x = 207$

$x = \frac{207}{99}$ or $2\frac{1}{11}$

Subtract x from one side of the equation and its equivalent $2.\overline{09}$ from the other side of the equation.

Use Structure How do you know that subtracting x from one side of the equation and subtracting $2.\overline{09}$ from the other side results in an equivalent equation?

Try It!

Write the repeating decimal 4.1363636… as a fraction. $4\frac{135}{990}$ or $4\frac{3}{22}$

Go Online | PearsonRealize.com   1-1 Rational Numbers as Decimals   9

ADDITIONAL EXAMPLES

For additional examples go to PearsonRealize.com.

ELL English Language Learners

BEGINNING Before completing Example 3, teach some of the vocabulary students will need.

Q: What does it mean to mix things? How does this explain what a *mixed number* is? [Sample answer: To put them together; a *mixed number* has a whole number and a fraction]

Q: Things that are *equal* have the same value. What word does *equivalent* sound like? How could you use that to figure out the meaning of equivalent? [Sample answer: Equal; equivalent means equal in value.]

INTERMEDIATE After completing Example 3, have students work in pairs. Ask them to read the problem and summarize the known information.

Q: What are the repeating digits in this example? How do you know? [0, 9; Repeat means that something happens over and over.]

Q: What is the difference between the words *multiple* and *multiply*? [Sample answer: Multiple means more than one. Multiply is an operation where you use repeated addition.]

ADVANCED After completing Example 3, have students read the problem, gathering important information from the question. Have a class discussion about the given information.

Q: Teach the person next to you how to solve the problem. Then list the steps you would use to write a repeating decimal as a fraction. [Check students' work.]

Key Concept   Activity

KEY CONCEPT

ETP **Pose Purposeful Questions**

Q: What are two ways a repeating decimal can be written as a rational number in fraction form? [Sample answer: Make an estimate by using a number line, or find an exact answer using equations.]

Do You Understand/Do You Know How?

ETP **Build Procedural Fluency from Conceptual Understanding**

Essential Question Students should understand that the patterns in repeating decimals are related to the place value of the repeating digits. Knowing the place value helps identify which power of 10 to multiply the equation by to convert the decimal expansion to a fraction.

ITEM 2

Q: What is the importance of subtracting to eliminate the repeating digits? [Sample answer: Eliminating the repeating digits results in an equation that allows you to solve for the variable and write the repeating decimal in fraction form.]

Prevent Misconceptions

ITEM 4 Make sure students understand that the percent must be written as a decimal before converting to a fraction.

Q: How do you write a percent as a decimal? [Sample answer: Divide a percent by 100 and remove the percent symbol.]

Q: What is the percent written as a repeating decimal? [0.6363…]

Available Online

KEY CONCEPT

Because repeating decimals are rational numbers, you can write them in fraction form.

STEP 1 Assign a variable to represent the repeating decimal.

STEP 2 Write an equation: *variable = decimal*.

STEP 3 Multiply each side of the equation by 10^d, where d is the number of repeating digits in the repeating decimal.

STEP 4 Subtract equivalent expressions of the variable and the repeating decimal from each side of the equation.

STEP 5 Solve for the variable. Write an equivalent fraction so that the numerator and denominator are integers, if necessary.

Do You Understand?

1. **Essential Question** How can you write repeating decimals as fractions?
Sample answer: Set the repeating decimal equal to a variable. Then, use a power of ten to write an equivalent equation. Subtract equivalent expressions of the variable and the repeating decimal from the equivalent equation to eliminate the repeating portion of the decimal. Lastly, solve for the variable.

2. **Use Structure** Why do you multiply by a power of 10 when writing a repeating decimal as a rational number?
Sample answer: Multiplying both sides of the equation by the same power of 10 makes an equivalent equation where the repeating decimal now has a whole number portion and a repeating decimal portion. By subtracting equivalent expressions of the variable and the repeating decimal, you are able to eliminate the repeating decimal portion. Then, you can solve for x which gives you the rational number in fraction form.

3. **Be Precise** How do you decide by which power of 10 to multiply an equation when writing a decimal with repeating digits as a fraction?
Sample answer: You multiply by the power of ten that matches the number of repeating digits. For example, if you are writing $0.12\overline{6}$ as a fraction, multiply by 10^2 because there are 2 repeating digits.

Do You Know How?

4. A survey reported that $63.\overline{63}\%$ of moviegoers prefer action films. This percent represents a repeating decimal. Write it as a fraction.
$\frac{7}{11}$

5. A student estimates the weight of astronauts on the Moon by multiplying their weight by the decimal 0.16666…. What fraction can be used for the same estimation?
$\frac{1}{6}$

6. Write 2.3181818… as a mixed number.
$2\frac{7}{22}$

10   **1-1** Rational Numbers as Decimals   Go Online | PearsonRealize.com

---

ADDITIONAL EXAMPLE **1**

Help students transition to writing a repeating decimal greater than 1 as a fraction.

Make sure students understand that the steps for writing a repeating decimal greater than 1 as a fraction are similar to those for writing a repeating decimal as a fraction.

Q: Why do you multiply by 10? [Sample answer: Only one digit repeats.]

Q: How do you compare the mixed numbers? [Sample answer: You could write $5\frac{2}{3}$ as an equivalent mixed number with a denominator of 9. $5\frac{2}{3}$ is equivalent to $5\frac{6}{9}$.]

Available Online

Go back

Additional Example

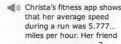

Christa's fitness app shows that her average speed during a run was 5.777… miles per hour. Her friend ran an average of $5\frac{2}{3}$ miles per hour. What fraction will allow Christa to compare her average speed to her friend's average speed?

Practice & Problem Solving

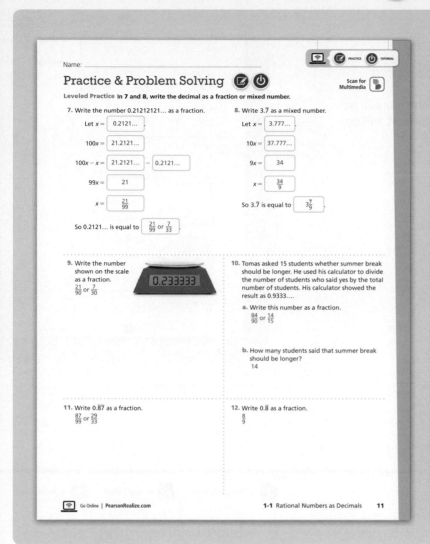

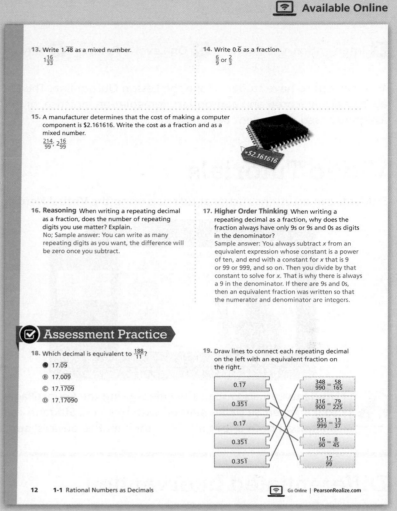

📶 **Available Online**

Name: _____

Practice & Problem Solving

Scan for Multimedia

Leveled Practice In 7 and 8, write the decimal as a fraction or mixed number.

7. Write the number 0.21212121... as a fraction.

Let x = | 0.2121...

100x = | 21.2121...

100$x - x$ = | 21.2121... | − | 0.2121...

99x = | 21

x = | $\frac{21}{99}$

So 0.2121... is equal to | $\frac{21}{99}$ or $\frac{7}{33}$

8. Write 3.$\overline{7}$ as a mixed number.

Let x = | 3.777...

10x = | 37.777...

9x = | 34

x = | $\frac{34}{9}$

So 3.$\overline{7}$ is equal to | $3\frac{7}{9}$

9. Write the number shown on the scale as a fraction.
0.233333
$\frac{21}{90}$ or $\frac{7}{30}$

10. Tomas asked 15 students whether summer break should be longer. He used his calculator to divide the number of students who said yes by the total number of students. His calculator showed the result as 0.9333....

a. Write this number as a fraction.
$\frac{84}{90}$ or $\frac{14}{15}$

b. How many students said that summer break should be longer?
14

11. Write 0.$\overline{87}$ as a fraction.
$\frac{87}{99}$ or $\frac{29}{33}$

12. Write 0.$\overline{8}$ as a fraction.
$\frac{8}{9}$

Go Online | PearsonRealize.com   1-1 Rational Numbers as Decimals   **11**

---

13. Write 1.$\overline{48}$ as a mixed number.
$1\frac{16}{33}$

14. Write 0.$\overline{6}$ as a fraction.
$\frac{6}{9}$ or $\frac{2}{3}$

15. A manufacturer determines that the cost of making a computer component is $2.161616. Write the cost as a fraction and as a mixed number.
$\frac{214}{99}$; $2\frac{16}{99}$

$2.161616

16. Reasoning When writing a repeating decimal as a fraction, does the number of repeating digits you use matter? Explain.
No; Sample answer: You can write as many repeating digits as you want, the difference will be zero once you subtract.

17. Higher Order Thinking When writing a repeating decimal as a fraction, why does the fraction always have only 9s or 9s and 0s as digits in the denominator?
Sample answer: You always subtract x from an equivalent expression whose constant is a power of ten, and end with a constant for x that is 9 or 99 or 999, and so on. Then you divide by that constant to solve for x. That is why there is always a 9 in the denominator. If there are 9s and 0s, then an equivalent fraction was written so that the numerator and denominator are integers.

✓ Assessment Practice

18. Which decimal is equivalent to $\frac{188}{11}$?
Ⓐ 17.0$\overline{9}$
Ⓑ 17.0$\overline{09}$
Ⓒ 17.$\overline{1709}$
Ⓓ 17.$\overline{17090}$

19. Draw lines to connect each repeating decimal on the left with an equivalent fraction on the right.

0.$\overline{17}$		$\frac{348}{990} = \frac{58}{165}$
0.3$\overline{51}$		$\frac{316}{900} = \frac{79}{225}$
0.1$\overline{7}$		$\frac{351}{999} = \frac{13}{37}$
0.$\overline{351}$		$\frac{16}{90} = \frac{8}{45}$
0.35$\overline{1}$		$\frac{17}{99}$

12   1-1 Rational Numbers as Decimals   Go Online | PearsonRealize.com

---

You may opt to have students complete the automatically scored Practice & Problem Solving items online.

🔴 Error Intervention

ITEM 10 Students may not recognize how to write an equivalent fraction form that is useful for answering part b.

Q: What does the numerator of the fraction represent? [It represents the total number of students who said yes.]

Q: What denominator value represents the total number of people Tomas surveyed? [15]

🏆 Challenge

ITEM 14 Extend students' understanding of repeating decimals by having them write and solve their own problem.

Q: Write a decimal with repeating digits to the thousandths place. Write this decimal in fraction form. [Sample answer: 0.532532...; 1,000$x - x$ = 532.$\overline{532}$ − 0.$\overline{532}$, 999x = 532, $x = \frac{532}{999}$]

Item Analysis

Example	Items	DOK
1	8, 12, 14	2
	17	3
2	9, 10, 15, 18	2
3	7, 11, 13	2
	16	3

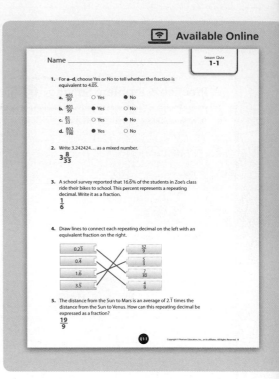
☑ **Lesson Quiz**

R+I Use the student scores on the Lesson Quiz to prescribe differentiated assignments.

I Intervention 0–3 Points **O** On-Level 4 Points **A** Advanced 5 Points

You may opt to have students take the Lesson Quiz online. The Lesson Quiz will be automatically scored and appropriate remediation, practice, or enrichment will be assigned based on student performance.

⏻ **Video Tutorials**

Students can access instructional tutorials using the **Virtual Nerd app**.

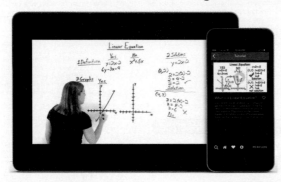

Students can also access the videos using the **BouncePages app** to scan exercise pages marked with this icon. Students can download both apps for free in their mobile devices' app store.

Differentiated Intervention

I = Intervention **O** = On-Level **A** = Advanced

Reteach to Build Understanding **I**
Provides scaffolded reteaching for the key lesson concepts.

Additional Vocabulary Support **I** **O**
Helps students develop and reinforce understanding of key terms and concepts.

Build Mathematical Literacy **I**
Provides support for struggling readers to build mathematical literacy.

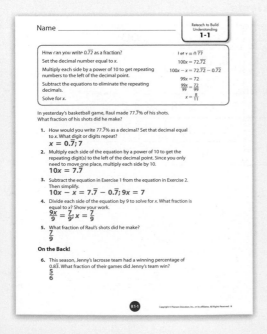

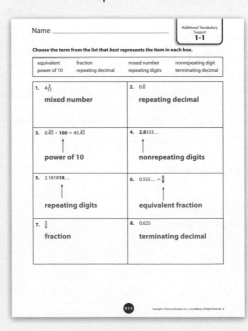

Additional Practice

You may opt to have students complete the automatically scored Additional Practice items online.

Item Analysis

Example	Items	DOK
1	1, 2, 12	1
1	7	2
1	11	3
2	3, 6, 10	2
2	5, 11	3
3	4, 9	2
3	8, 11	3

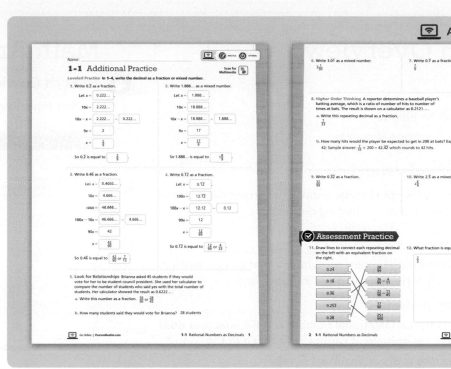

🛜 Available Online

Differentiated Intervention

I = Intervention   **O** = On-Level   **A** = Advanced

Enrichment **O** **A**

Presents engaging problems and activities that extend the lesson concepts.

Math Tools and Games **I** **O** **A**

Offers additional activities and games to build understanding and fluency.

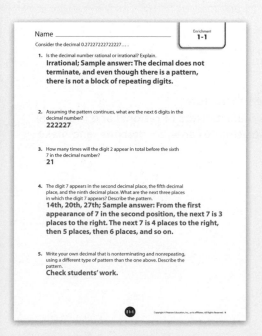

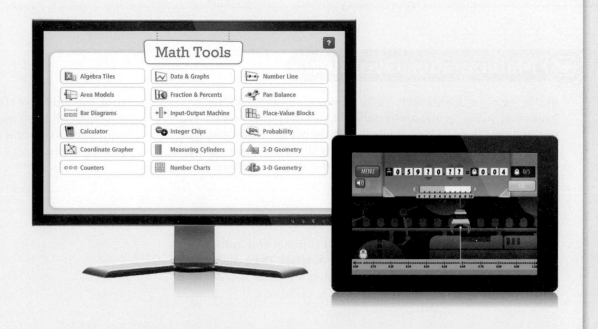

Lesson 1-2

Understand Irrational Numbers

Lesson Overview

FOCUS

Objective

Students will be able to:

✔ identify an irrational number.

Essential Understanding

Any number that is not rational is irrational. Irrational numbers are nonrepeating, nonterminating decimals.

COHERENCE

In Grade 7, students:

- identified rational numbers as numbers that can be written in the form $\frac{a}{b}$, where a and b are integers, and $b \neq 0$.

In this lesson, students:

- understand that an irrational number is a decimal that does not repeat or terminate; it cannot be written in the form $\frac{a}{b}$.
- identify square roots as irrational numbers.
- classify numbers as rational or irrational.

Later in this topic, students will:

- compare and order rational and irrational numbers.
- develop processes to estimate the value of irrational square roots.

RIGOR

This lesson emphasizes a blend of **conceptual understanding** and **procedural skill and fluency**.

- Students extend their understanding of rational numbers to identify irrational numbers. They understand that these categories make up the system of real numbers.
- Students explain how they classify numbers as rational or irrational.

Math Anytime

👆 Today's Challenge

Use the Topic 1 problems any time during this topic.

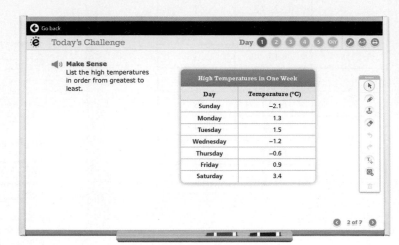

✅ Mathematics Overview

In this lesson, students will classify numbers as either rational or irrational. Students will understand that an irrational number is a decimal that does not repeat or terminate. Students will also learn to recognize perfect squares and identify that the square root of a number that is not a perfect square is an irrational number.

Applying Math Practices

Critique Reasoning

Students will use their knowledge about rational and irrational numbers to justify how they classified a number. They will critique the reasoning of others and decide if other students' explanations make sense when classifying a number.

Look for and Make Use of Structure

Students will learn the characteristics of rational and irrational numbers and use this structure to analyze, describe, and make classifications.

STEP 1 | Develop: Problem-Based Learning

15-20 min

Activity

Explain It!

Critique Reasoning As students work through the *Explain It*, listen and look for different ways in which students analyze Sofia's work. Incorporate their critiques into the classroom discussion.

Before [WHOLE CLASS]

TP **1 Implement Tasks that Promote Reasoning and Problem Solving**

Q: Do all of the digits in a repeating decimal need to repeat? Explain. [No; 0.12222…; Sample answer: Not all of the digits in a repeating decimal need to repeat, just as long as the digits farthest to the right in the decimal repeat.]

Q: Why is 0.1212 not a repeating decimal? [Sample answer: This number has a pattern of 12, but 12 does not repeat forever.]

2 Build Understanding

Q: Could the decimal given in the problem be written as a repeating decimal? Explain. [No; Sample answer: There is a pattern in the decimal, 12, 112, 1112, and so on, but it does not have any digits that keep repeating in the same order.]

During [SMALL GROUP]

TP **3 Support Productive Struggle in Learning Mathematics**

Q: How is Sofia's answer, $\frac{12}{99}$, written as a decimal different from the given decimal? [Sample answer: Sofia's fraction would be written as 0.121212…, which shows the 12 repeating in the same order. The given decimal does not show any digits repeating.]

Q: Write a rule for identifying a repeating decimal. [Sample answer: A repeating decimal is a decimal in which a digit or digits repeat in the same order forever.]

After [WHOLE CLASS]

TP **4 Facilitate Meaningful Mathematical Discourse**

Ask students to share their solutions. If needed, project Mary's and Devon's work and ask:

Q: If a decimal does not terminate or repeat, do you think that you can write the decimal as a fraction? Explain. [No; Sample answer: Only a terminating or repeating decimal can be written as a fraction.]

5 Transition to Visual Learning

Q: If a decimal can be written as a fraction, it is called a rational number. Do you think a number that cannot be written as a fraction has a name? Explain. [Yes; Sample answer: These numbers that cannot be written as a fraction are called irrational numbers.]

6 Extension for Early Finishers

Q: Is $\frac{0.24}{1.7}$ a rational number? Explain your reasoning. [Sample answer: It is a rational number. If you multiply both the numerator and denominator by 100, the result is a ratio of integers: $\frac{24}{170}$.]

Analyze Student Work

Available Online

Go back

Explain It!

Make Sense and Persevere

Sofia wrote a decimal as a fraction. Her classmate Nora says that her method and answer are not correct. Sofia disagrees and says that this Is the method she learned.

B. Use Structure What is another nonterminating decimal number that can not be written as a fraction?

0.121121112112…

$x = 0.12$
$100 \cdot x = 100 \cdot 0.12$
$100x = 12.12$
$99x = 12$
$x = \frac{12}{99}$

Mary's Work

0.020020002000200002…

I used the same digits, but my pattern did not repeat.

1 of 1

Mary's decimal contains the same digits, but they do not repeat in the same pattern.

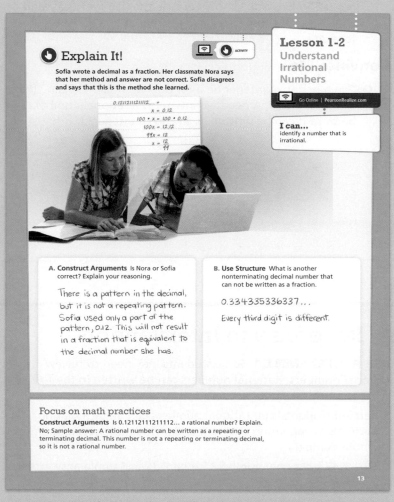

Explain It!

Lesson 1-2
Understand Irrational Numbers

Sofia wrote a decimal as a fraction. Her classmate Nora says that her method and answer are not correct. Sofia disagrees and says that this is the method she learned.

0.121121112112… =
$x = 0.12$
$100 \cdot x = 100 \cdot 0.12$
$100x = 12.12$
$99x = 12$
$x = \frac{12}{99}$

Go Online | PearsonRealize.com

I can…
identify a number that is irrational.

A. Construct Arguments Is Nora or Sofia correct? Explain your reasoning.

There is a pattern in the decimal, but it is not a repeating pattern. Sofia used only a part of the pattern, 0.12. This will not result in a fraction that is equivalent to the decimal number she has.

B. Use Structure What is another nonterminating decimal number that can not be written as a fraction?

0.334335336337…

Every third digit is different.

Focus on math practices

Construct Arguments Is 0.12112111112… a rational number? Explain. No; Sample answer: A rational number can be written as a repeating or terminating decimal. This number is not a repeating or terminating decimal, so it is not a rational number.

13

Devon studies the pattern in Sofia's decimal to determine that she is correct. He writes a decimal without a repeating pattern, even though some of the digits do repeat.

STEP 2 | Develop: Visual Learning

Visual Learning | Assess

ETP Establish Mathematics Goals to Focus Learning

Engage students in a discussion about the *Essential Question*. Make sure they have mastered identifying rational numbers, and understand that a number is irrational if it is not rational.

EXAMPLE 1 Identify Irrational Numbers

ETP Use and Connect Mathematical Representations

Q: Is the given decimal a terminating decimal? Explain.
[No; Sample answer: The three dots at the end of the decimal mean that the digits continue without end, but may or may not repeat.]

Q: Suppose the given decimal was written as 0.24758326. Would this decimal be a rational number? Explain.
[Yes; Sample answer: The decimal would be a rational number because it terminates.]

Try It!

ETP Elicit and Use Evidence of Student Thinking

Q: What type of decimal is $0.\overline{76}$? How do you know? [It is a repeating decimal. I know because the bar over the 7 and 6 means that those specific digits repeat in a pattern forever.]

Convince Me!

Q: Can a negative integer be a rational number? Explain. [Yes; Sample answer: A negative integer is a rational number because it can be written as a ratio of integers.]

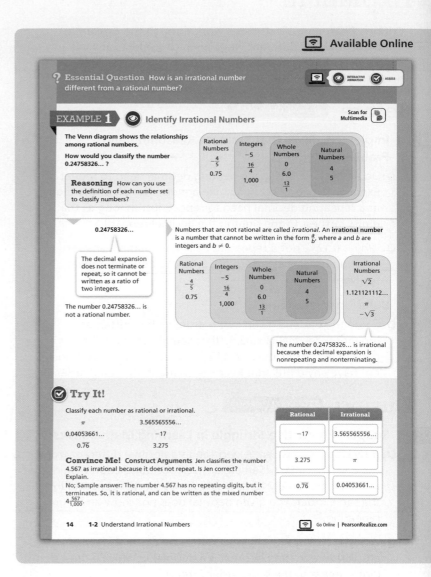

Available Online

? **Essential Question** How is an irrational number different from a rational number?

EXAMPLE 1 Identify Irrational Numbers

Scan for Multimedia

The Venn diagram shows the relationships among rational numbers.

How would you classify the number 0.24758326... ?

Reasoning How can you use the definition of each number set to classify numbers?

0.24758326...

The decimal expansion does not terminate or repeat, so it cannot be written as a ratio of two integers.

The number 0.24758326... is not a rational number.

Numbers that are not rational are called *irrational*. An **irrational number** is a number that cannot be written in the form $\frac{a}{b}$, where a and b are integers and $b \neq 0$.

The number 0.24758326... is irrational because the decimal expansion is nonrepeating and nonterminating.

Try It!

Classify each number as rational or irrational.

π 3.565565556...
0.04053661...   −17
$0.\overline{76}$ 3.275

Rational	Irrational
−17	3.565565556...
3.275	π
$0.\overline{76}$	0.04053661...

Convince Me! Construct Arguments Jen classifies the number 4.567 as irrational because it does not repeat. Is Jen correct? Explain.
No; Sample answer: The number 4.567 has no repeating digits, but it terminates. So, it is rational, and can be written as the mixed number $4\frac{567}{1,000}$.

14   **1-2** Understand Irrational Numbers   Go Online | PearsonRealize.com

 Students can access the *Visual Learning Animation Plus* by using the **BouncePages app** to scan this page. Students can download the app for free in their mobile devices' app store.

Response to Intervention

USE WITH EXAMPLE 1 Some students may need to review rational numbers. Rational numbers can be written in the form $\frac{a}{b}$, where a and b are integers, and $b \neq 0$.

- Remind students that rational numbers can be terminating decimals or repeating decimals and include integers and whole numbers.

  Q: Is 3.45 a rational number? Explain. [Yes; Sample answer: It is a rational number because it is a terminating decimal.]

  Q: Is $3.\overline{45}$ a rational number? Explain. [Yes; Sample answer: It is a rational number because it is a repeating decimal.]

Enrichment

USE WITH EXAMPLE 2 Challenge advanced students to find the first fifteen perfect squares. [1, 4, 9, 16, 25, 36, 49, 64, 81, 100, 121, 144, 169, 196, 225]

Q: Look at the differences between consecutive perfect squares. Identify a pattern that could help you to find the 16th perfect square.
[Sample answer: The difference between consecutive perfect squares follows the pattern 3, 5, 7, 9, 11,....]

EXAMPLE 2 · Identify Square Roots and Irrational Numbers

TP Pose Purposeful Questions

Write $\sqrt{7}$ on the board and ask the students the following questions:

Q: How would you read this number? [The nonnegative square root of 7]

Q: What does this number mean? [Sample answer: It is the number that, when multiplied by itself, equals 7.]

Q: Do you think that $\sqrt{7}$ is rational or irrational? Explain. [Irrational; Sample answer: It is irrational because there is no number that, when multiplied by itself, equals 7.]

EXAMPLE 3 · Classify Numbers as Rational or Irrational

TP Pose Purposeful Questions

Q: What is the value of $\sqrt{16}$? Explain. [4; Sample answer: $4 \times 4 = 16$]

Q: How can you use what you know about $-81,572$ to make a general rule about all integers? Explain how this rule will help you identify whether all integers are rational or irrational. [Sample answer: Since any integer can be written in the form $\frac{a}{b}$, where $b = 1$, all integers are rational numbers.]

▶ Try It!

TP Elicit and Use Evidence of Student Thinking

Q: How do you know if a square root is rational or irrational? [Sample answer: If the number under the radical is a perfect square, it is rational. If not, it is irrational.]

Q: Do you have to know how to write $-0.7\overline{5}$ as a ratio of integers to be able to classify it as rational? Explain. [No; Sample answer: Since the decimal is a repeating decimal, it is rational.]

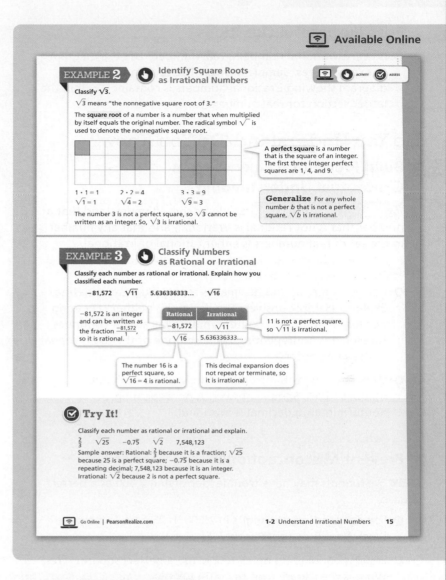

Available Online

EXAMPLE 2 · Identify Square Roots as Irrational Numbers

Classify $\sqrt{3}$.

$\sqrt{3}$ means "the nonnegative square root of 3."

The **square root** of a number is a number that when multiplied by itself equals the original number. The radical symbol $\sqrt{}$ is used to denote the nonnegative square root.

A **perfect square** is a number that is the square of an integer. The first three integer perfect squares are 1, 4, and 9.

$1 \cdot 1 = 1$ $2 \cdot 2 = 4$ $3 \cdot 3 = 9$
$\sqrt{1} = 1$ $\sqrt{4} = 2$ $\sqrt{9} = 3$

The number 3 is not a perfect square, so $\sqrt{3}$ cannot be written as an integer. So, $\sqrt{3}$ is irrational.

Generalize For any whole number b that is not a perfect square, $\sqrt{b}$ is irrational.

EXAMPLE 3 · Classify Numbers as Rational or Irrational

Classify each number as rational or irrational. Explain how you classified each number.
$$-81,572 \quad \sqrt{11} \quad 5.636336333... \quad \sqrt{16}$$

$-81,572$ is an integer and can be written as the fraction $\frac{-81,572}{1}$, so it is rational.

Rational	Irrational
$-81,572$	$\sqrt{11}$
$\sqrt{16}$	$5.636336333...$

11 is not a perfect square, so $\sqrt{11}$ is irrational.

The number 16 is a perfect square, so $\sqrt{16} = 4$ is rational.

This decimal expansion does not repeat or terminate, so it is irrational.

☑ Try It!

Classify each number as rational or irrational and explain.
$\frac{2}{3}$ $\sqrt{25}$ -0.75 $\sqrt{2}$ $7,548,123$

Sample answer: Rational: $\frac{2}{3}$ because it is a fraction; $\sqrt{25}$ because 25 is a perfect square; -0.75 because it is a repeating decimal; $7,548,123$ because it is an integer. Irrational: $\sqrt{2}$ because 2 is not a perfect square.

Go Online | PearsonRealize.com   1-2 Understand Irrational Numbers   **15**

ADDITIONAL EXAMPLES

For additional examples go to PearsonRealize.com.

ⒺⒷⓛ English Language Learners

BEGINNING Before Example 1, teach the terms from the Venn diagram. Provide vocabulary terms and examples to students as they express their thoughts in English.

Q: Which groups include the number 0.5? [Rational numbers]

Q: How are natural numbers different from whole numbers? [Sample answer: Whole numbers include 0.]

Q: Why is $\frac{16}{4}$ an integer but $-\frac{4}{5}$ is not? [Sample answer: $\frac{16}{4}$ simplifies to 4.]

INTERMEDIATE Ask students to review Example 2. Have volunteers complete and read these sentences.

The number that can be multiplied by itself to equal a given number is the _____ of that number. [square root]

The square root of a perfect square is a(n) _____ number. [rational]

The square root of a nonperfect square is a(n) _____ number. [irrational]

ADVANCED After completing Example 2, have students share information by speaking with a partner or in a small group.

Q: In your own words, explain to your partner what a perfect square is. [Sample answer: A number that is equal to an integer times itself.]

Q: Why do you think the word *square* is used to describe this type of number? [Sample answer: You can form that number of squares into a larger square with an equal number of columns and rows.]

STEP **2** | Develop: Visual Learning *continued*

Key Concept Activity

KEY CONCEPT

ETP Pose Purposeful Questions

Q: Is every irrational number a real number? Use the diagram to explain. [Yes. Sample answer: The section in the Venn diagram showing irrational numbers is contained within the larger section for real numbers.]

Do You Understand/Do You Know?

ETP Build Procedural Fluency from Conceptual Understanding

 Essential Question Students should understand that a number that is not rational is irrational, and that any number in the set of real numbers is either rational or irrational.

ITEM 4

Q: Can you describe this decimal as repeating or terminating? Explain. [Sample answer: The decimal is neither repeating nor terminating. It is nonterminating because it continues forever. It is nonrepeating because none of the digits repeat in the same order.]

Q: Does knowing this information help you classify the number? [Yes; Sample answer: A nonrepeating, nonterminating decimal is irrational.]

Prevent Misconceptions

ITEM 5 Students may have trouble identifying 2,500 as a perfect square.

Q: Look at the first two digits in 2,500. Is 25 a perfect square? [Yes] What is its square root? [5]

Q: 2,500 is equal to 25 times 100. Is 100 a perfect square? [Yes] What is the square root of 100? [10]

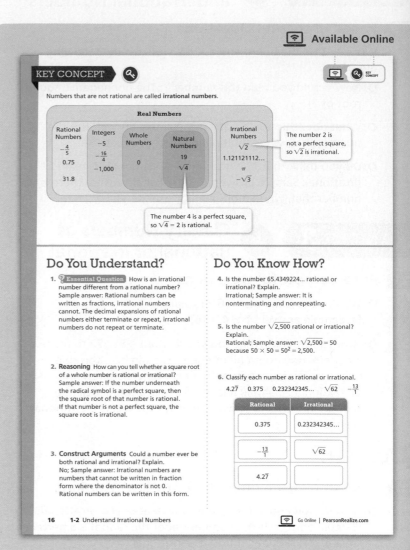

KEY CONCEPT

Numbers that are not rational are called **irrational numbers**.

Real Numbers

Rational Numbers $-\frac{4}{5}$ 0.75 31.8 | Integers -5 $-\frac{16}{4}$ $-1,000$ | Whole Numbers 0 | Natural Numbers 19 $\sqrt{4}$

Irrational Numbers $\sqrt{2}$ 1.121121112... π $-\sqrt{3}$

The number 2 is not a perfect square, so $\sqrt{2}$ is irrational.

The number 4 is a perfect square, so $\sqrt{4} = 2$ is rational.

Do You Understand?

1. **Essential Question** How is an irrational number different from a rational number? Sample answer: Rational numbers can be written as fractions, irrational numbers cannot. The decimal expansions of rational numbers either terminate or repeat, irrational numbers do not repeat or terminate.

2. **Reasoning** How can you tell whether a square root of a whole number is rational or irrational? Sample answer: If the number underneath the radical symbol is a perfect square, then the square root of that number is rational. If that number is not a perfect square, the square root is irrational.

3. **Construct Arguments** Could a number ever be both rational and irrational? Explain. No; Sample answer: Irrational numbers are numbers that cannot be written in fraction form where the denominator is not 0. Rational numbers can be written in this form.

Do You Know How?

4. Is the number 65.4349224... rational or irrational? Explain. Irrational; Sample answer: It is nonterminating and nonrepeating.

5. Is the number $\sqrt{2,500}$ rational or irrational? Explain. Rational; Sample answer: $\sqrt{2,500} = 50$ because $50 \times 50 = 50^2 = 2,500$.

6. Classify each number as rational or irrational. $4.2\overline{7}$ 0.375 0.232342345... $\sqrt{62}$ $-\frac{13}{1}$

Rational	Irrational
0.375	0.232342345...
$-\frac{13}{1}$	$\sqrt{62}$
$4.2\overline{7}$	

16 1-2 Understand Irrational Numbers Go Online | PearsonRealize.com

ADDITIONAL EXAMPLE **3**

Help students transition to classifying numbers written in fraction form as rational or irrational.

Make sure students remember that the fraction bar indicates division, to clear up confusion about why an irrational number is written in fraction form.

Q: Why is $\sqrt{\frac{1}{2}}$ irrational and $\frac{-\sqrt{4}}{2}$ rational? [Since $\sqrt{\frac{1}{2}} = \frac{\sqrt{1}}{\sqrt{2}}$, $\sqrt{\frac{1}{2}}$ is irrational because it has an irrational number in the denominator. The quotient of $\frac{-\sqrt{4}}{2} = \frac{-2}{2} = -1$. This is an integer, so it's a rational number.]

Q: The 2 and 6 in 8.262662666... repeat. Why isn't this number a repeating decimal? [Sample answer: Even though there is a pattern, 26, 266, 2666 and so on, the same digits in the same order do not repeat forever.]

Go back

Additional Example

Classify each number as rational or irrational. Explain how you classified each number.

$\frac{2}{0.5}$ $\frac{22}{7}$ $\sqrt{\frac{1}{2}}$ $\frac{-\sqrt{4}}{2}$

8.262662666...

Answer: $\frac{2}{0.5}$, $\frac{22}{7}$, and $\frac{-\sqrt{4}}{2}$ are rational; $\sqrt{\frac{1}{2}}$ and 8.262662666... are irrational.

Practice & Problem Solving

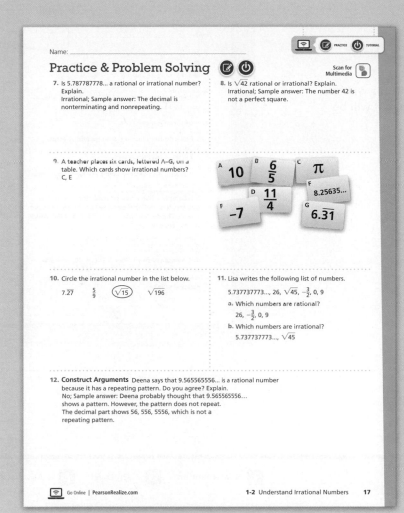

Name: _____

Practice & Problem Solving

Scan for Multimedia

7. Is 5.787787778... a rational or irrational number? Explain.

Irrational; Sample answer: The decimal is nonterminating and nonrepeating.

8. Is $\sqrt{42}$ rational or irrational? Explain.

Irrational; Sample answer: The number 42 is not a perfect square.

9. A teacher places six cards, lettered A–G, on a table. Which cards show irrational numbers?

C, E

A 10
B $\frac{6}{5}$
C π
D $\frac{11}{4}$
E 8.25635...
F −7
G $6.\overline{31}$

10. Circle the irrational number in the list below.

$7.\overline{27}$ $\frac{5}{9}$ $\boxed{\sqrt{15}}$ $\sqrt{196}$

11. Lisa writes the following list of numbers.

5.737737773..., 26, $\sqrt{45}$, $-\frac{3}{2}$, 0, 9

a. Which numbers are rational?

26, $-\frac{3}{2}$, 0, 9

b. Which numbers are irrational?

5.737737773..., $\sqrt{45}$

12. Construct Arguments Deena says that 9.565565556... is a rational number because it has a repeating pattern. Do you agree? Explain.

No; Sample answer: Deena probably thought that 9.565565556... shows a pattern. However, the pattern does not repeat. The decimal part shows 56, 556, 5556, which is not a repeating pattern.

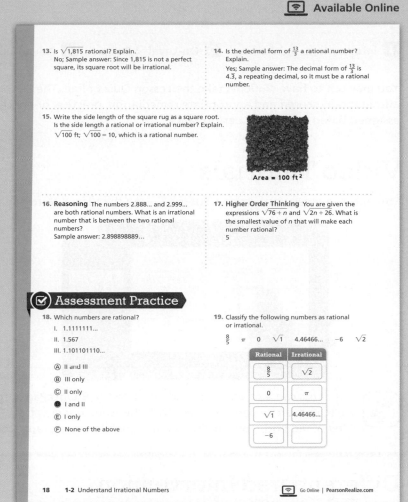

13. Is $\sqrt{1,815}$ rational? Explain.

No; Sample answer: Since 1,815 is not a perfect square, its square root will be irrational.

14. Is the decimal form of $\frac{13}{3}$ a rational number? Explain.

Yes; Sample answer: The decimal form of $\frac{13}{3}$ is $4.\overline{3}$, a repeating decimal, so it must be a rational number.

15. Write the side length of the square rug as a square root. Is the side length a rational or irrational number? Explain.

$\sqrt{100}$ ft; $\sqrt{100}$ = 10, which is a rational number.

Area = 100 ft^2

16. Reasoning The numbers 2.888... and 2.999... are both rational numbers. What is an irrational number that is between the two rational numbers?

Sample answer: 2.898898889...

17. Higher Order Thinking You are given the expressions $\sqrt{76 + n}$ and $\sqrt{2n + 26}$. What is the smallest value of n that will make each number rational?

5

☑ Assessment Practice

18. Which numbers are rational?

I.   1.1111111...

II. 1.567

III. 1.101101110...

Ⓐ II and III

Ⓑ III only

Ⓒ II only

● I and II

Ⓔ I only

Ⓕ None of the above

19. Classify the following numbers as rational or irrational.

$\frac{8}{5}$ π 0 $\sqrt{1}$ 4.46466...   −6 $\sqrt{2}$

Rational	Irrational
$\frac{8}{5}$	$\sqrt{2}$
0	π
$\sqrt{1}$	4.46466...
−6	

ⒺⓁⓁ English Language Learners

ITEM 8 English Language Learners may know the answer, but struggle to explain how they know. Give them this list of vocabulary words that they can use in their explanations, reviewing definitions as needed.

perfect square   nonperfect square

square root   radical sign

🏆 Challenge

ITEM 9 Challenge students to extend their knowledge of irrational numbers.

Q: Suppose another index card shows the number 3π. Is this number rational or irrational? Justify your answer.

[Irrational; Sample answer: Multiplying a nonrepeating, nonterminating decimal by 3 will not make it terminate or repeat. The product will still be irrational.]

You may opt to have students complete the automatically scored Practice & Problem Solving items online.

Item Analysis

Example	Items	DOK
1	9, 18	1
1	7, 12, 14, 16	2
2	10	1
2	8, 13	2
3	11, 15, 19	2
3	17	3

PearsonRealize.com

Assess   Tutorials   Worksheets

Lesson Quiz

 Use the student scores on the Lesson Quiz to prescribe differentiated assignments.

I Intervention 0–3 Points   **O** On-Level 4 Points   **A** Advanced 5 Points

You may opt to have students take the Lesson Quiz online. The Lesson Quiz will be automatically scored and appropriate remediation, practice, or enrichment will be assigned based on student performance.

Video Tutorials

Students can access instructional tutorials using the **Virtual Nerd app**.

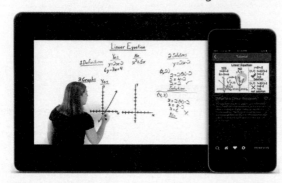

Students can also access the videos using the **BouncePages app** to scan exercise pages marked with this icon. Students can download both apps for free in their mobile devices' app store.

Available Online

Name _____   Lesson Quiz 1-2

1. Which numbers can be classified as rational? Select all that apply.
   ☑ 9/2   ☐ √11   ☑ 6.565656…
   ☑ 0.23   ☐ 0.32416…   ☑ −5⅝

2. Is the number √3,600 rational or irrational? Explain.
   Rational; Sample answer: 3,600 is a perfect square, so √3,600 = 60.

3. Explain why each number is irrational.
   a. π
   Pi is a nonterminating, nonrepeating decimal.
   b. √7
   7 is not a perfect square.
   c. 7.1234…
   7.1234… is a nonterminating, nonrepeating decimal.

4. Isaiah says that the number 6.787887888… is a rational number because it has a repeating pattern. Do you agree? Explain.
   No; Sample answer: Even though the number has a pattern, it is irrational because the pattern does not repeat. The decimal part shows 78, 788, 7888, which is not a repeating pattern.

5. A ballroom has a square dance floor. The area of the floor is 400 square feet. If the length of each side of the square increased by one foot, would its area be a rational number? Explain.
   Yes; Sample answer: Since √400 = 20, each side would now be 20 + 1 = 21 feet. (21)² = 441 which is a perfect square. A perfect square is a rational number.

Differentiated Intervention

I = Intervention   **O** = On-Level   **A** = Advanced

Reteach to Build Understanding **I**

Provides scaffolded reteaching for the key lesson concepts.

Additional Vocabulary Support **I O**

Helps students develop and reinforce understanding of key terms and concepts.

Build Mathematical Literacy **I**

Provides support for struggling readers to build mathematical literacy.

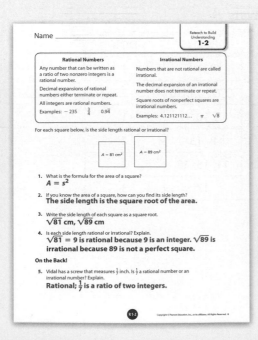

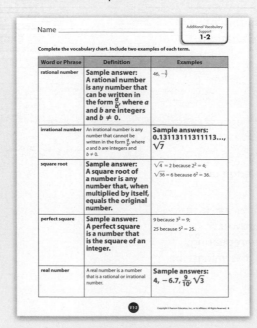

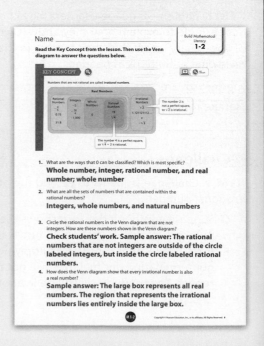

Practice   Worksheets   Math Tools   Math Games

Additional Practice

You may opt to have students complete the automatically scored Additional Practice items online.

Item Analysis

Example	Items	DOK
1	1, 9	1
	5	2
2	2, 6	2
	8	3
3	3, 4, 7, 10	2

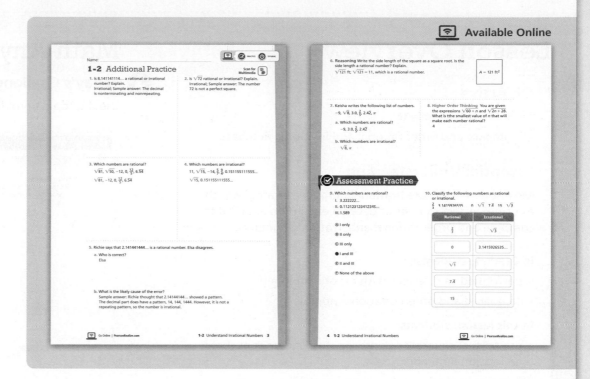

Available Online

Differentiated Intervention

I = Intervention   **O** = On-Level   **A** = Advanced

Enrichment **O** **A**

Presents engaging problems and activities that extend the lesson concepts.

Math Tools and Games **I** **O** **A**

Offers additional activities and games to build understanding and fluency.

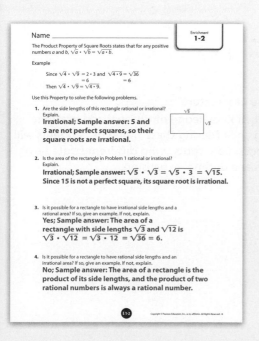

Lesson 1-3 — Compare and Order Real Numbers

Lesson Overview

FOCUS

Objective

Students will be able to:

✔ compare and order rational and irrational numbers.

Essential Understanding

Most square roots are irrational numbers. Strategies such as using perfect squares or decimal expansion are used to compare and order rational and irrational numbers.

COHERENCE

In Grade 7, students:

- performed calculations with rational numbers.
- compared and ordered rational numbers.

In this lesson, students:

- use perfect squares to approximate a square root that is an irrational number.
- compare and order rational and irrational numbers.

Later in this topic, students will:

- evaluate square roots and cube roots.
- solve equations using square roots and cube roots.

RIGOR

This lesson emphasizes a blend of **conceptual understanding** and **application**.

- Students reinforce and extend their understanding of rational numbers and irrational numbers to compare and order rational and irrational numbers.
- Students apply their knowledge of perfect squares and decimals to approximate a square root that is an irrational number.

Math Anytime

⬇ **Today's Challenge**

Use the Topic 1 problems any time during this topic.

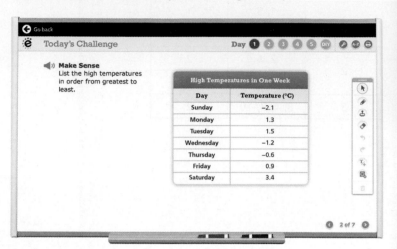

▶ Watch the **Listen and Look For Video** for strategies and habits of mind to look for as students complete work on this lesson.

☑ Mathematics Overview

In this lesson, students will compare and order rational and irrational numbers. Students will learn to approximate the value of a square root by using perfect squares and decimal approximations. Students will also use the number line to compare and order rational and irrational numbers.

Applying Math Practices

Model with Math

Students have opportunities to use a number line to determine the approximate value of an irrational number. By graphing, they are also able to compare and order real numbers, even when ordering or comparing rational and irrational numbers.

Look For and Make Use of Structure

Students will expand their knowledge of rational and irrational numbers by comparing and ordering these numbers. Students will approximate nonperfect square roots using different strategies such as perfect squares and decimal expansion.

STEP 1 | Develop: Problem-Based Learning

15-20 min

Activity

Solve & Discuss It!

Modeling with Math As students work through the *Solve & Discuss It*, listen and look for students who use their reasoning skills to determine the rug Courtney and Malik should purchase.

Before [WHOLE CLASS]

1 Implement Tasks that Promote Reasoning and Problem Solving

Q: How can you determine which rug Courtney and Malik should purchase? [Sample answer: Since all the rugs are the same price, determine which rug or rugs will fit in the 50 square foot space by finding the area of each rug.]

2 Build Understanding

Q: How will you determine which rugs will fit in the space? [Sample answer: After finding the area of each rug, compare each area with 50 square feet. The rug needs to be 50 square feet or less.]

During [SMALL GROUP]

3 Support Productive Struggle in Learning Mathematics

Q: Which formulas will you use to find the area of each rug? [Sample answer: The formula for the area of a circle is $A = \pi r^2$, where A represents the area, and the r represents the radius. Area of rectangle: $A = l \times w$. Area of square: $A = s^2$]

Q: Why would you want to use value 3.14 for π? [Sample answer: You need to be able to compare the area of the circular rug with the other areas, so you need to use a rational approximation for π.]

After [WHOLE CLASS]

4 Facilitate Meaningful Mathematical Discourse

Ask students to share their solutions. If needed, project Nathan's and Lindsey's work and ask:

Q: How can you use modeling to compare the areas of the three rugs? [Sample answer: You could make scale models of each rug using the scale of 1 inch equals 1 foot. You could then cut out the models and compare them.]

5 Transition to Visual Learning

Q: Do you think that π is a rational number or an irrational number? Explain. [Sample answer: π is an irrational number because its decimal form is nonterminating and nonrepeating.]

6 Extension for Early Finishers

Q: Give the dimensions of a room that would fit one of the rugs that is too large for Courtney and Malik's space. How do you know it will fit? [Sample Answer: The circular rug would fit in a square room with side lengths of 8 feet. The rug covers about 50.24 square feet. Its diameter is 8 feet and would just fit in the room.]

Analyze Student Work

Available Online

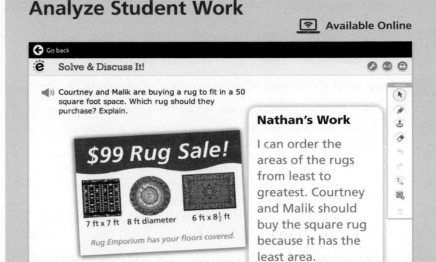

Go back

Solve & Discuss It!

Courtney and Malik are buying a rug to fit in a 50 square foot space. Which rug should they purchase? Explain.

$99 Rug Sale!

7 ft × 7 ft   8 ft diameter   6 ft × 8½ ft

Rug Emporium has your floors covered.

Nathan's Work

I can order the areas of the rugs from least to greatest. Courtney and Malik should buy the square rug because it has the least area.

1 of 1

Nathan ordered the areas of the rugs from least to greatest and determined that they should buy the rug with the least area.

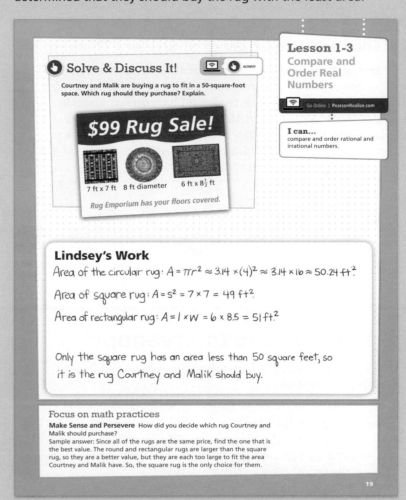

Solve & Discuss It!

ACTIVITY

Courtney and Malik are buying a rug to fit in a 50-square-foot space. Which rug should they purchase? Explain.

$99 Rug Sale!

7 ft × 7 ft   8 ft diameter   6 ft × 8½ ft

Rug Emporium has your floors covered.

Lesson 1-3
Compare and Order Real Numbers

Go Online | PearsonRealize.com

I can...
compare and order rational and irrational numbers.

Lindsey's Work

Area of the circular rug: $A = \pi r^2 \approx 3.14 \times (4)^2 \approx 3.14 \times 16 \approx 50.24 \text{ ft}^2$.

Area of square rug: $A = s^2 = 7 \times 7 = 49 \text{ ft}^2$.

Area of rectangular rug: $A = l \times w = 6 \times 8.5 = 51 \text{ ft}^2$.

Only the square rug has an area less than 50 square feet, so it is the rug Courtney and Malik should buy.

Focus on math practices
Make Sense and Persevere How did you decide which rug Courtney and Malik should purchase?
Sample answer: Since all of the rugs are the same price, find the one that is the best value. The round and rectangular rugs are larger than the square rug, so they are a better value, but they are each too large to fit the area Courtney and Malik have. So, the square rug is the only choice for them.

19

Lindsey compared the areas of the rugs to 50 square feet.

ETP Establish Mathematics Goals to Focus Learning

Engage students in a discussion about the *Essential Question*. Make sure they understand the concepts of perfect squares and irrational numbers.

EXAMPLE 1 **Approximate an Irrational Number**

ETP Use and Connect Mathematical Representations

Q: Why must you approximate $\sqrt{74}$? [Sample answer: Since $\sqrt{74}$ is not a perfect square, it is irrational. A rational approximation must be done to compare numbers.]

Q: Is knowing that $\sqrt{74}$ ft is between 8 ft and 9 ft enough information for Darcy to know whether she has enough ribbon? Explain. [No; Sample answer: Since Darcy has 8.5 feet, she still wouldn't know if the amount of ribbon is long enough for the diagonal.]

Q: Reasoning Why do you think 8.5 is the first number used as an approximate value for $\sqrt{74}$? [Sample answer: The $\sqrt{74}$ is between the $\sqrt{64}$ and $\sqrt{81}$ and Darcy has 8.5 feet of ribbon, so it is a good place to start.]

 Try It!

ETP Elicit and Use Evidence of Student Thinking

Q: Suppose someone chooses 4 and 16 as perfect squares because they are on opposite sides of 12 on the number line. Explain why this reasoning is incorrect. [Sample answer: While 4 and 16 are perfect squares, with square roots of 2 and 4 respectively, 9 is also a perfect square. Using the $\sqrt{9}$ would give a more accurate range for the approximate square root.]

Convince Me!

Q: How could you determine a closer approximation for $\sqrt{12}$? Explain. [Sample answer: Using square numbers like 3.4 and 3.5 to determine the best approximation.]

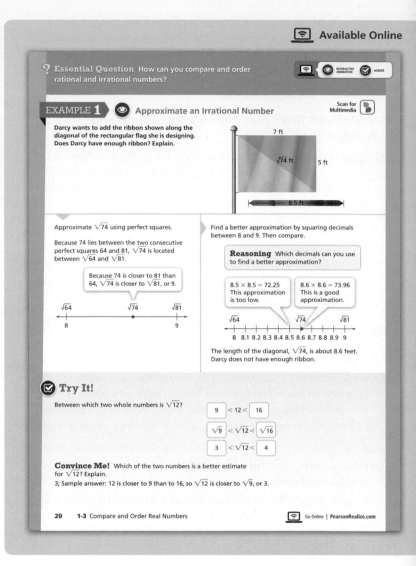

Available Online

? Essential Question How can you compare and order rational and irrational numbers?

EXAMPLE 1 Approximate an Irrational Number
Scan for Multimedia

Darcy wants to add the ribbon shown along the diagonal of the rectangular flag she is designing. Does Darcy have enough ribbon? Explain.

7 ft

$\sqrt{74}$ ft   5 ft

8.5 ft

Approximate $\sqrt{74}$ using perfect squares.

Because 74 lies between the two consecutive perfect squares 64 and 81, $\sqrt{74}$ is located between $\sqrt{64}$ and $\sqrt{81}$.

Because 74 is closer to 81 than 64, $\sqrt{74}$ is closer to $\sqrt{81}$, or 9.

$\sqrt{64}$ $\sqrt{74}$ $\sqrt{81}$
8   9

Find a better approximation by squaring decimals between 8 and 9. Then compare.

Reasoning Which decimals can you use to find a better approximation?

$8.5 \times 8.5 = 72.25$ This approximation is too low.

$8.6 \times 8.6 = 73.96$ This is a good approximation.

$\sqrt{64}$ $\sqrt{74}$ $\sqrt{81}$
8 8.1 8.2 8.3 8.4 8.5 8.6 8.7 8.8 8.9 9

The length of the diagonal, $\sqrt{74}$, is about 8.6 feet. Darcy does not have enough ribbon.

 Try It!

Between which two whole numbers is $\sqrt{12}$?

9 < 12 < 16

$\sqrt{9}$ < $\sqrt{12}$ < $\sqrt{16}$

3 < $\sqrt{12}$ < 4

Convince Me! Which of the two numbers is a better estimate for $\sqrt{12}$? Explain.
3; Sample answer: 12 is closer to 9 than to 16, so $\sqrt{12}$ is closer to $\sqrt{9}$, or 3.

20   1-3 Compare and Order Real Numbers   Go Online | PearsonRealize.com

Students can access the *Visual Learning Animation Plus* by using the **BouncePages app** to scan this page. Students can download the app for free in their mobile devices' app store.

RtI Response to Intervention

USE WITH EXAMPLE 2 Some students may have difficulty multiplying decimals.

• Ask students questions to help with multiplying decimals.

Q: How many decimal places will the product of 20.6×0.7 have? Explain. [Sample answer: The product will have two decimal places. Each factor has one decimal place, so the product must have two decimal places.]

Q: How can you determine where to place the decimal in the product of two decimals? [Sample answer: Count the number of decimal places for each factor, and determine the total number of decimal places for both factors. Place that many numbers to the right of the decimal point. Adjust for zeros that are the last numbers to the right of the decimal point.]

E Enrichment

USE WITH EXAMPLE 1 Challenge advanced students to use this process to find an approximation, to the hundredths place, for the square root of 10.8.

Q: Find an approximation for $\sqrt{10.8}$ to the hundredths place. Explain. [3.29; Sample answer: $\sqrt{10.8}$ is between 3.2 and 3.3. Determine a closer approximation by trying numbers that lie between 3.2 and 3.3 and squaring them. $3.29 \times 3.29 = 10.8241$]

EXAMPLE 2 Compare Irrational Numbers

TP Pose Purposeful Questions

Q: How can you find an approximation of $\sqrt{32}$ to compare it to 5.51326...? [Sample answer: Find an approximation by using perfect squares and decimals that are either greater or less than 5.51326....]

Q: Why is it enough to know that $\sqrt{32}$ is between 5.6 and 5.7? Explain. [Sample answer: You only need to know if the number is greater that 5.51326... and if the number is between 5.6 and 5.7, you know it is greater.]

EXAMPLE 3 Compare and Order Rational and Irrational Numbers

TP Pose Purposeful Questions

Q: Why are irrational numbers being written as their rational approximations? [Sample answer: So they can be placed on the number line and be compared with rational numbers]

Q: Explain how you would determine the rational approximation of $\sqrt{94}$. [Sample answer: First you would find the perfect squares greater than and less than 94, which are 81 and 100. Since 94 is closer to 100 than 81, you would begin multiplying 9.5×9.5 until you found the decimal closest to 94.]

Q: Why is $9.\overline{5}$ greater than 9.5? [Sample answer: The line over the 5 means that the digit 5 repeats forever. So the number 0.9555... is greater than 9.5, which has a 0 in the hundredths place.]

Try It!

TP Elicit and Use Evidence of Student Thinking

Q: What should you do to help compare and order the numbers? [Sample answer: Each irrational number needs to written as its rational approximation. All numbers should be written as decimals.]

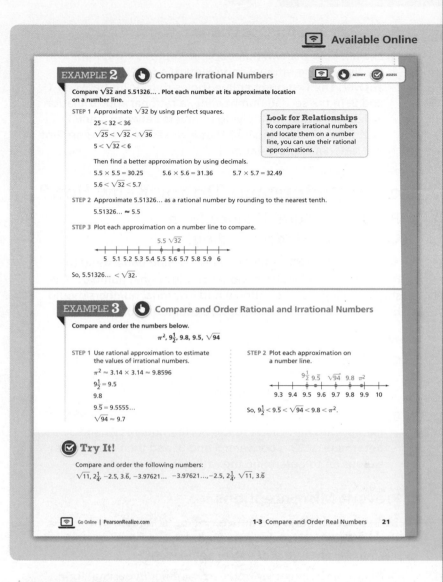

Available Online

EXAMPLE 2 — Compare Irrational Numbers — ACTIVITY — ASSESS

Compare $\sqrt{32}$ and 5.51326.... Plot each number at its approximate location on a number line.

STEP 1 Approximate $\sqrt{32}$ by using perfect squares.

$25 < 32 < 36$
$\sqrt{25} < \sqrt{32} < \sqrt{36}$
$5 < \sqrt{32} < 6$

Look for Relationships
To compare irrational numbers and locate them on a number line, you can use their rational approximations.

Then find a better approximation by using decimals.

$5.5 \times 5.5 = 30.25 \qquad 5.6 \times 5.6 = 31.36 \qquad 5.7 \times 5.7 = 32.49$
$5.6 < \sqrt{32} < 5.7$

STEP 2 Approximate 5.51326... as a rational number by rounding to the nearest tenth.

$5.51326... \approx 5.5$

STEP 3 Plot each approximation on a number line to compare.

5.5 $\sqrt{32}$
5 5.1 5.2 5.3 5.4 5.5 5.6 5.7 5.8 5.9 6

So, $5.51326... < \sqrt{32}$.

EXAMPLE 3 — Compare and Order Rational and Irrational Numbers

Compare and order the numbers below.
$\pi^2, 9\frac{1}{2}, 9.8, 9.5, \sqrt{94}$

STEP 1 Use rational approximation to estimate the values of irrational numbers.

$\pi^2 \approx 3.14 \times 3.14 \approx 9.8596$
$9\frac{1}{2} = 9.5$
9.8
$9.5 = 9.5555...$
$\sqrt{94} \approx 9.7$

STEP 2 Plot each approximation on a number line.

$9\frac{1}{2}$ 9.5 $\sqrt{94}$ 9.8 π^2
9.3 9.4 9.5 9.6 9.7 9.8 9.9 10

So, $9\frac{1}{2} < 9.5 < \sqrt{94} < 9.8 < \pi^2$.

Try It!

Compare and order the following numbers:
$\sqrt{11}, 2\frac{1}{4}, -2.5, 3.\overline{6}, -3.97621...$ $-3.97621..., -2.5, 2\frac{1}{4}, \sqrt{11}, 3.\overline{6}$

Go Online | PearsonRealize.com   1-3 Compare and Order Real Numbers   21

ADDITIONAL EXAMPLES

For additional examples go to PearsonRealize.com.

E L L English Language Learners

BEGINNING After reading Example 1 to students, review the terms *ribbon*, *diagonal*, *rectangular*, *approximation*, and *below*. Use the diagram to support instruction. Ask:

Q: What shape is the flag? Where does Darcy want to add the ribbon to the flag? [Rectangle; Sample answer: She wants to add the ribbon on the diagonal.]

Q: What does the word *approximation* mean? What number does Darcy need to approximate? [Sample answer: An approximation is an estimate. She needs to find an approximation of $\sqrt{74}$.]

INTERMEDIATE Use with Example 2.

Assign students into pairs and have them read the problem aloud. Then ask:

Q: Explain in your own words what *approximation* means. [Sample answer: *Approximation* means an estimate.]

Q: What is meant by a *better approximation* in terms of the problem? [Sample answer: A better approximation would be a closer estimate.]

ADVANCED Use with Example 2.

Assign students into pairs and read the problem aloud. Then have students write the steps for comparing irrational numbers in their own words. Have students read their steps to each other. Then ask:

Q: What was similar about the steps you wrote? [Students should include a first step involving using perfect squares and then include a step using decimal expansion to find a rational approximation.]

KEY CONCEPT

ETP **Pose Purposeful Questions**

Q: Explain how the two number lines represent the steps for finding the rational approximation for $\sqrt{2}$. [Sample answer: The first number line shows that $\sqrt{2}$ is between 1 and 2. In the second number line, a rational approximation is determined by multiplying numbers between 1 and 2. The decimal when squared that is closest to 2 will represent the rational approximation.]

Do You Understand/Do You Know How?

ETP **Build Procedural Fluency from Conceptual Understanding**

? Essential Question Students should understand that it is possible to compare rational and irrational numbers. They should recognize that rational and irrational numbers should be written in decimal form before comparing or ordering.

ITEM 6

Q: What is the first step you should do before comparing 5.7145 and $\sqrt{29}$? [Sample answer: You should first determine the rational approximation of $\sqrt{29}$.

Q: How can you determine the rational approximation of $\sqrt{29}$? [Sample answer: First, use the perfect squares 25 and 36 to determine $\sqrt{29}$ is between 5 and 6, and then use decimal expansion to determine the rational approximation.]

Prevent Misconceptions

ITEM 7 Students may have difficulty comparing negative numbers to positive numbers. Remind students to check the sign of the numbers before ordering or comparing.

Q: Before ordering or writing each number in decimal form, how can you determine which number will be the least? [Sample answer: I know that -5.6 will be least since it is the only negative number.]

Available Online

KEY CONCEPT

To compare rational and irrational numbers, you must first find rational approximations of the irrational numbers. You can approximate irrational numbers using perfect squares or by rounding.

Do You Understand?

1. **? Essential Question** How can you compare and order rational and irrational numbers? Sample answer: You can use perfect squares or rounding to approximate irrational numbers as rational numbers. Then you can compare.

2. **Reasoning** The "leech" is a technical term for the slanted edge of a sail. Is the length of the leech shown closer to 5 meters or 6 meters? Explain. $\sqrt{30}$
5 meters; Sample answer: 30 lies between perfect squares 25 and 36. Since 30 is closer to 25, $\sqrt{30}$ is closer to $\sqrt{25}$, or 5.

3. **Construct Arguments** Which is a better approximation of $\sqrt{20}$, 4.5 or 4.47? Explain.
4.47; Sample answer: The more decimal places in the answer, the more precise the approximation.

Do You Know How?

4. Approximate $\sqrt{39}$ to the nearest whole number.
6

5. Approximate $\sqrt{18}$ to the nearest tenth and plot the number on a number line.
4.2; Check students' number lines.
$\sqrt{18}$
4 4.1 4.2 4.3 4.4 4.5 4.6 4.7 4.8 4.9 5

6. Compare 5.7145... and $\sqrt{29}$. Show your work.
$\sqrt{29} < 5.7145...$; Check students' work.

7. Compare and order the following numbers:
5.2, $-5.\overline{6}$, $3\frac{9}{10}$, $\sqrt{21}$
$-5.\overline{6} < 3\frac{9}{10} < \sqrt{21} < 5.2$

22 1-3 Compare and Order Real Numbers   Go Online | **PearsonRealize.com**

ADDITIONAL EXAMPLE **3**

Available Online

Help students transition to comparing and ordering negative numbers with this additional example.

Make sure students remember that numbers decrease as they move farther to the left of zero on the number line.

Q: Why isn't -3.1 equal to $-3.\overline{1}$? How do you know which number is greater? [Sample answer: $-3.1 = -3.10...$, So when you compare -3.10 with $-3.111...$, you see that $-3.1 > -3.\overline{1}$.]

Q: Why do you convert to decimals instead of fractions? [Sample answer: If you converted the numbers to fractions, you would have to further convert them to have common denominators before comparing. Converting to decimals eliminates this extra step.]

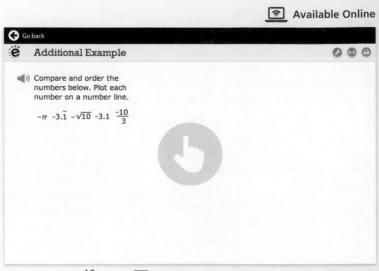

← Go back

é **Additional Example**

🔊 Compare and order the numbers below. Plot each number on a number line.

$-\pi$ $-3.\overline{1}$ $-\sqrt{10}$ -3.1 $\frac{-10}{3}$

Answer: So, $\frac{-10}{3} < -\sqrt{10} < -\pi < -3.\overline{1} < -3.1$

Practice & Problem Solving

 Available Online

Practice & Problem Solving

Scan for Multimedia

8. Leveled Practice Find the rational approximation of $\sqrt{15}$.

a. Approximate using perfect squares.

$$\boxed{9} < 15 < \boxed{16}$$

$$\boxed{\sqrt{9}} < \sqrt{15} < \boxed{\sqrt{16}}$$

$$\boxed{3} < \sqrt{15} < \boxed{4}$$

b. Locate and plot $\sqrt{15}$ on a number line.
Find a better approximation using decimals.

$$3.8 \times 3.8 = \boxed{14.44}$$

$$3.9 \times 3.9 = \boxed{15.21}$$

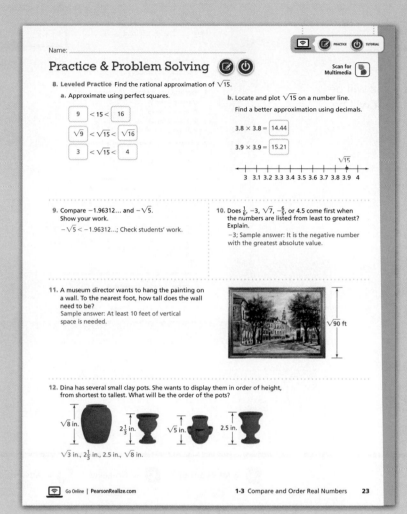

3 3.1 3.2 3.3 3.4 3.5 3.6 3.7 3.8 3.9 4

9. Compare $-1.96312...$ and $-\sqrt{5}$.
Show your work.

$-\sqrt{5} < -1.96312...$; Check students' work.

10. Does $\frac{1}{6}$, -3, $\sqrt{7}$, $-\frac{6}{5}$, or 4.5 come first when the numbers are listed from least to greatest? Explain.

-3; Sample answer: It is the negative number with the greatest absolute value.

11. A museum director wants to hang the painting on a wall. To the nearest foot, how tall does the wall need to be?
Sample answer: At least 10 feet of vertical space is needed.

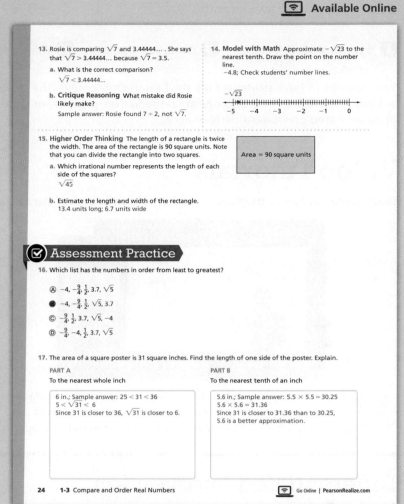

$\sqrt{90}$ ft

12. Dina has several small clay pots. She wants to display them in order of height, from shortest to tallest. What will be the order of the pots?

$\sqrt{8}$ in. $2\frac{1}{3}$ in. $\sqrt{5}$ in. 2.5 in.

$\sqrt{3}$ in., $2\frac{1}{3}$ in., 2.5 in., $\sqrt{8}$ in.

13. Rosie is comparing $\sqrt{7}$ and $3.44444...$. She says that $\sqrt{7} > 3.44444...$ because $\sqrt{7} = 3.5$.

a. What is the correct comparison?
$\sqrt{7} < 3.44444...$

b. **Critique Reasoning** What mistake did Rosie likely make?
Sample answer: Rosie found $7 \div 2$, not $\sqrt{7}$.

14. Model with Math Approximate $-\sqrt{23}$ to the nearest tenth. Draw the point on the number line.
-4.8; Check students' number lines.

$-\sqrt{23}$

-5   -4   -3   -2   -1   0

15. Higher Order Thinking The length of a rectangle is twice the width. The area of the rectangle is 90 square units. Note that you can divide the rectangle into two squares.

Area = 90 square units

a. Which irrational number represents the length of each side of the squares?
$\sqrt{45}$

b. Estimate the length and width of the rectangle.
13.4 units long; 6.7 units wide

✓ Assessment Practice

16. Which list has the numbers in order from least to greatest?

Ⓐ $-4, -\frac{9}{4}, \frac{1}{2}, 3.7, \sqrt{5}$

Ⓑ $-4, -\frac{9}{4}, \frac{1}{2}, \sqrt{5}, 3.7$

Ⓒ $-\frac{9}{4}, \frac{1}{2}, 3.7, \sqrt{5}, -4$

Ⓓ $-\frac{9}{4}, -4, \frac{1}{2}, 3.7, \sqrt{5}$

17. The area of a square poster is 31 square inches. Find the length of one side of the poster. Explain.

PART A
To the nearest whole inch

6 in.; Sample answer: $25 < 31 < 36$
$5 < \sqrt{31} < 6$
Since 31 is closer to 36, $\sqrt{31}$ is closer to 6.

PART B
To the nearest tenth of an inch

5.6 in.; Sample answer: $5.5 \times 5.5 = 30.25$
$5.6 \times 5.6 = 31.36$
Since 31 is closer to 31.36 than to 30.25, 5.6 is a better approximation.

You may opt to have students complete the automatically scored Practice & Problem Solving items online.

🅁 Error Intervention

ITEM 9 Remind students that when comparing two negative numbers, the number closest to 0 is the greater number.

Q: Why is $-\sqrt{5}$ less than $-1.96312...$? [Sample answer: $-\sqrt{5}$ is approximately -2.3 which is less that $-1.96312...$]

Q: How could you use a model to justify your reasoning? [Sample answer: You could draw a number line and plot both points using their rational approximations. On the number line, -1.96312 is closer to 0 than -2.3.]

🏆 Challenge

ITEM 8 You can use this item to expand students' understanding of approximation.

Q: Is it possible to determine a closer rational approximation for $\sqrt{15}$? Explain. [Yes; Sample answer: Find the rational approximation to the hundredths place.]

Q: How would you find the closer approximation? Sample answer: Square 3.85 and then make adjustments.]

Item Analysis

Example	Items	DOK
	11	1
1	8, 14, 17	2
	15	3
2	9	2
	13	3
3	10, 12, 16	2

☑ Lesson Quiz

RtI Use the student scores on the Lesson Quiz to prescribe differentiated assignments.

I Intervention 0–3 Points   **O** On-Level 4 Points   **A** Advanced 5 Points

You may opt to have students take the Lesson Quiz online. The Lesson Quiz will be automatically scored and appropriate remediation, practice, or enrichment will be assigned based on student performance.

⏻ Video Tutorials

Students can access instructional tutorials using the **Virtual Nerd app**.

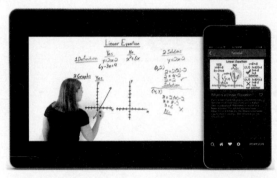

 Students can also access the videos using the **BouncePages app** to scan exercise pages marked with this icon. Students can download both apps for free in their mobile devices' app store.

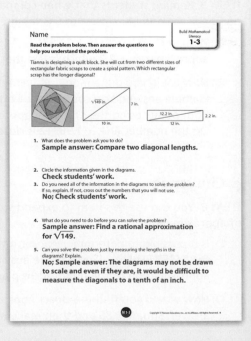

📶 **Available Online**

Name _____

Lesson Quiz
1-3

1. Compare $\sqrt{24}$ and 4.256 by plotting each number on the number line.

4.256 $\sqrt{24}$
4.0 4.1 4.2 4.3 4.4 4.5 4.6 4.7 4.8 4.9 5.0

2. What is the approximate value of $\sqrt{8}$ to the nearest tenth?
   Ⓐ between 2.9 and 3.0
   ● between 2.8 and 2.9
   Ⓒ between 2.7 and 2.8
   Ⓓ between 2.6 and 2.7

3. Compare and order the numbers below from least to greatest.
   $4.6, 2.\overline{8}, \pi, \sqrt{17}, \sqrt{7}$
   $\sqrt{7}, 2.\overline{8}, \pi, \sqrt{17}, 4.6$

4. For **a–d**, choose True or False for each statement.
   a. You can compare irrational numbers using rational approximation. ● True ○ False
   b. Square roots can be compared and ordered by comparing and ordering the numbers underneath the radical symbol. ● True ○ False
   c. You cannot compare the value of rational and irrational numbers. ○ True ● False
   d. The closer together the numbers being compared, the more decimal places you need to use. ● True ○ False

5. Between which two consecutive whole numbers does the length of the diagonal fall? Indicate which whole number it is closer to.
   Between 4 and 5; closer to 4

Differentiated Intervention

I = Intervention   **O** = On-Level   **A** = Advanced

Reteach to Build Understanding **I**

Provides scaffolded reteaching for the key lesson concepts.

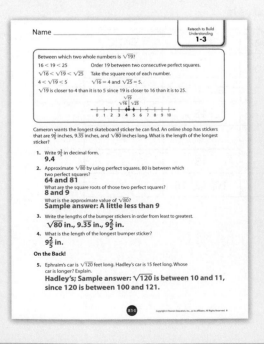

Name _____   Reteach to Build Understanding **1-3**

Between which two whole numbers is $\sqrt{19}$?
$16 < 19 < 25$ Order 19 between two consecutive perfect squares.
$\sqrt{16} < \sqrt{19} < \sqrt{25}$ Take the square root of each number.
$4 < \sqrt{19} < 5$ $\sqrt{16} = 4$ and $\sqrt{25} = 5$.
$\sqrt{19}$ is closer to 4 than it is to 5 since 19 is closer to 16 than it is to 25.

$\sqrt{16}$ $\sqrt{25}$
0 1 2 3 4 5 6 7 8 9 10

Cameron wants the longest skateboard sticker he can find. An online shop has stickers that are $9\frac{2}{5}$ inches, 9.35 inches, and $\sqrt{80}$ inches long. What is the length of the longest sticker?

1. Write $9\frac{2}{5}$ in decimal form.
   9.4
2. Approximate $\sqrt{80}$ by using perfect squares. 80 is between which two perfect squares?
   64 and 81
   What are the square roots of those two perfect squares?
   8 and 9
   What is the approximate value of $\sqrt{80}$?
   Sample answer: A little less than 9
3. Write the lengths of the bumper stickers in order from least to greatest.
   $\sqrt{80}$ in., 9.35 in., $9\frac{2}{5}$ in.
4. What is the length of the longest bumper sticker?
   $9\frac{2}{5}$ in.

On the Back!

5. Ephraim's car is $\sqrt{120}$ feet long. Hadley's car is 15 feet long. Whose car is longer? Explain.
   Hadley's; Sample answer: $\sqrt{120}$ is between 10 and 11, since 120 is between 100 and 121.

Additional Vocabulary Support **I** **O**

Helps students develop and reinforce understanding of key terms and concepts.

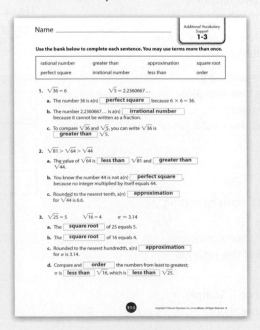

Name _____   Additional Vocabulary Support **1-3**

Use the bank below to complete each sentence. You may use terms more than once.

| rational number | greater than | approximation | square root |
| perfect square | irrational number | less than | order |

1. $\sqrt{36} = 6$ $\sqrt{5} = 2.2360667\ldots$
   a. The number 36 is a(n) **perfect square** because $6 \times 6 = 36$.
   b. The number $2.2360667\ldots$ is a(n) **irrational number** because it cannot be written as a fraction.
   c. To compare $\sqrt{36}$ and $\sqrt{5}$, you can write $\sqrt{36}$ is **greater than** $\sqrt{5}$.

2. $\sqrt{81} > \sqrt{64} > \sqrt{44}$
   a. The value of $\sqrt{64}$ is **less than** $\sqrt{81}$ and **greater than** $\sqrt{44}$.
   b. You know the number 44 is not a(n) **perfect square**, because no integer multiplied by itself equals 44.
   c. Rounded to the nearest tenth, a(n) **approximation** for $\sqrt{44}$ is 6.6.

3. $\sqrt{25} = 5$ $\sqrt{16} = 4$ $\pi \approx 3.14$
   a. The **square root** of 25 equals 5.
   b. The **square root** of 16 equals 4.
   c. Rounded to the nearest hundredth, a(n) **approximation** for π is 3.14.
   d. Compare and **order** the numbers from least to greatest; π is **less than** $\sqrt{16}$, which is **less than** $\sqrt{25}$.

Build Mathematical Literacy **I**

Provides support for struggling readers to build mathematical literacy.

Name _____   Build Mathematical Literacy **1-3**

Read the problem below. Then answer the questions to help you understand the problem.

Tianna is designing a quilt block. She will cut from two different sizes of rectangular fabric scraps to create a spiral pattern. Which rectangular scrap has the longer diagonal?

$\sqrt{149}$ in.   7 in.
10 in.
12.2 in.   2.2 in.
12 in.

1. What does the problem ask you to do?
   Sample answer: Compare two diagonal lengths.
2. Circle the information given in the diagrams.
   Check students' work.
3. Do you need all of the information in the diagrams to solve the problem? If so, explain. If not, cross out the numbers that you will not use.
   No; Check students' work.
4. What do you need to do before you can solve the problem?
   Sample answer: Find a rational approximation for $\sqrt{149}$.
5. Can you solve the problem just by measuring the lengths in the diagrams? Explain.
   No; Sample answer: The diagrams may not be drawn to scale and even if they are, it would be difficult to measure the diagonals to a tenth of an inch.

Additional Practice

You may opt to have students complete the automatically scored Additional Practice items online.

Item Analysis

Example	Items	DOK
	1	1
1	2, 10	2
	8	3
2	3, 6	2
3	4, 5	2
	7, 9	3

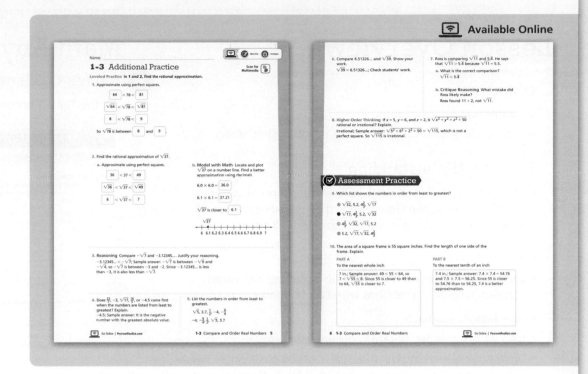

Differentiated Intervention

I = Intervention   **O** = On-Level   **A** = Advanced

Enrichment O A

Presents engaging problems and activities that extend the lesson concepts.

Math Tools and Games I O A

Offers additional activities and games to build understanding and fluency.

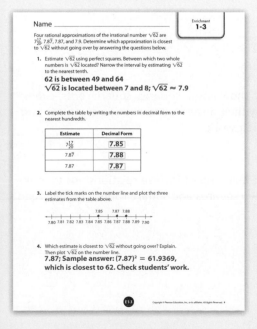

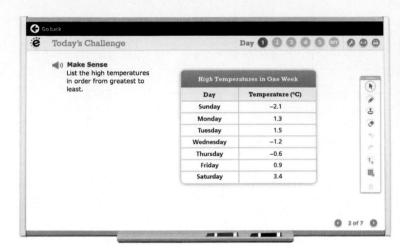

Lesson 1-4

Evaluate Square Roots and Cube Roots

PearsonRealize.com

Video   Activity

Lesson Overview

FOCUS

Objective

Students will be able to:

✔ find square roots and cube roots of rational numbers.

Essential Understanding

Finding the square root is the inverse operation of squaring a number. Finding the cube root is the inverse operation of cubing, which is raising a number to the third power.

COHERENCE

In Grade 6, students:

• showed fluency involved with whole number exponents through writing expressions with whole number exponents.

In this lesson, students:

• find whole number square roots and cube roots.

• build fluency with square and cube roots by classifying a whole number as a perfect square, a perfect cube, both, or neither.

Later in this topic, students will:

• solve equations using square and cube roots.

• explore and develop fluency involving integer exponents.

RIGOR

This lesson emphasizes a blend of **conceptual understanding** and **application**.

• Students reinforce their knowledge of perfect squares and square roots. They expand their knowledge to include developing an understanding of perfect cubes and cube roots.

• Students solve real-world problems with square roots and cube roots. They explore the relationship between the edge of a cube and its volume.

Math Anytime

Today's Challenge

Use the Topic 1 problems any time during this topic.

✅ Mathematics Overview

In this lesson, students will learn how to evaluate perfect squares and perfect cubes, and solve problems using perfect squares and perfect cubes. Students will also classify a whole number as either a perfect square, perfect cube, or both or neither.

Applying Math Practices

Reason Abstractly and Quantitatively
Students use their knowledge of squares, square roots, cubes, and cube roots to solve real-world problems. They will determine when to use squares, square roots, cubes, and cube roots for their calculations.

Construct Arguments
Students use what they know about squares, square roots, cubes, and cube roots to justify their answers and provide complete and clear explanations of their work.

Look for Relationships
Students use their understanding of inverse relationships to look for relationships between squares and square roots, and between cubes and cube roots.

STEP 1 | Develop: Problem-Based Learning

15-20 min

Activity

Solve & Discuss It!

Look for Relationships As students work through the *Solve & Discuss It*, listen and look for a variety of ways in which students analyze and describe what the problem is asking.

Before [WHOLE CLASS]

TP 1 Implement Tasks that Promote Reasoning and Problem Solving

Q: How do you find the area of a rectangle? [Multiply the rectangle's length by its width.]

Q: What do Matt and his dad need to find out? Explain. [Sample answer: They need to find out possible dimensions for the floor of a tree house they are building so that its area will equal 36 square feet.]

2 Build Understanding

Q: Is there more than one set of dimensions for a rectangular 36 square foot floor? Explain. [Yes; Sample answer: 36 is a composite number, so it has several factors. Each set of factors gives a different set of dimensions.]

During [SMALL GROUP]

TP 3 Support Productive Struggle in Learning Mathematics

Q: How can you find the dimensions for each rectangle that is 36 square feet? [Sample answer: Find the factors of 36.]

After [WHOLE CLASS]

TP 4 Facilitate Meaningful Mathematical Discourse

Ask students to share their solutions. If needed, project Grant's and Talia's work and ask:

Q: Do you think Grant's approach was effective? Explain. [Sample answer: Knowing the factors of 36 is important in finding the possible dimensions of the floor.]

Q: How does Talia's work compare to Grant's work? [Sample answer: Talia's work lets her visualize what the different dimensions would look like.]

5 Transition to Visual Learning

Q: If Matt and his dad build a floor that is 6 feet by 6 feet, how can they make the house a cube? How could they find its volume? [Sample answer: They could make each wall 6 feet high. The volume would be the area of the floor, 36, times the height, 6, which equals 216 cubic feet.]

6 Extension for Early Finishers

Q: Of all of the possible floor dimensions, which floor dimensions has the greatest perimeter? The least? [Greatest: 1 ft × 36 ft; Least: 6 ft × 6 ft]

Analyze Student Work

Available Online

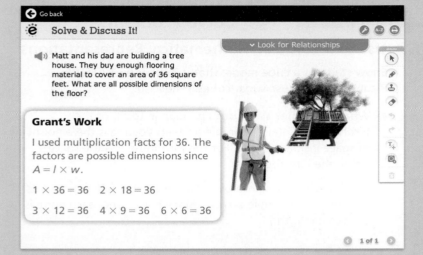

Grant's Work

I used multiplication facts for 36. The factors are possible dimensions since $A = l \times w$.

$1 \times 36 = 36$ $2 \times 18 = 36$
$3 \times 12 = 36$ $4 \times 9 = 36$ $6 \times 6 = 36$

Grant uses the factors of 36 to find possible dimensions.

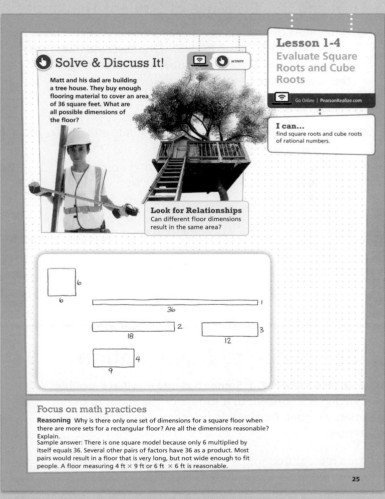

Talia draws diagrams to understand and solve the problem.

ETP **Establish Mathematics Goals to Focus Learning**

Engage students in a discussion about the *Essential Question*. Make sure they understand the concepts of squares, square roots, cubes, and cube roots.

 EXAMPLE **1** **Evaluate Cube Roots to Solve Problems**

ETP **Use and Connect Mathematical Representations**

Show students a cube model that is 3 cubes by 3 cubes by 3 cubes. You can use sugar cubes, if needed.

Q: What is volume? What does it mean in terms of the birdhouse? Explain. [Sample answer: Volume is the amount of space inside a figure. For the birdhouse it is the space inside the birdhouse.]

Q: How does knowing the birdhouse is a cube help you find its dimensions? [Sample answer: Since it is a cube, each edge is the same length.]

 Try It!

ETP **Elicit and Use Evidence of Student Thinking**

Q: What must be true of the three numbers that you fill in under the radical sign? Explain. [The three numbers are 4. Sample answer: Since it is a cube, each edge length must be the same, 4 feet.]

Convince Me!

Q: How would you find the $\sqrt[3]{125}$? [Sample answer: Try 5^3 first since you know 4^3 is 64. $5^3 = 125$.]

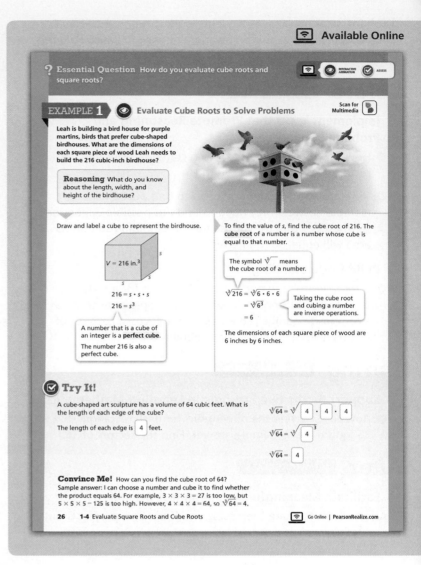

Available Online

? Essential Question How do you evaluate cube roots and square roots?

EXAMPLE **1** Evaluate Cube Roots to Solve Problems   Scan for Multimedia

Leah is building a bird house for purple martins, birds that prefer cube-shaped birdhouses. What are the dimensions of each square piece of wood Leah needs to build the 216 cubic-inch birdhouse?

Reasoning What do you know about the length, width, and height of the birdhouse?

Draw and label a cube to represent the birdhouse.

$V = 216$ in.^{3}

$216 = s \cdot s \cdot s$
$216 = s^3$

A number that is a cube of an integer is a **perfect cube**. The number 216 is also a perfect cube.

To find the value of s, find the cube root of 216. The **cube root** of a number is a number whose cube is equal to that number.

The symbol $\sqrt[3]{}$ means the cube root of a number.

$\sqrt[3]{216} = \sqrt[3]{6 \cdot 6 \cdot 6}$
$= \sqrt[3]{6^3}$
$= 6$

Taking the cube root and cubing a number are inverse operations.

The dimensions of each square piece of wood are 6 inches by 6 inches.

Try It!

A cube-shaped art sculpture has a volume of 64 cubic feet. What is the length of each edge of the cube?

The length of each edge is [4] feet.

$\sqrt[3]{64} = \sqrt[3]{\boxed{4} \cdot \boxed{4} \cdot \boxed{4}}$

$\sqrt[3]{64} = \sqrt[3]{\boxed{4}^3}$

$\sqrt[3]{64} = \boxed{4}$

Convince Me! How can you find the cube root of 64? Sample answer: I can choose a number and cube it to find whether the product equals 64. For example, $3 \times 3 \times 3 = 27$ is too low, but $5 \times 5 \times 5 = 125$ is too high. However, $4 \times 4 \times 4 = 64$, so $\sqrt[3]{64} = 4$.

26   1-4 Evaluate Square Roots and Cube Roots   Go Online | PearsonRealize.com

 Students can access the *Visual Learning Animation Plus* by using the **BouncePages app** to scan this page. Students can download the app for free in their mobile devices' app store.

 Response to Intervention

USE WITH EXAMPLE 1 Some students may have trouble connecting the concept of a square or cube root to the geometric model. Have students complete the following sentences.

Area is measured in _____ [square] units. Volume is measured in _____ [cubic] units.

The side length of a square with a given area is equal to the _____ [square root] of that area.

The side length of a cube with a given volume is equal to the _____ [cube root] of that volume.

Enrichment

USE WITH EXAMPLE 1 Challenge advanced students to find square roots and cube roots of larger numbers.

Q: A square has an area of 441 square centimeters. What is the length of each side? [21 centimeters]

Q: A cube has a volume of 3,375 cubic centimeters. What is the length of each edge? Use the fact that the last digit is 5 to help find the cube root. [15 centimeters]

EXAMPLE 2 **Evaluate Perfect Squares and Perfect Cubes**

ETP **Pose Purposeful Questions**

Q: How do you know if a number is a perfect square? [Sample answer: It is a number that is the square of an integer.]

Q: How do you know if a number is a perfect cube? [Sample answer: It is a number that is a cube of an integer.]

Q: Why is 64 both a perfect square and a perfect cube? [Sample answer: Because $8^2 = 64$ and $4^3 = 64$.]

Try It!

ETP **Elicit and Use Evidence of Student Thinking**

Q: Why are the square root and the cube root of 1 the same number? [Sample answer: One multiplied by itself is always equal to 1.]

EXAMPLE 3 **Evaluate Square Roots to Solve Problems**

ETP **Pose Purposeful Questions**

Q: Why is Sean using $\sqrt{144}$ instead of the cube root? [Sample answer: Sean is finding the area of the square bulletin board, not the volume of a cube.]

Q: What is a benchmark perfect square you could use to determine $\sqrt{144}$? [100; Sample answer: Start with 10×10 since it is equal to 100, and then square each integer after 10.]

Try It!

ETP **Elicit and Use Evidence of Student Thinking**

Q: Why is the answer given with the phrase "at least?" [Sample answer: A tablecloth can sometimes have greater dimensions than the table top itself. Therefore, the tablecloth must be at least large enough to cover the table top.]

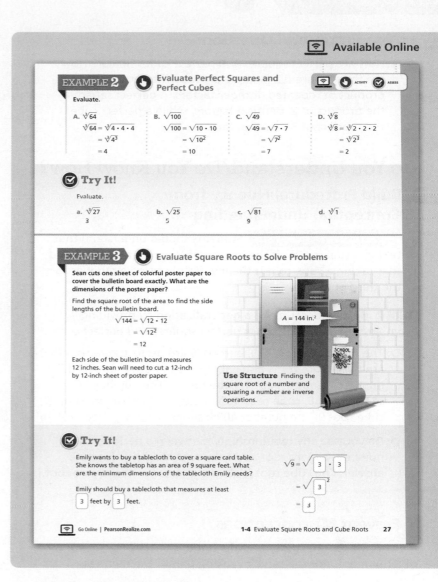

ADDITIONAL EXAMPLES

For additional examples go to PearsonRealize.com.

English Language Learners

BEGINNING Before reading Example 1, draw or display a square and a cube with the same length for a side and an edge.

Q: How are these shapes the same, and how are they different? [Sample answer: The side of the square and edget of the cube are the same length. The cube has height, and the square does not.]

Q: What does the word root mean? [Sample answer: The *root* is the part of a plant that grows underground.]

Explain that, in math, the *root* is the factor that is squared or cubed.

INTERMEDIATE Complete Example 2.

Organize students into small groups. Have them practice using content-based vocabulary in their explanation.

Q: What is a perfect square? [Sample answer: A perfect square is a number that is the square of an integer.]

Q: What is a perfect cube? [Sample answer: A perfect cube is the cube of an integer.]

ADVANCED Complete Example 3.

Have students work with a partner to answer and discuss the following questions.

Q: How can you use the illustration to help you understand the problem? [Sample answer: The illustration shows the shape of the bulletin board and its area.]

Q: Explain to a partner how to show that 12 is $\sqrt{144}$. [Sample answer: You can multiply 12 by 12 to get 144.]

PearsonRealize.com

Key Concept   Activity

KEY CONCEPT

ETP Pose Purposeful Questions

Q: How are perfect squares and perfect cubes similar? How are they different? [Sample answer: They are both the product of repeated, integer factors. A perfect square is the product of 2 identical factors, while a perfect cube is the product of 3 identical factors.]

Do You Understand/Do You Know How?

ETP Build Procedural Fluency from Conceptual Understanding

? Essential Question Students should understand that taking a square root is the inverse of squaring a number, and that taking a cube root is the inverse of raising a number to the third power.

ITEM 2 Help students make a generalization by providing examples of numbers that are perfect squares and perfect cubes.

Q: The numbers 1, 64, 729, and 4096 are perfect squares. What are the square roots and cube roots of each number? [The number 1: square root 1, cube root 1; The number 64: square root 8, cube root 4; The number 729: square root 27, cube root 9; The number 4096: square root 64, cube root 16]

Q: Do you see any relationship(s) between a perfect square number's square root and cube root? Explain. [Sample answer: The cube root is always a factor of the square root.]

Prevent Misconceptions

ITEM 5 Make sure students understand that taking a square root of a number is not the same as taking half of the number.

Q: True or false: The square root of 16 is 8. Explain. [False; Sample answer: 8×8 is 64, not 16.]

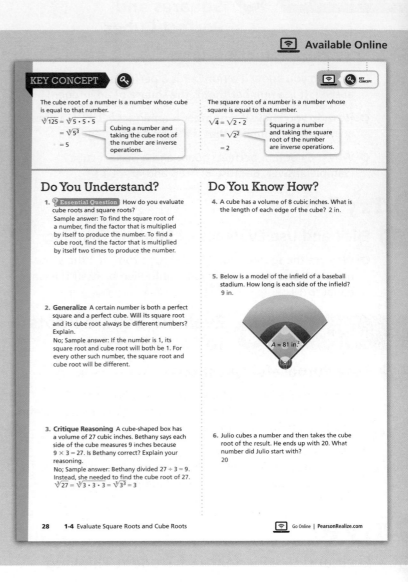

Available Online

KEY CONCEPT

The cube root of a number is a number whose cube is equal to that number.
$\sqrt[3]{125} = \sqrt[3]{5 \cdot 5 \cdot 5}$
$= \sqrt[3]{5^3}$
$= 5$

Cubing a number and taking the cube root of the number are inverse operations.

The square root of a number is a number whose square is equal to that number.
$\sqrt{4} = \sqrt{2 \cdot 2}$
$= \sqrt{2^2}$
$= 2$

Squaring a number and taking the square root of the number are inverse operations.

Do You Understand?

1. **? Essential Question** How do you evaluate cube roots and square roots?
Sample answer: To find the square root of a number, find the factor that is multiplied by itself to produce the number. To find a cube root, find the factor that is multiplied by itself two times to produce the number.

2. **Generalize** A certain number is both a perfect square and a perfect cube. Will its square root and its cube root always be different numbers? Explain.
No; Sample answer: If the number is 1, its square root and cube root will both be 1. For every other such number, the square root and cube root will be different.

3. **Critique Reasoning** A cube-shaped box has a volume of 27 cubic inches. Bethany says each side of the cube measures 9 inches because $9 \times 3 = 27$. Is Bethany correct? Explain your reasoning.
No; Sample answer: Bethany divided $27 \div 3 = 9$. Instead, she needed to find the cube root of 27. $\sqrt[3]{27} = \sqrt[3]{3 \cdot 3 \cdot 3} = \sqrt[3]{3^3} = 3$

Do You Know How?

4. A cube has a volume of 8 cubic inches. What is the length of each edge of the cube? 2 in.

5. Below is a model of the infield of a baseball stadium. How long is each side of the infield? 9 in.

$A = 81$ in.²

6. Julio cubes a number and then takes the cube root of the result. He ends up with 20. What number did Julio start with? 20

28   1-4 Evaluate Square Roots and Cube Roots   Go Online | PearsonRealize.com

ADDITIONAL EXAMPLE 3

Help students transition from finding the missing length of a square to finding the radius of a circle when the area is given.

Make sure students understand that the area of a circle is equal to pi times the radius squared.

Q: If the area of the given circle is 49π square centimeters, then what is the radius of the circle? Explain. [Sample answer: You know that the formula for the area of a circle is $A = \pi r^2$. Since the area of the given circle is 49π centimeters, $49\pi = \pi r^2$. To solve for the radius, find the square root of 49.]

Q: Why don't you take the square root of π? [Sample answer: Since $49\pi = \pi r^2$, to solve you need to divide both sides of the equation by π. You are left with the equation $49 = r^2$. So, π is eliminated by the Division Property of Equality.]

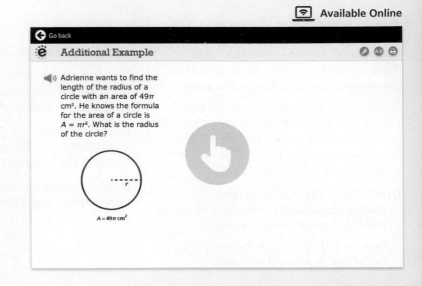

Available Online

Go back

Additional Example

Adrienne wants to find the length of the radius of a circle with an area of 49π cm². He knows the formula for the area of a circle is $A = \pi r^2$. What is the radius of the circle?

$A = 49\pi$ cm²

Practice & Problem Solving

📶 **Available Online**

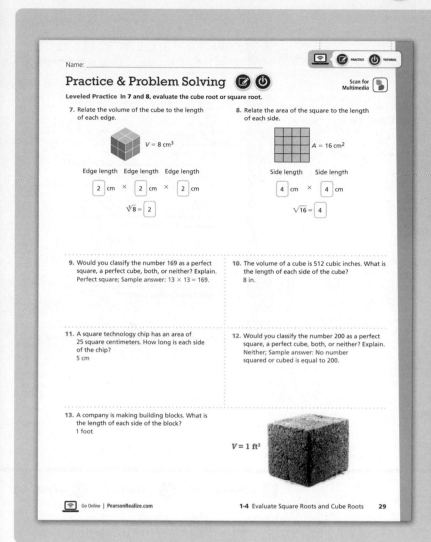

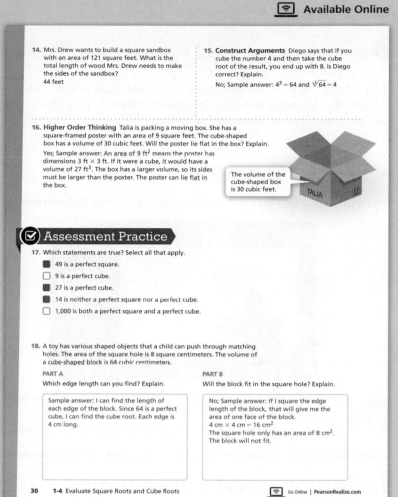

You may opt to have students complete the automatically scored Practice & Problem Solving items online.

🅡 Error Intervention

ITEM 14 Students may take the square root of the area to find the side length, and then stop without answering the question.

- **Q:** What do you need to find? [The total length of wood needed.]
- **Q:** Fill in the blank: You need to find the _____ of the square. [perimeter]

🏆 Challenge

ITEM 12 Expand students' understanding of the definitions of squares and cubes with these equations.

$$1.2^2 = 1.44 \qquad (0.5)^3 = 0.125$$

- **Q:** What is $\sqrt{1.44}$? Explain. [1.2; Sample answer: I know that 12 is the square root of 144, so I tried 1.2 to see if it is the square root of 1.44.]
- **Q:** What is the cube root of 0.125? [0.5]
- **Q:** Why is the cube root, 0.5, greater than the cube, 0.125? [Sample answer: Because the cube root is greater than 0 and less than 1]

Item Analysis

Example	Items	DOK
1	7, 10, 13	1
	15	3
2	8, 11, 14, 17	1
	12	2
	16	3
3	9, 18	2

Lesson Quiz

 Use the student scores on the Lesson Quiz to prescribe differentiated assignments.

I Intervention 0–3 Points   **O** On-Level 4 Points   **A** Advanced 5 Points

You may opt to have students take the Lesson Quiz online. The Lesson Quiz will be automatically scored and appropriate remediation, practice, or enrichment will be assigned based on student performance.

Video Tutorials

Students can access instructional tutorials using the **Virtual Nerd app**.

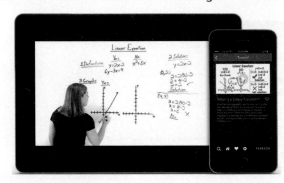

Students can also access the videos using the **BouncePages app** to scan exercise pages marked with this icon. Students can download both apps for free in their mobile devices' app store.

Available Online

Name _____   Lesson Quiz 1-4

1. A cube has a volume of 125 cubic inches. What is the length of each edge?
   5 in.

2. Kai is making a chessboard using pieces of wood that measure 1 square inch. When he finishes, the chessboard will have an area of 64 square inches. How many pieces of wood should he put along each side?
   Ⓐ 64 pieces of wood
   Ⓑ 64² pieces of wood
   ● 8 pieces of wood
   Ⓓ 8² pieces of wood

3. Sonya wants to sew ribbon along each side of a square pillow. If the pillow has an area of 144 square inches, how much ribbon must she buy to have the exact amount that she needs?
   48 in.

4. Maria has a cube-shaped box that measures 9 inches along each edge. Can she fit 1,000 square-inch cubes inside the box? Explain.
   No; Sample answer: $9^3 = 9 \times 9 \times 9 = 729$, **which is less than 1,000.**

5. What pattern do you notice in the numbers below?
   $1 = 1 \times 1$, and $1 \times 1 \times 1$
   $64 = 8 \times 8$, and $4 \times 4 \times 4$
   $729 = 27 \times 27$, and $9 \times 9 \times 9$
   $4,096 = 64 \times 64$, and $16 \times 16 \times 16$
   Sample answer: They are both perfect squares and perfect cubes.

Differentiated Intervention

I = Intervention   **O** = On-Level   **A** = Advanced

Reteach to Build Understanding **I**

Provides scaffolded reteaching for the key lesson concepts.

Additional Vocabulary Support **I O**

Helps students develop and reinforce understanding of key terms and concepts.

Build Mathematical Literacy **I**

Provides support for struggling readers to build mathematical literacy.

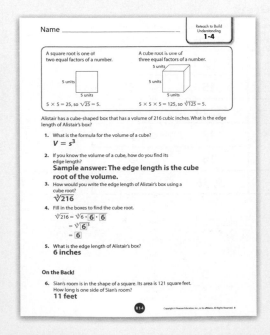

Name _____   Reteach to Build Understanding 1-4

| A square root is one of two equal factors of a number. | A cube root is one of three equal factors of a number. |

5 units

$5 \times 5 = 25$, so $\sqrt{25} = 5$. $5 \times 5 \times 5 = 125$, so $\sqrt[3]{125} = 5$.

Alistair has a cube-shaped box that has a volume of 216 cubic inches. What is the edge length of Alistair's box?

1. What is the formula for the volume of a cube?
   $V = s^3$

2. If you know the volume of a cube, how do you find its edge length?
   Sample answer: The edge length is the cube root of the volume.

3. How would you write the edge length of Alistair's box using a cube root?
   $\sqrt[3]{216}$

4. Fill in the boxes to find the cube root.
   $\sqrt[3]{216} = \sqrt[3]{6 \cdot 6 \cdot 6}$
   $= \sqrt[3]{6^3}$
   $= 6$

5. What is the edge length of Alistair's box?
   6 inches

On the Back!

6. Sian's room is in the shape of a square. Its area is 121 square feet. How long is one side of Sian's room?
   11 feet

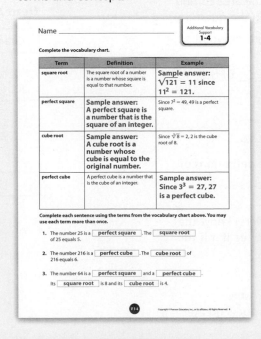

Name _____   Additional Vocabulary Support 1-4

Complete the vocabulary chart.

Term	Definition	Example
square root	The square root of a number is a number whose square is equal to that number.	**Sample answer:** $\sqrt{121} = 11$ since $11^2 = 121$.
perfect square	**Sample answer: A perfect square is a number that is the square of an integer.**	Since $7^2 = 49$, 49 is a perfect square.
cube root	**Sample answer: A cube root is a number whose cube is equal to the original number.**	Since $\sqrt[3]{8} = 2$, 2 is the cube root of 8.
perfect cube	A perfect cube is a number that is the cube of an integer.	**Sample answer: Since** $3^3 = 27$, **27 is a perfect cube.**

Complete each sentence using the terms from the vocabulary chart above. You may use each term more than once.

1. The number 25 is a [perfect square]. The [square root] of 25 equals 5.

2. The number 216 is a [perfect cube]. The [cube root] of 216 equals 6.

3. The number 64 is a [perfect square] and a [perfect cube]. Its [square root] is 8 and its [cube root] is 4.

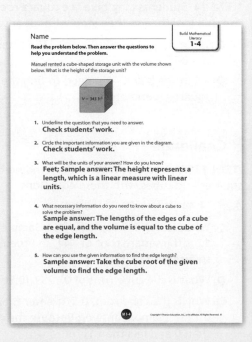

Name _____   Build Mathematical Literacy 1-4

Read the problem below. Then answer the questions to help you understand the problem.

Manuel rented a cube-shaped storage unit with the volume shown below. What is the height of the storage unit?

$V = 343 \text{ ft}^3$

1. Underline the question that you need to answer.
   Check students' work.

2. Circle the important information you are given in the diagram.
   Check students' work.

3. What will be the units of your answer? How do you know?
   Feet; Sample answer: The height represents a length, which is a linear measure with linear units.

4. What necessary information do you need to know about a cube to solve the problem?
   Sample answer: The lengths of the edges of a cube are equal, and the volume is equal to the cube of the edge length.

5. How can you use the given information to find the edge length?
   Sample answer: Take the cube root of the given volume to find the edge length.

Practice   Worksheets   Math Tools   Math Games

Additional Practice

You may opt to have students complete the automatically scored Additional Practice items online.

Item Analysis

Example	Items	DOK
1	4	1
	3, 7	2
2	1, 2	1
	8, 9, 11, 12	2
3	5, 6	2
	10	3

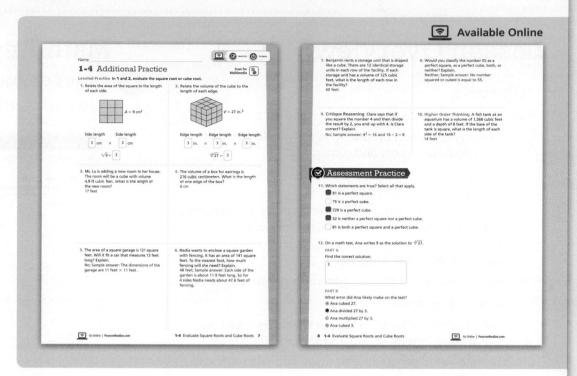

Available Online

Differentiated Intervention

I = Intervention   **O** = On-Level   **A** = Advanced

Enrichment O A

Presents engaging problems and activities that extend the lesson concepts.

Math Tools and Games I O A

Offers additional activities and games to build understanding and fluency.

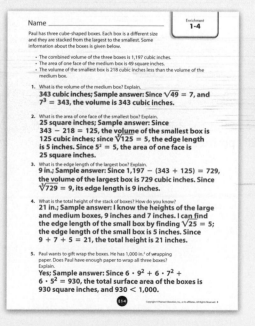

Activity

Lesson 1-5
Solve Equations Using Square Roots and Cube Roots

Lesson Overview

FOCUS

Objective

Students will be able to:

✔ solve equations and problems, in real-world contexts, involving square roots and cube roots.

Essential Understanding

The square root of a positive squared number is that number. The cube root of a cubed number is that number.

COHERENCE

Previously in this topic, students:

- evaluated square roots and cube roots of rational numbers.

In this lesson, students:

- extend their knowledge of square roots and cube roots to solve equations using square roots and cube roots.
- solve real-world problems that involve square roots and cube roots.

Later in this topic, students will:

- explore and develop fluency with integer exponents.
- operate with numbers in scientific notation.

RIGOR

This lesson emphasizes a blend of **conceptual understanding** and **procedural skill and fluency**.

- Students understand the mathematical relationship between the square root and square of a number, and the cube root and cube of a number.
- Students use their conceptual understanding of square roots and cube roots to solve equations, including those presented in real-world problems.

Math Anytime

Today's Challenge

Use the Topic 1 problems any time during this topic.

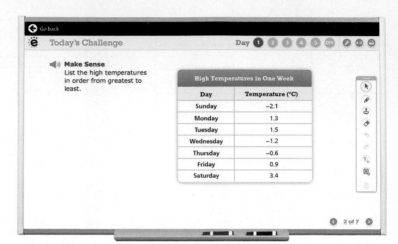

Mathematics Overview

In this lesson, students will solve equations involving square roots and cube roots. Students will extend this knowledge to solve real-world problems using square roots and cube roots.

Applying Math Practices

Construct Arguments and Critique Reasoning

Students will construct arguments and critique reasoning related to the solutions of equations that are solved using square roots or cube roots.

Generalize

Students will generalize about the solutions of equations of the form $x^2 = p$, where p is a positive rational number and of the form $x^3 = p$.

STEP 1 | Develop: Problem-Based Learning

15-20 min

Activity

Solve & Discuss It!

Look for Relationships As students work through the *Solve & Discuss It!*, listen and look for students who relate the dimensions of the cube to its volume.

Before [WHOLE CLASS]

TP **1 Implement Tasks That Promote Reasoning and Problem Solving**

> **Q:** What information is given about each possible model that Janine can build? [Sample answer: All the possible models will be cube-shaped and made with one-inch cubes. The models can contain up to 150 one-inch cubes.]

2 Build Understanding

> **Q:** Will you use the square or cube of a number to solve this problem? Explain. [Cube of a number. The problem states that Janine is building a solid, *cube*-shaped model.]

During [SMALL GROUP]

TP **3 Support Productive Struggle in Learning Mathematics**

> **Q:** How many possible models could Janine create that do not exceed 150 one-inch cubes? Explain. [5; Sample answer: Start with a one-inch model and cube that number, which will equal 1 cube ($1 \times 1 \times 1$). Then increase the one-inch model configuration to a two-inch model and cube that number, which will equal 8 cubes ($2 \times 2 \times 2$). Repeat until the cube of a number exceeds 150.]

After [WHOLE CLASS]

TP **4 Facilitate Meaningful Mathematical Discourse**

Ask students to share their solutions. If needed, project Camilla's and Julian's work and ask:

> **Q:** What is the difference between Camilla's and Julian's approaches to the solution? [Sample answer: Camilla used an equation. Julian used a longhand format that included words with the mathematical operators.]

> **Q:** Why must the numbers in either approach be the same for each model? [Sample answer: Janine is building a *solid*, cube-shaped model. If there are 5 rows of 5 cubes, there must be 5 layers in order for the model to be a cube. The product of $5 \times 5 \times 5$ is always 125.]

5 Transition to Visual Learning

> **Q:** If you were given the number of cubes in the model, how could you find the side length? [Sample answer: Use "guess and check" to choose a number, n, that might be a side length. Multiply $n \cdot n \cdot n$ to see if the product equals the number of cubes in the model. Revise n as needed.]

6 Extension for Early Finishers

> **Q:** How many $\frac{1}{2}$-inch cubes would Janine need to build a model that has the dimensions 5 in. by 5 in. by 5 in.? Explain. [1,000; Sample answer: It would take ten $\frac{1}{2}$-inch cubes to cover the length, width, and height of the cube. So, Janine would need $10 \times 10 \times 10 = 1,000$ cubes.]

Analyze Student Work

 Available Online

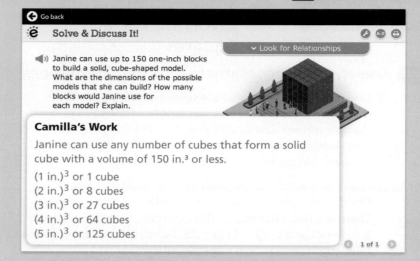

← Go back

Solve & Discuss It!

Janine can use up to 150 one-inch blocks to build a solid, cube-shaped model. What are the dimensions of the possible models that she can build? How many blocks would Janine use for each model? Explain.

✓ Look for Relationships

Camilla's Work

Janine can use any number of cubes that form a solid cube with a volume of 150 in.³ or less.

$(1 \text{ in.})^3$ or 1 cube
$(2 \text{ in.})^3$ or 8 cubes
$(3 \text{ in.})^3$ or 27 cubes
$(4 \text{ in.})^3$ or 64 cubes
$(5 \text{ in.})^3$ or 125 cubes

1 of 1

Camilla's approach to solving the problem is a mathematical approach. She uses the volume formula, $V = s^3$.

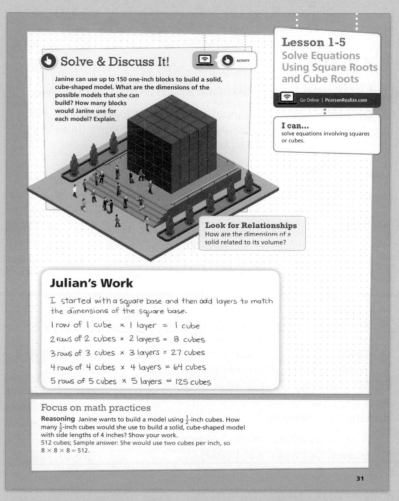

Solve & Discuss It!

Janine can use up to 150 one-inch blocks to build a solid, cube-shaped model. What are the dimensions of the possible models that she can build? How many blocks would Janine use for each model? Explain.

Look for Relationships
How are the dimensions of a solid related to its volume?

Lesson 1-5
Solve Equations Using Square Roots and Cube Roots

Go Online | PearsonRealize.com

I can...
solve equations involving squares or cubes.

Julian's Work

I started with a square base and then add layers to match the dimensions of the square base.

1 row of 1 cube × 1 layer = 1 cube
2 rows of 2 cubes × 2 layers = 8 cubes
3 rows of 3 cubes × 3 layers = 27 cubes
4 rows of 4 cubes × 4 layers = 64 cubes
5 rows of 5 cubes × 5 layers = 125 cubes

Focus on math practices
Reasoning Janine wants to build a model using $\frac{1}{2}$-inch cubes. How many $\frac{1}{2}$-inch cubes would she use to build a solid, cube-shaped model with side lengths of 4 inches? Show your work.
512 cubes; Sample answer: She would use two cubes per inch, so $8 \times 8 \times 8 = 512$.

31

Julian's approach to solving the problem is a longhand format that includes words with the mathematical operators.

ETP Establish Mathematics Goals to Focus Learning

Engage students in a discussion about the *Essential Question*. Make sure they understand what it means to square or cube a number.

EXAMPLE 1 **Solve Equations Involving Perfect Squares**

ETP Use and Connect Mathematical Representations

Q: Explain why Darius found the square root instead of the cube root to determine the side length of the square. [Sample answer: Darius needs to find the side length of a square table top when given its area. The side length is squared, not cubed.]

Q: How many solutions are there to this equation? Explain. Which solution will Darius use and why? [Sample answer: There are two solutions to this equation, 5 and −5, because 5 × 5 = 25 and (−5) × (−5) = 25. Darius will use 5, because a side length cannot be a negative integer.]

Q: Why does Darius need a total of 20 feet of decorative molding? [Sample answer: The table is square-shaped, which means it has four sides of equal length. If each side is 5 feet and there are 4 sides, 4 (sides) × 5 (feet) = 20 feet.]

☑ **Try It!**

ETP Elicit and Use Evidence of Student Thinking

Q: Suppose decorative molding is needed for the figure. How much decorative molding would be needed to finish the edges of the figure? [40 m]

Convince Me!

Q: Why is the length of a table that is 100 m² the positive square root of 100, not the negative square root of 100? [Sample answer: Both 10 and −10 are square roots of 100, but length is represented by a positive number, not a negative number.]

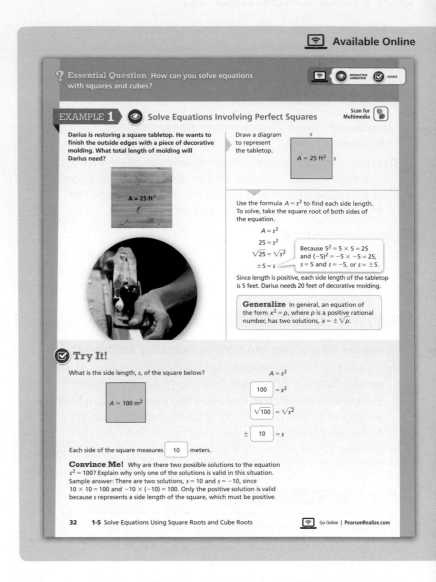

Students can access the *Visual Learning Animation Plus* by using the **BouncePages app** to scan this page. Students can download the app for free in their mobile devices' app store.

 English Language Learners

BEGINNING Before reading Example 1 to students, explain that molding is material such as wood, plastic, or stone that is shaped for use as a decorative or architectural feature.

Q: What does *outside* mean? [Sample answer: Outdoors; not inside]

Use the diagram or classroom objects to demonstrate Example 1.

INTERMEDIATE Ask students to review Example 2.

Use the following questions and diagram to ensure they understand the vocabulary used in the question.

Q: What is a terrarium? [Sample answer: A terrarium is a glass container that is used to house land animals or to display plants.]

Q: What do the words "minimum dimensions" mean for this problem? [Sample answer: The smallest possible length and width of the screen for the terrarium.]

ADVANCED Ask students to review Example 2.

Have students explain number of solutions in this problem, and why there are this many solutions.

Q: How many solutions are there to this problem? [1]

Q: How do you know the answer must be positive? [Sample answer: The equation was set equal to a positive number.]

EXAMPLE 2 Solve Equations Involving Perfect Cubes

ETP Pose Purposeful Questions

Q: Why was a cube root equation used to solve this problem when only the length and width of the terrarium are needed? [Sample answer: The volume of the terrarium is given, so a cube root equation is needed to find each edge length. By solving the cube root equation, the dimensions of the screen are found.]

Try It!

ETP Elicit and Use Evidence of Student Thinking

Q: How can you find the value of x? [Sample answer: Take the cube root of both sides of the equation.]

 EXAMPLE 3 Solve Equations Involving Imperfect Squares and Cubes

ETP Pose Purposeful Questions

Q: Do you need to change your process when solving equations with imperfect squares and cubes? Explain. [No; Sample answer: You still take the square root (or cube root) of both sides of the equation to solve for the variable.]

Q: Will nonperfect squares still have two square roots? Explain. [Yes; Sample answer: One square root will be positive, and the other will be negative.]

Q: How many cube roots will nonperfect cubes have? Explain. [1; Sample answer: nonperfect cubes have one cube root, which is not an integer, that when multiplied three times gives the nonperfect cube.]

Try It!

ETP Elicit and Use Evidence of Student Thinking

Q: If the second equation was $c^2 = 11$, what is the value of c? Explain. [$\pm\sqrt{11}$; Sample answer: Take the square root of both sides of the equation. $\sqrt{11} \times \sqrt{11} = 11$, so $c = \sqrt{11}$. $(-\sqrt{11}) \times (-\sqrt{11}) = 11$, so $c = -\sqrt{11}$.]

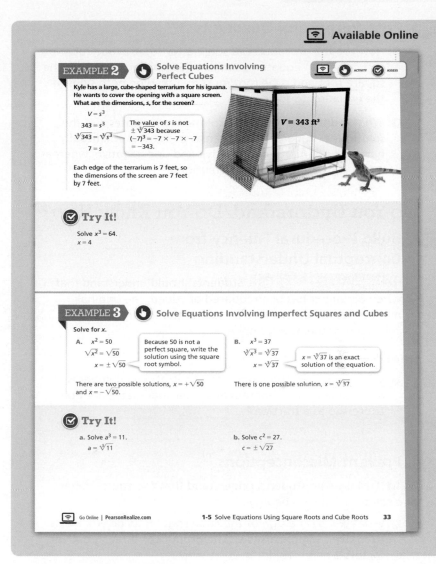

Available Online

EXAMPLE 2 Solve Equations Involving Perfect Cubes

Kyle has a large, cube-shaped terrarium for his iguana. He wants to cover the opening with a square screen. What are the dimensions, s, for the screen?

$V = s^3$

$343 = s^3$

$\sqrt[3]{343} = \sqrt[3]{s^3}$

$7 = s$

The value of s is not $\pm\sqrt[3]{343}$ because $(-7)^3 = -7 \times -7 \times -7 = -343$.

$V = 343\ \text{ft}^3$

Each edge of the terrarium is 7 feet, so the dimensions of the screen are 7 feet by 7 feet.

Try It!

Solve $x^3 = 64$.

$x = 4$

EXAMPLE 3 Solve Equations Involving Imperfect Squares and Cubes

Solve for x.

A. $x^2 = 50$
$\sqrt{x^2} = \sqrt{50}$
$x = \pm\sqrt{50}$

Because 50 is not a perfect square, write the solution using the square root symbol.

There are two possible solutions, $x = +\sqrt{50}$ and $x = -\sqrt{50}$.

B. $x^3 = 37$
$\sqrt[3]{x^3} = \sqrt[3]{37}$
$x = \sqrt[3]{37}$

$x = \sqrt[3]{37}$ is an exact solution of the equation.

There is one possible solution, $x = \sqrt[3]{37}$

Try It!

a. Solve $a^3 = 11$.
$a = \sqrt[3]{11}$

b. Solve $c^2 = 27$.
$c = \pm\sqrt{27}$

Go Online | PearsonRealize.com   1-5 Solve Equations Using Square Roots and Cube Roots   **33**

ADDITIONAL EXAMPLES

For additional examples go to PearsonRealize.com.

 Response to Intervention

USE WITH EXAMPLE 2 Some students may need to review multiplication tables in order to work with squares and cubes.

• Have students make a list of the squares and cubes using factors from 1 to 9. To get them started, ask:

Q: What is 5×5, or 5^2? [25]

Q: What is 7×7, or 7^2? [49]

Q: What is $5 \times 5 \times 5$, or 5^3? [125]

 Enrichment

USE WITH EXAMPLE 2 Challenge students to recognize that the size of the number in an equation does not change the procedure used to solve the equation.

• Have students solve these problems and show their work.

Q: What is the value of x in the equation $x^3 = -1,728$? [$x = -12$ because $(-12) \times (-12) \times (-12) = -1,728$]

Q: A cube-shaped tank has a volume of 15,625 cubic inches. How much paint is needed for the front panel of the tank? [625 square inches]

STEP 2 | Develop: Visual Learning *continued*

KEY CONCEPT

ETP Pose Purposeful Questions

Q: How are the procedures of solving for square root equations and cube root equations similar? [Sample answer: Both the square root and cube root must be taken on both sides of the equation to solve.]

Q: What is different about the solutions of squares and the solutions of cubes? [Sample answer: Squares will **usually** have *two* solutions, one positive and one negative, whereas cubes will **always** have one solution.]

Do You Understand/Do You Know How?

ETP Build Procedural Fluency from Conceptual Understanding

? Essential Question Students should understand that when a number has been squared or cubed, the original number can be determined by taking the square root or cube root of the new number.

ITEM 4

Q: What is an irrational number? [An irrational number is a nonterminating, nonrepeating decimal that cannot be expressed as a fraction.]

RtI Prevent Misconceptions

ITEM 7 Make sure students understand that the equation has one solution, which is negative.

Q: What will be the sign of the cube root? How do you know? [Negative; Sample answer: The product of three negative factors is negative.]

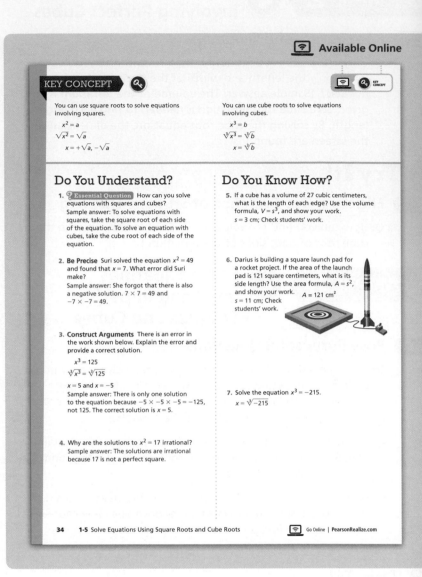

Available Online

KEY CONCEPT

You can use square roots to solve equations involving squares.

$x^2 = a$
$\sqrt{x^2} = \sqrt{a}$
$x = +\sqrt{a}, -\sqrt{a}$

You can use cube roots to solve equations involving cubes.

$x^3 = b$
$\sqrt[3]{x^3} = \sqrt[3]{b}$
$x = \sqrt[3]{b}$

Do You Understand?

1. **? Essential Question** How can you solve equations with squares and cubes?
Sample answer: To solve equations with squares, take the square root of each side of the equation. To solve an equation with cubes, take the cube root of each side of the equation.

2. **Be Precise** Suri solved the equation $x^2 = 49$ and found that $x = 7$. What error did Suri make?
Sample answer: She forgot that there is also a negative solution. $7 \times 7 = 49$ and $-7 \times -7 = 49$.

3. **Construct Arguments** There is an error in the work shown below. Explain the error and provide a correct solution.
$x^3 = 125$
$\sqrt[3]{x^3} = \sqrt[3]{125}$
$x = 5$ and $x = -5$
Sample answer: There is only one solution to the equation because $-5 \times -5 \times -5 = -125$, not 125. The correct solution is $x = 5$.

4. Why are the solutions to $x^2 = 17$ irrational?
Sample answer: The solutions are irrational because 17 is not a perfect square.

Do You Know How?

5. If a cube has a volume of 27 cubic centimeters, what is the length of each edge? Use the volume formula, $V = s^3$, and show your work.
$s = 3$ cm; Check students' work.

6. Darius is building a square launch pad for a rocket project. If the area of the launch pad is 121 square centimeters, what is its side length? Use the area formula, $A = s^2$, and show your work. $A = 121$ cm²
$s = 11$ cm; Check students' work.

7. Solve the equation $x^3 = -215$.
$x = \sqrt[3]{-215}$

ADDITIONAL EXAMPLE 1

Help students transition from finding the missing length of a square to finding the missing length of a triangle.

Make sure students understand the steps for solving.

Q: Why does the product change from $\frac{1}{8}$ to $\frac{1}{4}$ from the second to the third step? [Sample answer: Both sides were multiplied by 2 to simplify $\frac{1}{2}b \cdot b$.]

Q: How do you take the square root of a fraction? [Sample answer: Take the square root of the numerator and the square root of the denominator. Write the roots in fraction form.]

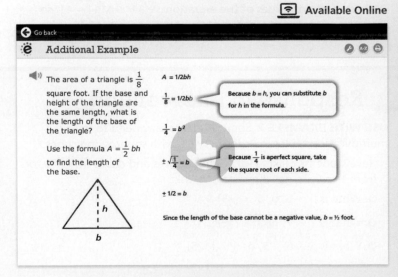

Go back

Additional Example

The area of a triangle is $\frac{1}{8}$ square foot. If the base and height of the triangle are the same length, what is the length of the base of the triangle?

Use the formula $A = \frac{1}{2}bh$ to find the length of the base.

$A = 1/2bh$

$\frac{1}{8} = 1/2bb$

Because $b = h$, you can substitute b for h in the formula.

$\frac{1}{4} = b^2$

$\pm\sqrt{\frac{1}{4}} = b$

Because $\frac{1}{4}$ is a perfect square, take the square root of each side.

$\pm 1/2 = b$

Since the length of the base cannot be a negative value, $b = \frac{1}{2}$ foot.

Answer: $\frac{1}{2}$ foot

Practice & Problem Solving

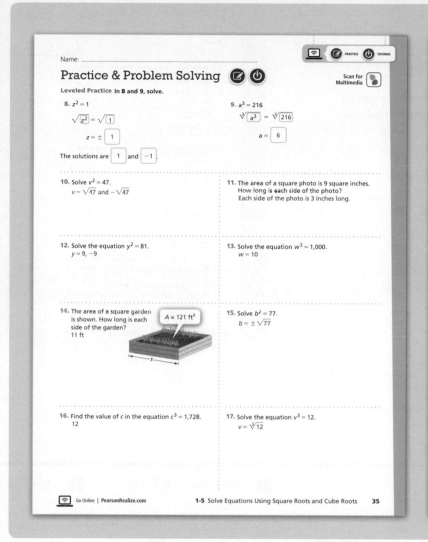

Available Online

Name: _____

Practice & Problem Solving

Scan for Multimedia

Leveled Practice In 8 and 9, solve.

8. $z^2 = 1$

$\sqrt{z^2} = \sqrt{1}$

$z = \pm \boxed{1}$

The solutions are $\boxed{1}$ and $\boxed{-1}$.

9. $a^3 = 216$

$\sqrt[3]{a^3} = \sqrt[3]{216}$

$a = \boxed{6}$

10. Solve $v^2 = 47$.
$v = \sqrt{47}$ and $-\sqrt{47}$

11. The area of a square photo is 9 square inches. How long is each side of the photo?
Each side of the photo is 3 inches long.

12. Solve the equation $y^2 = 81$.
$y = 9, -9$

13. Solve the equation $w^3 = 1,000$.
$w = 10$

14. The area of a square garden is shown. How long is each side of the garden?
$A = 121\ ft^2$
11 ft

15. Solve $b^2 = 77$.
$b = \pm\sqrt{77}$

16. Find the value of c in the equation $c^3 = 1,728$.
12

17. Solve the equation $v^3 = 12$.
$v = \sqrt[3]{12}$

18. **Higher Order Thinking** Explain why $\sqrt[3]{-\frac{8}{27}}$ is $-\frac{2}{3}$.

Sample answer: $\sqrt[3]{-\frac{8}{27}}$ is $-\frac{2}{3}$ because $-\frac{2}{3} \cdot -\frac{2}{3} \cdot -\frac{2}{3} = -\frac{8}{27}$.

19. **Critique Reasoning** Manolo says that the solution of the equation $g^2 = 36$ is $g = 6$ because $6 \times 6 = 36$. Is Manolo's reasoning complete? Explain.
No; Sample answer: Manolo needs to include both the positive and negative solutions of the equation.

20. Evaluate $\sqrt[3]{-512}$.
   a. Write your answer as an integer.
   -8

   b. Explain how you can check that your result is correct.
   Sample answer: I can cube the result.
   $-8^3 = -512$

21. Yael has a square-shaped garage with 228 square feet of floor space. She plans to build an addition that will increase the floor space by 50%. What will be the length, to the nearest tenth, of one side of the new garage?
18.5 ft

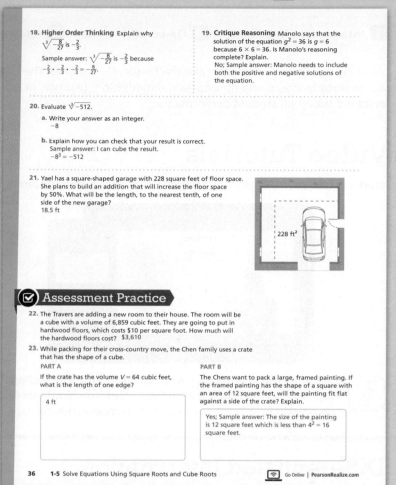

228 ft²

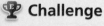 Assessment Practice

22. The Travers are adding a new room to their house. The room will be a cube with a volume of 6,859 cubic feet. They are going to put in hardwood floors, which costs $10 per square foot. How much will the hardwood floors cost? $3,610

23. While packing for their cross-country move, the Chen family uses a crate that has the shape of a cube.

PART A
If the crate has the volume $V = 64$ cubic feet, what is the length of one edge?

4 ft

PART B
The Chens want to pack a large, framed painting. If the framed painting has the shape of a square with an area of 12 square feet, will the painting fit flat against a side of the crate? Explain.

Yes; Sample answer: The size of the painting is 12 square feet which is less than $4^2 = 16$ square feet.

Error Intervention

ITEM 14 Students may forget that when a problem includes the word *area*, they need to use $A = s^2$. Likewise, when they see the keyword *volume*, they need to use $V = s^3$.

Q: Will you need to determine the square root or the cube root to determine the side length? Explain. [Square root. Sample answer: Area has two dimensions, length and width, so find the square root.]

You may opt to have students complete the automatically scored Practice & Problem Solving items online.

Item Analysis

Example	Items	DOK
1	8, 11, 12, 14	1
	19	3
2	9, 13	1
	16, 18, 20, 22	2
	23	3
3	10, 15, 17	1
	21	3

Challenge

ITEM 14 You can use this question to extend the students' understanding of exponents and radicals.

Q: How do you think you would evaluate $\sqrt[4]{625}$? Explain.
[Sample answer: If $\sqrt[3]{}$ means the cube root, then the expressed solution must represent the number that when multiplied 4 times gives the product 625. $5 \times 5 \times 5 \times 5 = 625$, so $\sqrt[4]{625} = 5$.]

PearsonRealize.com

Assess   Tutorials   Worksheets

Lesson Quiz

Use the student scores on the Lesson Quiz to prescribe differentiated assignments.

I Intervention 0–3 Points   **O** On-Level 4 Points   **A** Advanced 5 Points

You may opt to have students take the Lesson Quiz online. The Lesson Quiz will be automatically scored and appropriate remediation, practice, or enrichment will be assigned based on student performance.

Video Tutorials

Students can access instructional tutorials using the **Virtual Nerd app**.

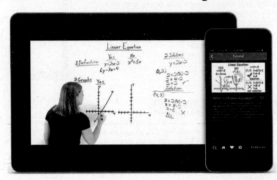

 Students can also access the videos using the **BouncePages app** to scan exercise pages marked with this icon. Students can download both apps for free in their mobile devices' app store.

Available Online

Name _____   Lesson Quiz 1-5

1. If the volume of a cube-shaped box is 729 cubic inches, what equation would you use to determine how many 1-inch cubes could fit along one side?
   - ● $s = \sqrt[3]{729}$
   - Ⓑ $s = \sqrt{729}$
   - Ⓒ $s = 729^2$
   - Ⓓ $s = 729^3$

2. Solve the equation $x^2 = 121$.
   $x = +11, -11$

3. Mr. Yueng graded his students' math quizzes. Students came up with four different answers when solving the equation $x^3 = 22$. Which answer is correct?
   - Ⓐ $x = 22^3$
   - ● $x = \sqrt[3]{22}$
   - Ⓒ $x = \pm\sqrt[3]{22}$
   - Ⓓ $x = \sqrt{22}$

4. Solve the equation $x = \sqrt[3]{27}$.
   $x = 3$

5. Sachiko is framing the border of a square picture. If she knows the area of the picture, how could Sachiko determine the amount of framing material she needs to buy?
   - Ⓐ Divide the area by 2, and then multiply the quotient by 4.
   - ● Set the area equal to x^2, solve for x, and then multiply the value of x by 4.
   - Ⓒ Set the area equal to x^3, and then solve for x.
   - Ⓓ Set the area equal to x^2, solve for x, and then divide the value of x by 4.

Differentiated Intervention

I = Intervention   **O** = On-Level   **A** = Advanced

Reteach to Build Understanding **I**

Provides scaffolded reteaching for the key lesson concepts.

Additional Vocabulary Support **I** **O**

Helps students develop and reinforce understanding of key terms and concepts.

Build Mathematical Literacy **I**

Provides support for struggling readers to build mathematical literacy.

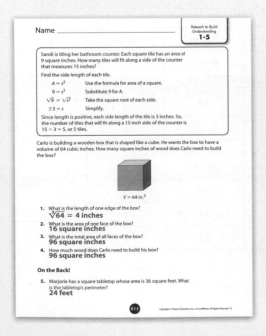

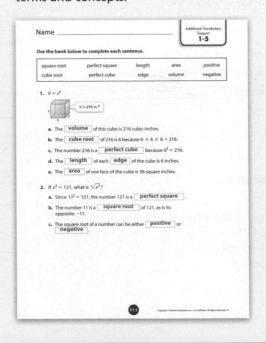

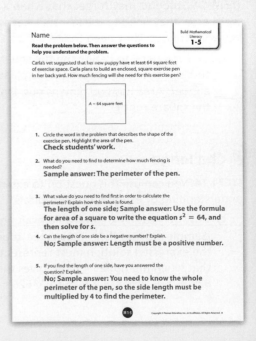

Practice Worksheets Math Tools Math Games

✎ Additional Practice

You may opt to have students complete the automatically scored Additional Practice items online.

Item Analysis

Example	Items	DOK
1	1, 5	1
	4	2
	10, 11	3
2	2	1
	3, 7, 9, 12	2
3	8	1
	6	2

📶 **Available Online**

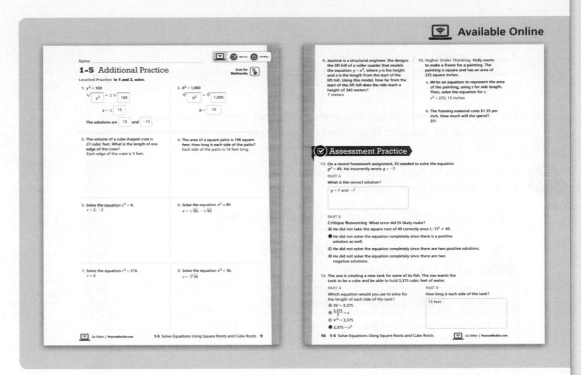

Differentiated Intervention

I = Intervention   **O** = On-Level   **A** = Advanced

Enrichment **O** **A**

Presents engaging problems and activities that extend the lesson concepts.

Math Tools and Games **I** **O** **A**

Offers additional activities and games to build understanding and fluency.

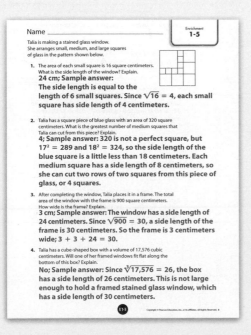

Math Tools

Algebra Tiles	Data & Graphs	Number Line
Area Models	Fraction & Percents	Pan Balance
Bar Diagrams	Input-Output Machine	Place-Value Blocks
Calculator	Integer Chips	Probability
Coordinate Grapher	Measuring Cylinders	2-D Geometry
Counters	Number Charts	3-D Geometry

MID-TOPIC CHECKPOINT

Assign the Mid-Topic Checkpoint to monitor students' understandings of concepts and skills taught in the first lessons in this topic.

Encourage students to use the self-assessment form at the bottom of the page to describe their level of understanding.

 You may opt to have students take the automatically-scored Mid-Topic Assessment online.

Use students' results to adjust instruction as needed.

 ## Item Analysis for Diagnosis and Intervention

Item	DOK	MDIS	Lesson
1	2	L80	1-2
2	1	M23	1-1
3	2	L81	1-3
4	1	L81	1-5
5	3	L82	1-4
6	1	M23	1-1

Available Online

Name: _____

MID-TOPIC CHECKPOINT TOPIC 1

1. **Vocabulary** How can you show that a number is a rational number? *Lesson 1-2*
Sample answer: A number can be shown to be rational by writing it in the form $\frac{a}{b}$, where a and b are integers and $b \neq 0$. If the number cannot be written in this form, then it is not rational.

2. Which shows $0.2\overline{3}$ as a fraction? *Lesson 1-1*

   Ⓐ $\frac{2}{33}$

   Ⓑ $\frac{7}{33}$

   Ⓒ $\frac{23}{99}$

   ● $\frac{7}{30}$

3. Is $\sqrt{8}$ greater than, less than, or equal to 4? Explain. *Lesson 1-3*
Less than 4; Sample answer: The square root of 4 is 2. The square root of 9 is 3. 8 is between 4 and 9, so the square root of 8 is between 2 and 3. This means that the square root of 8 is less than 4.

4. Solve the equation $m^2 = 14$. *Lesson 1-5* $m = \pm\sqrt{14}$.

5. A fish tank is in the shape of a cube. Its volume is 125 ft³. What is the area of one face of the tank? *Lesson 1-4* 25 ft²

6. Write $1.\overline{12}$ as a mixed number. Show your work. *Lesson 1-1*
$1\frac{4}{33}$; Sample answer: Let $x = 1.\overline{12}$. Multiply each side by 100: $100x = 112.\overline{12}$. Subtract the two equations: $100x - x = 112.\overline{12} - 1.\overline{12}$. Simplify: $99x = 111$. Divide each side by 9: $x = \frac{111}{99} = \frac{37}{33} = 1\frac{4}{33}$.

How well did you do on the mid-topic checkpoint? Fill in the stars. ☆☆☆

Go Online | PearsonRealize.com   **Topic 1** Real Numbers **37**

Mid-Topic Assessment Master

Name _____   Topic **1**
                               Mid-Topic Assessment

1. Vocabulary Is a repeating decimal a rational number? Explain.
Yes; Sample answer: A repeating decimal is a rational number because it can be written in the form $\frac{a}{b}$, where a and b are integers and $b \neq 0$.

2. Which fraction is equivalent to $0.1\overline{6}$?
   Ⓐ $\frac{1}{16}$ ● $\frac{1}{6}$
   Ⓑ $\frac{16}{100}$ Ⓓ $\frac{1}{3}$

3. Is $\sqrt{10}$ greater than, less than, or equal to 5? Explain.
Less than 5; Sample answer: Because 10 lies between two consecutive perfect squares 9 and 16, $\sqrt{10}$ is located between $\sqrt{9}$ and $\sqrt{16}$. This means that $\sqrt{10}$ is located between 3 and 4, so $\sqrt{10}$ is less than 5.

4. Solve the equation $x^2 = 5$.
$x = \pm\sqrt{5}$

5. Cassie has a small cube-shaped box. Its volume is 64 cubic centimeters. What is the area of one face of the box?
16 cm²

6. Write $2.\overline{1}$ as a mixed number. Show your work.
$2\frac{1}{9}$; Sample answer: Let $x = 2.\overline{1}$. Multiply each side by 10: $10x = 21.\overline{1}$. Subtract the two equations: $10x - x = 21.\overline{1} - 2.\overline{1}$. Simplify: $9x = 19$. Divide each side by 9: $x = \frac{19}{9} = 2\frac{1}{9}$.

Mid-Topic Assessment 1 of 1   Copyright © Pearson Education, Inc., or its affiliates. All Rights Reserved. 8

MID-TOPIC PERFORMANCE TASK

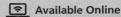

Assess

Assess students' ability to apply the concepts and skills in the first part of the topic using the Mid-Topic Performance Task, found in the Student's Edition or at PearsonRealize.com.

RtI Item Analysis for Diagnosis and Intervention

Part	DOK	MDIS	Lesson
A	1	L80	1-1, 1-2
B	2	L80	1-3
C	2	L80	1-3

Scoring Guide

Part	Points	Mid-Topic Performance Task
A	1	Correct answer and explanation
B	2	Correct answer and work shown
B	1	Correct answer without work shown or mostly-correct work shown
C	2	Correct answer and work shown
C	1	Correct answer without work shown or mostly-correct work shown

---

📶 Available Online

TOPIC 1 MID-TOPIC PERFORMANCE TASK

Six members of the math club are forming two teams for a contest. The teams will be determined by having each student draw a number from a box.

Student	Number Drawn
Lydia	$\sqrt{38}$
Marcy	$6.3\overline{4}$
Caleb	$\sqrt{36}$
Ryan	$6.343443444\ldots$
Anya	$6.\overline{34}$
Chan	$\sqrt{34}$

PART A

The table shows the results of the draw. The students who drew rational numbers will form the team called the Tigers. The students who drew irrational numbers will form the team called the Lions.

List the members of each team.
Tigers: Marcy, Caleb, Anya; Lions: Lydia, Ryan, Chan

PART B

The student on each team who drew the greatest number will be the captain of that team. Who will be the captain of the Tigers? Show your work.
Marcy will be the captain of the Tigers. Sample answer: Write each number to the same number of decimal places and compare to find the greatest number. For Marcy, $6.3\overline{4} \approx 6.3444$; for Caleb, $\sqrt{36} = 6.0000$; for Anya, $6.\overline{34} = 6.3434$. The greatest number is 6.3444, so Marcy will be the captain.

PART C

Who will be the captain of the Lions? Show your work.
Ryan will be the captain of the Lions. Sample answer: The three numbers are $\sqrt{38}$, $6.343443444\ldots$, and $\sqrt{34}$. Since 34 is less than 38, $\sqrt{34}$ is less than $\sqrt{38}$. Since $6.1^2 = 37.21$ and $6.2^2 = 38.44$, $\sqrt{38}$ is between 6.1 and 6.2. Therefore, $\sqrt{38}$ is less than $6.343443444\ldots$ So the greatest number is $6.343443444\ldots$, which is Ryan's number, so Ryan will be the captain.

38 **Topic 1** Real Numbers   📶 Go Online | PearsonRealize.com

Activity

Lesson 1-6

Use Properties of Integer Exponents

Lesson Overview

FOCUS

Objective

Students will be able to:

✔ understand the properties of exponents.

✔ generate equivalent expressions with exponents.

Essential Understanding

Expressions with integer exponents can be simplified using the properties of exponents. The simplified expression will always be equivalent to the original expression.

COHERENCE

Previously in this topic, students:

• evaluated square root and cube root expressions and equations.

In this lesson, students:

• explore and use properties of exponents to generate equivalent expressions.

Later in this topic, students will:

• explore and apply the Zero Exponent Property and the Negative Exponent Property.

• evaluate expressions that include numbers with negative exponents and zero exponents.

RIGOR

This lesson emphasizes a blend of **conceptual understanding** and **procedural skill and fluency**.

• Students develop an understanding of the properties of integer exponents and how they can be used in evaluating expressions with exponents.

• Students apply the properties of integer exponents to generate equivalent expressions with simplified exponents.

Math Anytime

Today's Challenge

Use the Topic 1 problems any time during this topic.

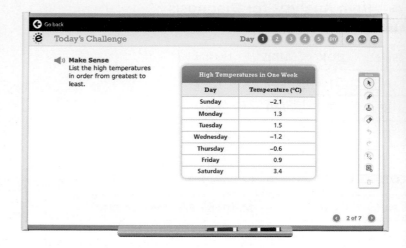

Mathematics Overview

In this lesson, students will use properties of integer exponents to simplify exponential expressions. Students will learn to multiply and divide exponential expressions with the same base, to multiply exponential expressions with different bases, and to find the power of a power.

Applying Math Practices

Construct Arguments

Students analyze given data within the lesson and use this information to explain mathematical properties involving exponents. They also have the opportunity to analyze student work and determine which student is correct given the exponential properties learned within this lesson.

Look for and Make Use of Structure

Students examine patterns and structure as they understand the properties of integer exponents and their relationships. They use this structure to solve problems involving equivalent expressions.

STEP 1 | Develop: Problem-Based Learning

15-20 min

Activity

Solve & Discuss It!

Use Structure As students work through the *Solve & Discuss It*, listen and look for a variety of strategies students use to determine the total number of views that can be incorporated into the classroom discussion.

Before [WHOLE CLASS]

1 Implement Tasks that Promote Reasoning and Problem Solving

Q: What is 2,187 written as a power of 3? [3^7]

2 Build Understanding

Q: What is happening to the number of views each day? [It is tripling each day.]

During [SMALL GROUP]

3 Support Productive Struggle in Learning Mathematics

Q: What is the total number of views for the first three days using exponents? [$3^7 \cdot 3 \cdot 3 = 3^9$]

Q: What is the total number of views at the end of the week using exponents? [$3^9 \cdot 3 \cdot 3 \cdot 3 \cdot 3 = 3^{13}$]

After [WHOLE CLASS]

4 Facilitate Meaningful Mathematical Discourse

Ask students to share their solutions. If needed, project Jeremy's and Chloe's work and ask:

Q: What is the same about Jeremy's and Chloe's work? What is different? [Sample answer: Both students find the number of views each day and add them together. Jeremy uses repeated multiplication, while Chloe uses patterns.]

5 Transition to Visual Learning

Q: The number 2,187 is equal to 3 · 3 · 3 · 3 · 3 · 3 · 3. How could you write this number in exponential form? [Sample answer: Write the factor that is being multiplied by itself, 3, as the base, and the number of times the factor is multiplied by itself as the exponent, 7; 3 · 3 · 3 · 3 · 3 · 3 · 3 = 3^7.]

6 Extension for Early Finishers

Q: How could you write the number of views each day using exponents? [Day 2: 3^8; Day 3: 3^9; Day 4: 3^{10}; Day 5: 3^{11}; Day 6: 3^{12}; Day 7: 3^{13}]

Analyze Student Work

📶 Available Online

← Go back

ё))) **Solve & Discuss It!**

))) One band's streaming video concert to benefit a global charity costs $1.00 to view.

The first day, the concert got 2,187 views. The second day, it got about three times as many views. On the third, it got 3 times as many views as on Day 2. If the trend continues, how much money will the band have raised in one week?

Jeremy's Work

I made a table to show 7 days.
Then I added the products to get $2,390,391 raised in one week.

Day	1	2	3	4	5	6	7
Number of Views	2,187	3(2,187) = 6,561	3(3 · 2,187) = 19,683	3(19,683) = 59,049	3(59,049) = 177,147	3(177,147) = 531,441	3(531,441) = 1,594,323

1 of 1

Jeremy uses repeated multiplication to find the number of views for each day, and then he finds the sum.

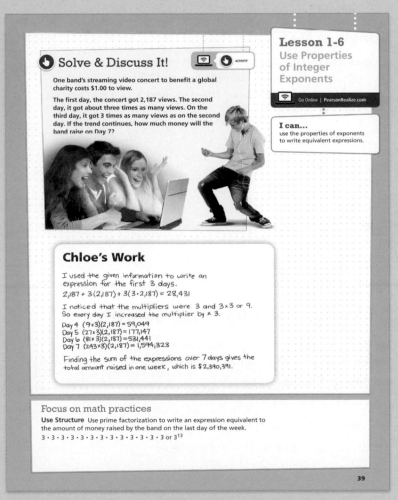

Solve & Discuss It!

One band's streaming video concert to benefit a global charity costs $1.00 to view.

The first day, the concert got 2,187 views. The second day, it got about three times as many views. On the third day, it got 3 times as many views as on the second day. If the trend continues, how much money will the band raise on Day 7?

Lesson 1-6
Use Properties of Integer Exponents

📶 Go Online | PearsonRealize.com

I can...
use the properties of exponents to write equivalent expressions.

Chloe's Work

I used the given information to write an expression for the first 3 days.
2,187 + 3(2,187) + 3(3 · 2,187) = 28,431

I noticed that the multipliers were 3 and 3×3 or 9. So every day I increased the multiplier by × 3.
Day 4 (9×3)(2,187) = 59,049
Day 5 (27×3)(2,187) = 177,147
Day 6 (81×3)(2,187) = 531,441
Day 7 (243×3)(2,187) = 1,594,323

Finding the sum of the expressions over 7 days gives the total amount raised in one week, which is $2,390,391.

Focus on math practices

Use Structure Use prime factorization to write an expression equivalent to the amount of money raised by the band on the last day of the week.
3 · 3 · 3 · 3 · 3 · 3 · 3 · 3 · 3 · 3 · 3 · 3 · 3 or 3^{13}

39

Chloe uses the pattern of multipliers to find the number of views for each day and then finds the sum.

STEP **2** | Develop: Visual Learning

ETP **Establish Mathematics Goals to Focus Learning**

Engage students in a discussion about the *Essential Question*. Make sure they understand that the number of factors and the exponent are the same.

EXAMPLE **1** **Multiply Exponential Expressions: Same Base**

ETP **Use and Connect Mathematical Representations**

Q: Describe what the expression 2^6 represents. [Sample answer: It means to use 2 as a factor 6 times.]

Q: What is the difference between the processes shown in One Way and Another Way? [Sample answer: In One Way, the terms are expanded to visualize the number of 2s being multiplied. In Another Way, the Product of Powers Property is used to add the exponents.]

 Try It!

ETP **Elicit and Use Evidence of Student Thinking**

Q: Explain why the answer is not 3^{16}. [Sample answer: Four factors of 3 multiplied by four more factors of 3 is a total of 8 factors of 3, not 16.]

Convince Me!

Q: State the Product of Powers Property in your own words. Give an example. [Sample answer: The total number of factors is the sum of the exponents, not the product: $6^2 \cdot 6^3 = 6^5$.]

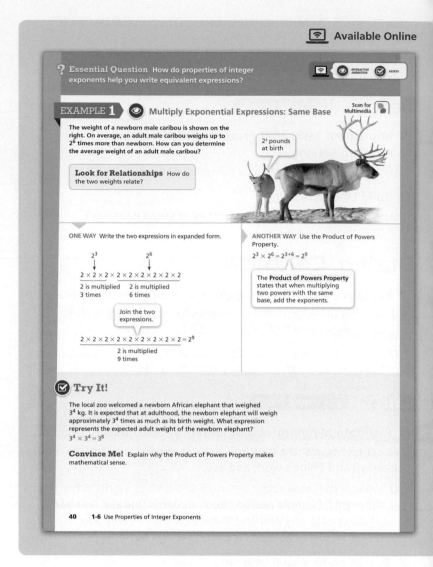

Available Online

? Essential Question How do properties of integer exponents help you write equivalent expressions?

EXAMPLE **1** Multiply Exponential Expressions: Same Base

Scan for Multimedia

The weight of a newborn male caribou is shown on the right. On average, an adult male caribou weighs up to 2^6 times more than newborn. How can you determine the average weight of an adult male caribou?

2^3 pounds at birth

Look for Relationships How do the two weights relate?

ONE WAY Write the two expressions in expanded form.

2^3
↓
$2 \times 2 \times 2$
2 is multiplied 3 times

2^6
↓
$2 \times 2 \times 2 \times 2 \times 2 \times 2$
2 is multiplied 6 times

Join the two expressions.

$2 \times 2 \times 2 \times 2 \times 2 \times 2 \times 2 \times 2 \times 2 = 2^9$
2 is multiplied 9 times

ANOTHER WAY Use the Product of Powers Property.

$2^3 \times 2^6 = 2^{3+6} = 2^9$

The **Product of Powers Property** states that when multiplying two powers with the same base, add the exponents.

 Try It!

The local zoo welcomed a newborn African elephant that weighed 3^4 kg. It is expected that at adulthood, the newborn elephant will weigh approximately 3^4 times as much as its birth weight. What expression represents the expected adult weight of the newborn elephant?

$3^4 \times 3^4 = 3^8$

Convince Me! Explain why the Product of Powers Property makes mathematical sense.

40   1-6 Use Properties of Integer Exponents

 Students can access the *Visual Learning Animation Plus* by using the **BouncePages app** to scan this page. Students can download the app for free in their mobile devices' app store.

RtI **Response to Intervention**

USE WITH EXAMPLE 1 Students may need to review the meaning of an expression with exponents.

• Consider the expression 2^5.

Q: What is the base? [2]

Q: What is the exponent? [5]

Q: Show how to evaluate the expression. [$2^5 = 2 \cdot 2 \cdot 2 \cdot 2 \cdot 2 = 32$]

E **Enrichment**

USE WITH EXAMPLE 1 Challenge students to simplify algebraic expressions with exponents.

• Simplify each expression.

$n^3 \cdot n^4$ [n^7]

$a^4 \cdot b^5 \cdot a^6 \cdot b^7$ [$a^{10} \cdot b^{12}$]

Activity   Assess

XAMPLE 2 — Multiply Exponential Expressions: Different Base

Pose Purposeful Questions

Q: What condition has to be met before this property can be applied? [The factors must have the same exponent.]

XAMPLE 3 — Find the Power of a Power

Pose Purposeful Questions

Q: What is the base in the expression? [5^2]

Q: How many times is this base used as a factor? [4 times]

XAMPLE 4 — Divide Exponential Expressions: Same Base

Pose Purposeful Questions

Q: Why do the bases have to be the same? [Sample answer: So that common factors can be divided out]

 Try It!

Elicit and Use Evidence of Student Thinking

Q: In part d, why not divide the exponent to get 8^3? [Sample answer: The rule is to subtract exponents, not divide.]

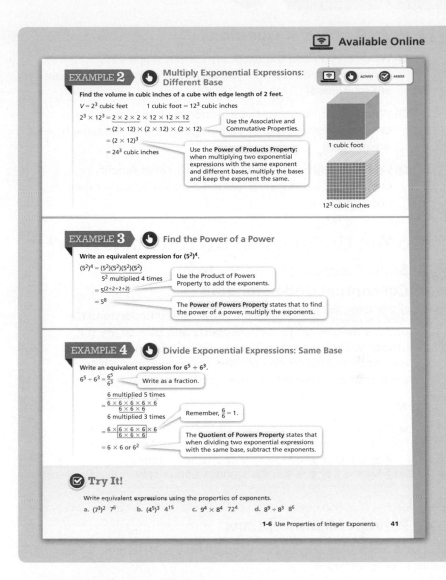

📱 Available Online

EXAMPLE 2 — Multiply Exponential Expressions: Different Base

Find the volume in cubic inches of a cube with edge length of 2 feet.

$V = 2^3$ cubic feet   1 cubic foot $= 12^3$ cubic inches

$2^3 \times 12^3 = 2 \times 2 \times 2 \times 12 \times 12 \times 12$

$= (2 \times 12) \times (2 \times 12) \times (2 \times 12)$ — Use the Associative and Commutative Properties.

$= (2 \times 12)^3$

$= 24^3$ cubic inches

Use the **Power of Products Property**: when multiplying two exponential expressions with the same exponent and different bases, multiply the bases and keep the exponent the same.

1 cubic foot

12^3 cubic inches

EXAMPLE 3 — Find the Power of a Power

Write an equivalent expression for $(5^2)^4$.

$(5^2)^4 = (5^2)(5^2)(5^2)(5^2)$
        5^2 multiplied 4 times — Use the Product of Powers Property to add the exponents.

$= 5^{(2+2+2+2)}$

$= 5^8$ — The **Power of Powers Property** states that to find the power of a power, multiply the exponents.

EXAMPLE 4 — Divide Exponential Expressions: Same Base

Write an equivalent expression for $6^5 \div 6^3$.

$6^5 \div 6^3 = \dfrac{6^5}{6^3}$ — Write as a fraction.

$= \dfrac{6 \times 6 \times 6 \times 6 \times 6}{6 \times 6 \times 6}$ 6 multiplied 5 times / 6 multiplied 3 times

$= \dfrac{6 \times 6 \times 6 \times 6 \times 6}{6 \times 6 \times 6}$ — Remember, $\frac{6}{6} = 1$.

$= 6 \times 6$ or 6^2 — The **Quotient of Powers Property** states that when dividing two exponential expressions with the same base, subtract the exponents.

 Try It!

Write equivalent expressions using the properties of exponents.

a. $(7^3)^2 \ 7^6$ b. $(4^5)^3 \ 4^{15}$ c. $9^4 \times 8^4 \ 72^4$ d. $8^9 \div 8^3 \ 8^6$

1-6 Use Properties of Integer Exponents   **41**

ADDITIONAL EXAMPLES

For additional examples go to PearsonRealize.com.

🄴🄻🄻 English Language Learners

BEGINNING See Example 2.

Review the terms *cube* and *cubic*. Explain that there are 12 inches in a foot. Ask questions to allow students to practice using the terms in context:

Q: How long is one edge of the cube in feet? In inches? [2 feet; 2 × 12 inches]

Review the terms *base* and *exponent*.

Q: What are the base and the exponent in 2^3? What does it mean? [Base is 2 and exponent is 3; it means that you multiply 2 three times.]

INTERMEDIATE See Example 2.

Have students supply the missing word or phrase in each statement to practice using new vocabulary words in context.

Q: The _____ of Multiplication allows the order of two numbers being multiplied to be switched. [Commutative Property]

Q: The _____ of Multiplication allows several numbers being multiplied to be regrouped. [Associative Property]

Q: The volume of a cube is measured in _____ units. [cubic]

ADVANCED See Example 2.

Help students internalize academic language by using vocabulary and properties correctly in their answers.

Q: Create your own example of an expression for which you can demonstrate the Power of Products Property. [Sample answer:

$6^3 \cdot 2^3 = (6 \cdot 6 \cdot 6) \cdot (2 \cdot 2 \cdot 2)$

$= (6 \cdot 2)(6 \cdot 2)(6 \cdot 2)$

$= (6 \cdot 2)^3$

$= 12^3$]

Share your example with a partner. Justify each mathematical step in your example with the name of the corresponding term, procedure, or property.

STEP **2** | Develop: Visual Learning *continued*

Key Concept   Activity

KEY CONCEPT

ETP **Pose Purposeful Questions**

Q: When do you add the exponents when simplifying exponential expressions? [When powers with the same base are multiplied]

Q: When do you subtract the exponents when simplifying exponential expressions? [When powers with the same base are divided]

Q: When do you multiply the exponents when simplifying exponential expressions? [When a power is being raised to another power]

Do You Understand/Do You Know How?

ETP **Build Procedural Fluency from Conceptual Understanding**

? Essential Question Students should understand the underlying concept for each property and how to use the property. This understanding should help them see that it is sometimes possible to use different properties with an expression to generate an equivalent expression.

ITEM 4

Q: How could Tyler have checked to see if he was correct? Explain. [Sample answer: He could have expanded 2 as a factor 3 times and 5 as a factor 3 times; $2 \times 2 \times 2 \times 5 \times 5 \times 5 = 1,000$. $1,000 \neq 10^9$]

⚠ Prevent Misconceptions

ITEM 3 Students may not understand how to determine which answer is correct.

Q: What property do you apply to simplify the expression? Explain. [The Power of a Power Property; $(5^2)^4 = 5^{2 \cdot 4} = 5^8$]

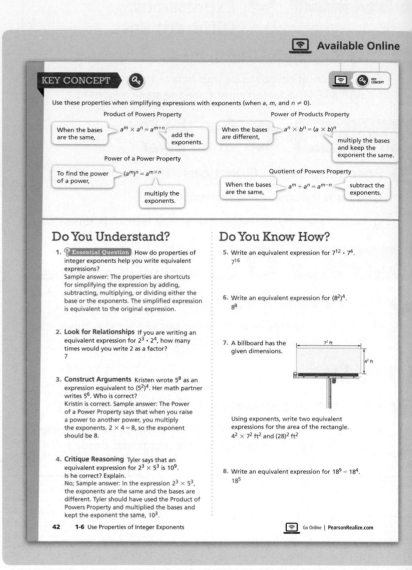

ADDITIONAL EXAMPLE **4**

Available Online

Help students transition from dividing exponential expressions to performing multiple operations with exponential expressions.

Make sure students understand how to determine the order in which you apply the operations.

Q: How does order of operations help you to evaluate the expression? [Simplify within the parentheses first, next find the power of a power, then divide.]

Q: How are the properties of exponents applied? [To simplify the numerator, use the Product of Powers Property first to multiply the expression within the parentheses, and then use the Power of a Power Property. Finally, use the Quotient of Powers Property and subtract the exponents.]

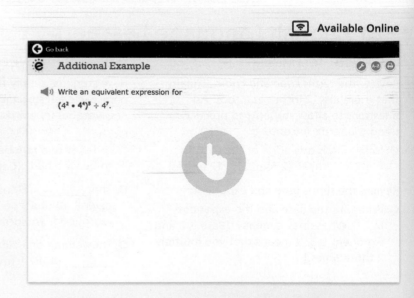

Answer: 4^{23}

Practice & Problem Solving

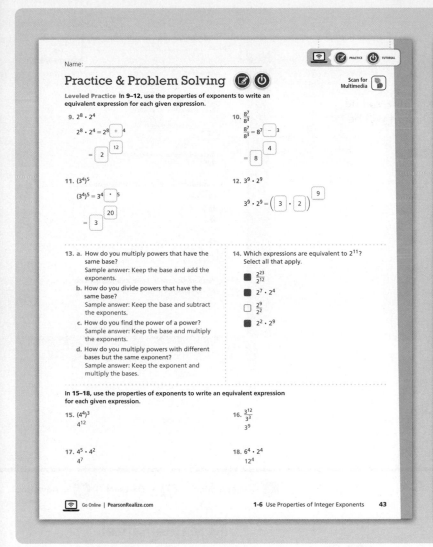

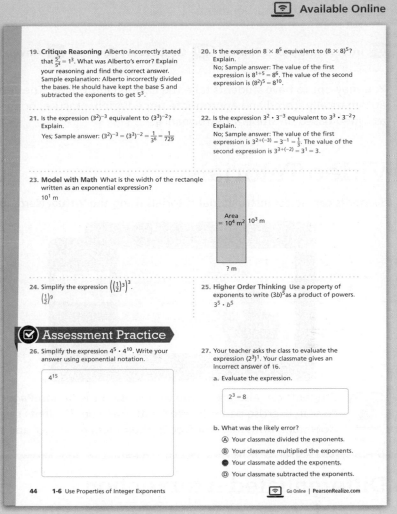

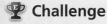

Error Intervention

ITEM 20 Students may incorrectly identify these expressions as equivalent.

Q: What properties would help you write an equivalent expression for 8×8^5? $(8 \times 8)^5$? [8×8^5: Product of Powers Property; $(8 \times 8)^5$: Product of Powers and Power of a Power Properties]

Challenge

ITEM 23 Model with Math Challenge students to see how many rectangles they can make that have an area of 10^8 square meters.

Q: What are some rectangles that have an area of 10^8 square meters? [Sample answer: 10^1 by 10^7, 10^2 by 10^6, 10^3 by 10^5, 10^4 by 10^4]

You may opt to have students complete the automatically scored Practice & Problem Solving items online.

Item Analysis

Example	Items	DOK
1	9, 17, 26	1
	13, 14	2
2	12, 18	1
3	11, 15	1
	20, 21, 22, 24	2
	25, 27	3
	10, 16	1
4	23	2
	19	3

PearsonRealize.com

 Lesson Quiz

Use the student scores on the Lesson Quiz to prescribe differentiated assignments.

I Intervention 0–3 Points **O** On-Level 4 Points **A** Advanced 5 Points

You may opt to have students take the Lesson Quiz online. The Lesson Quiz will be automatically scored and appropriate remediation, practice, or enrichment will be assigned based on student performance.

 Video Tutorials

Students can access instructional tutorials using the **Virtual Nerd app**.

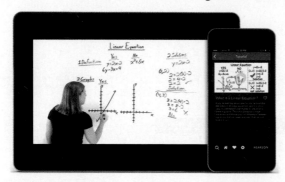

Students can also access the videos using the **BouncePages app** to scan exercise pages marked with this icon. Students can download both apps for free in their mobile devices' app store.

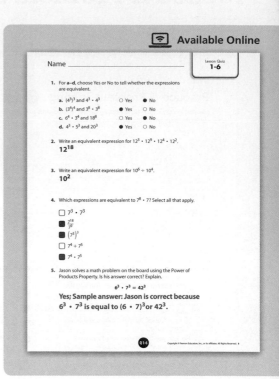

Available Online

1. For **a–d**, choose Yes or No to tell whether the expressions are equivalent.
   a. $(4^3)^3$ and $4^3 \cdot 4^3$ ○ Yes ● No
   b. $(3^4)^4$ and $3^8 \cdot 3^8$ ● Yes ○ No
   c. $6^4 \cdot 3^4$ and 18^8 ○ Yes ● No
   d. $4^3 \cdot 5^3$ and 20^3 ● Yes ○ No

2. Write an equivalent expression for $12^3 \cdot 12^9 \cdot 12^4 \cdot 12^2$.
   12^{18}

3. Write an equivalent expression for $10^6 \div 10^4$.
   10^2

4. Which expressions are equivalent to $7^6 \cdot 7$? Select all that apply.
   ☐ $7^3 \cdot 7^3$
   ■ $\frac{7^{18}}{7^4}$
   ■ $(7^3)^3$
   ☐ $7^4 + 7^5$
   ■ $7^4 \cdot 7^5$

5. Jason solves a math problem on the board using the Power of Products Property. Is his answer correct? Explain.
   $6^3 \cdot 7^3 = 42^3$
   Yes; Sample answer: Jason is correct because $6^3 \cdot 7^3$ is equal to $(6 \cdot 7)^3$ or 42^3.

Differentiated Intervention

I = Intervention **O** = On-Level **A** = Advanced

Reteach to Build Understanding **I**
Provides scaffolded reteaching for the key lesson concepts.

Additional Vocabulary Support **I** **O**
Helps students develop and reinforce understanding of key terms and concepts.

Build Mathematical Literacy **I**
Provides support for struggling readers to build mathematical literacy.

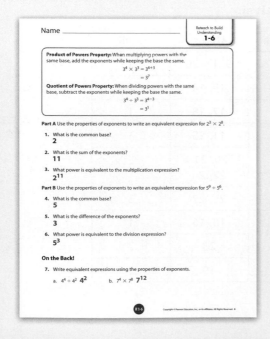

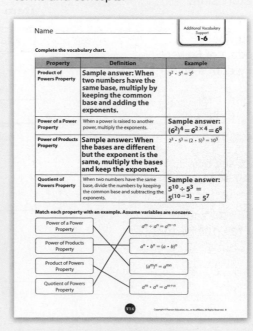

Practice | Worksheets | Math Tools | Math Games

Additional Practice

You may opt to have students complete the automatically scored Additional Practice items online.

Item Analysis

Example	Items	DOK
1	1, 13	1
	6, 9	2
2	4, 8	1
	11	2
3	3, 5	1
	10	2
	12	3
4	2, 7, 14	1

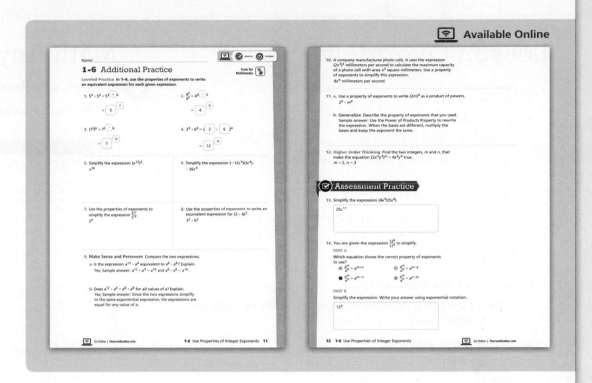

🔊 Available Online

Differentiated Intervention

I = Intervention **O** = On-Level **A** = Advanced

Enrichment O A

Presents engaging problems and activities that extend the lesson concepts.

Math Tools and Games I O A

Offers additional activities and games to build understanding and fluency.

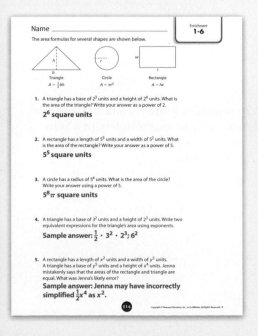

Activity

Lesson 1-7
More Properties of Integer Exponents

Lesson Overview

FOCUS

Objective

Students will be able to:

✔ simplify expressions with negative and zero exponents.

✔ evaluate expressions with negative and zero exponents.

Essential Understanding

A number with a negative exponent indicates multiplication by the reciprocal of that number. A number with an exponent of zero is equal to 1.

COHERENCE

Previously in this topic, students:

• learned how the properties of exponents can be used to simplify exponential expressions.

In this lesson, students:

• explore and apply the Zero Exponent Property and the Negative Exponent Property.

Later in this topic, students will:

• add, subtract, multiply, and divide very large and very small numbers written in scientific notation.

RIGOR

This lesson emphasizes a blend of **conceptual understanding** and **procedural skill and fluency**.

• Students reinforce their understanding of the Zero Exponent Property and the Negative Exponent Property by analyzing patterns to understand the properties.

• Students learn and apply the Zero Exponent Property and the Negative Exponent Property to write equivalent exponential expressions.

Math Anytime

Today's Challenge

Use the Topic 1 problems any time during this topic.

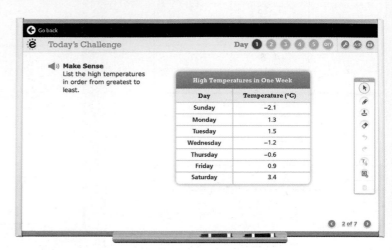

Mathematics Overview

In this lesson, students will learn the Zero Exponent Property and Negative Exponent Property, and use these properties to simplify expressions and to solve problems.

Applying Math Practices

Reason Abstractly and Quantitatively
Students will use their reasoning skills and explore the meaning of a zero exponent and a negative exponent. They will apply the Zero Exponent Property and the Negative Exponent Property to write equivalent exponential expressions.

Construct Arguments
Students will use the Zero Exponent Property and the Negative Exponent Property to explain why an expression with a zero exponent or negative exponents can be simplified using no exponent or only positive exponents.

STEP 1 | Develop: Problem-Based Learning

15-20 min

Activity

Explore It!

Look for Relationships As students work through the *Explore It*, listen and look for students who are able to find the relationship of each set to the following set and reduce the ratio.

Before 〔 WHOLE CLASS 〕

1 Implement Tasks that Promote Reasoning and Problem Solving

Q: What information should you put in the last column of the table? [Sample answer: Put the ratio of the number of sit-ups in each set to the number of sit-ups in the previous set.]

2 Build Understanding

Q: What do you notice about the number of sit-ups as the set number increases? [The number of sit-ups decreases.]

Q: What pattern do you notice between each set of sit-ups? [Sample answer: The next set of sit-ups is half the number of sit-ups as the previous set.]

During 〔 SMALL GROUP 〕

3 Support Productive Struggle in Learning Mathematics

Q: How many sit-ups will they do in the second set? [32]

Q: How can you predict the number of sit-ups in Set 5? [Divide the number of sit-ups in Set 4 by 2.]

After 〔 WHOLE CLASS 〕

4 Facilitate Meaningful Mathematical Discourse

Ask students to share their solutions. If needed, project Ethan's and Donovan's work and ask:

Q: How did Ethan solve the problem? How does this compare with Donovan's solution? [Sample answer: Ethan makes a table and divides the number of sit-ups in each set by 2 to find the number in the subsequent set. Donovan multiplies the number of sit-ups in each set by $\frac{1}{2}$ to find the number of sit-ups in the subsequent set.]

5 Transition to Visual Learning

Q: How could you represent the total number of sit-ups in each set using exponents? [Starting from Set 1: 2^6, 2^5, 2^4, and so on]

6 Extension for Early Finishers

Q: Predict the number of sit-ups for Sets 6, 7, 8, and 9. Does the number of sit-ups in these sets make sense? [Sample answer: The number of sit-ups for Set 6 is 2, for Set 7 is 1, for Set 8 is $\frac{1}{2}$, and for Set 9 is $\frac{1}{4}$. The values become unrealistically small for this situation and do not make sense in sets 8 and 9.]

Analyze Student Work

Available Online

Go back

Explore It!

✓ Look for Relationships

Calvin and Mike do sit-ups when they work out. They start with 64 sit-ups for the first set and do half as many each subsequent set.

B. What conclusion can you make about the relationship between the number of sit-ups in each set?

Ethan's work

I made a table to show the number of sit-ups in each set. Each set has half the number of sit-ups as the previous set. The relationship is 2 to 1. The pattern is divide by 2.

1 of 1

Ethan finds that each set was half the number of the previous set, so the pattern was to divide by 2.

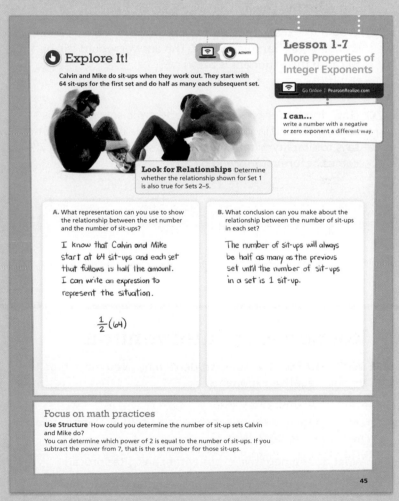

Explore It!

ACTIVITY

Calvin and Mike do sit-ups when they work out. They start with 64 sit-ups for the first set and do half as many each subsequent set.

Lesson 1-7
More Properties of Integer Exponents

Go Online | PearsonRealize.com

I can...
write a number with a negative or zero exponent a different way.

Look for Relationships Determine whether the relationship shown for Set 1 is also true for Sets 2–5.

A. What representation can you use to show the relationship between the set number and the number of sit-ups?

I know that Calvin and Mike start at 64 sit-ups and each set that follows is half the amount. I can write an expression to represent the situation.

$$\frac{1}{2}(64)$$

B. What conclusion can you make about the relationship between the number of sit-ups in each set?

The number of sit-ups will always be half as many as the previous set until the number of sit-ups in a set is 1 sit-up.

Focus on math practices

Use Structure How could you determine the number of sit-up sets Calvin and Mike do?
You can determine which power of 2 is equal to the number of sit-ups. If you subtract the power from 7, that is the set number for those sit-ups.

45

Donovan writes an expression to model the relationship between each set and the previous one.

ETP Establish Mathematics Goals to Focus Learning

Engage students in a discussion about the *Essential Question*. Make sure they understand the procedure for simplifying numbers with exponents.

EXAMPLE **1** The Zero Exponent Property

ETP Use and Connect Mathematical Representations

Q: As the exponent decreases by 1 in the exponent form, what pattern do you notice when finding the value of the simplified form in the table? [The previous number is divided by 3.]

Q: How would you determine the value of 3^0 using this pattern? [Sample answer: Divide the previous number, 3, by 3.]

 Try It!

ETP Elicit and Use Evidence of Student Thinking

Q: In all four problems, what do you notice about the base in relation to the answers? [Sample answer: If the exponent is zero, the value of the base does not matter as long as it is not zero. The answer will always equal 1.]

Q: Would the answer be different if the base were a variable? Explain. [No; Sample answer: The answer would still be 1 because the exponent is zero.]

Convince Me!

Q: How does order of operations affect the solving of this problem? Explain. [Sample answer: The order of operations says to simplify within the parenthesis first, so finding 7^0 comes before multiplying by 2.]

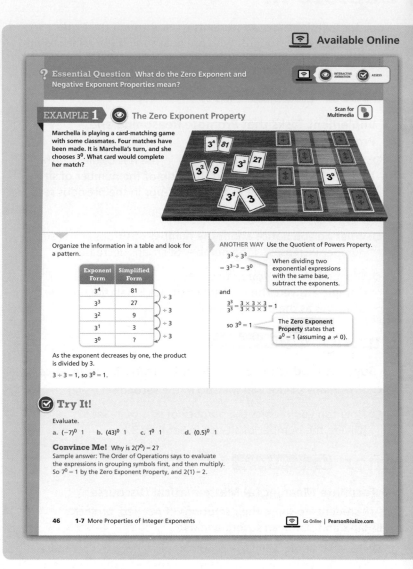

Available Online

? Essential Question What do the Zero Exponent and Negative Exponent Properties mean?

EXAMPLE **1** The Zero Exponent Property

Scan for Multimedia

Marchella is playing a card-matching game with some classmates. Four matches have been made. It is Marchella's turn, and she chooses 3^0. What card would complete her match?

Organize the information in a table and look for a pattern.

Exponent Form	Simplified Form	
3^4	81	÷3
3^3	27	÷3
3^2	9	÷3
3^1	3	÷3
3^0	?	÷3

As the exponent decreases by one, the product is divided by 3.
$3 \div 3 = 1$, so $3^0 = 1$.

ANOTHER WAY Use the Quotient of Powers Property.

$3^3 \div 3^3$
$= 3^{3-3} = 3^0$

When dividing two exponential expressions with the same base, subtract the exponents.

and

$\frac{3^3}{3^3} = \frac{3 \times 3 \times 3}{3 \times 3 \times 3} = 1$

so $3^0 = 1$

The Zero Exponent Property states that $a^0 = 1$ (assuming $a \neq 0$).

 Try It!

Evaluate.
a. $(-7)^0$ 1   b. $(43)^0$ 1   c. 1^0 1   d. $(0.5)^0$ 1

Convince Me! Why is $2(7^0) = 2$?
Sample answer: The Order of Operations says to evaluate the expressions in grouping symbols first, and then multiply. So $7^0 = 1$ by the Zero Exponent Property, and $2(1) = 2$.

46   1-7 More Properties of Integer Exponents   Go Online | PearsonRealize.com

Students can access the *Visual Learning Animation Plus* by using the **BouncePages app** to scan this page. Students can download the app for free in their mobile devices' app store.

 Response to Intervention

USE WITH EXAMPLE 2 Some students may need more time to understand negative exponents.

- Ask the following questions.

  Q: Does a negative exponent change a positive number to a negative number? [No]

  Q: What does a negative exponent mean? [Reciprocal]

  Q: What effect does a negative exponent have on a base? [Sample answer: A negative exponent moves a factor from the numerator to the denominator with a positive exponent; or, a negative exponent moves a factor from the denominator to the numerator with a positive exponent.]

 Enrichment

USE WITH EXAMPLE 3 Challenge students to further explore the meaning of negative exponents.

Q: How can you use the fact that a number multiplied by its reciprocal is 1 and the Power of Products Property to explain negative exponents? [Sample answer: $9 \times \frac{1}{9} = 1$, so $3^2 \times 3^n = 3^0$. Using the Power of Products Property, $2 + n = 0$, so $n = -2$. Therefore, $3^{-2} = \frac{1}{3^2} = \frac{1}{9}$.]

XAMPLE 2 The Negative Exponent Property

TP Pose Purposeful Questions

Q: Using the Negative Exponent Property, how do you know that $4^{-2} = \frac{1}{16}$? [Sample answer: $4^{-2} = \frac{1}{4^2} \cdot \frac{1}{4 \times 4} = \frac{1}{16}$.]

Try It!

TP Elicit and Use Evidence of Student Thinking

Q: What property could you use to help you simplify 8^{-2}? Explain. [Sample answer: You can use the Negative Exponent Property to write expressions with negative exponents as expressions with positive exponents.]

XAMPLE 3 Expressions with Negative Exponents

TP Pose Purposeful Questions

Q: Why is the exponent positive in the answer? [Sample answer: The exponent is positive in the answer because 7^{-3} in the denominator was simplified to $\frac{1}{7^3}$. Dividing 1 by $\frac{1}{7^3}$ is the same as multiplying 1 by 7^3.]

Try It!

TP Elicit and Use Evidence of Student Thinking

Q: What is the reciprocal of the reciprocal of a number? [It is the number itself.]

Q: How does knowing this help to solve these problems? [Sample answer: The "one over a number" is a reciprocal, and the negative exponent means to take the reciprocal of the base with a positive exponent, so the expression is the reciprocal of a reciprocal.]

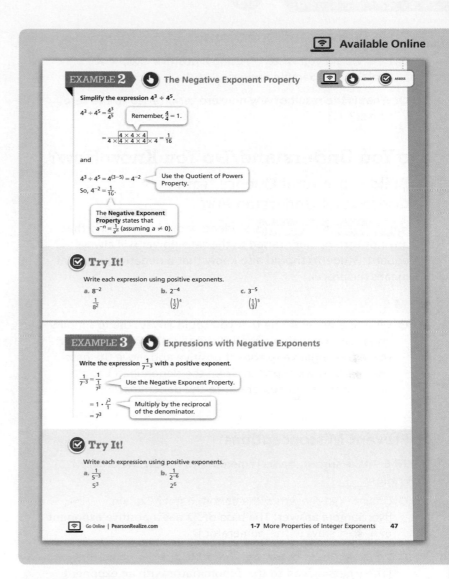

📶 Available Online

EXAMPLE 2 The Negative Exponent Property

Simplify the expression $4^3 \div 4^5$.

$4^3 \div 4^5 = \frac{4^3}{4^5}$ — Remember, $\frac{4}{4} = 1$.

$= \frac{4 \times 4 \times 4}{4 \times \boxed{4 \times 4 \times 4} \times 4} = \frac{1}{16}$

and

$4^3 \div 4^5 = 4^{(3-5)} = 4^{-2}$ — Use the Quotient of Powers Property.

So, $4^{-2} = \frac{1}{16}$.

The **Negative Exponent Property** states that $a^{-n} = \frac{1}{a^n}$ (assuming $a \neq 0$).

Try It!

Write each expression using positive exponents.

a. 8^{-2} b. 2^{-4} c. 3^{-5}

$\frac{1}{8^2}$ $\left(\frac{1}{2}\right)^4$ $\left(\frac{1}{3}\right)^5$

EXAMPLE 3 Expressions with Negative Exponents

Write the expression $\frac{1}{7^{-3}}$ with a positive exponent.

$\frac{1}{7^{-3}} = \frac{1}{\frac{1}{7^3}}$ — Use the Negative Exponent Property.

$= 1 \cdot \frac{7^3}{1}$ — Multiply by the reciprocal of the denominator.

$= 7^3$

Try It!

Write each expression using positive exponents.

a. $\frac{1}{5^{-3}}$ b. $\frac{1}{2^{-6}}$

5^3 2^6

Go Online | PearsonRealize.com   1-7 More Properties of Integer Exponents   47

ADDITIONAL EXAMPLES

For additional examples go to **PearsonRealize.com.**

English Language Learners

BEGINNING Before reading Example 1, have students identify what they see in the illustration, either in their first language or in English. Point to the words *card-matching* and ask:

Q: What is a *card*? What does it mean to *match cards*? [Sample answer: A card is a small piece of paper. Matching cards means to pair cards with the same value.]

Use the table to review the term *pattern*.

Q: What is a *pattern*? [A pattern is something that repeats. The exponents in the table decrease by 1, so that is a pattern.]

INTERMEDIATE Read Example 1 to students. Ask students to identify which parts of the illustration show "four matches." Ask the students:

Q: What other meanings do you know for the word *match*? Explain. [Sample answer: Pair, complement, suit; You can match two things that are alike.]

Q: How can the illustration help you know which meaning to use? [Sample answer: The illustration shows cards with equal values. In this problem, *match* means to find things that are alike.]

ADVANCED Read Example 1. Have students explain how the illustration represents the problem. Ask supporting questions, such as:

Q: What matches does the illustration show? [$3^1 = 3$; $3^2 = 9$; $3^3 = 27$; $3^4 = 81$]

Q: What is the meaning of the last sentence of the problem? [Sample answer: It means "What card is equal in value to 3^0?"]

Ask students to explain the pattern in the table using their own words.

STEP **2** | Develop: Visual Learning *continued*

KEY CONCEPT

ETP **Pose Purposeful Questions**

Q: How would you write $\frac{1}{2^{-3}}$ using a positive exponent? Explain. [2^3; Sample answer: $\frac{1}{2^{-3}} = 1 \cdot \frac{2^3}{1} = 2^3$]

Q: What is the result of any nonzero term raised to the zero power? [1]

Do You Understand/Do You Know How?

ETP **Build Procedural Fluency from Conceptual Understanding**

? Essential Question Students should understand that any nonzero number raised to the zero power will always equal 1. Students should also know that a negative exponent means reciprocal.

ITEM 5

Q: What is a general rule that you could always use to simplify an expression with a negative exponent? [Sample answer: Make the negative exponent positive and move the base and this positive exponent from the denominator to the numerator, or the numerator to the denominator.]

Prevent Misconceptions

ITEM 6 Make sure students remember to follow the order of operations.

Q: Does 27 get moved to the denominator? Explain. [No; Sample answer: The base of 27 has a positive exponent of 1, so it stays in the numerator.]

Q: What factor or factors get moved to the denominator? [The *y* gets moved to the denominator with an exponent of positive 2.]

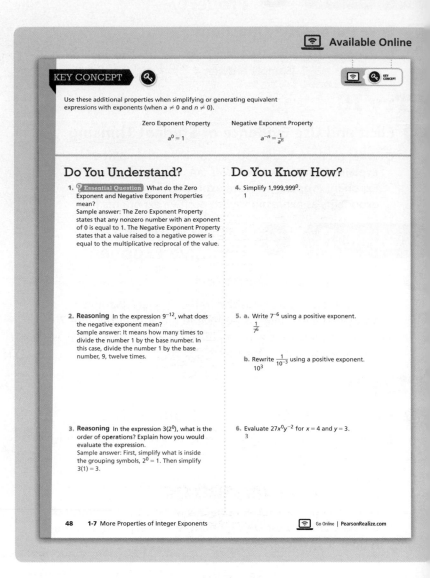

Available Online

KEY CONCEPT

Use these additional properties when simplifying or generating equivalent expressions with exponents (when $a \neq 0$ and $n \neq 0$).

Zero Exponent Property	Negative Exponent Property
$a^0 = 1$	$a^{-n} = \frac{1}{a^n}$

Do You Understand?

1. **? Essential Question** What do the Zero Exponent and Negative Exponent Properties mean?
   Sample answer: The Zero Exponent Property states that any nonzero number with an exponent of 0 is equal to 1. The Negative Exponent Property states that a value raised to a negative power is equal to the multiplicative reciprocal of the value.

2. **Reasoning** In the expression 9^{-12}, what does the negative exponent mean?
   Sample answer: It means how many times to divide the number 1 by the base number. In this case, divide the number 1 by the base number, 9, twelve times.

3. **Reasoning** In the expression $3(2^0)$, what is the order of operations? Explain how you would evaluate the expression.
   Sample answer: First, simplify what is inside the grouping symbols, $2^0 = 1$. Then simplify $3(1) = 3$.

Do You Know How?

4. Simplify $1,999,999^0$.
   1

5. a. Write 7^{-6} using a positive exponent.
      $\frac{1}{7^6}$

   b. Rewrite $\frac{1}{10^{-3}}$ using a positive exponent.
      10^3

6. Evaluate $27x^0y^{-2}$ for $x = 4$ and $y = 3$.
   3

48   1-7 More Properties of Integer Exponents   Go Online | PearsonRealize.com

---

ADDITIONAL EXAMPLE **2**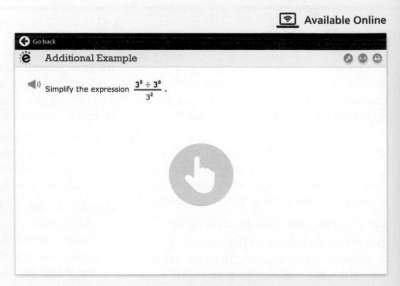

Available Online

Help students transition from applying the Negative Exponent Property to an expression containing division twice.

Make sure students remember that they use order of operations to simplify the exponential expression in the numerator first.

Q: How do you use the Quotient of Powers Property? [Sample answer: When the bases are the same, subtract the exponents.]

Q: Why do you apply the same property twice here? [Sample answer: The expression calls for division twice, and both times the division involves exponents.]

Q: What is another way you could write $\frac{1}{3^5}$? [3^{-5}]

Go back

Additional Example

Simplify the expression $\frac{3^5 \div 3^8}{3^2}$.

Answer: $\frac{1}{243}$

Practice & Problem Solving

 Available Online

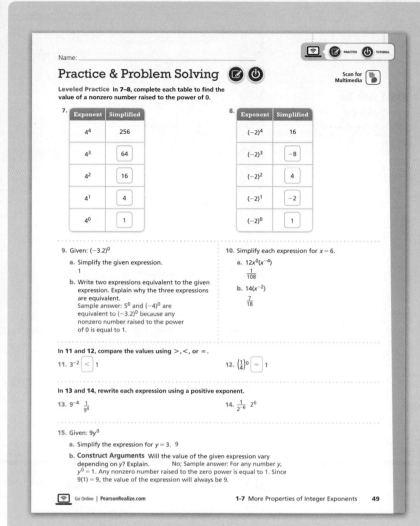

Name: _____

Practice & Problem Solving

Scan for Multimedia

Leveled Practice In **7–8**, complete each table to find the value of a nonzero number raised to the power of 0.

7.

Exponent	Simplified
4^4	256
4^3	64
4^2	16
4^1	4
4^0	1

8.

Exponent	Simplified
$(-2)^4$	16
$(-2)^3$	-8
$(-2)^2$	4
$(-2)^1$	-2
$(-2)^0$	1

9. Given: $(-3.2)^0$

  a. Simplify the given expression.
  1

  b. Write two expressions equivalent to the given expression. Explain why the three expressions are equivalent.
  Sample answer: 5^0 and $(-4)^0$ are equivalent to $(-3.2)^0$ because any nonzero number raised to the power of 0 is equal to 1.

10. Simplify each expression for $x = 6$.

  a. $12x^0(x^{-4})$
  $\frac{1}{108}$

  b. $14(x^{-2})$
  $\frac{7}{18}$

In **11** and **12**, compare the values using $>$, $<$, or $=$.

11. 3^{-2} $<$ 1   **12.** $\left(\frac{1}{4}\right)^0$ $=$ 1

In **13** and **14**, rewrite each expression using a positive exponent.

13. 9^{-4} $\frac{1}{9^4}$ **14.** $\frac{1}{2^{-6}}$ 2^6

15. Given: $9y^0$

  a. Simplify the expression for $y = 3$.   9

  b. **Construct Arguments** Will the value of the given expression vary depending on y? Explain.   No; Sample answer: For any number y, $y^0 = 1$. Any nonzero number raised to the zero power is equal to 1. Since $9(1) = 9$, the value of the expression will always be 9.

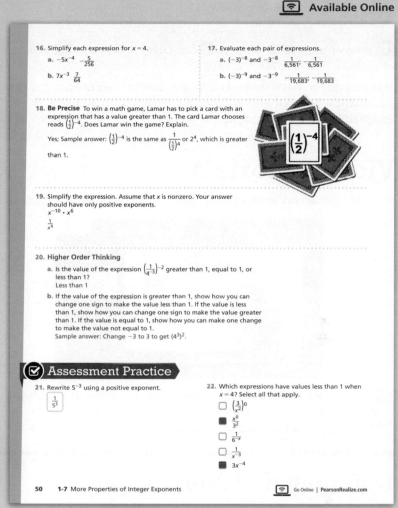

16. Simplify each expression for $x = 4$.

  a. $-5x^{-4}$ $-\frac{5}{256}$

  b. $7x^{-3}$ $\frac{7}{64}$

17. Evaluate each pair of expressions.

  a. $(-3)^{-8}$ and -3^{-8} $\frac{1}{6,561}$, $-\frac{1}{6,561}$

  b. $(-3)^{-9}$ and -3^{-9} $-\frac{1}{19,683}$, $\frac{1}{19,683}$

18. **Be Precise** To win a math game, Lamar has to pick a card with an expression that has a value greater than 1. The card Lamar chooses reads $\left(\frac{1}{2}\right)^{-4}$. Does Lamar win the game? Explain.

  Yes; Sample answer: $\left(\frac{1}{2}\right)^{-4}$ is the same as $\frac{1}{\left(\frac{1}{2}\right)^4}$ or 2^4, which is greater than 1.

$\left(\frac{1}{2}\right)^{-4}$

19. Simplify the expression. Assume that x is nonzero. Your answer should have only positive exponents.
  $x^{-10} \cdot x^6$
  $\frac{1}{x^4}$

20. **Higher Order Thinking**

  a. Is the value of the expression $\left(\frac{1}{4^{-3}}\right)^{-2}$ greater than 1, equal to 1, or less than 1?
  Less than 1

  b. If the value of the expression is greater than 1, show how you can change one sign to make the value less than 1. If the value is less than 1, show how you can change one sign to make the value greater than 1. If the value is equal to 1, show how you can make one change to make the value not equal to 1.
  Sample answer: Change -3 to 3 to get $(4^3)^2$.

✅ Assessment Practice

21. Rewrite 5^{-3} using a positive exponent.
  $\frac{1}{5^3}$

22. Which expressions have values less than 1 when $x = 4$? Select all that apply.
  ☐ $\left(\frac{3}{x^2}\right)^0$
  ☒ $\frac{x^0}{3^2}$
  ☐ $\frac{1}{6^{-x}}$
  ☐ $\frac{1}{x^{-3}}$
  ☒ $3x^{-4}$

🛑 Error Intervention

ITEM 16 Students may think that the coefficient should move to the denominator.

  Q: Should the coefficient be part of the denominator? Explain. [No; Sample answer: The negative exponent applies only to the base x, not to the coefficient.]

  Q: How could you write the problem so that the coefficient becomes part of the denominator? [Sample answer: Use parentheses, such as $(-5x)^{-4}$.]

🄴🄻🄻 English Language Learners

ITEM 20 Higher Order Thinking English Language Learners may not understand the questions asked. Have students state the problem in their own words.

  Q: In your own words, explain what the question is asking in part A. [Sample answer: Compare the value of $\left(\frac{1}{4^{-3}}\right)^{-2}$ to 1.]

You may opt to have students complete the automatically scored Practice & Problem Solving items online.

Item Analysis

Example	Items	DOK
	7, 8, 9	1
1	12	2
	15	3
2	13, 14, 21	1
	11, 19	2
	10, 17	1
3	16, 22	2
	18, 20	3

Lesson Quiz

Use the student scores on the Lesson Quiz to prescribe differentiated assignments.

I Intervention 0–3 Points   **O** On-Level 4 Points   **A** Advanced 5 Points

You may opt to have students take the Lesson Quiz online. The Lesson Quiz will be automatically scored and appropriate remediation, practice, or enrichment will be assigned based on student performance.

Video Tutorials

Students can access instructional tutorials using the **Virtual Nerd app**.

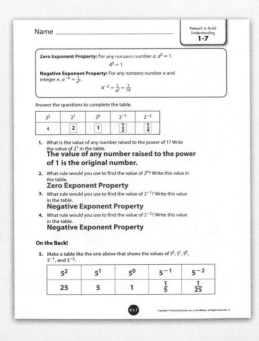

Students can also access the videos using the **BouncePages app** to scan exercise pages marked with this icon. Students can download both apps for free in their mobile devices' app store.

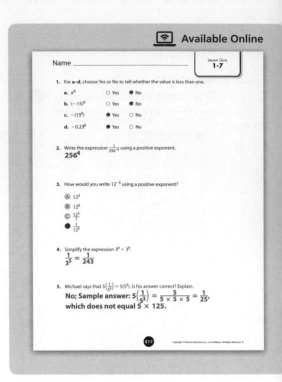

Available Online

Name _____   Lesson Quiz 1-7

1. For **a–d**, choose Yes or No to tell whether the value is less than one.
   a. x^0 ○ Yes ● No
   b. $(-15)^0$ ○ Yes ● No
   c. $-(15^0)$ ● Yes ○ No
   d. -0.23^0 ● Yes ○ No

2. Write the expression $\frac{1}{256^4}$ using a positive exponent.
   256^4

3. How would you write 12^{-3} using a positive exponent?
   Ⓐ 12^3
   Ⓑ 12^0
   Ⓒ $\frac{12^3}{1}$
   ● $\frac{1}{12^3}$

4. Simplify the expression $3^4 \div 3^9$.
   $\frac{1}{3^5} = \frac{1}{243}$

5. Michael says that $5\left(\frac{1}{5^3}\right) = 5(5^3)$. Is his answer correct? Explain.
   No; Sample answer: $5\left(\frac{1}{5^3}\right) = \frac{5}{5 \times 5 \times 5} = \frac{1}{25}$, which does not equal 5×125.

Differentiated Intervention

I = Intervention   **O** = On-Level   **A** = Advanced

Reteach to Build Understanding **I**

Provides scaffolded reteaching for the key lesson concepts.

Name _____   Reteach to Build Understanding 1-7

Zero Exponent Property: For any nonzero number a, $a^0 = 1$.
$$4^0 = 1$$

Negative Exponent Property: For any nonzero number a and integer n, $a^{-n} = \frac{1}{a^n}$.
$$4^{-2} = \frac{1}{4^2} = \frac{1}{16}$$

Answer the questions to complete the table.

2^2	2^1	2^0	2^{-1}	2^{-2}
4	2	1	$\frac{1}{2}$	$\frac{1}{4}$

1. What is the value of any number raised to the power of 1? Write the value of 2^1 in the table.
   The value of any number raised to the power of 1 is the original number.
2. What rule would you use to find the value of 2^0? Write this value in the table.
   Zero Exponent Property
3. What rule would you use to find the value of 2^{-1}? Write this value in the table.
   Negative Exponent Property
4. What rule would you use to find the value of 2^{-2}? Write this value in the table.
   Negative Exponent Property

On the Back!

5. Make a table like the one above that shows the values of 5^2, 5^1, 5^0, 5^{-1}, and 5^{-2}.

5^2	5^1	5^0	5^{-1}	5^{-2}
25	5	1	$\frac{1}{5}$	$\frac{1}{25}$

Additional Vocabulary Support **I O**

Helps students develop and reinforce understanding of key terms and concepts.

Name _____   Additional Vocabulary Support 1-7

Complete the sentences using the bank below.

| Negative Exponent Property | zero | positive |
| Zero Exponent Property | expression | negative |

1. According to the   Zero Exponent Property , any nonzero number with an exponent of   zero   is equal to 1.
2. According to the   Negative Exponent Property , the   expression a^{-n} can be rewritten as $\frac{1}{a^n}$, when a and $n \neq 0$.
3. An exponent changes from   negative   to   positive   when it moves from the numerator to the denominator.

For each equation, write Zero Exponent Property or Negative Exponent Property.

$5^{-3} = \frac{1}{125}$ **Negative Exponent Property**	$82^0 = 1$ **Zero Exponent Property**
$-(6^0) = -1$ **Zero Exponent Property**	$7^{-2} = \frac{1}{49}$ **Negative Exponent Property**

Build Mathematical Literacy **I**

Provides support for struggling readers to build mathematical literacy.

Name _____   Build Mathematical Literacy 1-7

Read the Key Concept from the lesson. Then answer the questions to help you understand the Key Concept.

KEY CONCEPT

Use these additional properties when simplifying or generating equivalent expressions with exponents (when a and $n \neq 0$).

Zero Exponent Property   Negative Exponent Property
$a^0 = 1$ $a^{-n} = \frac{1}{a^n}$

1. Why is the property on the left called the Zero Exponent Property?
   Sample answer: When $a \neq 0$, it describes the value of a number whose exponent is 0.
2. What does the Zero Exponent Property tell you about a number raised to the power of 0?
   Sample answer: The value is equal to 1, unless the base is 0.
3. Can you use the Zero Exponent Property to find the value of 0^0? Explain.
   No; Sample answer: The property says that the base cannot be equal to 0.
4. In the expression 4^{-3}, underline the number that corresponds to a in the Negative Exponent Property and circle the number that corresponds to n. What does the Negative Exponent Property tell you about the expression 4^{-3}?
   Check students' work; $4^{-3} = \frac{1}{4^3}$.
5. The Negative Exponent Property cannot be applied to what base? Why do you think this base is not included?
   0; Sample answer: Zero cannot be the denominator of a fraction because division by zero is undefined.

Practice Worksheets Math Tools Math Games

Additional Practice

You may opt to have students complete the automatically scored Additional Practice items online.

Item Analysis

Example	Items	DOK
1	2, 3, 6	1
	13, 15	2
2	1, 14	1
	4, 7, 10	2
	11, 12	3
3	5, 8, 9, 15	2

 Available Online

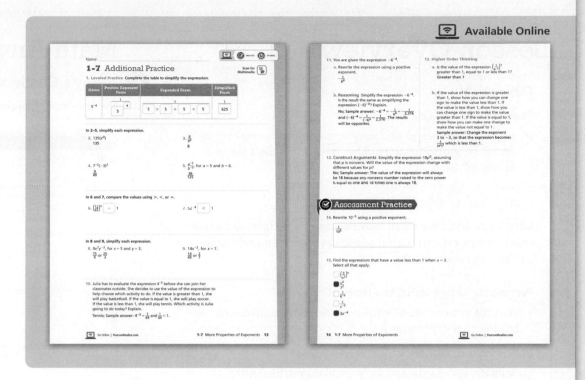

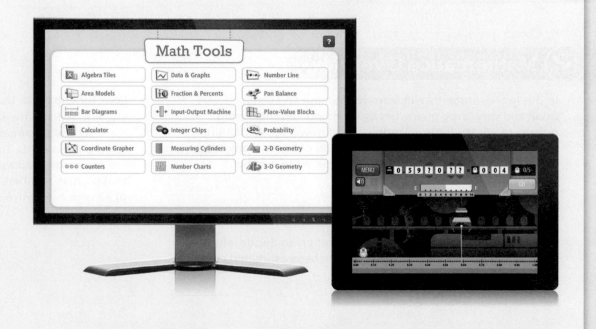

Differentiated Intervention

I = Intervention   **O** = On-Level   **A** = Advanced

Enrichment O A

Presents engaging problems and activities that extend the lesson concepts.

Math Tools and Games I O A

Offers additional activities and games to build understanding and fluency.

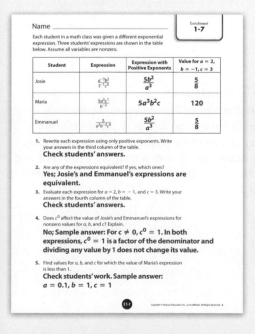

Lesson 1-8

Use Powers of 10 to Estimate Quantities

Lesson Overview

FOCUS

Objective

Students will be able to:

✔ estimate very large and very small quantities by rounding and then writing that number as a single digit times a power of 10.

Essential Understanding

Very large and very small numbers can be estimated to help make computations easier, as well as create an understanding of the size of a quantity.

COHERENCE

Previously in this topic, students:

• used the properties of exponents to write equivalent exponential expressions.

In this lesson, students:

• estimate very large and very small quantities using powers of 10.

Later in this topic, students will:

• perform operations with numbers written in scientific notation.

RIGOR

This lesson emphasizes a blend of **conceptual understanding** and **application**.

• Students extend their knowledge of integer exponents to estimate very large and very small quantities using powers of 10.

• Students apply estimation with powers of 10 to situations when comparing quantities to find out how many times larger or smaller one quantity is in comparison to another.

Math Anytime

Today's Challenge

Use the Topic 1 problems any time during this topic.

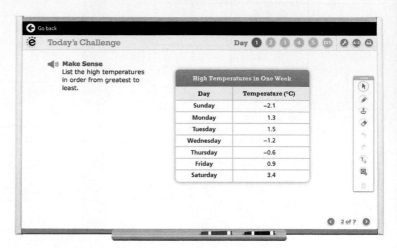

Watch the **Listen and Look For Video** for strategies and habits of mind to look for as students complete work on this lesson.

✓ Mathematics Overview

In this lesson, students will learn to estimate and compare very small and very large quantities by rounding and then using powers of 10. Students will apply their knowledge to real-life situations by comparing quantities to find out how many times larger or smaller one quantity is as compared to another.

Applying Math Practices

Construct Arguments

Students will critique the reasoning of others to decide whether very large and very small quantities have been estimated correctly using powers of 10.

Look for and Make Use of Structure

Students will use the structure of the place-value system to correctly make estimates of very large and very small quantities using powers of 10. They will determine that very large numbers can be represented as a power of 10 with a positive exponent and that positive numbers less than 1 can be represented as a power of 10 with a negative exponent.

STEP 1 | Develop: Problem-Based Learning

15-20 min

Activity

Explain It!

Reasoning As students work through the *Explain It*, listen and look for the process that students use to round numbers before multiplying by a power of ten.

Before [WHOLE CLASS]

TP 1 Implement Tasks that Promote Reasoning and Problem Solving

Q: How would you simplify 10^2? 10^3? Explain the relationship between the exponent and the number of zeros in the simplified form. [$10^2 = 100$ and $10^3 = 1,000$; Sample answer: The number of zeros after the 1 is the same as the exponent.]

2 Build Understanding

Q: What is 10^{15} written in standard form? [1,000,000,000,000,000]

Q: Why might you want to express 1,000,000,000,000,000,000 using powers of 10? [Sample answer: It can be easier to understand this very large number by looking at the exponent of 10 rather than trying to read and understand all the zeros.]

During [SMALL GROUP]

TP 3 Support Productive Struggle in Learning Mathematics

Q: Why is the leading digit rounded to 7 instead of 8? [The number in the place value to the right of 7 is 4, which is less than 5, so the leading digit remains the same.]

After [WHOLE CLASS]

TP 4 Facilitate Meaningful Mathematical Discourse

Ask students to share their solutions. If needed, project Dylan's and Amelia's work and ask:

Q: How do Dylan's and Amelia's reasoning compare? [Sample answer: Dylan says that Jeff counted zeros, while Keegan counted the number of places to the right of 7. Amelia says that Jeff and Keegan wrote the powers in standard form and then multiplied by 7.]

5 Transition to Visual Learning

Q: How can you estimate very large quantities using a power of 10? [Sample answer: Estimate the number by rounding to its greatest place value. Then count the number of places after the first digit, which will be the exponent of the power of 10.]

6 Extension for Early Finishers

Q: Find an estimate for half the number of grains of sand. [Sample answer: 3.5×10^{18}]

Analyze Student Work

Available Online

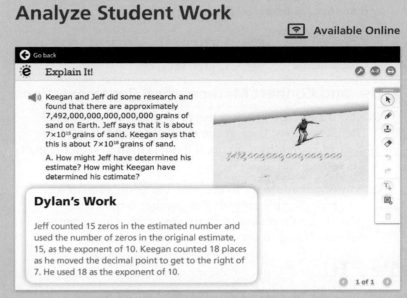

Keegan and Jeff did some research and found that there are approximately 7,492,000,000,000,000,000 grains of sand on Earth. Jeff says that it is about 7×10^{15} grains of sand. Keegan says that this is about 7×10^{18} grains of sand.

A. How might Jeff have determined his estimate? How might Keegan have determined his estimate?

Dylan's Work

Jeff counted 15 zeros in the estimated number and used the number of zeros in the original estimate, 15, as the exponent of 10. Keegan counted 18 places as he moved the decimal point to get to the right of 7. He used 18 as the exponent of 10.

1 of 1

Dylan notices that Jeff counted the number of zeros and that Keegan counted the 18 places the decimal point moved.

Explain It!

Keegan and Jeff did some research and found that there are approximately 7,492,000,000,000,000,000 grains of sand on Earth. Jeff says that it is about 7×10^{15} grains of sand. Keegan says that this is about 7×10^{18} grains of sand.

Lesson 1-8
Use Powers of 10 to Estimate Quantities

Go Online | PearsonRealize.com

I can... estimate large and small quantities using a power of 10.

$$7,492,000,000,000,000,000$$

A. How might Jeff have determined his estimate? How might Keegan have determined his estimate?

I think Jeff wrote 10^{15} in standard form, multiplied by 7, and compared it to 7,492,000,000,000,000,000.

Keegan wrote 10^{18} in standard form, multiplied by 7, and compared it to 7,492,000,000,000,000,000.

B. Whose estimate, Jeff's or Keegan's, is more logical? Explain.

Keegan's estimate is closer.

Focus on math practices

Be Precise Do you think the two estimates are close in value? Explain your reasoning.
Sample answer: No. I divided 10^{18} and 10^{15} to determine how many times as great is 10^{18} than 10^{15}.
$\frac{10^{18}}{10^{15}} = 10^{18-15} = 10^3$
Keegan's estimate is 1,000 times greater than Jeff's.

51

Amelia reasons that both boys wrote the power of 10 in standard form and multiplied by 7.

STEP **2** | Develop: Visual Learning

ETP **Establish Mathematics Goals to Focus Learning**

Engage students in a discussion about the *Essential Question*. Make sure they understand how to work with powers of 10 and multiply numbers by powers of 10.

 EXAMPLE 1 **Estimate Very Large Quantities**

ETP **Use and Connect Mathematical Representations**

Q: How do you round a number to its greatest place value? [Sample answer: Look at the digit to its right. If it is 5 or greater, round the digit up; if it is less than 5, keep the digit the same.]

Q: Why might you want to estimate the population of a country? [Sample answer: The number is constantly changing, so it makes sense to work with a more general number. Doing so also makes comparisons easier.]

 Try It!

ETP **Elicit and Use Evidence of Student Thinking**

Q: How do you determine the power of ten for each estimated number? [Sample answer: Count the number of zeros that follow the estimated whole number.]

Convince Me!

Q: What rule could you write for comparing similar powers of 10 that round to the same whole number? [Sample answer: If the greatest place values round to the same whole number, then you have to round to the next place value to the right of the greatest place.]

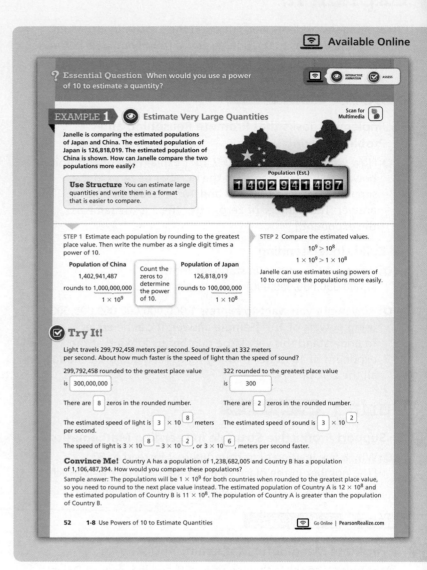

Students can access the *Visual Learning Animation Plus* by using the **BouncePages app** to scan this page. Students can download the app for free in their mobile devices' app store.

R+I **Response to Intervention**

USE WITH EXAMPLE 2 Some students may need to review how to interpret negative powers of 10.

- Remind students that a negative power of 10 moves the decimal point that number of places to the left.

  Q: What effect does multiplying by 10^{-3} have on the placement of the decimal point? [Sample answer: It moves the decimal point three places to the left.]

  Q: Write the number 7×10^{-3} in standard form. How many zeros are there after the decimal point? Explain. [0.007; Sample answer: There are 2 zeros because one decimal place is used to move the decimal point from the right of 7 to the left of 7, then zeros are used as the decimal point continues to move to the left.]

E **Enrichment**

USE WITH EXAMPLE 3 Have students use estimated quantities with powers of 10 to perform calculations.

Q: How many times greater is 27×10^5 than 9×10^3? Explain. [3×10^2, or 300 times greater; Sample answer: Divide 27 by 9 to get 3. Then divide 10^5 by 10^3. To divide numbers with the same base, subtract the exponents: $10^{5-3} = 10^2$.]

Q: How does 6×10^2 compare to 3×10^3? Explain. [2×10^{-1}, or 0.2 times as large; Sample answer: Divide 6 by 3 to get 2. Then divide 10^2 by 10^3. To divide numbers with the same base, subtract the exponents: $10^{2-3} = 10^{-1}$. So 6×10^2 is 0.2 times as large as than 3×10^3.]

EXAMPLE 2 ▸ Estimate Very Small Quantities

STEP Pose Purposeful Questions

Q: How is the procedure similar to that in Example 1? [Sample answer: The place value of the leading digit is used to determine the power of 10.]

Q: Why are the exponents in these two numbers negative? [Sample answer: Because both measurements are between 0 and 1]

EXAMPLE 3 ▸ Find How Many Times as Much

STEP Pose Purposeful Questions

Q: After writing each number as a single digit times a power of 10, how can you tell that the U.S. GDP is about 10 times greater than the GDP of Canada? [Sample answer: 10^{16} is 10 times greater than 10^{15}.]

Q: How could you use division to compare the two quantities? [Sample answer: when you divide 2×10^{16} by 2×10^{15}, $2 \div 2 = 1$. Then divide the powers of 10 using the Quotient of Powers Property; $\frac{10^{16}}{10^{15}} = 10^{16-15} = 10^1$ or 10.]

Try It!

STEP Elicit and Use Evidence of Student Thinking

Q: Explain the steps you would use to compare these quantities. [Sample answer: Estimate each number by writing it as a single digit times a power of 10. Then compare the estimates.]

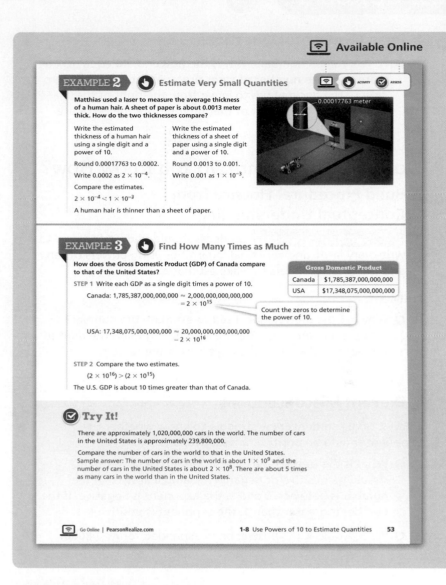

ADDITIONAL EXAMPLES ▸

For additional examples go to PearsonRealize.com.

ⒺⓁⓁ English Language Learners

BEGINNING See Example 3.

Point out the acronym "GDP" in line 1 and explain that the words "gross domestic product" are shortened to these three letters. Tell students that the GDP is the total value of the goods and services produced by the United States in a set period. Have students share examples of goods and services that they are familiar with.

INTERMEDIATE See Example 3.

Have a student read the question to the class. Then ask:

Q: What does it mean to compare the GDPs of the two countries? [Sample answer: Compare means to find how many times greater one country's GDP is than the other country's GDP.]

Q: What are some other things that you compare between two countries? [Sample answer: Population; number of births each year, average income]

ADVANCED See Example 3.

Have a student read the question to the class. Then, encourage students to start by summarizing the steps needed to solve the problem and reading them aloud. After solving, have students share some other situations in which they might say "10 times greater."

STEP **2** | Develop: Visual Learning *continued*

Key Concept   Activity

KEY CONCEPT

ETP **Pose Purposeful Questions**

Q: For very small numbers, why is the power of 10 equal to one more than the number of zeros preceding the first nonzero digit? [The decimal has to move from the right of the leading digit to the left of that digit before the zeros are written.]

Do You Understand/Do You Know How?

ETP **Build Procedural Fluency from Conceptual Understanding**

? Essential Question Students should understand how to write very large and very small quantities using powers of ten and use those numbers to make estimates.

ITEM 3

Q: Why is 3 the digit Raquel used to estimate the number? [Sample answer: Since 3 is the leading digit and the digit to the right of the 3 is 0, the digit 3 stays the same.]

RH Prevent Misconceptions

ITEM 2 Some students may struggle to know whether the exponent should be positive or negative.

Q: What is the rule for deciding whether the power of 10 should be positive or negative? [Sample answer: If the number is between 0 and 1, the exponent is negative. If the number is greater than 1, the exponent is positive.]

Q: What would Kim's answer be in expanded form? [4,000]

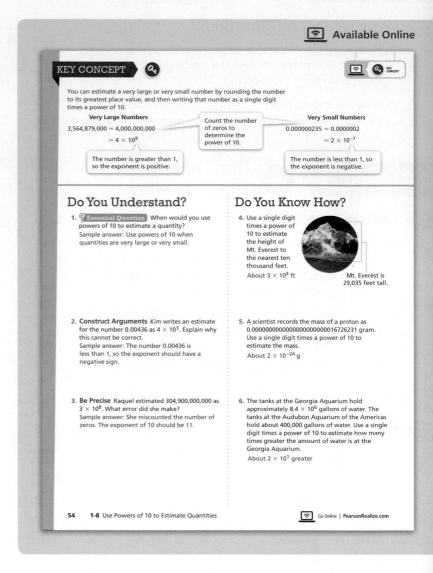

Available Online

KEY CONCEPT

You can estimate a very large or very small number by rounding the number to its greatest place value, and then writing that number as a single digit times a power of 10.

Very Large Numbers
$3,564,879,000 \approx 4,000,000,000$
$\approx 4 \times 10^9$

Count the number of zeros to determine the power of 10.

Very Small Numbers
$0.000000235 \approx 0.0000002$
$\approx 2 \times 10^{-7}$

The number is greater than 1, so the exponent is positive.

The number is less than 1, so the exponent is negative.

Do You Understand?

1. **? Essential Question** When would you use powers of 10 to estimate a quantity? Sample answer: Use powers of 10 when quantities are very large or very small.

2. **Construct Arguments** Kim writes an estimate for the number 0.00436 as 4×10^3. Explain why this cannot be correct. Sample answer: The number 0.00436 is less than 1, so the exponent should have a negative sign.

3. **Be Precise** Raquel estimated 304,900,000,000 as 3×10^8. What error did she make? Sample answer: She miscounted the number of zeros. The exponent of 10 should be 11.

Do You Know How?

4. Use a single digit times a power of 10 to estimate the height of Mt. Everest to the nearest ten thousand feet. About 3×10^4 ft

Mt. Everest is 29,035 feet tall.

5. A scientist records the mass of a proton as 0.0000000000000000000000016726231 gram. Use a single digit times a power of 10 to estimate the mass. About 2×10^{-24} g

6. The tanks at the Georgia Aquarium hold approximately 8.4×10^6 gallons of water. The tanks at the Audubon Aquarium of the Americas hold about 400,000 gallons of water. Use a single digit times a power of 10 to estimate how many times greater the amount of water is at the Georgia Aquarium. About 2×10^1 greater

54   1-8 Use Powers of 10 to Estimate Quantities   Go Online | PearsonRealize.com

ADDITIONAL EXAMPLE **3**

Available Online

Help students transition from comparing large numbers to comparing small numbers with this additional example.

Q: How do you know that the length of spiral bacterium B is greater than the length of spiral bacterium A? [Sample answer: The decimal point moves 6 places for spiral bacterium A and only 5 places for spiral bacterium B.]

Q: After writing each length as a single digit times a power of 10, what is another way to tell that spiral bacterium B is greater than spiral bacterium A? [Sample answer: Compare 10^{-5} and 10^{-6}. 10^{-5} is 10 times greater than 10^{-6}.]

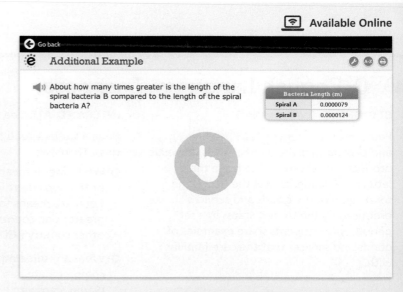

Go back

Additional Example

About how many times greater is the length of the spiral bacteria B compared to the length of the spiral bacteria A?

Bacteria Length (m)	
Spiral A	0.0000079
Spiral B	0.0000124

Answer: The length of spiral bacterium B is about 1.5 times greater than the length of spiral bacterium A.

Practice & Problem Solving

 Available Online

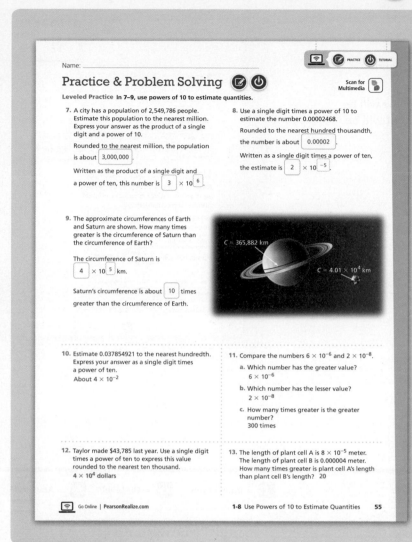

Name: _____

Practice & Problem Solving

Scan for Multimedia

Leveled Practice In 7–9, use powers of 10 to estimate quantities.

7. A city has a population of 2,549,786 people. Estimate this population to the nearest million. Express your answer as the product of a single digit and a power of 10.

Rounded to the nearest million, the population is about ⟨3,000,000⟩.

Written as the product of a single digit and a power of ten, this number is ⟨3⟩ × 10^⟨6⟩.

8. Use a single digit times a power of 10 to estimate the number 0.00002468.

Rounded to the nearest hundred thousandth, the number is about ⟨0.00002⟩.

Written as a single digit times a power of ten, the estimate is ⟨2⟩ × 10^⟨−5⟩.

9. The approximate circumferences of Earth and Saturn are shown. How many times greater is the circumference of Saturn than the circumference of Earth?

C ≈ 365,882 km

C ≈ 4.01 × 10^4 km

The circumference of Saturn is ⟨4⟩ × 10^⟨5⟩ km.

Saturn's circumference is about ⟨10⟩ times greater than the circumference of Earth.

10. Estimate 0.037854921 to the nearest hundredth. Express your answer as a single digit times a power of ten.
About 4 × 10^{−2}

11. Compare the numbers 6 × 10^{−6} and 2 × 10^{−8}.

a. Which number has the greater value?
6 × 10^{−6}

b. Which number has the lesser value?
2 × 10^{−8}

c. How many times greater is the greater number?
300 times

12. Taylor made $43,785 last year. Use a single digit times a power of ten to express this value rounded to the nearest ten thousand.
4 × 10^4 dollars

13. The length of plant cell A is 8 × 10^{−5} meter. The length of plant cell B is 0.000004 meter. How many times greater is plant cell A's length than plant cell B's length? 20

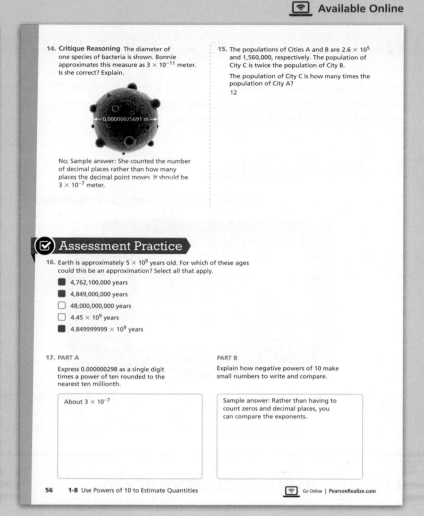

14. Critique Reasoning The diameter of one species of bacteria is shown. Bonnie approximates this measure as 3 × 10^{−11} meter. Is she correct? Explain.

0.00000025691 m

No; Sample answer: She counted the number of decimal places rather than how many places the decimal point moves. It should be 3 × 10^{−7} meter.

15. The populations of Cities A and B are 2.6 × 10^5 and 1,560,000, respectively. The population of City C is twice the population of City B.

The population of City C is how many times the population of City A?
12

☑ Assessment Practice

16. Earth is approximately 5 × 10^9 years old. For which of these ages could this be an approximation? Select all that apply.

■ 4,762,100,000 years
■ 4,849,000,000 years
☐ 48,000,000,000 years
☐ 4.45 × 10^9 years
■ 4.849999999 × 10^9 years

17. PART A

Express 0.000000298 as a single digit times a power of ten rounded to the nearest ten millionth.

About 3 × 10^{−7}

PART B

Explain how negative powers of 10 make small numbers to write and compare.

Sample answer: Rather than having to count zeros and decimal places, you can compare the exponents.

⚠ Error Intervention

You may opt to have students complete the automatically scored Practice & Problem Solving items online.

ITEM 14 Critique Reasoning Students might not correctly determine how many decimal places to count to determine the power of 10.

Q: How do you find the correct number of decimal places?
[Sample answer: Count the number of decimal places from the original starting place of the decimal point to the right of the first nonzero digit. This will give you a single digit value between 1 and 10.]

Item Analysis

Example	Items	DOK
1	7, 12, 16	2
2	8, 10	2
2	14, 17	3
3	9, 11, 13, 15	2

🏆 Challenge

ITEM 11 Challenge students to multiply estimates that use powers of ten.

Q: How could you estimate the product of 2,950,000,000 and 215,000,000,000? [(3 × 10^9) × (2 × 10^{11}) = 6 × 10^{20}]

PearsonRealize.com

Assess | Tutorials | Worksheets

Lesson Quiz

Use the student scores on the Lesson Quiz to prescribe differentiated assignments.

I Intervention 0–3 Points   **O** On-Level 4 Points   **A** Advanced 5 Points

You may opt to have students take the Lesson Quiz online. The Lesson Quiz will be automatically scored and appropriate remediation, practice, or enrichment will be assigned based on student performance.

Video Tutorials

Students can access instructional tutorials using the **Virtual Nerd app**.

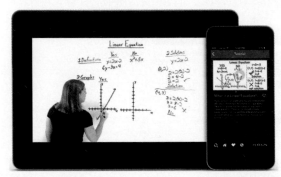

Students can also access the videos using the **BouncePages app** to scan exercise pages marked with this icon. Students can download both apps for free in their mobile devices' app store.

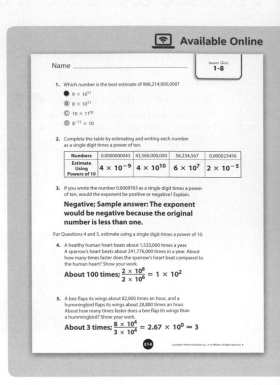

Available Online

Name _____   Lesson Quiz 1-8

1. Which number is the best estimate of 866,214,000,000?
   - (A) 9×10^{11} ●
   - (B) 8×10^{11}
   - (C) 10×11^{10}
   - (D) $8^{-11} \times 10$

2. Complete the table by estimating and writing each number as a single digit times a power of ten.

Numbers	0.0000000043	43,560,000,000	56,234,567	0.000023456
Estimate Using Powers of 10	4×10^{-9}	4×10^{10}	6×10^7	2×10^{-5}

3. If you wrote the number 0.0009763 as a single digit times a power of ten, would the exponent be positive or negative? Explain.
   Negative; Sample answer: The exponent would be negative because the original number is less than one.

For Questions 4 and 5, estimate using a single digit times a power of ten.

4. A healthy human heart beats about 1,533,000 times a year. A sparrow's heart beats about 241,776,000 times in a year. About how many times faster does the sparrow's heart beat compared to the human heart? Show your work.
   About 100 times; $\frac{2 \times 10^8}{2 \times 10^6} = 1 \times 10^2$

5. A bee flaps its wings about 82,800 times an hour, and a hummingbird flaps its wings about 28,800 times an hour. About how many times faster does a bee flap its wings than a hummingbird? Show your work.
   About 3 times; $\frac{8 \times 10^4}{3 \times 10^4} = 2.67 \times 10^0 \approx 3$

014

Copyright © Pearson Education, Inc., or its affiliates. All Rights Reserved.

Differentiated Intervention

I = Intervention   **O** = On-Level   **A** = Advanced

Reteach to Build Understanding **I**

Provides scaffolded reteaching for the key lesson concepts.

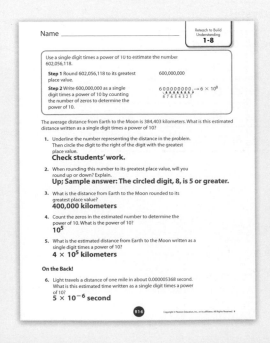

Name _____   Reteach to Build Understanding 1-8

Use a single digit times a power of 10 to estimate the number 602,056,118.

Step 1 Round 602,056,118 to its greatest place value.   600,000,000

Step 2 Write 600,000,000 as a single digit times a power of 10 by counting the number of zeros to determine the power of 10. $600000000 \rightarrow 6 \times 10^8$

The average distance from Earth to the Moon is 384,403 kilometers. What is this estimated distance written as a single digit times a power of 10?

1. Underline the number representing the distance in the problem. Then circle the digit to the right of the digit with the greatest place value.
   Check students' work.

2. When rounding this number to its greatest place value, will you round up or down? Explain.
   Up; Sample answer: The circled digit, 8, is 5 or greater.

3. What is the distance from Earth to the Moon rounded to its greatest place value?
   400,000 kilometers

4. Count the zeros in the estimated number to determine the power of 10. What is the power of 10?
   10^5

5. What is the estimated distance from Earth to the Moon written as a single digit times a power of 10?
   4×10^5 **kilometers**

On the Back!

6. Light travels a distance of one mile in about 0.000005368 second. What is this estimated time written as a single digit times a power of 10?
   5×10^{-6} **second**

R14

Additional Vocabulary Support **I** **O**

Helps students develop and reinforce understanding of key terms and concepts.

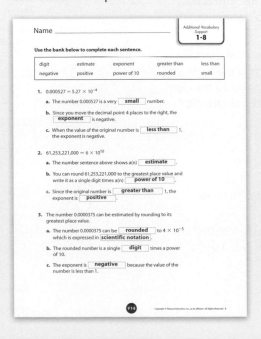

Name _____   Additional Vocabulary Support 1-8

Use the bank below to complete each sentence.

digit	estimate	exponent	greater than	less than
negative	positive	power of 10	rounded	small

1. $0.000527 = 5.27 \times 10^{-4}$
   a. The number 0.000527 is a very **small** number.
   b. Since you move the decimal point 4 places to the right, the **exponent** is negative.
   c. When the value of the original number is **less than** 1, the exponent is negative.

2. $61,253,221,000 \approx 6 \times 10^{10}$
   a. The number sentence above shows a(n) **estimate**.
   b. You can round 61,253,221,000 to the greatest place value and write it as a single digit times a(n) **power of 10**.
   c. Since the original number is **greater than** 1, the exponent is **positive**.

3. The number 0.0000375 can be estimated by rounding to its greatest place value.
   a. The number 0.0000375 can be **rounded** to 4×10^{-5} which is expressed in **scientific notation**.
   b. The rounded number is a single **digit** times a power of 10.
   c. The exponent is **negative** because the value of the number is less than 1.

V14

Build Mathematical Literacy **I**

Provides support for struggling readers to build mathematical literacy.

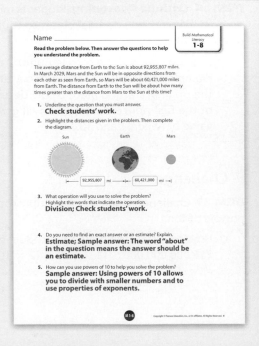

Name _____   Build Mathematical Literacy 1-8

Read the problem below. Then answer the questions to help you understand the problem.

The average distance from Earth to the Sun is about 92,955,807 miles. In March 2029, Mars and the Sun will be in opposite directions from each other as seen from Earth, so Mars will be about 60,421,000 miles from Earth. The distance from Earth to the Sun will be about how many times greater than the distance from Mars to the Sun at this time?

1. Underline the question that you must answer.
   Check students' work.

2. Highlight the distances given in the problem. Then complete the diagram.

   Sun — Earth — Mars
   92,955,807 mi | 60,421,000 mi

3. What operation will you use to solve the problem? Highlight the words that indicate the operation.
   Division; Check students' work.

4. Do you need to find an exact answer or an estimate? Explain.
   Estimate; Sample answer: The word "about" in the question means the answer should be an estimate.

5. How can you use powers of 10 to help you solve the problem?
   Sample answer: Using powers of 10 allows you to divide with smaller numbers and to use properties of exponents.

M14

Additional Practice

You may opt to have students complete the automatically scored Additional Practice items online.

Item Analysis

Example	Items	DOK
1	2, 8	1
	10, 12	2
	11	3
2	1, 5, 6, 13	1
3	3, 4, 7, 9	2

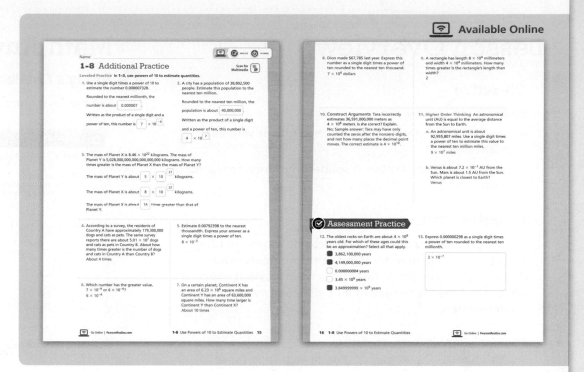

 Available Online

Differentiated Intervention

I = Intervention   **O** = On-Level   **A** = Advanced

Enrichment **O** **A**

Presents engaging problems and activities that extend the lesson concepts.

Math Tools and Games **I** **O** **A**

Offers additional activities and games to build understanding and fluency.

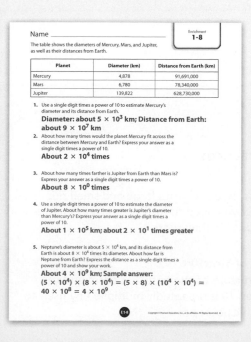

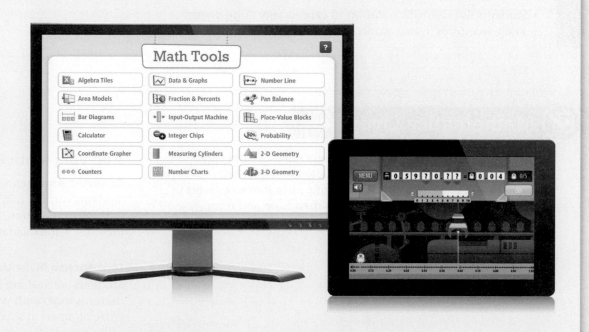

Lesson 1-9

Understand Scientific Notation

Activity

Lesson Overview

Objective

Students will be able to:

✔ use scientific notation to write very large or very small quantities.

✔ convert numbers written in scientific notation to standard form.

Essential Understanding

Very large and very small numbers can be estimated using scientific notation in order to make the numbers more convenient to use. Scientific notation also makes it easier to understand the magnitude of a number and compare it with other numbers.

Previously in this topic, students:

• estimated very large and very small quantities using powers of 10.

In this lesson, students:

• develop fluency in using scientific notation to write large and small numbers.

• convert numbers in scientific notation to standard form.

Later in this topic, students will:

• perform operations with quantities written in scientific notation.

This lesson emphasizes a blend of **procedural skill and fluency** and **application**.

• Students use powers of 10 to express large and small numbers in scientific notation.

• Students use scientific notation to express very large or very small quantities in real-world situations.

FOCUS

COHERENCE

RIGOR

Math Anytime

Today's Challenge

Use the Topic 1 problems any time during this topic.

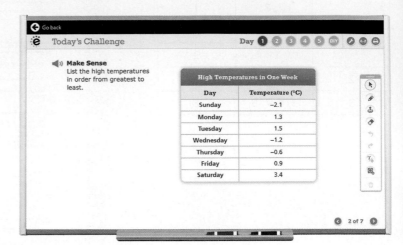

✅ Mathematics Overview

In this lesson, students will write very large numbers and very small numbers in scientific notation. Students extend their knowledge and understanding of scientific notations to convert numbers from scientific notation to standard form and from standard form to scientific notation.

Applying Math Practices

Construct Arguments

Students will not only be asked to write large and small numbers in scientific notation, but will need to justify their reasoning and provide clear explanations for their work.

Look for and Make Use of Structure

Students will use the structure of the base-10 system and the patterns that result when 10 is repeatedly multiplied by itself to write numbers in scientific notation.

STEP 1 | Develop: Problem-Based Learning

15-20 min

Activity

Solve & Discuss It!

Use Structure As students work through the *Solve & Discuss It*, listen and look for students who use their understanding of powers of 10 to write the number in another form.

Before [WHOLE CLASS]

TP

1 Implement Tasks that Promote Reasoning and Problem Solving

Q: How can you recognize a number that can be written as a power of 10? [Sample answer: It is a 1 followed by one or more zeros. It is the product of 10 and itself a specific number of times.]

2 Build Understanding

Q: Why might you want to estimate a number like the one on the board? [Sample answer: It would give you a simpler number to use, which would make calculation easier.]

During [SMALL GROUP]

TP

3 Support Productive Struggle in Learning Mathematics

Q: What methods can you use to estimate the number shown on the board? [Sample answer: You could round it to a place value that you choose, or estimate it using a single digit times a power of 10.]

After [WHOLE CLASS]

TP

4 Facilitate Meaningful Mathematical Discourse

Ask students to share their solutions. If needed, project Ty's and Alyssa's work and ask:

Q: How did each student choose what power of 10 to use to estimate the number on the board? [Sample answer: Ty rounds to the first nonzero digit to the right of the decimal point. Alyssa rounds to the third nonzero digit to the right of the decimal point. Both wrote their estimates as a power of 10.]

Q: Which student's estimate was more helpful? Explain. [Sample answer: It depends on the situation. If you want a quick idea of the magnitude, Ty made the better choice, but Alyssa kept more of the original digits in the answer.]

5 Transition to Visual Learning

Q: What potential issues could come from using different ways to estimate very large or very small numbers? [Sample answer: Without a rule, it could be more difficult to compare very large or very small numbers. Ty and Alyssa are estimating the same number, yet their estimates use different powers of 10. It seems as though they are estimating two different numbers, when they are not.]

6 Extension for Early Finishers

Q: How could you use powers of 10 to estimate very large numbers, such as 3,719,278,549,351? [Sample answer: Round to the greatest place value and then use a power of 10 to represent the zeros to the right of the greatest place. This number could be estimated as 4×10^{12}.]

Analyze Student Work

Available Online

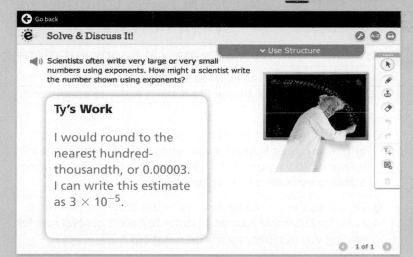

Go back

Solve & Discuss It!

⌄ Use Structure

Scientists often write very large or very small numbers using exponents. How might a scientist write the number shown using exponents?

Ty's Work

I would round to the nearest hundred-thousandth, or 0.00003. I can write this estimate as 3×10^{-5}.

1 of 1

Ty rounds to the nearest hundred-thousandth and wrote the estimate as a power of 10.

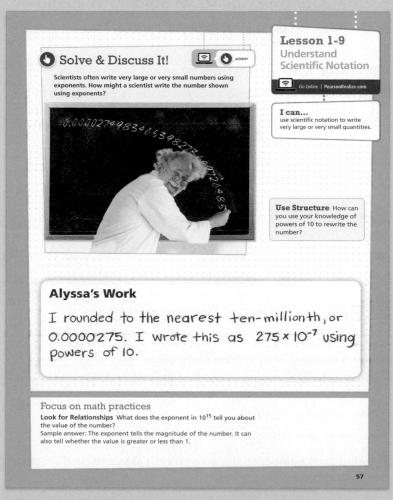

Solve & Discuss It!

Scientists often write very large or very small numbers using exponents. How might a scientist write the number shown using exponents?

0.00002749834653982740720485

Lesson 1-9
Understand Scientific Notation

Go Online | PearsonRealize.com

I can... use scientific notation to write very large or very small quantities.

Use Structure How can you use your knowledge of powers of 10 to rewrite the number?

Alyssa's Work

I rounded to the nearest ten-millionth, or 0.0000275. I wrote this as 275×10^{-7} using powers of 10.

Focus on math practices

Look for Relationships What does the exponent in 10^{15} tell you about the value of the number?
Sample answer: The exponent tells the magnitude of the number. It can also tell whether the value is greater or less than 1.

57

Alyssa rounds to the nearest ten-millionth and wrote the estimate as a power of 10.

📶 **Available Online**

ETP Establish Mathematics Goals to Focus Learning

Engage students in a discussion about the *Essential Question*. Make sure students understand how to round and how to write a number with a power of 10.

 EXAMPLE 1 ◉ **Write Large Numbers in Scientific Notation**

ETP Use and Connect Mathematical Representations

Q: Why might you want to write 92,960,000 in scientific notation? [Sample answer: To make it easier to understand and compare]

Q: Why is it important to keep some of the digits from the original number instead of just using a single digit times a power of 10 to estimate it? [Sample answer: It gives a more accurate estimate of the original number.]

Q: Why does the first factor have to be less than 10 in scientific notation? [Sample answer: In order to have a general rule for writing any number in scientific notation]

☑ **Try It!**

ETP Elicit and Use Evidence of Student Thinking

Q: What is the place value of the first digit in the height of the falls? [Thousands]

Convince Me!

Q: How do you use powers of 10 to write large numbers in scientific notation? [Sample answer: The power of 10 used in scientific notation is equal to the number of digits after the decimal point.]

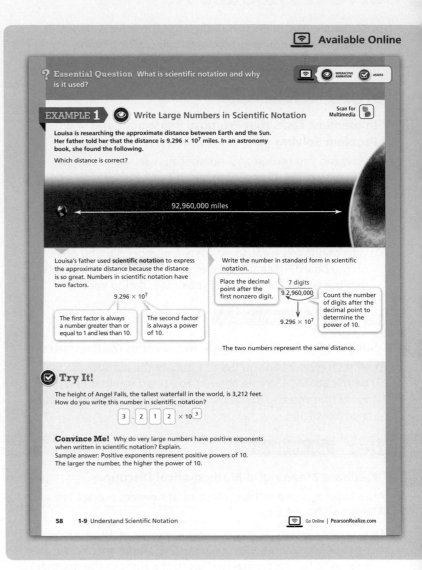

 Students can access the *Visual Learning Animation Plus* by using the **BouncePages app** to scan this page. Students can download the app for free in their mobile devices' app store.

🔺 Response to Intervention

USE WITH EXAMPLE 1 Some students may need to review how to use powers of 10 to express place value.

- What is the place value of the first digit of each number? (Write your answer as a power of 10.)

  Q: 4,678,861,034 [10^{10}]

  Q: 24,999,999 [10^8]

- Round each number to the given place value and then write the estimate in scientific notation.

  Q: 4,678,861,034 to the nearest million [4,679,000,000; 4.679×10^9]

  Q: 24,999,999 to the nearest ten million [20,000,000; 2×10^7]

🏆 Enrichment

USE WITH EXAMPLE 3 Have students explore how a calculator would display numbers that are too long for its screen capabilities.

- Calculator notation

  Q: Predict how a calculator would display 945,673,000,000,000. [9.45673 E14, or 9.45673×10^{14}]

  Q: How would a calculator display 0.000000000000945? [9.45 E-13 or 9.45×10^{-13}]

EXAMPLE 2 Write Small Numbers in Scientific Notation

ETP Pose Purposeful Questions

Q: What is the place value of the digit 7 in the decimal 0.00000703? [The 7 is in the millionths place.]

Q: How could you express that place value as a fraction and as a power of 10? [Sample answer: $\frac{1}{1,000,000}$, 10^{-6}]

Try It!

ETP Elicit and Use Evidence of Student Thinking

Q: Could you write 0.005 as a fraction and then use properties of exponents to write it in scientific notation? Explain. [Yes; Sample answer: You could write 0.005 $= \frac{5}{1,000} = \frac{5}{10^3} = 5 \times 10^{-3}$.]

EXAMPLE 3 Convert Scientific Notation to Standard Form

ETP Pose Purposeful Questions

Q: How do you know whether to move the decimal point to the right or to the left when converting scientific notation to standard form? [Sample answer: A positive power of 10 moves the decimal point to the right. A negative power of 10 moves the decimal point to the left.]

Q: How could you check that your answer is correct? [Sample answer: Convert your answer back to scientific notation.]

Try It!

ETP Elicit and Use Evidence of Student Thinking

Q: How does the sign of the exponent help you determine if your number is greater or less than 1? [Sample answer: If the exponent is positive, the number is greater than 1. If the exponent is negative, the number is less than 1.]

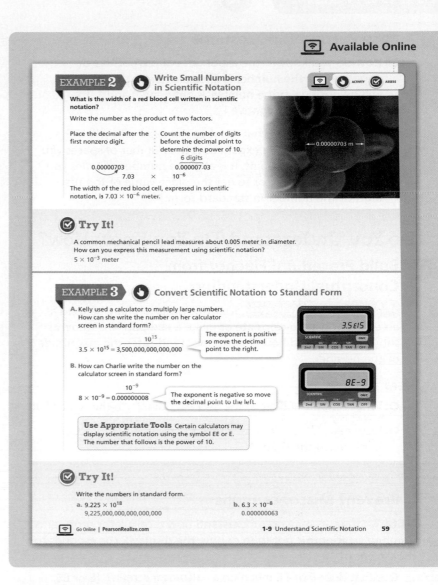

Available Online

EXAMPLE 2 Write Small Numbers in Scientific Notation

What is the width of a red blood cell written in scientific notation?

Write the number as the product of two factors.

| Place the decimal after the first nonzero digit. | Count the number of digits before the decimal point to determine the power of 10. |

6 digits

0.00000703 → 7.03   0.000007.03 → 10^{-6}

The width of the red blood cell, expressed in scientific notation, is 7.03×10^{-6} meter.

← 0.00000703 m

Try It!

A common mechanical pencil lead measures about 0.005 meter in diameter. How can you express this measurement using scientific notation?
5×10^{-3} meter

EXAMPLE 3 Convert Scientific Notation to Standard Form

A. Kelly used a calculator to multiply large numbers. How can she write the number on her calculator screen in standard form?

$3.5 E15$

10^{15}
$3.5 \times 10^{15} = 3,500,000,000,000,000$

The exponent is positive so move the decimal point to the right.

B. How can Charlie write the number on the calculator screen in standard form?

$8 E{-}9$

10^{-9}
$8 \times 10^{-9} = 0.000000008$

The exponent is negative so move the decimal point to the left.

Use Appropriate Tools Certain calculators may display scientific notation using the symbol EE or E. The number that follows is the power of 10.

Try It!

Write the numbers in standard form.
a. 9.225×10^{18} b. 6.3×10^{-8}
9,225,000,000,000,000,000   0.000000063

Go Online | PearsonRealize.com   **1-9 Understand Scientific Notation** 59

ADDITIONAL EXAMPLES

For additional examples go to PearsonRealize.com.

English Language Learners

BEGINNING After reading Example 1 to students, allow them to practice following the directions you give:

Q: Put your finger on the 3 in 3,500,000. Where are you when you move 6 places to the right? [To the right of the final zero at the decimal point]

Q: Put your finger on the 8 in 0.000000008. Where are you when you move 9 places to the left? [At the decimal point]

Give students the opportunity to practice counting aloud as they move left or right with different numbers.

INTERMEDIATE See Example 3.

Ask students to share questions they need to answer as they solve the problem.

Q: What questions must you ask before solving this problem? [Sample answer: Is 3.5 E15 a number greater or less than 1? Should I move the decimal point to the right or to the left?]

Then have students work with a partner to answer their questions and practice following oral directions.

ADVANCED See Example 3.

Ask students to explain how to solve each step in the problem. Have other students follow their directions to see if they arrive at the correct answer. Encourage them to use academic mathematical vocabulary terms such as factor, exponent, positive, negative, greater than, less than, multiply, divide, and scientific notation.

KEY CONCEPT

ETP **Pose Purposeful Questions**

Q: How do you know if the exponent will be positive or negative? [If the number is greater than 1, the exponent will be positive. If the number is between 0 and 1, the exponent will be negative.]

Q: How do you know what number the exponent will be? [Sample answer: The exponent is the number of spaces you move the decimal point. It is also the number of times you multiply 10 as a factor to get the place value of the first digit of the number in standard form.]

Do You Understand/Do You Know How?

ETP **Build Procedural Fluency from Conceptual Understanding**

? Essential Question Scientific notation may be used as an efficient way to calculate or make a comparison. Students should understand how the exponent indicates the magnitude of the number.

ITEM 3

Q: Where should she move the decimal point? [To the right of 3]

Q: How many places will she move it, and in what direction? [5 places to the right]

RH **Prevent Misconceptions**

ITEM 7 Students may not understand how a calculator represents numbers in scientific notation or how the display E corresponds to the power of 10.

Q: What does E or EE mean on a calculator screen? [E or EE means the number is in scientific notation. The number following E or EE is the power of 10.]

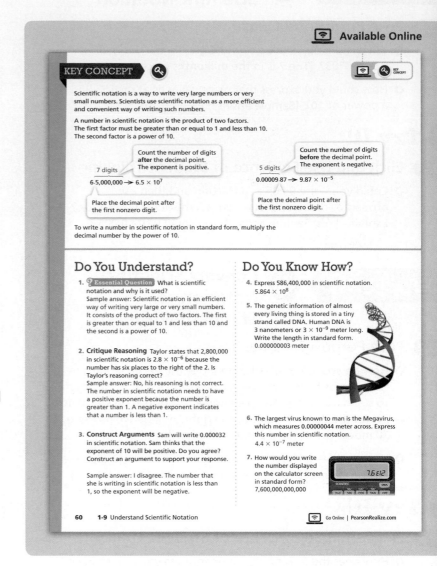

Available Online

KEY CONCEPT

Scientific notation is a way to write very large numbers or very small numbers. Scientists use scientific notation as a more efficient and convenient way of writing such numbers.

A number in scientific notation is the product of two factors. The first factor must be greater than or equal to 1 and less than 10. The second factor is a power of 10.

Count the number of digits **after** the decimal point. The exponent is positive.

7 digits

$6.5,000,000 \rightarrow 6.5 \times 10^7$

Place the decimal point after the first nonzero digit.

Count the number of digits **before** the decimal point. The exponent is negative.

5 digits

$0.00009.87 \rightarrow 9.87 \times 10^{-5}$

Place the decimal point after the first nonzero digit.

To write a number in scientific notation in standard form, multiply the decimal number by the power of 10.

Do You Understand?

1. **? Essential Question** What is scientific notation and why is it used?
Sample answer: Scientific notation is an efficient way of writing very large or very small numbers. It consists of the product of two factors. The first is greater than or equal to 1 and less than 10 and the second is a power of 10.

2. **Critique Reasoning** Taylor states that 2,800,000 in scientific notation is 2.8×10^{-6} because the number has six places to the right of the 2. Is Taylor's reasoning correct?
Sample answer: No, his reasoning is not correct. The number in scientific notation needs to have a positive exponent because the number is greater than 1. A negative exponent indicates that a number is less than 1.

3. **Construct Arguments** Sam will write 0.000032 in scientific notation. Sam thinks that the exponent of 10 will be positive. Do you agree? Construct an argument to support your response.

Sample answer: I disagree. The number that she is writing in scientific notation is less than 1, so the exponent will be negative.

Do You Know How?

4. Express 586,400,000 in scientific notation.
5.864×10^8

5. The genetic information of almost every living thing is stored in a tiny strand called DNA. Human DNA is 3 nanometers or 3×10^{-9} meter long. Write the length in standard form.
0.000000003 meter

6. The largest virus known to man is the Megavirus, which measures 0.00000044 meter across. Express this number in scientific notation.
4.4×10^{-7} meter

7. How would you write the number displayed on the calculator screen in standard form?
7,600,000,000,000

7.6 E12

60   **1-9** Understand Scientific Notation

Go Online | PearsonRealize.com

ADDITIONAL EXAMPLE **3**

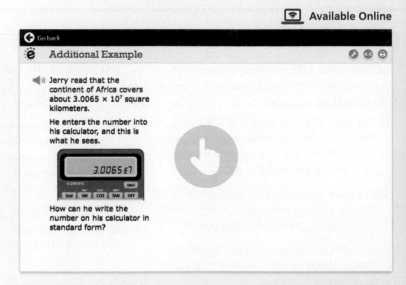

Available Online

Help students transition from writing decimals as shown on a calculator in standard form to writing decimals with zero in standard form.

Q: Can you write this number as 3.65×10^{13}? Explain. [Sample answer: 3.65×10^{13} is equal to 36,500,000,000,000. You need to include the zeros in the tenths and hundredths places to keep the scientific notation equal to the original number.]

Q: How would the number change if the calculator showed E-13? [The decimal moves 13 places to the left. Its value would be 0. 00000000000030065.]

Go back

Additional Example

Jerry read that the continent of Africa covers about 3.0065×10^7 square kilometers.

He enters the number into his calculator, and this is what he sees.

3.0065 E7

How can he write the number on his calculator in standard form?

Answer: 30,065,000

Practice & Problem Solving

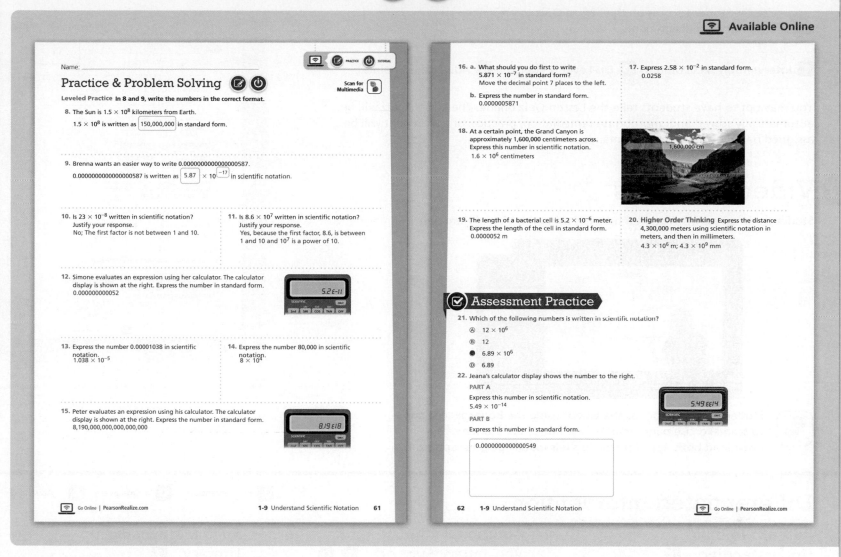

Available Online

Name: _____

Practice & Problem Solving

Scan for Multimedia

Leveled Practice In 8 and 9, write the numbers in the correct format.

8. The Sun is 1.5×10^8 kilometers from Earth.

1.5×10^8 is written as $150,000,000$ in standard form.

9. Brenna wants an easier way to write 0.0000000000000000587.

0.0000000000000000587 is written as 5.87×10^{-17} in scientific notation.

10. Is 23×10^{-8} written in scientific notation? Justify your response.
No; The first factor is not between 1 and 10.

11. Is 8.6×10^7 written in scientific notation? Justify your response.
Yes, because the first factor, 8.6, is between 1 and 10 and 10^7 is a power of 10.

12. Simone evaluates an expression using her calculator. The calculator display is shown at the right. Express the number in standard form.
0.000000000052

[Calculator display: 5.2 E-11]

13. Express the number 0.00001038 in scientific notation.
1.038×10^{-5}

14. Express the number 80,000 in scientific notation.
8×10^4

15. Peter evaluates an expression using his calculator. The calculator display is shown at the right. Express the number in standard form.
8,190,000,000,000,000,000

[Calculator display: 8.19 E18]

16. a. What should you do first to write 5.871×10^{-7} in standard form?
Move the decimal point 7 places to the left.

b. Express the number in standard form.
0.0000005871

17. Express 2.58×10^{-2} in standard form.
0.0258

18. At a certain point, the Grand Canyon is approximately 1,600,000 centimeters across. Express this number in scientific notation.
1.6×10^6 centimeters

[Image: 1,600,000 cm]

19. The length of a bacterial cell is 5.2×10^{-6} meter. Express the length of the cell in standard form.
0.0000052 m

20. Higher Order Thinking Express the distance 4,300,000 meters using scientific notation in meters, and then in millimeters.
4.3×10^6 m; 4.3×10^9 mm

Assessment Practice

21. Which of the following numbers is written in scientific notation?
- Ⓐ 12×10^6
- Ⓑ 12
- ● 6.89×10^6
- Ⓓ 6.89

22. Jeana's calculator display shows the number to the right.

PART A
Express this number in scientific notation.
5.49×10^{-14}

[Calculator display: 5.49 EE14]

PART B
Express this number in standard form.

0.0000000000000549

Error Intervention

ITEM 20 Higher Order Thinking Students may not remember the difference between meters and millimeters.

Q: How many millimeters are there in a meter? [1,000 mm = 1 m]

Q: How does *milli-* help you determine how many millimeters are in a meter? [Sample answer: The prefix *milli-* means 1,000, so there are 1,000 millimeters in 1 meter.]

Challenge

ITEM 19 Challenge students to perform operations with numbers in scientific notation.

Q: How many bacterial cells could you line up end-to-end along the length of a football field? Write the answer in scientific notation. (1 football field ≈ 105 meters) [About 2×10^7 cells]

You may opt to have students complete the automatically scored Practice & Problem Solving items online.

Item Analysis

Example	Items	DOK
	14, 18, 21	1
1	11	2
	20	3
2	9, 13	1
	10	2
3	8, 12, 15, 19	1
	16, 17, 22	2

Lesson Quiz

Use the student scores on the Lesson Quiz to prescribe differentiated assignments.

I Intervention 0–3 Points   **O** On-Level 4 Points   **A** Advanced 5 Points

You may opt to have students take the Lesson Quiz online. The Lesson Quiz will be automatically scored and appropriate remediation, practice, or enrichment will be assigned based on student performance.

Video Tutorials

Students can access instructional tutorials using the **Virtual Nerd app**.

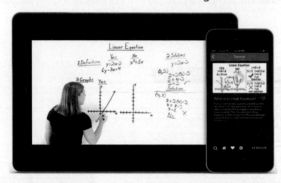

Students can also access the videos using the **BouncePages app** to scan exercise pages marked with this icon. Students can download both apps for free in their mobile devices' app store.

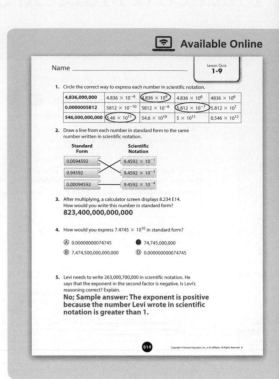

Differentiated Intervention

I = Intervention   **O** = On-Level   **A** = Advanced

Reteach to Build Understanding **I**

Provides scaffolded reteaching for the key lesson concepts.

Additional Vocabulary Support **I** **O**

Helps students develop and reinforce understanding of key terms and concepts.

Build Mathematical Literacy **I**

Provides support for struggling readers to build mathematical literacy.

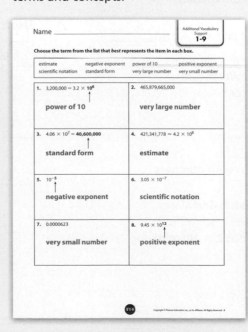

Practice Worksheets Math Tools Math Games

 # Additional Practice

You may opt to have students complete the automatically scored Additional Practice items online.

Item Analysis

Example	Items	DOK
1	2	1
	4, 6	2
	13, 14	3
2	3, 7, 11	2
	14	3
3	1	1
	5, 8, 9, 10, 12, 15	2

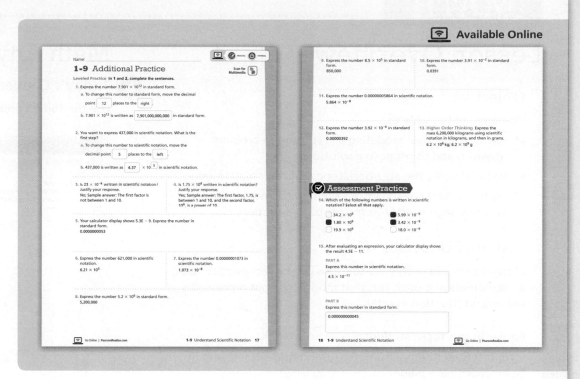

Available Online

Differentiated Intervention

I = Intervention O = On-Level A = Advanced

Enrichment O A

Presents engaging problems and activities that extend the lesson concepts.

Math Tools and Games I O A

Offers additional activities and games to build understanding and fluency.

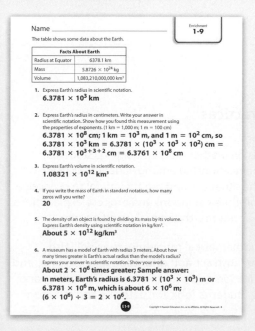

3-ACT MATH

3-Act Mathematical Modeling: Hard-Working Organs

Video   Activity

Lesson Overview

Objective

Students will be able to:

✔ use mathematical modeling to represent a problem situation and to propose a solution.

✔ test and verify the appropriateness of their math models.

✔ explain why the results from their mathematical models may not align exactly to the problem situation.

Essential Understanding

Many real-world problem situations can be represented with a mathematical model, but that model may not represent a real-world situation exactly.

Earlier in this topic, students:

• represented rational numbers on the number line and in the coordinate plane.

• identified opposites and absolute values of rational numbers.

In this lesson, students:

• develop a mathematical model to represent and propose a solution to a problem situation involving comparing rational numbers and absolute value.

Later in this course, students will:

• refine their mathematical modeling skills.

This mathematical modeling lesson focuses on **application** of both **math content** and **math practices and processes**.

• Students draw on their understanding of rational numbers and absolute value to develop a representative model.

• Students apply their mathematical model to test and validate its applicability to similar problem situations.

FOCUS

COHERENCE

RIGOR

Math Anytime

Today's Challenge

Use the Topic 1 problems any time during this topic.

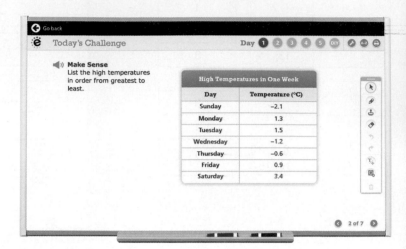

Mathematics Overview

In this lesson, students will develop and use a mathematical model to represent and propose a solution to a real-world problem involving comparing rational numbers and absolute value. Students will reinforce both their procedural skills with these concepts as well as their understanding of the limitations of some mathematical models for real-world situations.

Applying Math Practices

Model with Mathematics

The focus of this lesson is on mathematical modeling. Students identify variables and the relationship among variables, develop a model that represents the situation, and use the model to propose a solution. Students interpret their solutions and propose explanations for why their answers may not match the real-world answer.

As students carry out mathematical modeling, they will also engage in sense-making, abstract and quantitative reasoning, and mathematical communication and argumentation. In testing and validating their models, students look for patterns and structure.

3-Act Mathematical Modeling

Video

ACT 1 ▸ The Hook ▸

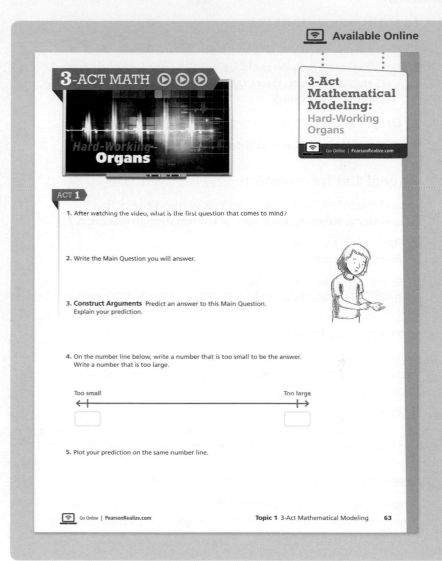

Students will be tasked with determining how many heartbeats and breaths a person experiences over a period of several years. They need to compare the two large numbers.

Play the Video and Brainstorm Questions

Have students complete Question 1. Encourage them to consider the situation and ask any questions that arise. Listen for interesting mathematical and non-mathematical questions. Ask students what makes each question interesting.

Q: What questions do you have? [Sample questions: Why are we listening to heartbeats and breathing? Is she measuring her heartbeats? Which is faster: your breathing rate or heart rate?]

Pose the Main Question

After the question brainstorming, pose the Main Question students will be tasked with answering. Have students complete **Question 2**.

Main Question
Q: How many times does your heart beat in a decade? How does that number compare to the number of breaths you take in a decade?

Ask about Predictions

Have students complete **Questions 3–5**. You can survey the class for the range of predictions.

Q: Why do you think your prediction is the answer to the Main Question?

Q: Who had a similar prediction?

Q: How many of you agree with that prediction?

Q: Who has a different prediction?

3-Act Mathematical Modeling *continued*

Activity

PearsonRealize.com

ACT 2 The Model

Identify Important Info

Have students complete **Question 6**.

Q: What information would be helpful to solve the problem? [Sample answers: Heart rate; breathing rate; how each rate changes over time]

Q: How could you get that information?

Q: Why do you need that information?

Reveal the Information

Reveal the information provided below using the online interactivity. Have students record information in **Question 7**.

Resting rates, 10 seconds
Breaths: 3, Heartbeats: 11

Exercising rates, 10 seconds
Breaths: 5, Heartbeats: 21

Develop a Model

As students answer **Questions 8 and 9**, look for inefficient methods that they are using and prompt them to think about more efficient solutions.

Q: How can scientific notation help you compare the two numbers? [Sample answer: You can use the powers of 10 to quickly see how much bigger one number is than the other.]

Use the Model to Propose a Solution

After students answer **Questions 8 and 9**, facilitate a discussion about solution methods. If needed, project the possible student solutions (shown below).

Available Online

ACT 2

6. What information in this situation would be helpful to know? How would you use that information?

7. **Use Appropriate Tools** What tools can you use to get the information you need? Record the information as you find it.

8. **Model with Math** Represent the situation using the mathematical content, concepts, and skills from this topic. Use your representation to answer the Main Question.

9. What is your answer to the Main Question? Is it greater or less than your prediction? Explain why.

64 **Topic 1** 3-Act Mathematical Modeling   Go Online | PearsonRealize.com

Possible Student Solutions

Jacinta's Work

$$\frac{4}{10}=\frac{24}{60} \qquad \frac{16}{10}=\frac{96}{60}$$

There are 5,256,000 minutes in a decade.

$$24 \times 5,256,000 \qquad 96 \times 5,256,000$$
$$=126,144,000 \qquad =504,576,000$$
$$=1.26 \times 10^8 \text{ breaths} \qquad =5.05 \times 10^8 \text{ heartbeats}$$

about 4 times as many

Jacinta uses the average of the two situations in the video and then compares the numbers in scientific notation.

Quinn's Work

$$\frac{11 \text{ heartbeats}}{10 \text{ seconds}}=\frac{66 \text{ heartbeats}}{1 \text{ minute}}=\frac{3,960 \text{ beats}}{1 \text{ hour}}=\frac{95,040 \text{ beats}}{1 \text{ day}}$$

$$95,040 \times 365 \times 10 = 346,896,000 \approx 3 \times 10^8 \text{ heartbeats}$$

In 10 seconds, the ratio of heartbeats to breaths is $\frac{11}{3}$.

It's the same ratio after 10 years.

Quinn uses the resting rates and equivalent rates. He realizes that the comparison after 10 seconds will be similar to the comparison after a decade.

TOPIC 1 | **64** | 3-Act Mathematical Modeling

CT 3 ▸ The Solution and Sequel ▸

🛜 Available Online

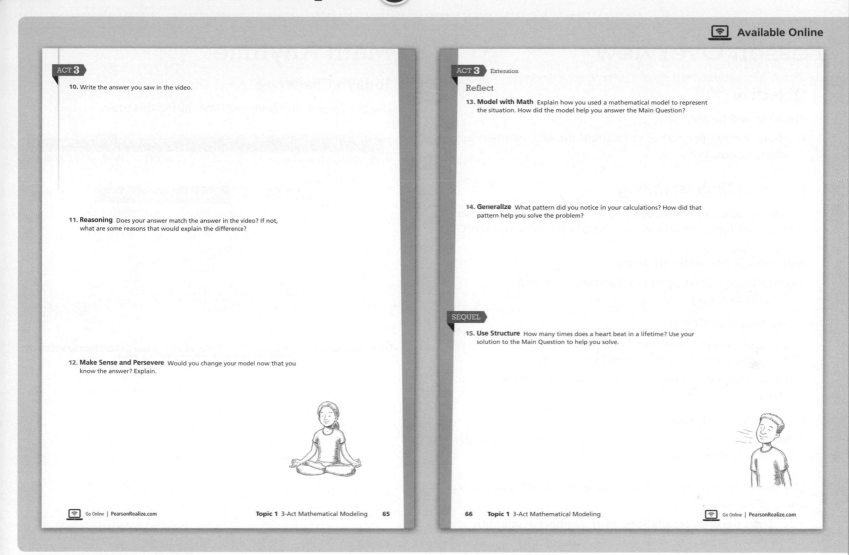

ACT 3

10. Write the answer you saw in the video.

11. Reasoning Does your answer match the answer in the video? If not, what are some reasons that would explain the difference?

12. Make Sense and Persevere Would you change your model now that you know the answer? Explain.

ACT 3 Extension

Reflect

13. Model with Math Explain how you used a mathematical model to represent the situation. How did the model help you answer the Main Question?

14. Generalize What pattern did you notice in your calculations? How did that pattern help you solve the problem?

SEQUEL

15. Use Structure How many times does a heart beat in a lifetime? Use your solution to the Main Question to help you solve.

Use the Video to Reveal the Answer

The final part of the video shows average data for both numbers over a ten-year period. Have students complete **Question 10**. Congratulate the students who were closest to the actual answer.

Main Question Answer

About 393 million heartbeats and 96 million breaths. The number of heartbeats is about 4 times the number of breaths.

Validate Conclusions

After students complete **Questions 11 and 12**, encourage them to discuss possible sources of error inherent in using math to model real-world situations. Look for students to point out that their models are still useful even though they are not perfect.

Q: Why does your answer not match the answer in the video? [Sample answer: The video shows that the water cooler is not completely full.]

Q: How useful was your model at predicting the answer?

Q: How could your model better represent the situation?

Reflect on Thinking

Generalize If time allows, have students complete **Questions 13 and 14** as an extension. Use this opportunity to discuss how students incorporate mathematical processes during the task.

Pose the Sequel

Use Structure Use **Question 15** to present a similar problem situation involving proportions. You can assign it to early finishers or as homework so students can test the usefulness of their models.

Q: How many times does a heart beat in a lifetime? Use your solution to the Main Question to help you solve.

Using their models and the answer in the video, look for student solutions between 30 and 40 billion heartbeats.

Q: What other factors do you need to consider to answer the Sequel? [Sample answer: Your heart rate may change as you get older.]

Activity

Lesson 1-10

Operations with Numbers in Scientific Notation

Lesson Overview

FOCUS

Objective

Students will be able to:

✔ apply number properties to calculations with numbers in scientific notation.

Essential Understanding

Number properties can be applied to understand how to add, subtract, multiply, and divide numbers in scientific notation.

COHERENCE

Previously in this topic, students:

- converted numbers between standard form and scientific notation.

In this lesson, students:

- apply properties of exponents to evaluate expressions involving operations with scientific notation.
- perform operations with quantities in scientific notation to solve real-world problems.

In Grade 9, students will:

- apply properties of exponents and use scientific notation to simplify equations with rational exponents.

RIGOR

This lesson emphasizes a blend of **procedural skill and fluency** and **application**.

- Students perform calculations with numbers in scientific notation.
- Students calculate using scientific notation to solve problems in situations containing very large or very small numbers.

Math Anytime

Today's Challenge

Use the Topic 1 problems any time during this topic.

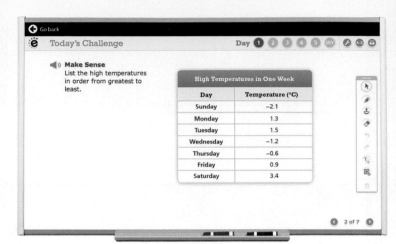

Mathematics Overview

In this lesson, students will use the Product of Powers Property and the Quotient of Powers Property to multiply and divide numbers written in scientific notation. Students will learn that to add and subtract numbers in scientific notation, the powers of 10 must have the same exponent.

Applying Math Practices

Attend to Precision
Students will perform calculations with numbers in scientific notation to solve real-world problems.

Look for and Make Use of Structure

Students will use number properties and properties of exponents to perform operations on numbers written in scientific notation. Students write their final answers to problems using correct scientific notation.

Solve & Discuss It!

Be Precise As students work through the *Solve & Discuss It*, listen and look for students who make sense of the problem and apply what they know about the area of a rectangle.

Before [WHOLE CLASS]

TP **1 Implement Tasks that Promote Reasoning and Problem Solving**

    Q: What do the numbers in the problem represent? [The height and length of a rectangular banner]

2 Build Understanding

    Q: How do you find the area of the banner? [Sample answer: Multiply its length by its width.]

During [SMALL GROUP]

TP **3 Support Productive Struggle in Learning Mathematics**

    Q: How could you use factors to find the area? [Sample answer: You could factor a 10 from both the length and the width.]

After [WHOLE CLASS]

TP **4 Facilitate Meaningful Mathematical Discourse**

    Ask students to share their solutions. If needed, project Amir's and Elsa's work and ask:

    Q: What is different about Amir's strategy compared to Elsa's strategy? [Sample answer: Amir uses standard multiplication, and then converts his answer to scientific notation. Elsa uses the Commutative Property to rearrange the factors before multiplying.]

    Q: When could Elsa's strategy be more helpful? Explain. [Sample answer: Elsa's strategy could be more helpful when the numbers are very large or very small.]

5 Transition to Visual Learning

    Q: How could you use scientific notation to multiply even larger numbers? [Sample answer: If the factors are multiples of 10, you can factor out powers of 10 and then multiply the other factors.]

6 Extension for Early Finishers

    Q: What other dimensions can you use to express the height and width of the banner? [Sample answer: Convert the measures to feet, yards, meters, or centimeters.]

Analyze Student Work

[🔲 Available Online]

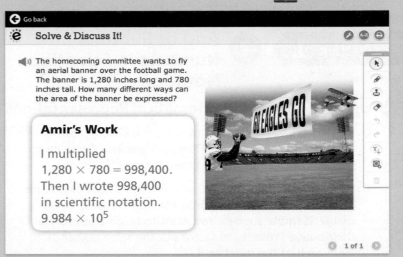

← Go back

e Solve & Discuss It!

🔊 The homecoming committee wants to fly an aerial banner over the football game. The banner is 1,280 inches long and 780 inches tall. How many different ways can the area of the banner be expressed?

Amir's Work

I multiplied
$1,280 \times 780 = 998,400$.
Then I wrote 998,400
in scientific notation.
9.984×10^5

1 of 1

Amir multiplies the dimensions and writes the area in scientific notation.

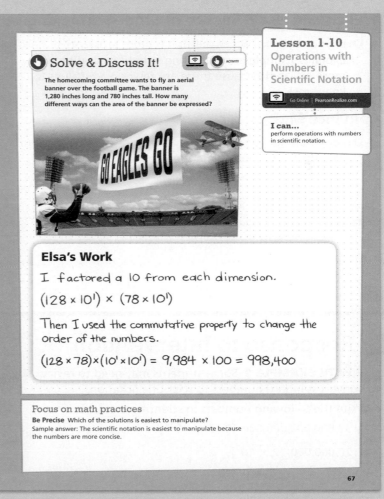

🕐 **Solve & Discuss It!**

The homecoming committee wants to fly an aerial banner over the football game. The banner is 1,280 inches long and 780 inches tall. How many different ways can the area of the banner be expressed?

Lesson 1-10
Operations with Numbers in Scientific Notation

🔲 Go Online | PearsonRealize.com

I can...
perform operations with numbers in scientific notation.

Elsa's Work

I factored a 10 from each dimension.

$(128 \times 10^1) \times (78 \times 10^1)$

Then I used the commutative property to change the order of the numbers.

$(128 \times 78) \times (10^1 \times 10^1) = 9,984 \times 100 = 998,400$

Focus on math practices
Be Precise Which of the solutions is easiest to manipulate?
Sample answer: The scientific notation is easiest to manipulate because the numbers are more concise.

67

Elsa factors a 10 from each number and uses the Commutative Property to rearrange the numbers before she multiplies.

STEP 2 | Develop: Visual Learning

ETP **Establish Mathematics Goals to Focus Learning**

Engage students in a discussion about the *Essential Question*. Make sure students understand how to write a number in scientific notation. Help students see how they can use properties to rearrange and combine terms in scientific notation to make calculations simpler.

 EXAMPLE 1 **Add or Subtract Numbers in Scientific Notation**

ETP **Use and Connect Mathematical Representations**

Q: Why was subtraction used to solve this problem rather than division? [Sample answer: The problem asks "How much greater?" not "How many times greater?"]

Q: In order to add or subtract, why is it important to rewrite the numbers so that they are raised to the same power of 10? [Sample answer: You want to be able to use the Distributive Property to factor out the same power of 10 from each of the numbers.]

 Try It!

ETP **Elicit and Use Evidence of Student Thinking**

Q: In your opinion, which method is more efficient? Explain. [Sample answer: Using scientific notation is more efficient because there are fewer place values to keep track of.]

Convince Me!

Q: For a number to properly be written in scientific notation, the first factor must be between which two numbers? [1 and 10]

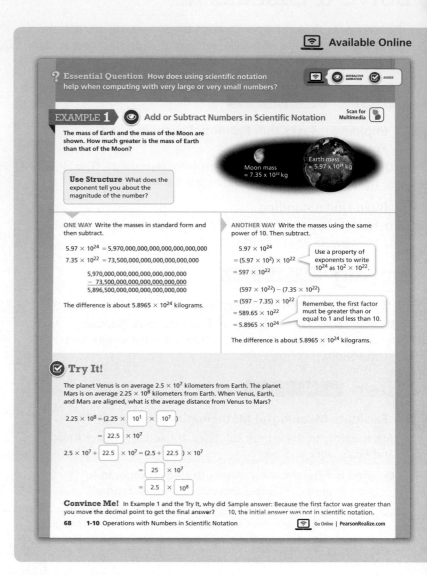

Available Online

? Essential Question How does using scientific notation help when computing with very large or very small numbers?

EXAMPLE 1 Add or Subtract Numbers in Scientific Notation   Scan for Multimedia

The mass of Earth and the mass of the Moon are shown. How much greater is the mass of Earth than that of the Moon?

Moon mass ≈ 7.35×10^{22} kg   Earth mass ≈ 5.97×10^{24} kg

Use Structure What does the exponent tell you about the magnitude of the number?

ONE WAY Write the masses in standard form and then subtract.

$5.97 \times 10^{24} = 5,970,000,000,000,000,000,000,000$
$7.35 \times 10^{22} = 73,500,000,000,000,000,000,000$

  5,970,000,000,000,000,000,000,000
− 73,500,000,000,000,000,000,000
  5,896,500,000,000,000,000,000,000

The difference is about 5.8965×10^{24} kilograms.

ANOTHER WAY Write the masses using the same power of 10. Then subtract.

5.97×10^{24}
$= (5.97 \times 10^2) \times 10^{22}$
$= 597 \times 10^{22}$

Use a property of exponents to write 10^{24} as $10^2 \times 10^{22}$.

$(597 \times 10^{22}) - (7.35 \times 10^{22})$
$= (597 - 7.35) \times 10^{22}$
$= 589.65 \times 10^{22}$
$= 5.8965 \times 10^{24}$

Remember, the first factor must be greater than or equal to 1 and less than 10.

The difference is about 5.8965×10^{24} kilograms.

Try It!

The planet Venus is on average 2.5×10^7 kilometers from Earth. The planet Mars is on average 2.25×10^8 kilometers from Earth. When Venus, Earth, and Mars are aligned, what is the average distance from Venus to Mars?

$2.25 \times 10^8 = (2.25 \times \boxed{10^1} \times \boxed{10^7})$

$= \boxed{22.5} \times 10^7$

$2.5 \times 10^7 + \boxed{22.5} \times 10^7 = (2.5 + \boxed{22.5}) \times 10^7$

$= \boxed{25} \times 10^7$

$= \boxed{2.5} \times \boxed{10^8}$

Convince Me! In Example 1 and the Try It, why did you move the decimal point to get the final answer? Sample answer: Because the first factor was greater than 10, the initial answer was not in scientific notation.

68   1-10 Operations with Numbers in Scientific Notation   Go Online | PearsonRealize.com

 Students can access the *Visual Learning Animation Plus* by using the **BouncePages app** to scan this page. Students can download the app for free in their mobile devices' app store.

RtI **Response to Intervention**

USE WITH EXAMPLE 1 Some students may need to review how to convert standard numbers to scientific notation.

- Write the following numbers in scientific notation.

  Q: 32,500,000,000,000 [3.25×10^{13}]

  Q: 20,000,000 [2×10^7]

  Q: 54.5×10^3 [5.45×10^4]

  Q: Write a rule to help you determine the exponent when writing a number in scientific notation. [Sample answer: First, identify the initial or leading digit in the number. Then count the number of places the decimal point was moved to make this number in the ones place. That number is the number to be used as the exponent.]

E **Enrichment**

USE WITH EXAMPLE 2 Challenge students to extend this problem by finding the approximate area of the main surface of the bridge.

  Q: What is the area of the surface of the bridge if its width is 3.6×10^1 feet? [The area is about 1.296×10^6 square feet.]

  Q: What is the area in standard form? [1,296,000 square feet]

XAMPLE 2 Multiply Numbers in Scientific Notation

TP Pose Purposeful Questions

Q: What you are trying to find? [The length of the main part of the bridge]

Q: What does 8.2×10^2 represent? [The distance between two piers]

XAMPLE 3 Divide Numbers in Scientific Notation

TP Pose Purposeful Questions

Q: What properties allow you to rewrite $(1.83 \times 10^6) \div (3.0 \times 10^1)$ as $(1.83 \div 3.0) \times (10^6 \div 10^1)$? [The Commutative and Associative Properties]

Q: How do you know that 0.61×10^5 is not in scientific notation? [The first factor has to be between 1 and 10, but 0.61 is less than 1.]

Try It!

TP Elicit and Use Evidence of Student Thinking

Q: Why can it be more convenient to divide numbers in scientific notation than numbers in standard form? [Sample answer: You can use the Properties of Exponents to divide the powers of 10 and then divide the factors of the powers of ten.]

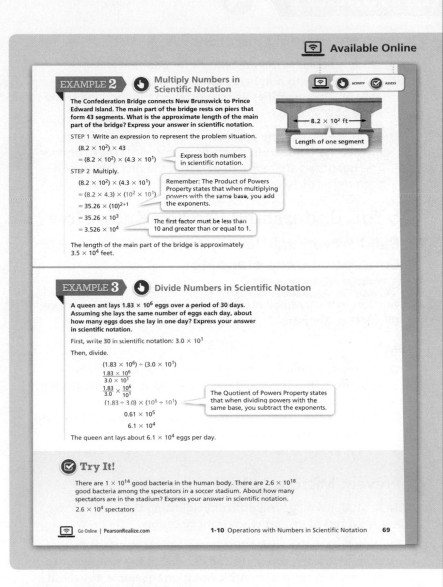

Available Online

EXAMPLE 2 Multiply Numbers in Scientific Notation

The Confederation Bridge connects New Brunswick to Prince Edward Island. The main part of the bridge rests on piers that form 43 segments. What is the approximate length of the main part of the bridge? Express your answer in scientific notation.

8.2×10^2 ft — Length of one segment

STEP 1 Write an expression to represent the problem situation.

$(8.2 \times 10^2) \times 43$

$= (8.2 \times 10^2) \times (4.3 \times 10^1)$ — Express both numbers in scientific notation.

STEP 2 Multiply.

$(8.2 \times 10^2) \times (4.3 \times 10^1)$

$= (8.2 \times 4.3) \times (10^2 \times 10^1)$ — Remember: The Product of Powers Property states that when multiplying powers with the same base, you add the exponents.

$= 35.26 \times (10)^{2+1}$

$= 35.26 \times 10^3$ — The first factor must be less than 10 and greater than or equal to 1.

$= 3.526 \times 10^4$

The length of the main part of the bridge is approximately 3.5×10^4 feet.

EXAMPLE 3 Divide Numbers in Scientific Notation

A queen ant lays 1.83×10^6 eggs over a period of 30 days. Assuming she lays the same number of eggs each day, about how many eggs does she lay in one day? Express your answer in scientific notation.

First, write 30 in scientific notation: 3.0×10^1

Then, divide.

$(1.83 \times 10^6) \div (3.0 \times 10^1)$

$\dfrac{1.83 \times 10^6}{3.0 \times 10^1}$

$\dfrac{1.83}{3.0} \times \dfrac{10^6}{10^1}$

$(1.83 \div 3.0) \times (10^6 \div 10^1)$ — The Quotient of Powers Property states that when dividing powers with the same base, you subtract the exponents.

0.61×10^5

6.1×10^4

The queen ant lays about 6.1×10^4 eggs per day.

Try It!

There are 1×10^{14} good bacteria in the human body. There are 2.6×10^{18} good bacteria among the spectators in a soccer stadium. About how many spectators are in the stadium? Express your answer in scientific notation.

2.6×10^4 spectators

Go Online | PearsonRealize.com   **1-10** Operations with Numbers in Scientific Notation   **69**

ADDITIONAL EXAMPLES

For additional examples go to PearsonRealize.com.

ELL English Language Learners

BEGINNING Read Example 1 aloud. Have students use the diagram to help them answer the following questions.

Q: What does the phrase *how much greater* mean? [Sample answer: It means how much larger one quantity is than another.]

Q: What operation should you use to compare the masses? [Subtraction]

INTERMEDIATE Read Example 1 aloud.

Have students fill in the missing words or phrases as the two solution methods are described.

Q: In the first method, line up the digits that have the same _____. Then you _____. [place value, subtract]

Q: In the second method, write both numbers using the _____ power of 10. Then factor out 10^{22} and _____ the first factors. Then write the answer in correct _____. [same, subtract, scientific notation]

ADVANCED Read Example 1 aloud.

Pair up students. Have each student write a summary of the steps used in the second method and then read it aloud to their partner. Suggest that each pair edit each other's work and combine their summaries into one.

KEY CONCEPT

ETP ## Pose Purposeful Questions

Q: What is similar in the procedures for addition and subtraction with numbers in scientific notation? [Sample answer: The quantities are rewritten so that both have the same power of 10.]

Q: What is similar in the procedures for multiplication and division for numbers in scientific notation? [Sample answer: The quantities are regrouped so that the first factors and the powers of 10 can be simplified.]

Do You Understand/Do You Know How?

ETP ## Build Procedural Fluency from Conceptual Understanding

? Essential Question Students should recognize that for very large or very small numbers, scientific notation can make calculations simpler.

ITEM 2

Q: In a multiplication problem involving two numbers in scientific notation, would the initial result after multiplying ever result in an answer greater than 100? Explain. [No; Sample answer: Since the first factors are both less than 10, their product will be less than 100.]

⚠ Prevent Misconceptions

ITEM 4 Students may have difficulty adjusting their answer so that it is expressed in correct scientific notation.

Q: How do you know whether to increase or decrease the exponent when you move the decimal in the first factor to express it in correct scientific notation? [Sample answer: If the first factor is greater than 10, you divide it by 10 when you move the decimal left, so you have to increase the exponent to keep the total value the same.]

Available Online

KEY CONCEPT

Operations with very large or very small numbers can be carried out more efficiently using scientific notation. The properties of exponents apply when carrying out operations.

Addition or Subtraction	Multiplication	Division
$(2.3 \times 10^6) + (1.6 \times 10^9)$	$(2.3 \times 10^6) \times (1.6 \times 10^9)$	$(2.3 \times 10^6) \div (1.6 \times 10^9)$
$(2.3 \times 10^6) + (1.6 \times 10^3) \times 10^6$	$(2.3 \times 1.6) \times (10^6 \times 10^9)$	$(2.3 \div 1.6) \times (10^6 \div 10^9)$
$(2.3 \times 10^6) + (1,600 \times 10^6)$	$3.68 \times 10^{6+9}$	$1.4375 \times 10^{6-9}$
$(2.3 + 1,600) \times 10^6$ — Use the Product of Powers Property.	3.68×10^{15} — Use the Product of Powers Property.	1.4375×10^{-3} — Use the Quotient of Powers Property.
$1,602.3 \times 10^6$		
1.6023×10^9		

Do You Understand?

1. **? Essential Question** How does using scientific notation help when computing with very small or very large numbers? Sample answer: Using scientific notation allows you to compute with fewer digits.

2. **Use Structure** When multiplying and dividing two numbers in scientific notation, why do you sometimes have to rewrite one factor? Sample answer: When multiplying and dividing numbers in scientific notation, the final answer must have a first factor that is less than 10. You may have to rewrite the calculated answer. For example, rewrite 12.15×10^4 as 1.215×10^5.

3. **Use Structure** For the sum of (5.2×10^4) and (6.95×10^4) in scientific notation, why will the power of 10 be 10^5? Sample answer: The exponent is 5 in the sum because the sum of 5.2 and 6.95 is 12.15, which is greater than 1. You move the decimal point one place to the left and increase the exponent by 1.

Do You Know How?

4. A bacteriologist estimates that there are 5.2×10^4 bacteria growing in each of 20 petri dishes. About how many bacteria in total are growing in the petri dishes? Express your answer in scientific notation.
about 1.04×10^6 bacteria

5. The distance from Earth to the Moon is approximately 1.2×10^9 feet. The Apollo 11 spacecraft was approximately 360 feet long. About how many spacecraft of that length would fit end to end from Earth to the Moon? Express your answer in scientific notation.

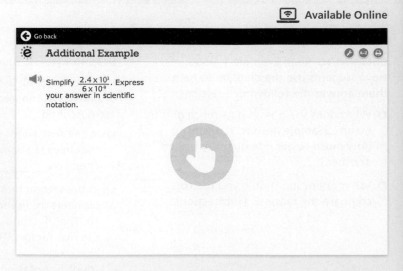

about 3.3×10^6 spacecraft

6. The mass of Mars is 6.42×10^{23} kilograms. The mass of Mercury is 3.3×10^{23} kilograms.
   a. What is the combined mass of Mars and Mercury expressed in scientific notation?
   9.72×10^{23} kg
   b. What is the difference in the mass of the two planets expressed in scientific notation?
   3.12×10^{23} kg

70   1-10 Operations with Numbers in Scientific Notation   Go Online | PearsonRealize.com

---

ADDITIONAL EXAMPLE **3**

Available Online

Help students transition from dividing quantities when one quantity is written in scientific notation to dividing when two quantities are written in scientific notation.

Make sure the students understand the properties used at each step to keep both sides of the equation equal.

Q: What is another way you can simplify the expression? [Sample answer: You can use the rules for simplifying fractions. If you think of $\frac{2.4 \times 10^{-3}}{6 \times 10^{-9}} = \frac{2.4}{6} \times \frac{10^{-3}}{10^{-9}}$, then you see how you can change the quantities and operations.]

Q: How could you check your answer? [Sample answer: Multiply your answer by the denominator of the first expression. The product should be the numerator.]

◀ Go back

ė **Additional Example**

🔊 Simplify $\frac{2.4 \times 10^3}{6 \times 10^{-9}}$. Express your answer in scientific notation.

Answer: 4.0×10^5

Practice & Problem Solving

Available Online

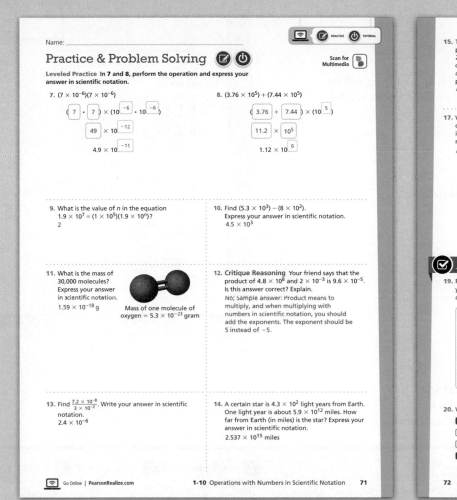

Name: _____

Practice & Problem Solving

Scan for Multimedia

Leveled Practice In 7 and 8, perform the operation and express your answer in scientific notation.

7. $(7 \times 10^{-6})(7 \times 10^{-6})$

$(\boxed{7} \cdot \boxed{7}) \times (10^{\boxed{-6}} \cdot 10^{\boxed{-6}})$

$\boxed{49} \times 10^{\boxed{-12}}$

$4.9 \times 10^{\boxed{-11}}$

8. $(3.76 \times 10^5) + (7.44 \times 10^5)$

$(\boxed{3.76} + \boxed{7.44}) \times (10^{\boxed{5}})$

$\boxed{11.2} \times \boxed{10^5}$

$1.12 \times 10^{\boxed{6}}$

9. What is the value of n in the equation $1.9 \times 10^7 = (1 \times 10^5)(1.9 \times 10^n)$?
   2

10. Find $(5.3 \times 10^3) - (8 \times 10^2)$. Express your answer in scientific notation.
    4.5×10^3

11. What is the mass of 30,000 molecules? Express your answer in scientific notation.
    1.59×10^{-18} g

    Mass of one molecule of oxygen $= 5.3 \times 10^{-23}$ gram

12. **Critique Reasoning** Your friend says that the product of 4.8×10^8 and 2×10^{-3} is 9.6×10^{-5}. Is this answer correct? Explain.
    No; Sample answer: Product means to multiply, and when multiplying with numbers in scientific notation, you should add the exponents. The exponent should be 5 instead of -5.

13. Find $\frac{7.2 \times 10^{-8}}{3 \times 10^{-2}}$. Write your answer in scientific notation.
    2.4×10^{-6}

14. A certain star is 4.3×10^2 light years from Earth. One light year is about 5.9×10^{12} miles. How far from Earth (in miles) is the star? Express your answer in scientific notation.
    2.537×10^{15} miles

Go Online | PearsonRealize.com

1-10 Operations with Numbers in Scientific Notation   71

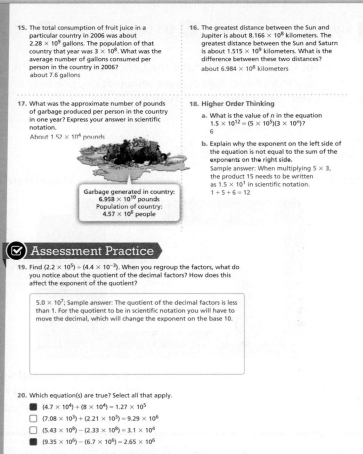

15. The total consumption of fruit juice in a particular country in 2006 was about 2.28×10^9 gallons. The population of that country that year was 3×10^8. What was the average number of gallons consumed per person in the country in 2006?
    about 7.6 gallons

16. The greatest distance between the Sun and Jupiter is about 8.166×10^8 kilometers. The greatest distance between the Sun and Saturn is about 1.515×10^9 kilometers. What is the difference between these two distances?
    about 6.984×10^8 kilometers

17. What was the approximate number of pounds of garbage produced per person in the country in one year? Express your answer in scientific notation.
    About 1.52×10^4 pounds

    Garbage generated in country: 6.958×10^{10} pounds
    Population of country: 4.57×10^6 people

18. **Higher Order Thinking**
    a. What is the value of n in the equation $1.5 \times 10^{12} = (5 \times 10^5)(3 \times 10^n)$?
       6
    b. Explain why the exponent on the left side of the equation is not equal to the sum of the exponents on the right side.
       Sample answer: When multiplying 5×3, the product 15 needs to be written as 1.5×10^1 in scientific notation. $1 + 5 + 6 = 12$

✓ Assessment Practice

19. Find $(2.2 \times 10^5) \div (4.4 \times 10^{-3})$. When you regroup the factors, what do you notice about the quotient of the decimal factors? How does this affect the exponent of the quotient?

    5.0×10^7; Sample answer: The quotient of the decimal factors is less than 1. For the quotient to be in scientific notation you will have to move the decimal, which will change the exponent on the base 10.

20. Which equation(s) are true? Select all that apply.
    ☑ $(4.7 \times 10^4) + (8 \times 10^4) = 1.27 \times 10^5$
    ☐ $(7.08 \times 10^3) + (2.21 \times 10^3) = 9.29 \times 10^6$
    ☐ $(5.43 \times 10^8) - (2.33 \times 10^8) = 3.1 \times 10^4$
    ☑ $(9.35 \times 10^6) - (6.7 \times 10^6) = 2.65 \times 10^6$

72   1-10 Operations with Numbers in Scientific Notation   Go Online | PearsonRealize.com

---

Error Intervention

You may opt to have students complete the automatically scored Practice & Problem Solving items online.

ITEM 16 Students may not understand or have trouble deciding which number is greater. Ask the following questions:

Q: Which number is greater? How do you know? [Sample answer: 1.515×10^9 is greater because it has a greater power of 10.]

Q: Why do you need to do to determine the greater number? [Sample answer: Both quantities must have the same power of 10 before they can be subtracted. One of the quantities will need to be rewritten.]

Item Analysis

Example	Items	DOK
1	8, 20	1
	10, 16	2
2	7	1
	9, 11, 14	2
	12, 18	3
3	13, 15, 17, 19	2

English Language Learners

ITEM 15 Students may need support in understanding the terms used in this question.

Q: What does *consumption* mean? How is it related to the word *consumed*? [Sample answer: *Consumption* means the act of eating or drinking something. *Consume* means to eat or drink. *Consumed* is a verb and *consumption* is a noun.]

☑ Lesson Quiz

 Use the student scores on the Lesson Quiz to prescribe differentiated assignments.

I Intervention 0–3 Points   **O** On-Level 4 Points   **A** Advanced 5 Points

You may opt to have students take the Lesson Quiz online. The Lesson Quiz will be automatically scored and appropriate remediation, practice, or enrichment will be assigned based on student performance.

⏻ Video Tutorials

Students can access instructional tutorials using the **Virtual Nerd app**.

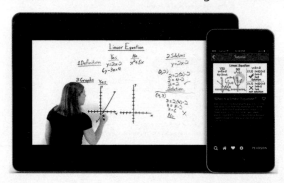

Students can also access the videos using the **BouncePages app** to scan exercise pages marked with this icon. Students can download both apps for free in their mobile devices' app store.

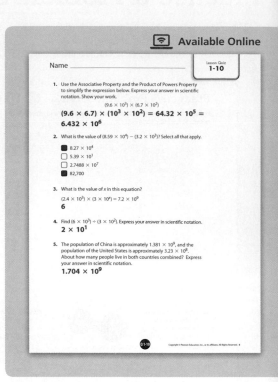

⎙ Available Online

Name _____   Lesson Quiz 1-10

1. Use the Associative Property and the Product of Powers Property to simplify the expression below. Express your answer in scientific notation. Show your work.

$(9.6 \times 10^3) \times (6.7 \times 10^2)$

$(9.6 \times 6.7) \times (10^3 \times 10^2) = 64.32 \times 10^5 = 6.432 \times 10^6$

2. What is the value of $(8.59 \times 10^4) - (3.2 \times 10^3)$? Select all that apply.
   - ☒ 8.27×10^4
   - ☐ 5.39×10^1
   - ☐ 2.7488×10^7
   - ☒ 82,700

3. What is the value of x in this equation?
   $(2.4 \times 10^3) \times (3 \times 10^6) = 7.2 \times 10^9$
   6

4. Find $(6 \times 10^3) \div (3 \times 10^2)$. Express your answer in scientific notation.
   2×10^1

5. The population of China is approximately 1.381×10^9, and the population of the United States is approximately 3.23×10^8. About how many people live in both countries combined? Express your answer in scientific notation.
   1.704×10^9

Differentiated Intervention

I = Intervention   **O** = On-Level   **A** = Advanced

Reteach to Build Understanding **I**

Provides scaffolded reteaching for the key lesson concepts.

Additional Vocabulary Support **I** **O**

Helps students develop and reinforce understanding of key terms and concepts.

Build Mathematical Literacy **I**

Provides support for struggling readers to build mathematical literacy.

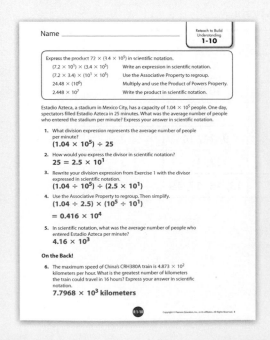

Name _____   Reteach to Build Understanding 1-10

Express the product $72 \times (3.4 \times 10^5)$ in scientific notation.
$(7.2 \times 10^1) \times (3.4 \times 10^5)$	Write an expression in scientific notation.
$(7.2 \times 3.4) \times (10^1 \times 10^5)$	Use the Associative Property to regroup.
$24.48 \times (10^6)$	Multiply and use the Product of Powers Property.
2.448×10^7	Write the product in scientific notation.

Estadio Azteca, a stadium in Mexico City, has a capacity of 1.04×10^5 people. One day, spectators filled Estadio Azteca in 25 minutes. What was the average number of people who entered the stadium per minute? Express your answer in scientific notation.

1. What division expression represents the average number of people per minute?
   $(1.04 \times 10^5) \div 25$

2. How would you express the divisor in scientific notation?
   $25 = 2.5 \times 10^1$

3. Rewrite your division expression from Exercise 1 with the divisor expressed in scientific notation.
   $(1.04 \times 10^5) \div (2.5 \times 10^1)$

4. Use the Associative Property to regroup. Then simplify.
   $(1.04 \div 2.5) \times (10^5 \div 10^1)$
   $= 0.416 \times 10^4$

5. In scientific notation, what was the average number of people who entered Estadio Azteca per minute?
   4.16×10^3

On the Back!

6. The maximum speed of China's CRH380A train is 4.873×10^2 kilometers per hour. What is the greatest number of kilometers the train could travel in 16 hours? Express your answer in scientific notation.
   7.7968×10^3 **kilometers**

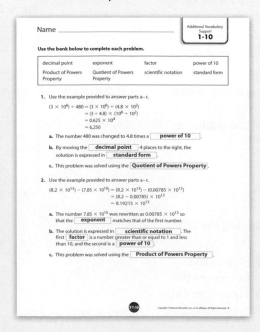

Name _____   Additional Vocabulary Support 1-10

Use the bank below to complete each problem.

decimal point	exponent	factor	power of 10
Product of Powers Property	Quotient of Powers Property	scientific notation	standard form

1. Use the example provided to answer parts a–c.
   $(3 \times 10^6) \div 480 = (3 \times 10^6) \div (4.8 \times 10^2)$
   $= (3 \div 4.8) \times (10^6 \div 10^2)$
   $= 0.625 \times 10^4$
   $= 6,250$

   a. The number 480 was changed to 4.8 times a **power of 10**.
   b. By moving the **decimal point** 4 places to the right, the solution is expressed in **standard form**.
   c. This problem was solved using the **Quotient of Powers Property**.

2. Use the example provided to answer parts a–c.
   $(8.2 \times 10^{13}) - (7.85 \times 10^{10}) = (8.2 \times 10^{13}) - (0.00785 \times 10^{13})$
   $= (8.2 - 0.00785) \times 10^{13}$
   $= 8.19215 \times 10^{13}$

   a. The number 7.85×10^{10} was rewritten as 0.00785×10^{13} so that the **exponent** matches that of the first number.
   b. The solution is expressed in **scientific notation**. The first **factor** is a number greater than or equal to 1 and less than 10, and the second is a **power of 10**.
   c. This problem was solved using the **Product of Powers Property**.

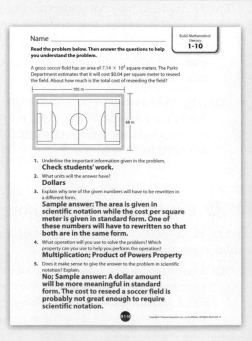

Name _____   Build Mathematical Literacy 1-10

Read the problem below. Then answer the questions to help you understand the problem.

A grass soccer field has an area of 7.14×10^3 square meters. The Parks Department estimates that it will cost $0.04 per square meter to reseed the field. About how much is the total cost of reseeding the field?

[diagram of soccer field: 105 m, 68 m]

1. Underline the important information given in the problem.
   Check students' work.

2. What units will the answer have?
   Dollars

3. Explain why one of the given numbers will have to be rewritten in a different form.
   Sample answer: The area is given in scientific notation while the cost per square meter is given in standard form. One of these numbers will have to rewritten so that both are in the same form.

4. What operation will you use to solve the problem? Which property can you use to help you perform the operation?
   Multiplication; Product of Powers Property

5. Does it make sense to give the answer to the problem in scientific notation? Explain.
   No; Sample answer: A dollar amount will be more meaningful in standard form. The cost to reseed a soccer field is probably not great enough to require scientific notation.

Practice · Worksheets · Math Tools · Math Games

Additional Practice

You may opt to have students complete the automatically scored Additional Practice items online.

Item Analysis

Example	Items	DOK
1	2	1
	4, 13, 14	2
2	5, 7, 10, 11	2
	12	3
3	1	1
	3, 6, 8, 9	2

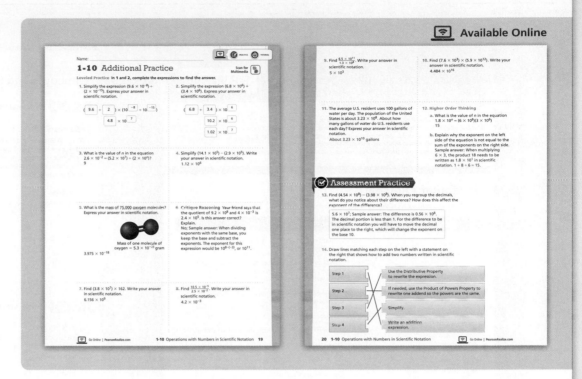

Available Online

Differentiated Intervention

I = Intervention **O** = On-Level **A** = Advanced

Enrichment **O** **A**

Presents engaging problems and activities that extend the lesson concepts.

Math Tools and Games **I** **O** **A**

Offers additional activities and games to build understanding and fluency.

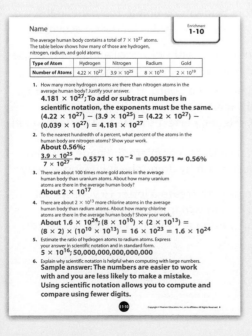

TOPIC 1 REVIEW — Real Numbers

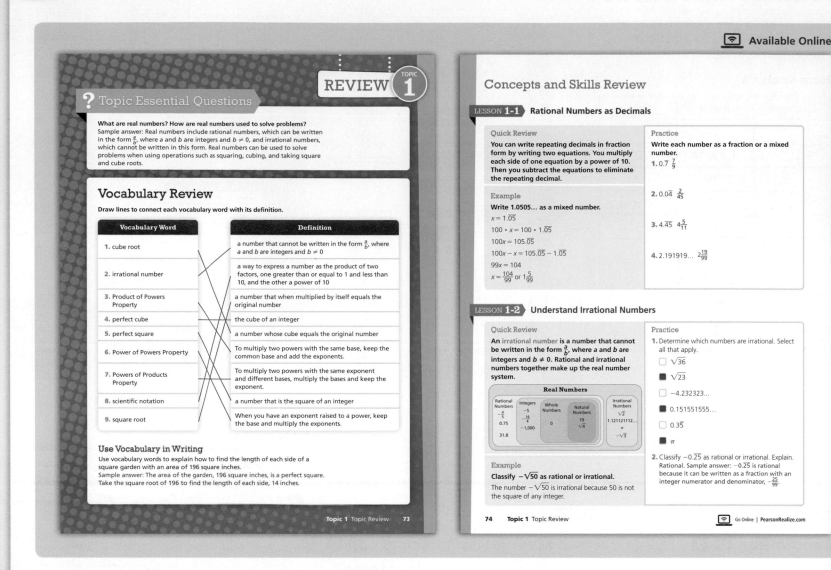

Available Online

REVIEW — TOPIC 1

Topic Essential Questions

What are real numbers? How are real numbers used to solve problems?
Sample answer: Real numbers include rational numbers, which can be written in the form $\frac{a}{b}$, where a and b are integers and $b \neq 0$, and irrational numbers, which cannot be written in this form. Real numbers can be used to solve problems when using operations such as squaring, cubing, and taking square and cube roots.

Vocabulary Review

Draw lines to connect each vocabulary word with its definition.

Vocabulary Word	Definition
1. cube root	a number that cannot be written in the form $\frac{a}{b}$, where a and b are integers and $b \neq 0$
2. irrational number	a way to express a number as the product of two factors, one greater than or equal to 1 and less than 10, and the other a power of 10
3. Product of Powers Property	a number that when multiplied by itself equals the original number
4. perfect cube	the cube of an integer
5. perfect square	a number whose cube equals the original number
6. Power of Powers Property	To multiply two powers with the same base, keep the common base and add the exponents.
7. Powers of Products Property	To multiply two powers with the same exponent and different bases, multiply the bases and keep the exponent.
8. scientific notation	a number that is the square of an integer
9. square root	When you have an exponent raised to a power, keep the base and multiply the exponents.

Use Vocabulary in Writing

Use vocabulary words to explain how to find the length of each side of a square garden with an area of 196 square inches.
Sample answer: The area of the garden, 196 square inches, is a perfect square. Take the square root of 196 to find the length of each side, 14 inches.

Topic 1 Topic Review   73

Concepts and Skills Review

LESSON 1-1 Rational Numbers as Decimals

Quick Review
You can write repeating decimals in fraction form by writing two equations. You multiply each side of one equation by a power of 10. Then you subtract the equations to eliminate the repeating decimal.

Example
Write $1.0505\ldots$ as a mixed number.
$x = 1.\overline{05}$
$100 \cdot x = 100 \cdot 1.\overline{05}$
$100x = 105.\overline{05}$
$100x - x = 105.\overline{05} - 1.\overline{05}$
$99x = 104$
$x = \frac{104}{99}$ or $1\frac{5}{99}$

Practice
Write each number as a fraction or a mixed number.
1. $0.\overline{7}$ $\frac{7}{9}$
2. $0.0\overline{4}$ $\frac{2}{45}$
3. $4.\overline{45}$ $4\frac{5}{11}$
4. $2.191919\ldots$ $2\frac{19}{99}$

LESSON 1-2 Understand Irrational Numbers

Quick Review
An irrational number is a number that cannot be written in the form $\frac{a}{b}$, where a and b are integers and $b \neq 0$. Rational and irrational numbers together make up the real number system.

Real Numbers
Rational Numbers: $-\frac{4}{5}$, 0.75, 31.8
Integers: -5, $-\frac{16}{4}$, $-1,000$
Whole Numbers: 0
Natural Numbers: 19, $\sqrt{4}$
Irrational Numbers: $\sqrt{2}$, $1.121121112\ldots$, π, $-\sqrt{3}$

Example
Classify $-\sqrt{50}$ as rational or irrational.
The number $-\sqrt{50}$ is irrational because 50 is not the square of any integer.

Practice
1. Determine which numbers are irrational. Select all that apply.
☐ $\sqrt{36}$
■ $\sqrt{23}$
☐ $-4.232323\ldots$
■ $0.151551555\ldots$
☐ $0.3\overline{5}$
■ π

2. Classify $-0.\overline{25}$ as rational or irrational. Explain.
Rational. Sample answer: $-0.\overline{25}$ is rational because it can be written as a fraction with an integer numerator and denominator, $-\frac{25}{99}$.

74   Topic 1 Topic Review   Go Online | PearsonRealize.com

Topic Essential Questions

What are real numbers? How are real numbers used to solve problems?

As students answer the Essential Questions in writing, encourage them to include definitions, examples, non-examples, models, and other representations that support their answers.

Be sure the following are made explicit while discussing students' answers.

- Real numbers are numbers that can be found on the number line.
- Real numbers are used to solve problems involving squares and square roots, cubes and cube roots, and all real-world situations.
- Real numbers can be added, subtracted, multiplied or divided with each other, and the result will be another real number.
- Very small and very large real numbers are often written in scientific notation.

Vocabulary Review

ORAL LANGUAGE Before students complete the page, reinforce oral language by using one or more of the following activities.

- Have students work in groups (without pencil and paper) to use each vocabulary word in an informative sentence.
- Write three real numbers on the board. Have students describe each one using as many math vocabulary words as possible. [Ex: 64 (Real, rational, integer, perfect square and perfect cube)]

WRITING IN MATH After students complete the page, you can further reinforce writing in math by doing the following activity.

- Have students work in pairs to create a letter to your school principal teaching her or him two interesting pieces of information from Topic 1 using at least two vocabulary words.

Concepts and Skills Review

📶 **Available Online**

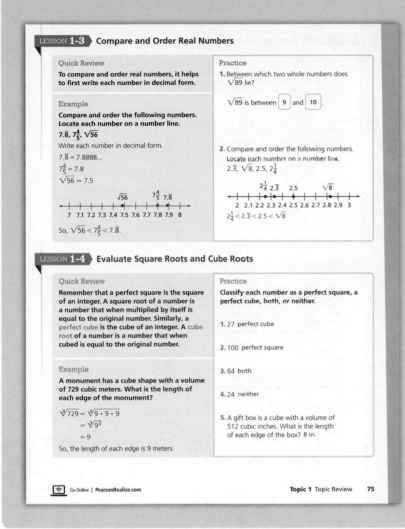

LESSON 1-3 Compare and Order Real Numbers

Quick Review
To compare and order real numbers, it helps to first write each number in decimal form.

Example
Compare and order the following numbers. Locate each number on a number line.

$7.\overline{8}$, $7\frac{4}{5}$, $\sqrt{56}$

Write each number in decimal form.

$7.\overline{8} = 7.8888...$

$7\frac{4}{5} = 7.8$

$\sqrt{56} \approx 7.5$

So, $\sqrt{56} < 7\frac{4}{5} < 7.\overline{8}$.

Practice
1. Between which two whole numbers does $\sqrt{89}$ lie?

$\sqrt{89}$ is between $\boxed{9}$ and $\boxed{10}$.

2. Compare and order the following numbers. Locate each number on a number line.

$2.\overline{3}$, $\sqrt{8}$, 2.5, $2\frac{1}{4}$

$2\frac{1}{4} < 2.\overline{3} < 2.5 < \sqrt{8}$

LESSON 1-4 Evaluate Square Roots and Cube Roots

Quick Review
Remember that a perfect square is the square of an integer. A square root of a number is a number that when multiplied by itself is equal to the original number. Similarly, a perfect cube is the cube of an integer. A cube root of a number is a number that when cubed is equal to the original number.

Example
A monument has a cube shape with a volume of 729 cubic meters. What is the length of each edge of the monument?

$\sqrt[3]{729} = \sqrt[3]{9 \cdot 9 \cdot 9}$

$\quad = \sqrt[3]{9^3}$

$\quad = 9$

So, the length of each edge is 9 meters.

Practice
Classify each number as a perfect square, a perfect cube, both, or neither.

1. 27 perfect cube

2. 100 perfect square

3. 64 both

4. 24 neither

5. A gift box is a cube with a volume of 512 cubic inches. What is the length of each edge of the box? 8 in.

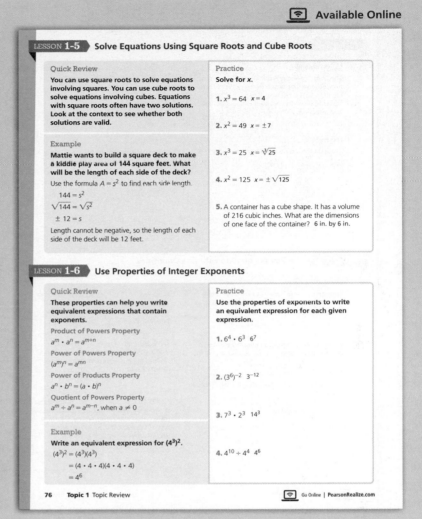

LESSON 1-5 Solve Equations Using Square Roots and Cube Roots

Quick Review
You can use square roots to solve equations involving squares. You can use cube roots to solve equations involving cubes. Equations with square roots often have two solutions. Look at the context to see whether both solutions are valid.

Example
Mattie wants to build a square deck to make a kiddie play area of 144 square feet. What will be the length of each side of the deck?

Use the formula $A = s^2$ to find each side length.

$144 = s^2$

$\sqrt{144} = \sqrt{s^2}$

$\pm 12 = s$

Length cannot be negative, so the length of each side of the deck will be 12 feet.

Practice
Solve for x.

1. $x^3 = 64$ $x = 4$

2. $x^2 = 49$ $x = \pm 7$

3. $x^3 = 25$ $x = \sqrt[3]{25}$

4. $x^2 = 125$ $x = \pm\sqrt{125}$

5. A container has a cube shape. It has a volume of 216 cubic inches. What are the dimensions of one face of the container? 6 in. by 6 in.

LESSON 1-6 Use Properties of Integer Exponents

Quick Review
These properties can help you write equivalent expressions that contain exponents.

Product of Powers Property
$a^m \cdot a^n = a^{m+n}$

Power of Powers Property
$(a^m)^n = a^{mn}$

Power of Products Property
$a^n \cdot b^n = (a \cdot b)^n$

Quotient of Powers Property
$a^m \div a^n = a^{m-n}$, when $a \neq 0$

Example
Write an equivalent expression for $(4^3)^2$.

$(4^3)^2 = (4^3)(4^3)$

$\quad = (4 \cdot 4 \cdot 4)(4 \cdot 4 \cdot 4)$

$\quad = 4^6$

Practice
Use the properties of exponents to write an equivalent expression for each given expression.

1. $6^4 \cdot 6^3$ 6^7

2. $(3^6)^{-2}$ 3^{-12}

3. $7^3 \cdot 2^3$ 14^3

4. $4^{10} \div 4^4$ 4^6

📶 Available Online

LESSON 1-7 More Properties of Integer Exponents

Quick Review

The Zero Exponent Property states that any nonzero number raised to the power of 0 is equal to 1. The Negative Exponent Property states that for any nonzero rational number a and integer n, $a^{-n} = \frac{1}{a^n}$.

Example

Evaluate the expression for $x = 2$ and $y = 4$.

$$\frac{2}{y^{-2}} + 5x^0 = \frac{2}{(4)^{-2}} + 5(2)^0$$
$$= \frac{2(4^2)}{1} + 5(1)$$
$$= 2(16) + 5(1)$$
$$= 32 + 5$$
$$= 37$$

Practice

Write each expression using positive exponents.

1. 9^{-4} $\frac{1}{9^4}$

2. $\frac{1}{3^{-5}}$ 3^5

Evaluate each expression for $x = 2$ and $y = 5$.

3. $-4x^{-2} + 3y^0$ 2

4. $2x^0y^{-2}$ $\frac{2}{25}$

LESSON 1-8 Use Powers of 10 to Estimate Quantities

Quick Review

You can estimate very large and very small quantities by writing the number as a single digit times a power of 10.

Example

Keisha is about 1,823,933 minutes old. Write this age as a single digit times a power of 10.

First round to the greatest place value.
1,823,933 is about 2,000,000.

Write the rounded number as a single digit times a power of 10.

$$2,000,000 = 2 \times 10^6$$

Keisha is about 2×10^6 minutes old.

Practice

1. In the year 2013 the population of California was about 38,332,521 people. Write the estimated population as a single digit times a power of 10. 4×10^7

2. The wavelength of green light is about 0.00000051 meter. What is this estimated wavelength as a single digit times a power of 10? 5×10^{-7}

3. The land area of Connecticut is about 12,549,000,000 square meters. The land area of Rhode Island is about 2,707,000,000 square meters. How many times greater is the land area of Connecticut than the land area of Rhode Island?   About 3 times greater

LESSON 1-9 Understand Scientific Notation

Quick Review

A number in scientific notation is written as a product of two factors, one greater than or equal to 1 and less than 10, and the other a power of 10.

Example

Write 65,700,000 in scientific notation.

First, place the decimal point to the right of the first nonzero digit.

Then, count the number of digits to the right of the decimal point to determine the power of 10.

65,700,000 in scientific notation is 6.57×10^7.

Practice

1. Write 803,000,000 in scientific notation.
   8.03×10^8

2. Write 0.0000000068 in scientific notation.
   6.8×10^{-9}

3. Write 1.359×10^5 in standard form.
   135,900

4. The radius of a hydrogen atom is 0.000000000025 meter. How would you express this radius in scientific notation?
   2.5×10^{-11} meter

LESSON 1-10 Operations with Numbers in Scientific Notation

Quick Review

When multiplying and dividing numbers in scientific notation, multiply or divide the first factors. Then multiply or divide the powers of 10. When adding and subtracting numbers in scientific notation, first write the numbers with the same power of 10. Then add or subtract the first factors, and keep the same power of 10.

If the decimal part of the result is not greater than or equal to 1 and less than 10, move the decimal point and adjust the exponent.

Example

Multiply $(4.2 \times 10^5) \times (2.5 \times 10^3)$.

$$(4.2 \times 10^5) \times (2.5 \times 10^3)$$
$$= (4.2 \times 2.5) \times (10^5 \times 10^3)$$
$$= 10.5 \times 10^8$$
$$= 1.05 \times 10^9$$

Practice

Perform each operation. Express your answers in scientific notation.

1. $(2.8 \times 10^4) \times (4 \times 10^5)$
   1.12×10^{10}

2. $(6 \times 10^9) \div (2.4 \times 10^3)$
   2.5×10^6

3. $(4.1 \times 10^4) + (5.6 \times 10^6)$
   5.641×10^6

4. The population of Town A is 1.26×10^5 people. The population of Town B is 2.8×10^4 people. How many times greater is the population of Town A than the population of Town B?
   4.5 times greater

Fluency Practice

Crisscrossed

Students maintain fluency for solving linear equations using addition and subtraction as they complete a crossword-style activity that reinforces mathematical practices.

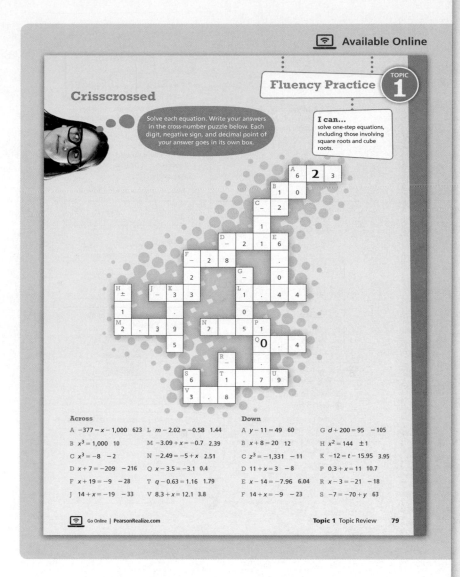

Getting Started Students may work independently or with a partner. Go over the directions. Point out that each digit, negative sign, and decimal point should be placed in its own box in the puzzle.

Students should solve each problem and complete their own puzzle. Encourage students to record their work on a separate sheet of paper.

As Students Do the Activity Remind students that the puzzle works like a crossword puzzle, so intersecting solutions share a common digit, negative sign, or decimal point. If the digit, negative sign, or decimal point isn't the same, students need to check their work and correct as needed.

Some students may find all of the answers first, and then fill in the puzzle. Allow this strategy as it provides the same fluency practice. Students should check each solution and compare and discuss their answers with their partner.

Another Activity Have students work together to write a new set of clues that result in the same solutions in the puzzle. Ask them to record the new clues on a separate sheet of paper.

Extra Challenge Create your own Crisscrossed puzzle activity. Write a new problem for each clue and use grid paper to create the puzzle. Then trade your activity with a partner and complete your partner's Crisscrossed activity. Do not forget to include decimals and negative integers in your clues.

TOPIC 1 Assessment

Assess

Available Online

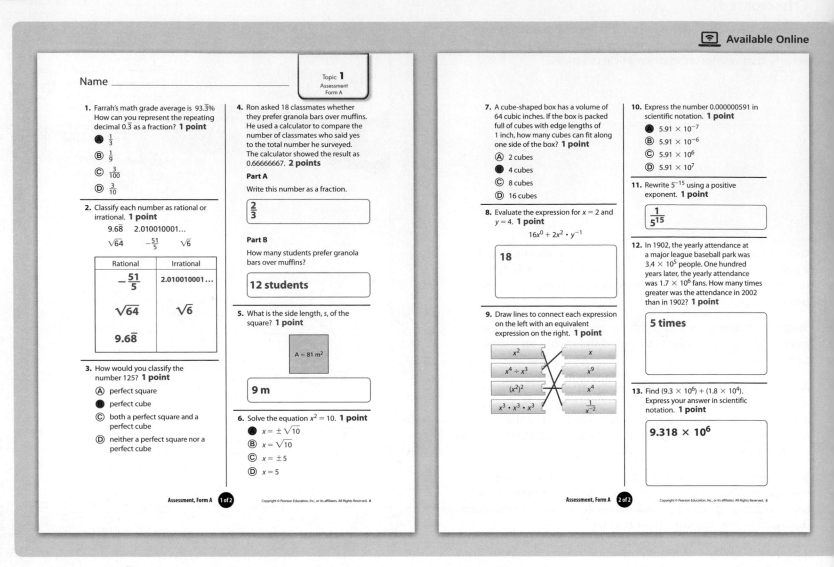

Name _____

Topic **1**
Assessment
Form A

1. Farrah's math grade average is $93.\overline{3}\%$. How can you represent the repeating decimal $0.\overline{3}$ as a fraction? **1 point**

Ⓐ $\frac{1}{3}$
Ⓑ $\frac{1}{9}$
Ⓒ $\frac{3}{100}$
Ⓓ $\frac{3}{10}$

2. Classify each number as rational or irrational. **1 point**

9.68   2.010010001...
$\sqrt{64}$ $-\frac{51}{5}$ $\sqrt{6}$

Rational	Irrational
$-\frac{51}{5}$	2.010010001...
$\sqrt{64}$	$\sqrt{6}$
$9.6\overline{8}$	

3. How would you classify the number 125? **1 point**

Ⓐ perfect square
Ⓑ perfect cube
Ⓒ both a perfect square and a perfect cube
Ⓓ neither a perfect square nor a perfect cube

4. Ron asked 18 classmates whether they prefer granola bars over muffins. He used a calculator to compare the number of classmates who said yes to the total number he surveyed. The calculator showed the result as 0.66666667. **2 points**

Part A

Write this number as a fraction.

$\frac{2}{3}$

Part B

How many students prefer granola bars over muffins?

12 students

5. What is the side length, s, of the square? **1 point**

$A = 81\ m^2$

9 m

6. Solve the equation $x^2 = 10$. **1 point**

Ⓐ $x = \pm\sqrt{10}$
Ⓑ $x = \sqrt{10}$
Ⓒ $x = \pm 5$
Ⓓ $x = 5$

Copyright © Pearson Education, Inc., or its affiliates. All Rights Reserved. 8

7. A cube-shaped box has a volume of 64 cubic inches. If the box is packed full of cubes with edge lengths of 1 inch, how many cubes can fit along one side of the box? **1 point**

Ⓐ 2 cubes
Ⓑ 4 cubes
Ⓒ 8 cubes
Ⓓ 16 cubes

8. Evaluate the expression for $x = 2$ and $y = 4$. **1 point**

$16x^0 + 2x^2 \cdot y^{-1}$

18

9. Draw lines to connect each expression on the left with an equivalent expression on the right. **1 point**

x^2		x
$x^4 \div x^3$		x^9
$(x^2)^2$		x^4
$x^3 \cdot x^3 \cdot x^3$		$\frac{1}{x^{-2}}$

10. Express the number 0.000000591 in scientific notation. **1 point**

Ⓐ 5.91×10^{-7}
Ⓑ 5.91×10^{-6}
Ⓒ 5.91×10^6
Ⓓ 5.91×10^7

11. Rewrite 5^{-15} using a positive exponent. **1 point**

$\frac{1}{5^{15}}$

12. In 1902, the yearly attendance at a major league baseball park was 3.4×10^5 people. One hundred years later, the yearly attendance was 1.7×10^6 fans. How many times greater was the attendance in 2002 than in 1902? **1 point**

5 times

13. Find $(9.3 \times 10^6) + (1.8 \times 10^4)$. Express your answer in scientific notation. **1 point**

9.318×10^6

Copyright © Pearson Education, Inc., or its affiliates. All Rights Reserved. 8

Assess students' understanding of the topic concepts and skills using the Topic Assessments found at PearsonRealize.com.

Use the Item Analysis Chart on the facing page to assign intervention to students based on their scores on the paper and pencil version of the Topic Assessments.

You may opt to have students take the Topic Assessment online at PearsonRealize.com. The online assessment is auto-scored, with differentiated intervention automatically assigned to students based on their scores.

You can use ExamView to generate additional Topic Assessments.

There are two versions of the Topic Assessment, Form A and Form B. These parallel versions assess the same content item for item. The Item Analysis chart on the next page can be used with both versions.

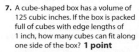
PearsonRealize.com

Assess

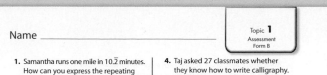

Available Online

Name _____

Topic **1**
Assessment
Form B

1. Samantha runs one mile in $10.\overline{2}$ minutes. How can you express the repeating decimal $0.\overline{2}$ as a fraction? **1 point**
- Ⓐ $\frac{1}{2}$
- Ⓑ $\frac{2}{10}$
- Ⓒ $\frac{1}{9}$
- ● $\frac{2}{9}$

2. Classify each number as rational or irrational. **1 point**

π $5.\overline{3}$ $\sqrt{36}$
$\sqrt{8}$ $-\frac{3}{7}$

Rational	Irrational
$5.\overline{3}$	π
$\sqrt{36}$	$\sqrt{8}$
$-\frac{3}{7}$	

3. How would you classify the number 121? **1 point**
- ● perfect square
- Ⓑ perfect cube
- Ⓒ both a perfect square and a perfect cube
- Ⓓ neither a perfect square nor a perfect cube

4. Taj asked 27 classmates whether they know how to write calligraphy. He used a calculator to compare the number of classmates who said yes to the total number he surveyed. The calculator showed the result as 0.1111111111. **2 points**

Part A

Write this number as a fraction.

$\frac{1}{9}$

Part B

How many students know how to write calligraphy?

3 students

5. What is the side length, s, of the square? **1 point**

$A = 169 \text{ m}^2$

13 m

6. Solve the equation $x^2 = 26$. **1 point**
- ● $x = \pm\sqrt{26}$
- Ⓑ $x = \sqrt{26}$
- Ⓒ $x = \pm13$
- Ⓓ $x = 13$

7. A cube-shaped box has a volume of 125 cubic inches. If the box is packed full of cubes with edge lengths of 1 inch, how many cubes can fit along one side of the box? **1 point**
- ● 5 cubes
- Ⓑ 10 cubes
- Ⓒ 25 cubes
- Ⓓ 125 cubes

8. Evaluate the expression for $x = 1$ and $y = 5$. **1 point**

$16x^0 + 5x^2 \cdot y^{-1}$

17

9. Draw lines to connect each expression on the left with an equivalent expression on the right. **1 point**

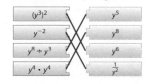

10. Express the number 3,440,000 in scientific notation. **1 point**
- Ⓐ 3.44×10^{-6}
- Ⓑ 3.44×10^{-5}
- Ⓒ 3.44×10^5
- ● 3.44×10^6

11. Rewrite 3^{-7} using a positive exponent. **1 point**

$\frac{1}{3^7}$

12. A large oak tree has 2×10^5 leaves during its lifespan. A large forest can have about 5×10^3 oak trees. Approximately how many leaves would be in the forest during the lifespan of those trees? **1 point**

About 1,000,000,000 or 1×10^9 leaves

13. Find $(1.6 \times 10^7) + (3.8 \times 10^8)$. Express your answer in scientific notation. **1 point**

3.96×10^8

Item Analysis for Diagnosis and Intervention

Item	DOK	MDIS
1	2	L80
2	1	L80, L81
3	1	L81
4A	2	L80
4B	1	M27
5	1	L81
6	1	L81
7	2	L82, N51
8	2	L83
9	1	L83
10	1	L84
11	1	L83
12	3	L85
13	2	L85

Performance Assessment

Available Online

Name _____

Nate and Elena participate in the "Keeper for a Day" program at the zoo, where they learn about the job of a zookeeper and help with some of the responsibilities.

1. Nate weighs and measures several animals in the "Mouse House," recording the data in a table.

Animal	Treeshrew	Chinchilla
Weight (lb)	$0.\overline{4}$	$1.\overline{2}$
Length (in.)	$5.\overline{3}$	$10.08\overline{3}$

Part A

The computer database only allows Nate to enter fractions. Complete the table to show how Nate should enter the data.

2 points

Animal	Treeshrew	Chinchilla
Weight (lb)	$\frac{4}{9}$	$1\frac{2}{9}$
Length (in.)	$5\frac{1}{3}$	$10\frac{1}{12}$

Part B

Nate says that repeating decimals are rational numbers. Is Nate correct? Explain. **1 point**

> **Yes; Sample answer: The decimal expansion does repeat, so each repeating decimal can be written as the ratio of two integers.**

2. Elena needs to find a table that will fit three cube-shaped cases, each containing a frog. If the volume of each case is 1,000 cubic inches, could she use a table with a top that measures $2\frac{1}{2}$ feet long and $1\frac{1}{2}$ feet wide? Explain. **2 points**

> **Yes; Sample answer: Each edge of a case is equal to $\sqrt[3]{1000}$, or 10 inches. The minimum length of the table must be 30 inches, or $2\frac{1}{2}$ feet. The minimum width must be 10 inches, which is less than $1\frac{1}{2}$ feet.**

---

3. There are 8 elephants in the zoo. Each elephant eats about 2.16×10^5 pounds of vegetation per year. The zookeeper asked Nate and Elena to determine how many pounds of vegetation are required to feed all of the elephants. They wrote their solutions in scientific notation.

Nate's Solution	Elena's Solution
$8 \times (2.16 \times 10^5)$	$8 \times (2.16 \times 10^5)$
$= (8 \times 2.16) \times 10^5$	$= (8 \times 2.16) \times (8 \times 10^5)$
$= 17.28 \times 10^5$	$= 17.28 \times 80^5$
$= 1.728 \times 10^6$	$= 1.728 \times 80^6$

Who is correct? Explain. **2 points**

> **Nate; Sample answer: Elena mistakenly distributes 8 to both 2.16 and the power of 10. Then, she incorrectly multiplies 8×10^5.**

4. Nate is curious to learn how much elephants eat compared to the largest animal on Earth, the blue whale. He does some research and finds that a full-grown blue whale eats about 1,460,000 pounds of krill per year. Write and solve a question similar to Problem 3 about how much blue whales eat. Use scientific notation in your solution. **3 points**

> **Check students' work.**
> **Sample answer: Each blue whale eats about 1,460,000 pounds of krill per year. How much krill would 8 blue whales eat? Express your answer using scientific notation.**
> $8 \times 1.46 \times 10^6 = 11.68 \times 10^6 = 1.168 \times 10^7$

Assess students' ability to apply the topic concepts and skills using the Topic Performance Assessments found at PearsonRealize.com.

 Item Analysis for Diagnosis and Intervention

Item	DOK	MDIS
1A	1	L80
1B	2	L80
2	3	L82
3	2	L84, L85
4	4	L85

Scoring Guide		
Item	**Points**	**Topic Performance Assessment (Form A)**
1A	2	Correct answers and complete table
	1	Two or three correct answers or incomplete table
1B	1	Correct answer and explanation
2	2	Correct answer and explanation
	1	Correct answer or explanation
3	2	Correct answer and explanation
	1	Correct answer or explanation
4	3	Clearly-written question that uses specified data with correct answer and recorded work
	2	Clearly-written question that uses specified data with incomplete answer or some recorded work
	1	Incomplete or no question written, and some recorded work

🖥 **Available Online**

Name _____

Topic **1**
Performance Assessment
Form B

A middle-school art teacher, Ms. Velez, and her students are turning the school's gymnasium into a student art museum for the day.

1. Ms. Velez types a program for the event and writes:
   The most popular art museum in the world, the Louvre, has approximately 9,300,000 visitors each year. About 1,900,000 of those visitors are young people age 18 to 25. **1 point**

   Part A
   How would you write the two numbers above in scientific notation?

   > 9.3×10^6; 1.9×10^6

   Part B
   Approximately what percent of visitors to the Louvre are young people? Express your answer in scientific notation. Show your work. **1 point**

   > About 20%; $1.9 \times 10^6 \div 9.3 \times 10^6 =$
   > $(1.9 \div 9.3) \times (10^6 \div 10^6) \approx 0.204$

2. For his art project, Dorian is using square tiles of different sizes and colors to make a mosaic. The first three tiles are shown below.

   Part A
   Which tile's side lengths will Dorian need to estimate? Explain. **2 points**

   Tile 1 — $A = 5\ cm^2$ Tile 2 — $A = 7\ cm^2$ Tile 3 — $A = 9\ cm^2$

   > Tiles 1 and 2; Sample answer: Dorian will need to estimate $\sqrt{5}$ and $\sqrt{7}$ because they are irrational numbers.

   Part B
   Find and plot the value of each side length on the number line. **2 points**

   $\sqrt{5}$ $\sqrt{7}$ $\sqrt{9}$
   2 2.1 2.2 2.3 2.4 2.5 2.6 2.7 2.8 2.9 3

   Performance Assessment, Form B **1 of 2** Copyright © Pearson Education, Inc., or its affiliates. All Rights Reserved. 8

3. Alysha's exhibit is about photography. She displays photos of a moving roller coaster using three different exposure times. Exposure time is the interval during which a camera's sensor collects light to capture an image.

   Part A
   Rewrite each exposure time in the table using a positive exponent. **1 point**

	Image 1	Image 2	Image 3
Exposure Time (seconds)	$2^{-5} = \dfrac{1}{2^5}$	$5^{-3} = \dfrac{1}{5^3}$	$10^{-4} = \dfrac{1}{10^4}$

   Part B
   Alysha explains how a shorter exposure time reduces the blurriness of an image. Based on her explanation, which image would you expect to be the least blurry? Explain. **1 point**

   > Image 3; Sample answer: It has the shortest exposure time, $\dfrac{1}{10,000}$ second.

4. Finn designs a sculpture that he wants to display on stacked cubes. If his sculpture is 1 foot tall, what will be the total height of the display after he places the sculpture on the three stacked cubes? Explain. **2 points**

   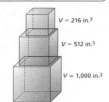
   $V = 216\ in.^3$
   $V = 512\ in.^3$
   $V = 1,000\ in.^3$

   > 36 in., or 3 ft; Sample answer: The edge lengths of the cubes are $\sqrt[3]{216} = 6$ inches; $\sqrt[3]{512} = 8$ inches; and $\sqrt[3]{1000} = 10$ inches; The total height is $6 + 8 + 10 + 12 = 36$ inches or 3 feet.

   Performance Assessment, Form B **2 of 2** Copyright © Pearson Education, Inc., or its affiliates. All Rights Reserved. 8

Assess students' ability to apply the topic concepts and skills using the Topic Performance Assessments found at PearsonRealize.com.

 Item Analysis for Diagnosis and Intervention

Item	DOK	MDIS
1A	1	L84
1B	2	L85
2A	2	L80, L81
2B	2	L80, L81
3A	2	L83
3B	3	L83
4	4	L82

	Scoring Guide	
Item	**Points**	**Topic Performance Assessment (Form B)**
1A	1	Correct expressions written in scientific notation
1B	1	Correct answer with work shown
2A	2	Correct answers and explanation
	1	One correct answer or incomplete explanation
2B	2	All points correctly labeled and plotted on number line
	1	Two points correctly labeled and plotted on number line
3A	1	All correct answers
3B	1	Correct answer and explanation
4	2	Correct answer and explanation
	1	Correct answer or explanation

Analyze and Solve Linear Equations

Math Background Focus

Solve Linear Equations

- **Inverse Operations** In Lesson 2-1, students combine like terms in equations with variables on one side of the equal sign, making it easier to solve for the unknown using inverse operations. In Lesson 2-2, students combine all like terms when solving equations with variables on both sides. They understand that inverse operations can be used to check the accuracy of an answer.
- **Compare Strategies** In Lesson 2-3, students develop multistep equations from bar diagrams and use the Distributive Property to solve the equations.
- **Simplify** In Lesson 2-4, students understand the importance of using different approaches to simplifying expressions with infinitely many, one, or no solution.

> Kelsey's amount after x weeks   Kris's amount after x weeks

$$550 - 25x = 10 + 15x + 20x$$
$$550 - 25x = 10 + 35x \quad \text{Combine like terms.}$$
$$550 - 25x + 25x = 10 + 35x + 25x$$
$$550 = 10 + 60x$$
$$550 - 10 = 10 - 10 + 60x$$
$$540 = 60x$$
$$540 \div 60 = 60x \div 60$$
$$9 = x$$

Proportional Relationships

- **Compare Proportional Relationships** In Lesson 2-5, students recognize that there are different models that can represent proportional relationships. They use various models to make comparisons between two different scenarios and give verbal descriptions of the result. In Lesson 2-6, students continue to work with proportional relationships as they review slope and how it is used to measure the steepness of a line. They use previous knowledge to find a unit rate for given scenarios.

Meera is researching cruising speeds of different planes. Which airplane has a greater cruising speed?

Cessna 310

Time (min)	5	15	30	45	60
Distance (km)	40	120	240	360	480

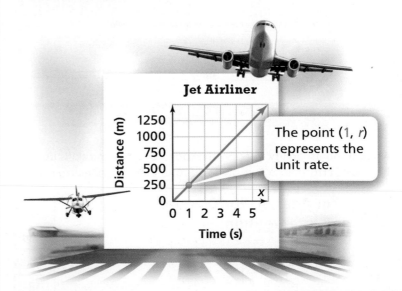

Jet Airliner

> The point $(1, r)$ represents the unit rate.

Represent Linear Equations

- **Equations** In Lesson 2-7, students relate slope to proportional relationships as they review the equation for a line passing through the origin. They write equations in the form $y = mx$ to represent given scenarios. In Lesson 2-9, students write the equation of a line in the form $y = mx + b$ to represent nonproportional relationships, substituting a value for one of the unknowns.

- **Graphs** In Lesson 2-7, students analyze and solve linear equations by plotting and graphing their solutions. In Lesson 2-8, they analyze structures needed to create models and make sense of the y-intercept. In Lesson 2-9, students graph nonproportional linear equations and write equations for a given graph.

Graph the equation $y = -4x + 3$.

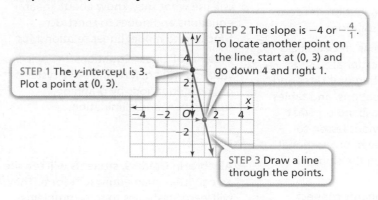

STEP 1 The y-intercept is 3. Plot a point at (0, 3).

STEP 2 The slope is -4 or $-\frac{4}{1}$. To locate another point on the line, start at (0, 3) and go down 4 and right 1.

STEP 3 Draw a line through the points.

Math Background Coherence

Students learn best when concepts are connected throughout the curriculum. This coherence is achieved within topics, across topics, across domains, and across grade levels.

Look Back

How does Topic 2 connect to what students learned earlier?

Grade 7

- **Expressions** In Grade 7, students learned to understand and write expressions by using variables to represent unknown quantities to solve problems. They used what they learned about order of operations to analyze and write equivalent expressions and solve multistep equations using the Distributive Property.

- **Proportional Relationships** In Grade 7, students learned to apply proportional reasoning to solve problems. They learned to compare ratios, written in fraction form or in tables, and compute unit rates to determine whether two quantities have a proportional relationship.

Topic 2

How is content connected within Topic 2?

- **Equations** In this topic, students collect like terms from one or both sides of an equation to solve problems using the Distributive Property and inverse operations. In Lesson 2-4, students determine whether an equation has zero, one, or infinitely many solutions.

- **Proportional Relationships** In Lesson 2-5, students compare proportional relationships by computing unit rates and using linear graphs, equations, and tables. In Lesson 2-6, students expand on what they learned in the previous lesson to make connections between proportional relationships and finding the slope of a line.

- **Slope** In Lesson 2-6, students connect the slope of a line with the unit rate in proportional relationships. In Lesson 2-7, students write and graph linear equations to describe a proportional relationship. In Lesson 2-8, students further extend their understanding of linear equations to include equations with non-zero y-intercepts. In Lesson 2-9, students learn to graph a line from an equation in the form $y = mx + b$. They learn to interpret the meaning of m and b in the linear equation.

$$\begin{array}{ccccc} \text{Total} & & \text{Hourly} & & \text{Initial} \\ \text{Cost} & = & \text{Rate} & + & \text{Fee} \\ y & = & 75x & + & 125 \end{array}$$

This equation is in **slope-intercept form**, $y = mx + b$, where m is the rate of change, or slope, and b is the initial value, or y-intercept.

Look Ahead

How does Topic 2 connect to what students will learn later?

Later in Grade 8

- **Functions** In Topic 3, students will use functions to model relationships. They will use what they know about linear equations and slopes to construct functions to model linear relationships.

- **Systems of Linear Equations** In Topic 5, students will analyze and solve systems of linear equations by graphing, substitution, and elimination.

Grade 9

- **Algebra** In Grade 9, students will rewrite an equation in an equivalent form. They will learn strategies to solve problems by manipulating complex equations into simpler equations.

- **Functions** In Grade 9, students will represent functions using graphs and algebraic expressions like $(x) = a + bx$. They will interpret functions in real-world contexts and build new functions from existing functions.

Math Background Rigor

A rigorous curriculum emphasizes conceptual understanding, procedural skill and fluency, and applications.

Conceptual Understanding

- **Understand Slope** Students understand the mathematical relationship between the equation of a line and the graph of that line. The coordinates of points on the graph can be substituted into the equation of the line to make a true statement. Students will use their understanding of ratios and proportional relationships to demonstrate how the unit rate or constant of proportionality can be used to measure the steepness of a line, or slope.
- **Solve Equations** Students will use equation-solving methods they learned previously in order to solve a variety of equations that have either zero, one, or infinitely many solutions. They will incorporate their knowledge of the Distributive Property to solve multistep equations.

  ONE WAY Draw bar diagrams to represent the perimeters. Then decompose and reorder the bar diagrams to solve for x.

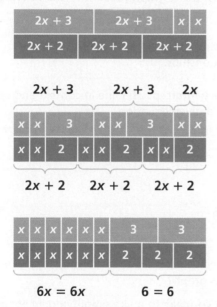

The expressions $6x = 6x$ and $6 = 6$ are true for any value of x. This equation has infinitely many solutions.

- **Representing Proportional Relationships** Students analyze equations, tables, and linear graphs to compare proportional relationships by interpreting the unit rates in context. They understand the characteristics of a graph and that the slope is the same as the constant of proportionality.

Procedural Skill and Fluency

- **Interpret Linear Equations and Slopes** In Lesson 2-2, students will become fluent in solving equations with variables on both sides by collecting like terms and using inverse operations to solve for the variable. In Lesson 2-8, students demonstrate the importance of the y-intercept in solving linear equations and understanding that in a proportional relationship the y-intercept is always 0. In Lesson 2-9, they develop procedural skills by providing the graph of a line when an equation is given or by providing the equation of a line when a graph is given.

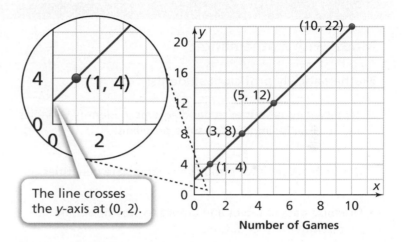

The line crosses the y-axis at (0, 2).

The y-intercept is 2. That means that the cost of shoe rental is \$2. Mathilde saves \$2 if she brings her mother's old bowling shoes.

Applications

- **Combine Like Terms** In Lesson 2-1, students apply the concept of combining like terms to simplify and solve equations involving one variable. In Lesson 2-2, students expand on the previous lesson by using models to construct and solve equations with variable terms on both sides of the equation. In Lesson 2-3, students plan different approaches using the Distributive Property to solve multistep equations. In Lesson 2-4, students solve and analyze equations to determine how many solutions they have.
- **Proportional Relationships** Throughout this topic, students apply their knowledge of ratios, unit rates, and tables to determine the relationship different quantities. They solve new problems in both mathematical and real-world contexts. In Lesson 2-7, students apply their knowledge of proportional relationships to graph linear equations in the form of $y = mx$, where m is the slope.

Math Practices

The math practices and processes describe the behaviors and thinking habits that mathematically proficient students demonstrate when actively engaged in mathematics work. Opportunities for engagement in the practices and to develop expertise with these important behaviors and thinking habits exist throughout the topic and program. Here we focus on mathematical reasoning and explanation.

As students solve problems involving linear relationships, look for these behaviors to assess and identify students who demonstrate proficiency with mathematical reasoning and explanation.

Math Practices Within Topic 2 Lessons

Model with mathematics.	Look for and make use of structure.
Mathematically proficient students:	Mathematically proficient students:
• Represent equations with bar diagrams to identify variables and to visually simplify and solve problems.	• Justify that a relationship is proportional when represented as a table, graph, or equation.
• Use both graphs and formulas to manipulate quantities.	• Use the structure of a line graph to identify and interpret its slope.
• Organize data in tables and graphs to provide visual representation of equations.	• Flexibly use tables, graphs, and equations to describe proportional relationships.
• Consider the slope and *y*-intercept of a given line and describe how it would look before graphing.	• Make sense of the *y*-intercept of a line in context and use it when graphing a given equation.

Help students become more proficient with mathematical reasoning and explanation.

If students do not understand the correlation between the constant of proportionality and the slope of the graph of the relationship, then use these questioning strategies to help them develop reasoning and explaining skills as they solve problems throughout the topic.

Q: What are some other ways to represent this situation?

Q: How can you find the slope of a line by looking at its graph?

Q: How can you decide whether two quantities are proportional by looking at a table of values?

Q: How does the slope of a line help you visualize the graph of the line?

Q: How can you decide whether a relationship is proportional by looking at its graph?

Q: What steps can you take to make simplifying an equation easier?

Q: How does the equation $y = mx$ relate to the equation $y = mx + b$?

Q: How does the *y*-intercept of a line help you draw the graph of the line?

Topic Readiness Assessment

Assess

Name _____

Topic **2**
Readiness Assessment

1. Samuel is deep-sea diving. He dives down 735 feet from the surface of the water, and then rises back up 418 feet. He then dives down another 271 feet. How far from the surface is he now?

Ⓐ −1,424 feet

Ⓑ −588 feet

Ⓒ 46 feet

Ⓓ 882 feet

2. Tina bought 15.25 gallons of gasoline at a price of $2.31 per gallon. What is the total cost of the gasoline rounded to the nearest hundredth?

Ⓐ $6.60   Ⓒ $17.56

Ⓑ $12.94   Ⓓ $35.23

3. Which expression is equivalent to $3x - \frac{1}{2}y + 2\frac{2}{3}y - \frac{5}{6}x$?

Ⓐ $2\frac{1}{6}x - 2\frac{1}{6}y$

Ⓑ $\frac{5}{6}x + 2\frac{1}{6}y$

Ⓒ $2\frac{1}{6}x + 2\frac{1}{6}y$

Ⓓ $2\frac{1}{6}x \quad \frac{5}{6}y$

4. Rayhana has a coupon for 15% off a single item at a store. If the item has a regular price of p dollars, then the sale price can be represented by $p - 0.15p$. Which expression is equivalent?

Ⓐ $0.85p$

Ⓑ $0.65p$

Ⓒ $0.15p$

Ⓓ $-0.15p$

5. Solve the equation $4(0.2x - 5) = 12$.

Ⓐ −10

Ⓑ 4

Ⓒ 13.75

Ⓓ 40

6. In Friday's volleyball game, Sam's team scored a point in 16.5% of his serves. Which of the following statements is true?

Ⓐ The team scored in more than $\frac{1}{6}$ of Sam's serves.

Ⓑ The team scored in less than $\frac{1}{10}$ of Sam's serves.

Ⓒ The team scored in exactly $\frac{1}{7}$ of Sam's serves.

Ⓓ The team scored in more than $\frac{1}{8}$ of Sam's serves.

7. Which table could represent a proportional relationship?

Ⓐ
x	1	2	5	11
y	1,300	2,600	6,500	14,300

Ⓑ
x	1	2	5	11
y	1,150	2,250	4,500	12,300

Ⓒ
x	1	2	5	11
y	900	1,800	3,500	7,640

Ⓓ
x	1	2	5	11
y	950	1,900	4,500	11,200

8. Angie drives a horse and buggy in the park. She charges a flat rate for each ride. Which graph could represent her earnings?

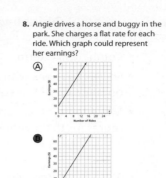

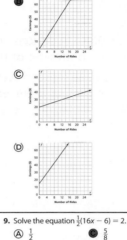

9. Solve the equation $\frac{1}{2}(16x - 6) = 2$.

Ⓐ $\frac{1}{2}$ Ⓒ $\frac{5}{8}$

Ⓑ $\frac{3}{5}$ Ⓓ $\frac{7}{10}$

10. The post office is 0.15 mile from Abdul's house. His school is $\frac{3}{8}$ mile from the post office. If Abdul stops at the post office on his way to school, how far will Abdul walk in all?

Ⓐ 0.15 mile

Ⓑ 0.225 mile

Ⓒ 0.375 mile

Ⓓ 0.525 mile

11. The audio-visual technician for a hotel ordered 4 boxes of microphone cords. There are 12 cords in each box. If there are now a total of 108 cords at the hotel, how many boxes of cords were there before the order?

Ⓐ 3 boxes

Ⓑ 5 boxes

Ⓒ 6 boxes

Ⓓ 8 boxes

12. Justin made 6 pounds of granola to sell at his community fair. He charges $6.35 for each $\frac{2}{3}$-pound bag of granola. How much money will Justin earn if he sells all of the granola?

Ⓐ $25.40

Ⓑ $38.10

Ⓒ $48.60

Ⓓ $57.15

 Copyright © Pearson Education, Inc., or its affiliates. All Rights Reserved. 8

 Copyright © Pearson Education, Inc., or its affiliates. All Rights Reserved. 8

Assess students' understanding of prerequisite concepts and skills using the Topic Readiness Assessment found at PearsonRealize.com.

 You may opt to have students take the Topic Readiness Assessment online.

RtI ## Item Analysis for Diagnosis and Remediation

Item	DOK	MDIS
1	2	L70, L74, L75
2	2	L64
3	1	K18, L56
4	2	K18, L77, L78
5	1	K26, K32
6	3	M38
7	2	M33
8	2	M33, K52
9	2	K32, K29
10	1	L77
11	2	K25
12	2	L79

Topic Planner

Analyze and Solve Linear Equations

Lesson	Vocabulary	Objective	Essential Understanding
2-1 Combine Like Terms to Solve Equations	none	• Combine like terms. • Solve equations with like terms on one side of the equation. • Make sense of scenarios and represent them with equations.	Combining like terms that are on one side of an equation makes it easier to solve for the variable by using inverse operations.
2-2 Solve Equations with Variables on Both Sides	none	• Solve equations with like terms on both sides of the equation. • Make sense of scenarios and represent them with equations.	To solve a linear equation that has variable terms on both sides of the equation, first use inverse operations to move all variable terms to one side of the equation and constant terms to the other. Then, isolate the variable.
2-3 Solve Multistep Equations	none	• Plan multiple solution pathways and choose one to find the solution.	The Distributive Property is an important tool for simplifying expressions and combining like terms.
2-4 Equations with No Solutions or Infinitely Many Solutions	none	• Determine the number of solutions to an equation.	Equations with one variable can have zero, one, or infinitely many solutions.
3-Act Mathematical Modeling: Powering Down	none		

Lesson Resources

 Digital

Student's Edition

Additional Practice workbook

 Print

Teaching Resources
- Reteach to Build Understanding
- Additional Vocabulary Support
- Build Mathematical Literacy
- Enrichment

Assessment Resources
- Lesson Quiz

 Digital

Digital Lesson Courseware
- Today's Challenge
- Visual Learning Animation Plus
- Key Concept
- Additional Examples
- 3-Act Mathematical Modeling
- Online Practice powered by MathXL for School

- Virtual Nerd Video Tutorials
- Animated Glossary
- Digital Math Tools
- Online Math Games

Lesson Support for Teachers
- Listen and Look For PD Lesson Video

The suggested pacing for each lesson is 2 days for a 45-minute math class and 1 day for a 90-minute class.

Lesson	Vocabulary	Objective	Essential Understanding
2-5 Compare Proportional Relationships	none	• Analyze equations, linear graphs, and tables to find unit rates and compare proportional relationships.	Proportional relationships can be represented using different models, including graphs, tables, and equations.
2-6 Connect Proportional Relationships and Slope	slope	• Find the slope of a line using different strategies. • Interpret a slope in context and relate it to steepness on a graph.	Slope is a measure of the steepness of a line and is equal to the rate of change between quantities. In a proportional relationship, slope is the same as the unit rate and the constant of proportionality.
2-7 Analyze Linear Equations: $y = mx$	none	• Understand how the constant of proportionality and the slope relate in a linear equation. • Write a linear equation in the form $y = mx$ when the slope is given. • Graph a linear equation in the form $y = mx$.	The slope, constant of proportionality, and unit rate are equal for proportional relationships.
2-8 Identify the y-intercept of a Line	y-intercept	• Interpret and extend the table or graph of a linear relationship to find its y-intercept. • Analyze graphs in context to determine and explain the meaning of the y-intercept.	The y-intercept of a line is the y-coordinate of the point where the graph of the line crosses the y-axis. Its meaning depends on the context of the graph.
2-9 Analyze Linear Equations: $y = mx + b$	slope-intercept form	• Graph a line from an equation in the form $y = mx + b$. • Write an equation that represents the given graph of a line.	The slope-intercept form for a linear equation, $y = mx + b$, gives information to sketch a graph of the line. It indicates that the point $(0, b)$ is on the graph of the line and shows that the slope of the line is m.

Topic Resources

Digital

Print

Student's Edition
- Review What You Know
- Build Literacy in Mathematics
- Mid-Topic Checkpoint and Performance Task
- Topic Review
- Fluency Practice Activity
- STEM Project

Assessment Resources
- Topic Readiness Assessment
- Mid-Topic Assessment
- Topic Assessment
- Topic Performance Task

Digital

Topic Support for Students
- Math Practice Animations
- STEM Project
- 3-Act Mathematical Modeling Lesson

Topic Support for Teachers
- Topic Overview Video
- ExamView Test Generator

Analyze and Solve Linear Equations

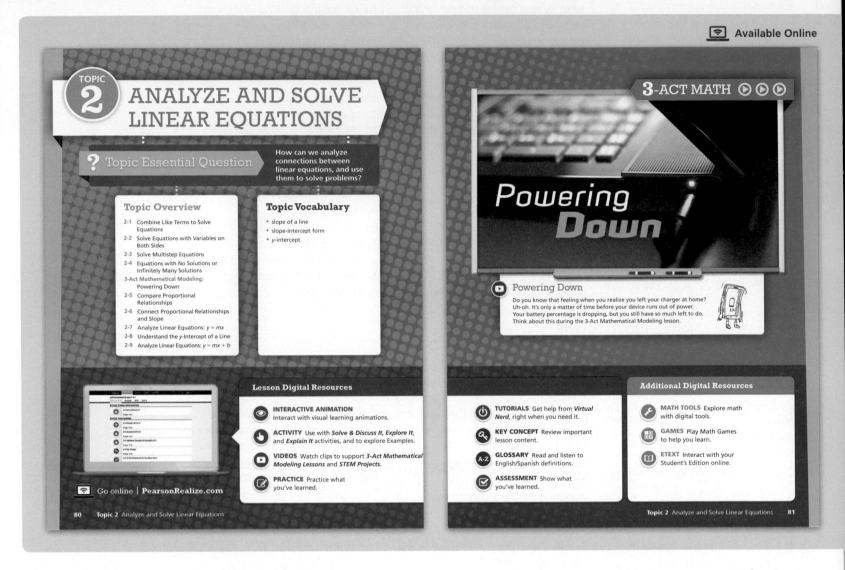

Topic Essential Question

How can we analyze connections between linear equations and use them to solve problems?

Revisit the Topic Essential Question throughout the topic. See the Teacher's Edition for the Topic Review for notes about answering the questions.

3-Act Mathematical Modeling

Have students read about the Math Modeling lesson for this topic. You can use the preview for this lesson to get students interested in learning the content of the topic.

The Mathematical Modeling in 3 Acts lesson appears after Lesson 4.

TOPIC 2 STEM Project

Modeling Population Growth

Project Overview

In this project, students will explore the science of demography. They will explore how birth rate, death rate, emigration, and immigration affect population growth. Students will analyze how changes in these indicators affect resource sustainability and how resource availability affects population growth.

What's the Math?

Students write linear equations in the form $y = mx + b$ to represent the population growth. They will use the equation to predict the population many years in the future. Students will analyze how the linear equation changes as the data changes.

What's the Science?

Students use mathematical representations to represent population growth and to support arguments about how the changes in population are affected by resource availability and sustainability. They will also analyze how these effects may differ for different communities.

What's the Engineering and Technology?

Students think like engineers as they gather, analyze, synthesize, and present data in clear and understandable ways. They recognize how technologies vary from region to region and how this impacts resource availability and population growth.

Introducing the Project

Present the project by having students discuss what they know about population growth. The questions below can be used to guide the discussion.

Q: What factors influence population growth? [Sample answer: birth rate, death rate, and immigration]

Q: Why is demography an important science? [Sample answer: Understanding the changes in populations allows for planning needed resources.]

Q: What are some reasons for emigration? [Sample answer: People may emigrate due to a lack of resources, natural disasters, and access to job opportunities, affordable housing, quality, and educational opportunities.]

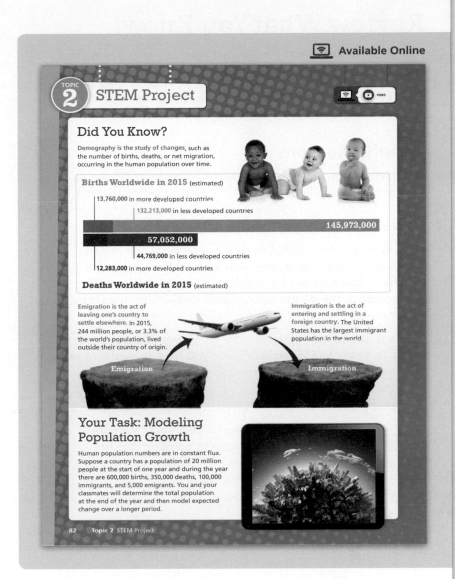

Available Online

TOPIC 2 STEM Project

Did You Know?

Demography is the study of changes, such as the number of births, deaths, or net migration, occurring in the human population over time.

Births Worldwide in 2015 (estimated)

13,760,000 in more developed countries

132,213,000 in less developed countries

145,973,000

57,052,000

44,769,000 in less developed countries

12,283,000 in more developed countries

Deaths Worldwide in 2015 (estimated)

Emigration is the act of leaving one's country to settle elsewhere. In 2015, 244 million people, or 3.3% of the world's population, lived outside their country of origin.

Immigration is the act of entering and settling in a foreign country. The United States has the largest immigrant population in the world.

Emigration   Immigration

Your Task: Modeling Population Growth

Human population numbers are in constant flux. Suppose a country has a population of 20 million people at the start of one year and during the year there are 600,000 births, 350,000 deaths, 100,000 immigrants, and 5,000 emigrants. You and your classmates will determine the total population at the end of the year and then model expected change over a longer period.

82   Topic 2 STEM Project

Q: How can you represent the population growth rate mathematically? [Sample answer: The ratio of population change to starting population can be used to represent the growth rate.]

You can launch this project any time after Topic 2 Lesson 5.

 Show the Topic 2 STEM video to generate interest in the project.

Teacher resources that provide students with project details and support are available at PearsonRealize.com.

Get Ready!

Review What You Know!

Assign the Review What You Know to activate prior knowledge and practice the prerequisite skills needed for success in this topic.

Encourage students to work independently or with a partner. Use these questioning strategies to help them get started.

Identify Like Terms

Q: What strategy can you use to identify like terms? [Sample answer: Match all the terms that have the same variable.]

Solve One-Step Equations

Q: How do you know what inverse operation to use in each question? [Sample answer: You look at the variable and see what is being done to it. If you're multiplying the variable by a constant, the inverse operation is to divide both sides by that constant.]

Q: What do you have to remember whenever you are operating on an equation? [Sample answer: You have to do the same thing to both sides of the equation.]

Simplify Fractions

Q: In what situations can it be helpful to simplify fractions? [Sample answer: To find unit rates or constant rate of proportionality]

 ### Item Analysis for Diagnosis and Remediation

Item	MDIS
1	K16
2	K13
3	M31
4	K22
5–6	K16
7–9	K23–K25
10	L4, M9

Vocabulary Review

You may choose to strengthen vocabulary with the following activity.

- Have students work in pairs to share two things they already know about each vocabulary term. Ask each pair in turn to write one of their ideas on the board, grouped by vocabulary word, until there are no more new ideas to share.

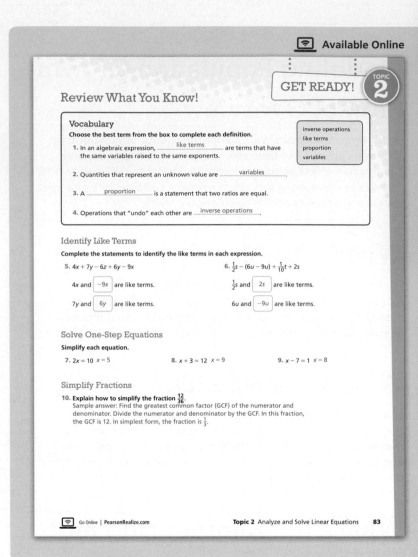

Available Online

Review What You Know!

Vocabulary
Choose the best term from the box to complete each definition.

> inverse operations
> like terms
> proportion
> variables

1. In an algebraic expression, ___like terms___ are terms that have the same variables raised to the same exponents.

2. Quantities that represent an unknown value are ___variables___.

3. A ___proportion___ is a statement that two ratios are equal.

4. Operations that "undo" each other are ___inverse operations___.

Identify Like Terms
Complete the statements to identify the like terms in each expression.

5. $4x + 7y - 6z + 6y - 9x$

$4x$ and $-9x$ are like terms.

$7y$ and $6y$ are like terms.

6. $\frac{1}{2}s - (6u - 9u) + \frac{1}{16}t + 2s$

$\frac{1}{2}s$ and $2s$ are like terms.

$6u$ and $-9u$ are like terms.

Solve One-Step Equations
Simplify each equation.

7. $2x = 10$ $x = 5$

8. $x + 3 = 12$ $x = 9$

9. $x - 7 = 1$ $x = 8$

Simplify Fractions
10. **Explain how to simplify the fraction $\frac{12}{36}$.**
Sample answer: Find the greatest common factor (GCF) of the numerator and denominator. Divide the numerator and denominator by the GCF. In this fraction, the GCF is 12. In simplest form, the fraction is $\frac{1}{3}$.

Go Online | PearsonRealize.com   **Topic 2** Analyze and Solve Linear Equations   83

GET READY! TOPIC 2

Prepare for Reading Success

Pre-reading Strategy: Outline

Have students preview lesson content and complete the table in order to build understanding of concepts covered in this topic.

Q: How does the table help you prepare for the lesson to come? [Sample answer: When you write down questions based on concepts you're not sure about, you can be ready to ask them when they come up in class.]

Q: Which column is used to express prior knowledge? [What I Know column]

Encourage students to recognize the continued benefits of using the information in the table to develop understanding of Topic 2.

Q: In what other ways can this table help with your success throughout this topic? [Sample answer: The table can also be used to review each lesson, and you can record answers to the questions you had.]

Encourage student to list additional questions and answers that they may have as they progress through each lesson.

Extension for All Readers

Challenge students to use their completed table to identify correlations among lessons. Help them develop a strong conceptual understanding by encouraging them to sort any similarities by concepts covered.

Available Online

Prepare for Reading Success

Before beginning each lesson, preview its content. Write what you already know about the lesson in the second column. In the third column, write a question that you want answered about the lesson. After the lesson, complete the fourth column with the answer to your question.

Lesson	What I Know	Questions I Have	Answer
2-1			
2-2			
2-3			
2-4			
2-5			
2-6			
2-7			
2-8			
2-9			

84   **Topic 2** Analyze and Solve Linear Equations   Go Online | **PearsonRealize.com**

Lesson 2-1

Combine Like Terms to Solve Equations

Video   Activity

Lesson Overview

Objective

Students will be able to:

✔ combine like terms.

✔ solve equations with like terms on one side of the equation.

✔ make sense of scenarios and represent them with equations.

Essential Understanding

Combining like terms that are on one side of an equation makes it easier to solve for the variable by using inverse operations.

In Grade 7, students:

• used variables to represent quantities.

• created simple equations to solve problems.

In this lesson, students:

• combine like terms.

• solve one- and two-step equations.

Later in this topic, students will:

• solve equations with variable terms on both sides of the equation.

This lesson emphasizes a blend of **procedural skill and fluency** and **application**.

• Students will use reasoning and planning to solve equations with like terms by combining like terms and using inverse operations to isolate the variable.

Math Anytime

Today's Challenge

Use the Topic 2 problems any time during this topic.

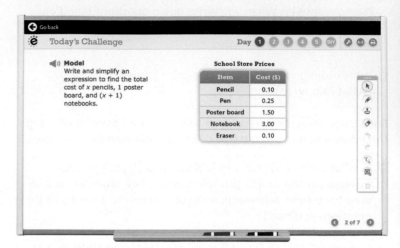

Watch the **Listen and Look For Video** for strategies and habits of mind to look for as students complete work on this lesson.

✓ Mathematics Overview

In this lesson, students will combine like terms on one side of the equal sign in equations with variables, making it easier to solve for the unknown. By using inverse operations, students will isolate the variable to solve the equation.

Applying Math Practices

Make Sense and Persevere
Throughout this lesson, students will examine problems to determine their meaning, model problems with equations, and identify and combine like terms in an equation. Students will explain the correspondence between equations and diagrams to understand the relationship of like terms.

Look for and Make Use of Structure
Students will use the structure of equations to solve problems. They will use inverse operations to find the solution after combining like terms.

STEP 1 | Develop: Problem-Based Learning

15-20 min

Activity

Explore It!

Model with Math As students work through the *Explore It*, listen and look for students who group the boxes together as like terms and apply equation-solving methods to determine the price of each laptop.

Before [WHOLE CLASS]

1 Implement Tasks that Promote Reasoning and Problem Solving

Q: How would you describe the problem in your own words? [Sample answer: A superintendent purchased some laptops for 2 schools. The total cost of the laptops is $7,500. How much does one laptop cost?]

2 Build Understanding

Q: Did each laptop cost the same amount? Why is that important? [Sample answer: It looks like the laptops are identical and would each cost the same. If they cost the same it will be easier to find the cost of one computer.]

During [SMALL GROUP]

3 Support Productive Struggle in Learning Mathematics

Q: How could you use a variable expression to show the cost of the laptops in the middle stack? [Sample answer: The middle stack has 4 laptops, so I could write 4L for their cost.]

Q: How can you use your drawing to help write an equation? [Sample answer: My drawing shows 10 total computers costing $7,500. I set up an equation, $7,500 = 10L.]

After [WHOLE CLASS]

4 Facilitate Meaningful Mathematical Discourse

Ask students to share their solutions. If needed, project Oscar's and Ani's work and ask:

Q: What is similar about Oscar's and Ani's work? [Sample answer: They both used a model that showed a total of 10 laptops.]

Q: What is different about Oscar's and Ani's work? [Sample answer: Oscar showed each laptop individually, and Ani used the variable L multiplied by the number of laptops in each stack.]

5 Transition to Visual Learning

Q: How could you use your diagram or equation to determine the cost of a laptop? [Sample answer: Both communicate that there are 10 laptops that cost $7,500. I can divide $7,500 by 10 to find the cost for each laptop.]

6 Extension for Early Finishers

Q: Suppose another school district ordered a different kind of laptop for its middle schools. There are 5 middle schools that each received 7 laptops. The bill for the middle schools is $14,875. How much did each laptop cost? [$425]

Analyze Student Work

📡 Available Online

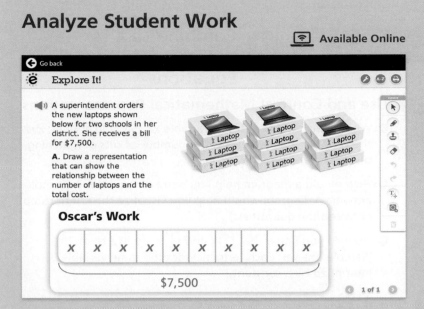

Oscar's Work

$7,500

Oscar uses x to represent the cost of each of the 10 laptops.

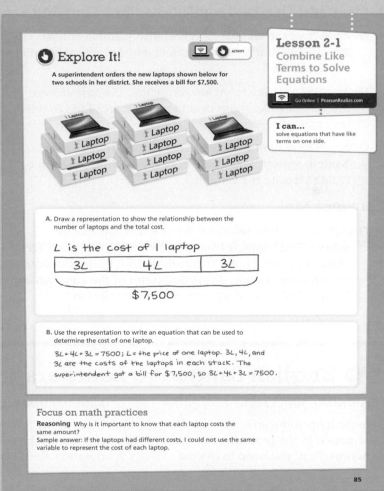

Ani uses L to represent the cost of each laptop and multiplies to show the cost of the laptops in each stack.

STEP 2 | Develop: Visual Learning

ETP **Establish Mathematics Goals to Focus Learning**

Engage students in a discussion about the *Essential Question*. Make sure students remember how to identify like terms.

EXAMPLE 1 **Combine Like Terms to Solve Addition Equations**

ETP **Use and Connect Mathematical Representations**

Q: What is the meaning of the variable x? [Sample answer: x is the variable that represents the number of sets of matching placemats and napkins.]

Q: How would a diagram help you write an equation? [Sample answer: A diagram would help you visualize the relationship between the quantities.]

Q: How do you know that $\left(\frac{8}{6}\right)x$ and $\left(\frac{1}{6}\right)x$ are like terms? [Sample answer: Each term includes the same variable, x, multiplied by a constant.]

Try It!

ETP **Elicit and Use Evidence of Student Thinking**

Q: What does the variable, s, represent? [Sample answer: s is the variable that represents the number of sets of bracelets and necklaces.]

Q: Describe how like terms are combined. [Sample answer: You combine like terms by adding $9.99s$ and $7.99s$ together for a sum of $17.98s$.]

Q: Which operation do you perform to isolate the variable? [Sample answer: You divide both sides of the equation by 17.98 to isolate the variable.]

Convince Me!

Q: Explain how you would solve this equation. [Sample answer: First combine like terms by adding $9.99s$ and $7.99s$, which results in $17.98s$. Then subtract 4.6 from both sides of the equation. Finally, divide both sides of the equation by 17.98 to isolate s, which determines the solution.]

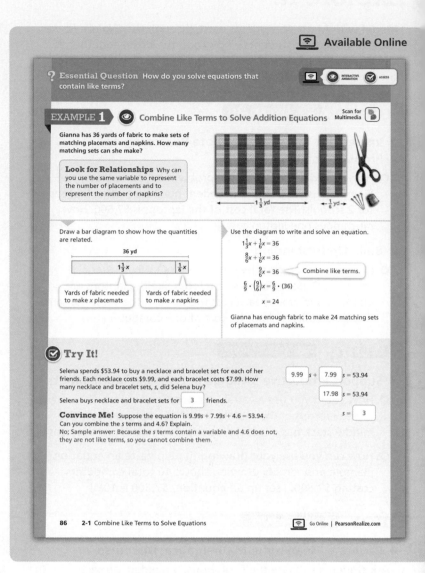

Available Online

? Essential Question How do you solve equations that contain like terms?

EXAMPLE 1 Combine Like Terms to Solve Addition Equations
Scan for Multimedia

Gianna has 36 yards of fabric to make sets of matching placemats and napkins. How many matching sets can she make?

Look for Relationships Why can you use the same variable to represent the number of placements and to represent the number of napkins?

$1\frac{1}{3}$ yd $\frac{1}{6}$ yd

Draw a bar diagram to show how the quantities are related.

36 yd

$1\frac{1}{3}x$ $\frac{1}{6}x$

Yards of fabric needed to make x placemats   Yards of fabric needed to make x napkins

Use the diagram to write and solve an equation.

$1\frac{1}{3}x + \frac{1}{6}x = 36$

$\frac{8}{6}x + \frac{1}{6}x = 36$

$\frac{9}{6}x = 36$ Combine like terms.

$\frac{6}{9} \cdot \left(\frac{9}{6}\right)x = \frac{6}{9} \cdot (36)$

$x = 24$

Gianna has enough fabric to make 24 matching sets of placemats and napkins.

Try It!

Selena spends $53.94 to buy a necklace and bracelet set for each of her friends. Each necklace costs $9.99, and each bracelet costs $7.99. How many necklace and bracelet sets, s, did Selena buy?

9.99 $s +$ 7.99 $s = 53.94$

17.98 $s = 53.94$

Selena buys necklace and bracelet sets for 3 friends.

$s =$ 3

Convince Me! Suppose the equation is $9.99s + 7.99s + 4.6 = 53.94$. Can you combine the s terms and 4.6? Explain.
No; Sample answer: Because the s terms contain a variable and 4.6 does not, they are not like terms, so you cannot combine them.

86   2-1 Combine Like Terms to Solve Equations   Go Online | PearsonRealize.com

Students can access the *Visual Learning Animation Plus* by using the **BouncePages app** to scan this page. Students can download the app for free in their mobile devices' app store.

ELL English Language Learners

BEGINNING See Example 1.

Help students summarize the necessary information in the problem with these sentences: First, you need to use the _____ property to rewrite $1\frac{1}{3}x + \frac{1}{6}x$ as $\left(1\frac{1}{3} + \frac{1}{6}\right)x$. Then you need to _____ $1\frac{1}{3}$ and $\frac{1}{6}$. Then, you will solve for x by multiplying both sides of the equation by the _____ of _____. Have students show their work. (Sample answers: distributive, add, reciprocal, $\frac{3}{2}$)

INTERMEDIATE See Example 1.

Have students reread the problem and summarize the known information and the question aloud. Ask students to share their summaries. Students should explain the meaning of the variable, how they know the two fabric quantities can be combined, and how to solve for the variable.

ADVANCED See Example 1.

Have students reread the problem and then rewrite it, shortening it to include only the necessary information. Have students edit each other's work to further shorten the summary.

Q: Read your summaries aloud. Which ones are accurate and concise?

Q: Write an equation to model this problem. How do you solve the equation? [$\frac{9x}{6} = 36$; Sample answer: Multiply each side by $\frac{6}{9}$ to find $x = 24$.]

PearsonRealize.com

Activity   Assess

XAMPLE 2 Combine Like Terms to Solve Subtraction Equations

TP Pose Purposeful Questions

Q: How does the diagram help you write an equation for this problem? [Sample answer: The diagram shows how to visualize the relationship between the discount, the original price, and the sale price.]

Q: When combining like terms, why does $p - 0.35p$ become $0.65p$? Explain. [Sample answer: p is actually $1p$. When you subtract $1p - 0.35p$ the difference is $0.65p$.]

Try It!

TP Elicit and Use Evidence of Student Thinking

Q: Why does it make sense that your answer is greater than $150? [Sample answer: Nat got a 5% discount, which means he paid less than the cost before the discount.]

XAMPLE 3 Combine Like Terms with Negative Coefficients to Solve Equations

TP Pose Purposeful Questions

Q: How do you combine the like terms in this equation? [Sample answer: Remember the method for subtracting positive integers from negative integers: add the absolute values of the numbers and keep the negative sign.]

Q: Why would it make sense for your answer to be positive? [Sample answer: When you divide a negative number by a negative number, the quotient is positive.]

Try It!

TP Elicit and Use Evidence of Student Thinking

Q: How can you tell if your answer is correct? [Sample answer: Substitute the value for the variable into the initial equation to check for accuracy.]

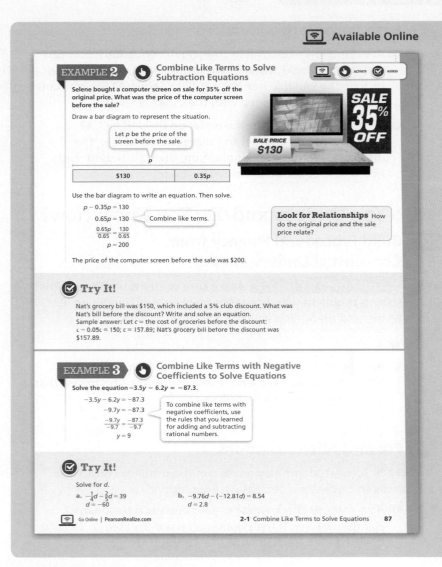

Available Online

EXAMPLE 2 Combine Like Terms to Solve Subtraction Equations

Selene bought a computer screen on sale for 35% off the original price. What was the price of the computer screen before the sale?

Draw a bar diagram to represent the situation.

Let p be the price of the screen before the sale.

| $130 | 0.35p |

Use the bar diagram to write an equation. Then solve.

$p - 0.35p = 130$
$0.65p = 130$ — Combine like terms.
$\frac{0.65p}{0.65} = \frac{130}{0.65}$
$p = 200$

Look for Relationships How do the original price and the sale price relate?

The price of the computer screen before the sale was $200.

Try It!

Nat's grocery bill was $150, which included a 5% club discount. What was Nat's bill before the discount? Write and solve an equation.
Sample answer: Let c = the cost of groceries before the discount:
$c - 0.05c = 150$; $c = 157.89$; Nat's grocery bill before the discount was $157.89.

EXAMPLE 3 Combine Like Terms with Negative Coefficients to Solve Equations

Solve the equation $-3.5y - 6.2y = -87.3$.

$-3.5y - 6.2y = -87.3$
$-9.7y = -87.3$
$\frac{-9.7y}{-9.7} = \frac{-87.3}{-9.7}$
$y = 9$

To combine like terms with negative coefficients, use the rules that you learned for adding and subtracting rational numbers.

Try It!

Solve for d.
a. $-\frac{1}{4}d - \frac{2}{5}d = 39$
$d = -60$
b. $-9.76d - (-12.81d) = 8.54$
$d = 2.8$

 Go Online | PearsonRealize.com   2-1 Combine Like Terms to Solve Equations   87

ADDITIONAL EXAMPLES

For additional examples go to PearsonRealize.com.

RtI Response to Intervention

USE WITH EXAMPLE 3 Some students may need to review the methods for adding and subtracting integers.

Q: Explain the method for adding integers with opposite signs. [Sample answer: Subtract their absolute values and use the sign of the number with the greater absolute value.]

Q: Explain the method for subtracting integers. [Sample answer: Change subtraction to adding the opposite of the integer. Then you use the rules for adding integers. For example, subtracting negative 3 is the same as adding positive 3.]

E Enrichment

USE WITH EXAMPLE 1 Students who need a challenge can try solving equations with variables on both sides.

- Solve the equation and explain how you determined your answer.

Q: $3x + 4 = 2x - 8$ [Sample answer: $x = -12$. I subtracted $2x$ from each side and then subtracted 4 from each side.]

Q: $1.5x - 0.75x = 7 - x$ [Sample answer: $x = 4$. I added x to both sides of the equations, and then combined like terms. Then I divided each side by 1.75 to solve for x.]

KEY CONCEPT

ETP Pose Purposeful Questions

Q: Are there any like terms in the original equation? How can you tell? [Sample answer: Two of the terms, 0.8*n* and 0.6*n*, include the variable *n* so they are like terms. 42 is a constant and cannot be combined with the other terms.]

Q: Why were both sides of the equation divided by 1.4? [Sample answer: In order to isolate the variable *n*, the inverse operation of multiplication, division, is used. Each side of the equation is divided by 1.4.]

Do You Understand/Do You Know How?

ETP Build Procedural Fluency from Conceptual Understanding

? Essential Question Make sure students understand that solving problems with like terms involves first combining like terms, and then using inverse operations to solve.

ITEM 3

Q: How do you convert 0.75 to a fraction? [Sample answer: 0.75 can be read as seventy-five-hundredths. This means that $0.75 = \frac{75}{100}$, which can be reduced to $\frac{3}{4}$.]

Prevent Misconceptions

ITEM 5 Some students may not set up the problem correctly so that it demonstrates a decrease in population.

Q: How can you check whether your answer is reasonable? [Sample answer: If the population has decreased to 350,000, then the answer must have been greater than 350,000.]

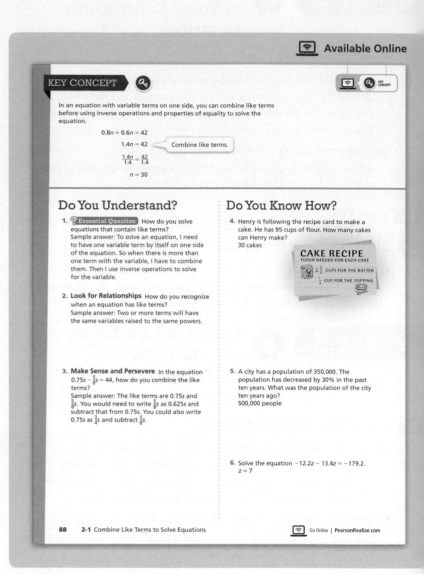

Available Online

KEY CONCEPT

In an equation with variable terms on one side, you can combine like terms before using inverse operations and properties of equality to solve the equation.

$$0.8n + 0.6n = 42$$
$$1.4n = 42 \quad \text{Combine like terms.}$$
$$\frac{1.4n}{1.4} = \frac{42}{1.4}$$
$$n = 30$$

Do You Understand?

1. **? Essential Question** How do you solve equations that contain like terms?
Sample answer: To solve an equation, I need to have one variable term by itself on one side of the equation. So when there is more than one term with the variable, I have to combine them. Then I use inverse operations to solve for the variable.

2. **Look for Relationships** How do you recognize when an equation has like terms?
Sample answer: Two or more terms will have the same variables raised to the same powers.

3. **Make Sense and Persevere** In the equation $0.75s - \frac{5}{8}s = 44$, how do you combine the like terms?
Sample answer: The like terms are 0.75s and $\frac{5}{8}$s. You would need to write $\frac{5}{8}$s as 0.625s and subtract that from 0.75s. You could also write 0.75s as $\frac{3}{4}$s and subtract $\frac{5}{8}$s.

Do You Know How?

4. Henry is following the recipe card to make a cake. He has 95 cups of flour. How many cakes can Henry make?
30 cakes

CAKE RECIPE
FLOUR NEEDED FOR EACH CAKE
$2\frac{5}{8}$ CUPS FOR THE BATTER
$\frac{1}{3}$ CUP FOR THE TOPPING

5. A city has a population of 350,000. The population has decreased by 30% in the past ten years. What was the population of the city ten years ago?
500,000 people

6. Solve the equation $-12.2z - 13.4z = -179.2$.
$z = 7$

88   2-1 Combine Like Terms to Solve Equations   Go Online | PearsonRealize.com

ADDITIONAL EXAMPLE **3**

Help students apply what they know about adding and subtracting fractions and about combining like terms with negative coefficients as they complete this additional example.

Make sure students understand how to change a negative mixed number to an improper fraction.

Q: How is changing a mixed number to an improper fraction different when the mixed numbers are negative? [Sample answer: Follow the same process as with positive mixed numbers, but keep the negative sign.]

Q: How do you combine the like terms in this equation? [Sample answer: Remember the method for subtracting positive rational numbers from negative rational numbers. Add their absolute values and keep the negative sign.]

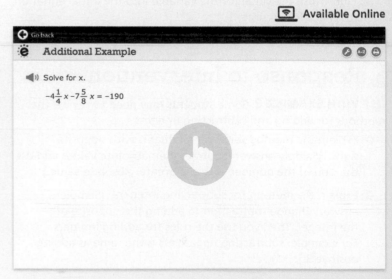

Available Online

Go back

ė Additional Example

◀) Solve for x.

$$-4\frac{1}{4}x - 7\frac{5}{8}x = -190$$

Answer: $x = 16$

Practice & Problem Solving

Practice Tutorials Math Tools

Available Online

Name: _____

Practice & Problem Solving

Scan for Multimedia

Leveled Practice In **7** and **8**, complete the steps to solve for x.

7. $\frac{4}{5}x - \frac{1}{4}x = 11$

$\boxed{\dfrac{11}{20}}x = 11$

$\boxed{\dfrac{20}{11}}\left(\boxed{\dfrac{11}{20}}x\right) = \boxed{\dfrac{20}{11}}(11)$

$x = \boxed{20}$

8. $-0.65x + 0.45x = 5.4$

$\boxed{-0.2}\,x = 5.4$

$x = \dfrac{5.4}{\boxed{-0.2}}$

$x = \boxed{-27}$

In **9–12**, solve for x.

9. $\frac{4}{9}x + \frac{1}{5}x = 87$
$x = 135$

10. $-3.8x - 5.9x = 223.1$
$x = -23$

11. $x + 0.15x = 3.45$
$x = 3$

12. $-\frac{3}{5}x - \frac{7}{10}x + \frac{1}{2}x = -56$
$x = 70$

13. A contractor buys 8.2 square feet of sheet metal. She used 2.1 square feet so far and has $183 worth of sheet metal remaining. Write and solve an equation to find out how much sheet metal costs per square foot.
$30 per square foot

14. **Make Sense and Persevere** Clint prepares and sells trail mixes at his store. This week, he uses $\frac{2}{3}$ of his supply of raisins to make regular trail mix and $\frac{1}{4}$ of his supply to make spicy trail mix. If Clint uses 20 pounds of raisins this week, how many pounds of raisins did he have at the beginning of the week?
32 pounds

15. **Make Sense and Persevere** A submarine descends to $\frac{1}{6}$ of its maximum depth. Then it descends another $\frac{2}{3}$ of its maximum depth. If it is now at 650 feet below sea level, what is its maximum depth?
780 feet below sea level

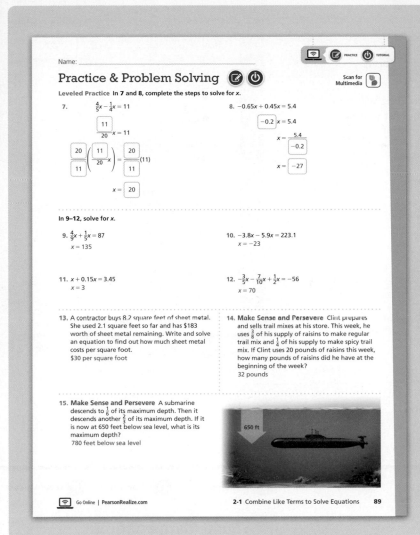

650 ft

---

16. **Model with Math** Write an equation that can be represented by the bar diagram, then solve.

-3.78	
$-1.2y$	$-4.2y$

Sample answer: $-1.2y - 4.2y = -3.78$; $y = 0.7$

17. **Higher Order Thinking** Solve $\frac{2}{3}h - 156 = 3\frac{13}{24}$.
$h = 239\frac{5}{16}$

18. **Model with Math** Nathan bought one notebook and one binder for each of his college classes. The total cost of the notebooks and binders was $27.08. Draw a bar diagram to represent the situation. How many classes is Nathan taking?
4 classes; Sample diagram:

$27.08	
$0.95x$	$5.82x$

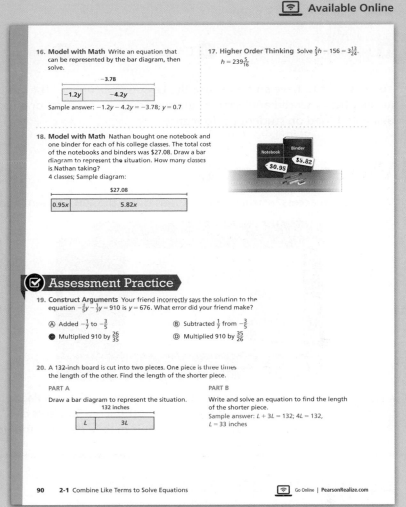

Notebook Binder $0.95 $5.82

Assessment Practice

19. **Construct Arguments** Your friend incorrectly says the solution to the equation $-\frac{2}{5}y - \frac{1}{7}y = 910$ is $y = 676$. What error did your friend make?

Ⓐ Added $-\frac{1}{7}$ to $-\frac{2}{5}$

Ⓑ Subtracted $\frac{1}{7}$ from $-\frac{2}{5}$

● Multiplied 910 by $\frac{26}{35}$

Ⓓ Multiplied 910 by $\frac{35}{26}$

20. A 132-inch board is cut into two pieces. One piece is three times the length of the other. Find the length of the shorter piece.

PART A

Draw a bar diagram to represent the situation.

132 inches	
L	$3L$

PART B

Write and solve an equation to find the length of the shorter piece.
Sample answer: $L + 3L = 132$; $4L = 132$,
$L = 33$ inches

You may opt to have students complete the automatically scored Practice & Problem Solving items online.

Error Intervention

ITEM 12 Some students may struggle when adding fractions with different denominators.

Q: What step must you perform first before combining like terms in this problem? Explain your answer. [Sample answer: You must rewrite each fraction with a common denominator because there are three fractions with different denominators. Then you can combine like terms.]

Challenge

ITEM 14 Some students may need a challenge and could begin solving equations with like terms and a constant on one side of the equation.

Q: Clint had 14 pounds of almonds at the end of the week. He used $\frac{1}{5}$ of his almonds for the regular trail mix and $\frac{1}{4}$ of his almonds for the spicy trail mix. He had to throw out 2.5 pounds of almonds that fell on the floor. How many pounds of almonds did Clint have at the start of the week? [30 pounds]

Item Analysis

Example	Items	DOK
1	9, 11	1
	14, 18, 20	2
2	7	1
	13, 17	2
3	8, 10, 12	1
	15, 16	2
	19	3

STEP 3 | Assess & Differentiate

☑ Lesson Quiz

 Use the student scores on the Lesson Quiz to prescribe differentiated assignments.

I Intervention 0–3 Points   **O** On-Level 4 Points   **A** Advanced 5 Points

You may opt to have students take the Lesson Quiz online. The Lesson Quiz will be automatically scored and appropriate remediation, practice, or enrichment will be assigned based on student performance.

⏻ Video Tutorials

Students can access instructional tutorials using the **Virtual Nerd app**.

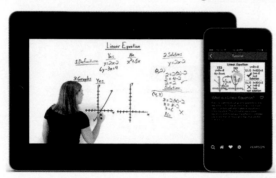

 Students can also access the videos using the **BouncePages app** to scan exercise pages marked with this icon. Students can download both apps for free in their mobile devices' app store.

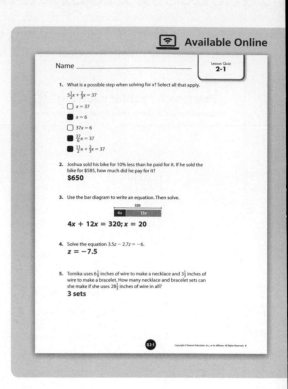

📶 **Available Online**

Name _____   Lesson Quiz 2-1

1. What is a possible step when solving for *x*? Select all that apply.

$5\frac{1}{2}x + \frac{2}{3}x = 37$

☐ $x = 37$
■ $x = 6$
☐ $37x = 6$
■ $\frac{37}{2}x = 37$
■ $1\frac{1}{2}x + \frac{2}{3}x = 37$

2. Joshua sold his bike for 10% less than he paid for it. If he sold the bike for $585, how much did he pay for it?
$650

3. Use the bar diagram to write an equation. Then solve.

320	
4x	12x

$4x + 12x = 320; x = 20$

4. Solve the equation $3.5z - 2.7z = -6$.
$z = -7.5$

5. Tomika uses $6\frac{1}{2}$ inches of wire to make a necklace and $3\frac{1}{2}$ inches of wire to make a bracelet. How many necklace and bracelet sets can she make if she uses $28\frac{1}{2}$ inches of wire in all?
3 sets

Differentiated Intervention

I = Intervention   **O** = On-Level   **A** = Advanced

Reteach to Build Understanding **I**

Provides scaffolded reteaching for the key lesson concepts.

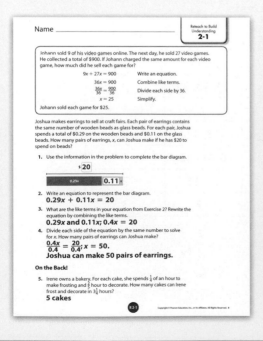

Additional Vocabulary Support **I** **O**

Helps students develop and reinforce understanding of key terms and concepts.

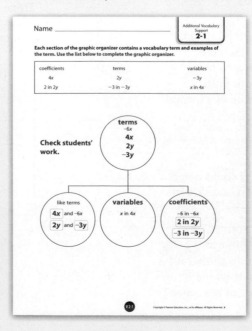

Build Mathematical Literacy **I**

Provides support for struggling readers to build mathematical literacy.

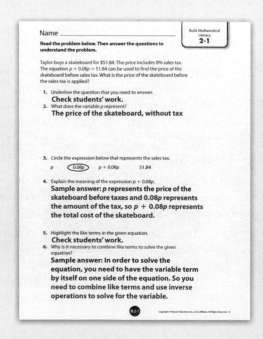

Additional Practice

You may opt to have students complete the automatically scored Additional Practice items online.

Item Analysis

Example	Items	DOK
1	1, 7, 8, 11, 12, 14	2
2	6, 9, 13	2
	10	3
3	2, 3, 4, 5	2

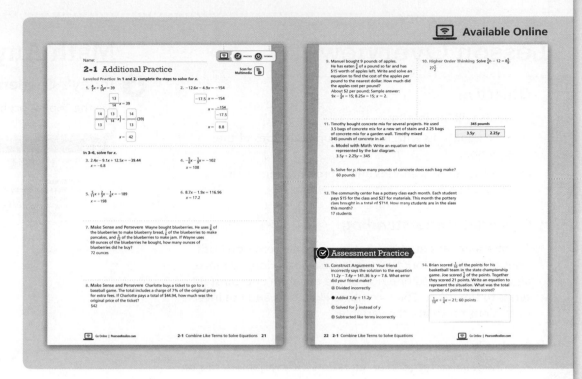

Available Online

Differentiated Intervention

I = Intervention   O = On-Level   A = Advanced

Enrichment O A

Presents engaging problems and activities that extend the lesson concepts.

Math Tools and Games I O A

Offers additional activities and games to build understanding and fluency.

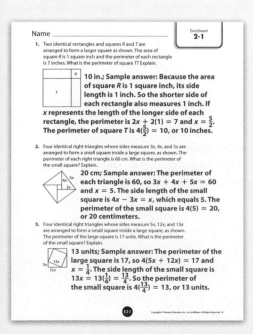

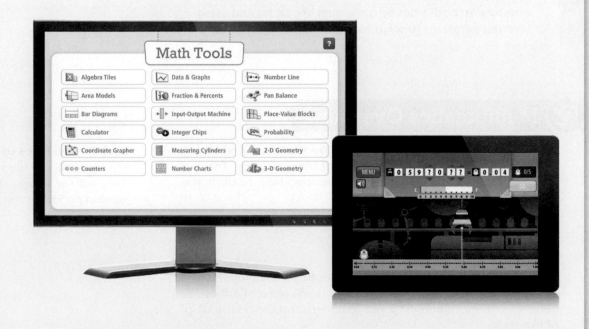

Lesson 2-2

Solve Equations with Variables on Both Sides

Lesson Overview

FOCUS

Objective

Students will be able to:

✔ solve equations with like terms on both sides of the equation.

✔ make sense of scenarios and represent them with equations.

Essential Understanding

To solve a linear equation that has variable terms on both sides of the equation, first use inverse operations to move all variable terms to one side of the equation and constant terms to the other. Then, combine like terms and use inverse operations to isolate the variable.

COHERENCE

Previously in this topic, students:

• combined like terms in an equation with variable terms on only one side of the equation.

• solved one- and two-step equations.

In this lesson, students:

• combine like terms from both sides of an equation onto one side by using inverse operations.

• solve equations to find the value of a variable.

Later in this topic, students will:

• solve multistep equations with like terms on both sides of the equation.

RIGOR

This lesson emphasizes a blend of **procedural skill and fluency** and **application**.

• Students will become fluent in solving equations with variables on both sides by combining like terms and using inverse operations to solve for the variable.

Math Anytime

Today's Challenge

Use the Topic 2 problems any time during this topic.

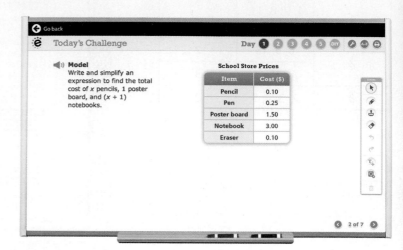

Mathematics Overview

In this lesson, students will combine all like terms when solving equations with variables on both sides of the equal sign. They will understand that they can use inverse operations to check the accuracy of an answer.

Applying Math Practices

Model with Math
Students will use diagrams and equations to build a model for a problem and find the solution. Students will use similarities between equations and diagrams to understand the relationship of like terms.

Look for and Make Use of Structure
Students will use the structure of equations to solve problems. They will use inverse operations to find the solution after combining like terms.

STEP 1 | Develop: Problem-Based Learning

15-20 min

Activity

Solve & Discuss It!

Reason Abstractly and Quantitatively As students work through the *Solve & Discuss It*, listen and look for students who make sense of the scenario and write expressions using the given information.

Before [WHOLE CLASS]

1 Implement Tasks that Promote Reasoning and Problem Solving

Q: How could you describe the money that each boy has collected? [Sample answer: Jaxson has 14 checks and $15 in cash. Bryon has 7 checks and $50 in cash.]

Q: What quantity will you represent with a variable? Explain. [Sample answer: I will use x to represent the value of each check. I can use that to determine the total amount of money.]

2 Build Understanding

Q: What is the relationship between Jaxson's earnings and Bryon's earnings? [Sample answer: The boys each collected the same amount of money.]

During [SMALL GROUP]

3 Support Productive Struggle in Learning Mathematics

Q: Would it help to create a diagram or table? Explain. [Sample answer: You could create a table of money earned and number of checks received.]

Q: What is an expression that represents the money that Jaxson earned? Explain. [Sample answer: Jaxson earned $14x + 15$. The $14x$ represents the checks, and the $+15$ is the cash he earned.]

After [WHOLE CLASS]

4 Facilitate Meaningful Mathematical Discourse

Ask students to share their solutions. If needed, project Danielle's and Vikram's work and ask:

Q: What did Danielle do that Vikram did not? [Sample answer: Danielle wrote expressions to represent each boy's earnings.]

Q: When would it be more difficult to use Vikram's strategy? [Sample answer: If a problem did not have a picture or had a situation that was too complicated for a picture]

5 Transition to Visual Learning

Q: How did Danielle combine all of her like terms? [Sample answer: She subtracted $15 from both sides to get all of the cash on one side of the equation. Then she subtracted $7x$ from both sides to get all of the checks on the other side of the equation.]

6 Extension for Early Finishers

Q: What are other combinations of checks and cash that would be equal to the amount earned by Jaxson or Bryon? [Sample answer: You could have $85 all in cash, or 1 check and $80.]

Analyze Student Work

Available Online

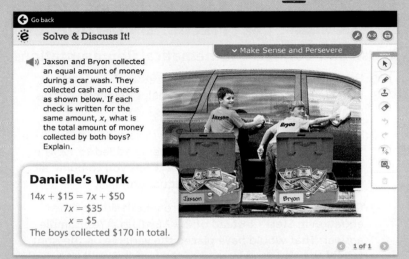

Go back

Solve & Discuss It!

Make Sense and Persevere

Jaxson and Bryon collected an equal amount of money during a car wash. They collected cash and checks as shown below. If each check is written for the same amount, x, what is the total amount of money collected by both boys? Explain.

Danielle's Work

$$14x + \$15 = 7x + \$50$$
$$7x = \$35$$
$$x = \$5$$

The boys collected $170 in total.

1 of 1

Danielle created an equation by writing an expression for each boy's earnings and setting them equal to each other. Then she combined like terms and solved for the variable.

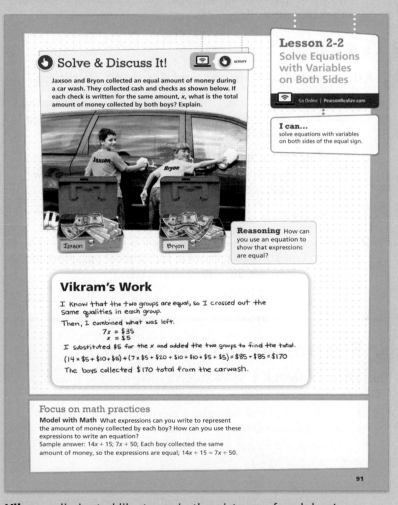

Lesson 2-2
Solve Equations with Variables on Both Sides

Go Online | PearsonRealize.com

I can...
solve equations with variables on both sides of the equal sign.

Solve & Discuss It!

Jaxson and Bryon collected an equal amount of money during a car wash. They collected cash and checks as shown below. If each check is written for the same amount, x, what is the total amount of money collected by both boys? Explain.

Reasoning How can you use an equation to show that expressions are equal?

Vikram's Work

I know that the two groups are equal, so I crossed out the same qualities in each group.
Then, I combined what was left.
$$7x = \$35$$
$$x = \$5$$
I substituted $5 for the x and added the two groups to find the total.
$$(14 \times \$5 + \$10 + \$5) + (7 \times \$5 + \$20 + \$10 + \$10 + \$5 + \$5) = \$85 + \$85 = \$170$$
The boys collected $170 total from the carwash.

Focus on math practices

Model with Math What expressions can you write to represent the amount of money collected by each boy? How can you use these expressions to write an equation?

Sample answer: $14x + 15$; $7x + 50$; Each boy collected the same amount of money, so the expressions are equal; $14x + 15 = 7x + 50$.

91

Vikram eliminated like terms in the pictures of each boy's earnings. He used what was left to write an equation and solve for the variable.

ETP Establish Mathematics Goals to Focus Learning

Engage students in a discussion about the *Essential Question*. Make sure students know how to combine like terms to one side of an equation.

EXAMPLE 1 Solve Equations with Fractional Coefficients

ETP Use and Connect Mathematical Representations

Q: How does the bar diagram help to set up the equation? [Sample answer: The bar diagram helps demonstrate the relationship between the quantities.]

Q: Why was $2\frac{1}{2}x$ subtracted from both sides of the equation in Step 1? [Sample answer: $2\frac{1}{2}x$ was being added to 12. The inverse operation of subtracting $2\frac{1}{2}x$ lets you combine all the x- terms on one side of the equation.]

Q: Could 4x have been subtracted from both sides of the equation in Step 1 instead of $2\frac{1}{2}x$? Explain. [Yes; Sample answer: That would have placed the variable on the right side of the equation instead of the left. It would have had a negative coefficient.]

Q: How could you find the number of fluid ounces in each smoothie? [Sample answer: You could substitute 4 for x on either side of the original equation and simplify.]

 Try It!

ETP Elicit and Use Evidence of Student Thinking

Q: How could you create a model that would help set up this equation? [Sample answer: A bar diagram could be used to show the relationship between the quantities.]

Q: What operations did you do to isolate the variable on one side of the equation? [Sample answer: I subtracted $3\frac{1}{4}w$ from each side, and then I subtracted 8 from each side.]

Convince Me!

Q: How do you know that your solution is correct? [Sample answer: I substituted 8 for w in the original equation and simplified it to get 36 = 36, which is true.]

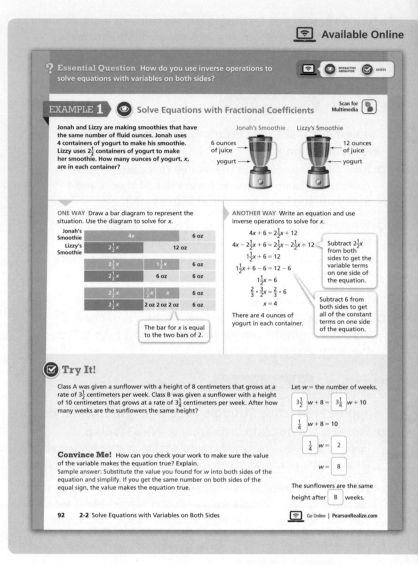

Available Online

? **Essential Question** How do you use inverse operations to solve equations with variables on both sides?

EXAMPLE 1 Solve Equations with Fractional Coefficients

Jonah and Lizzy are making smoothies that have the same number of fluid ounces. Jonah uses 4 containers of yogurt to make his smoothie. Lizzy uses $2\frac{1}{2}$ containers of yogurt to make her smoothie. How many ounces of yogurt, x, are in each container?

Try It!

Class A was given a sunflower with a height of 8 centimeters that grows at a rate of $3\frac{1}{2}$ centimeters per week. Class B was given a sunflower with a height of 10 centimeters that grows at a rate of $3\frac{1}{4}$ centimeters per week. After how many weeks are the sunflowers the same height?

Let w = the number of weeks.

$3\frac{1}{2}w + 8 = 3\frac{1}{4}w + 10$

$\frac{1}{4}w + 8 = 10$

$\frac{1}{4}w = 2$

$w = 8$

The sunflowers are the same height after 8 weeks.

Convince Me! How can you check your work to make sure the value of the variable makes the equation true? Explain.
Sample answer: Substitute the value you found for w into both sides of the equation and simplify. If you get the same number on both sides of the equal sign, the value makes the equation true.

92   2-2 Solve Equations with Variables on Both Sides   Go Online | PearsonRealize.com

 Students can access the *Visual Learning Animation Plus* by using the **BouncePages app** to scan this page. Students can download the app for free in their mobile devices' app store.

 Response to Intervention

USE WITH EXAMPLE 1 Some students may need help with addition and subtraction of fractions.

Q: How do you rewrite the mixed number $2\frac{1}{2}$ as a fraction? [Sample answer: Multiply the whole number 2 by the denominator 2 to get 4. Then add 4 to the numerator 1 to get the fraction $\frac{5}{2}$.]

Q: How do you simplify $4 - \frac{5}{2}$? [Sample answer: You rewrite 4 as a fraction with the denominator 2. Then you have $\frac{8}{2} - \frac{5}{2}$, so you subtract the numerators to get $\frac{3}{2}$.]

 Enrichment

USE WITH EXAMPLE 2 Challenge students to understand the relationship between Teresa's earnings and Brad's earnings.

• Answer the following.

Q: Who would earn more if Teresa and Brad each sold $20,000 of merchandise? Explain. [Sample answer: Teresa earns more if they both sell $20,000 because even though her weekly salary is less than Brad's, she gets a higher percentage of sales.]

Activity　Assess

XAMPLE 2 Solve Equations with Decimal Coefficients

TP Pose Purposeful Questions

Q: How can you write the percents as decimals to use in your equation? [Sample answer: Divide a percent by 100 to convert it to a decimal.]

Q: Could you solve this equation by subtracting $0.05x$ from both sides? Explain. [Yes; Sample answer: Then subtract $1,250 from both sides to get $-0.02x = -\$325$. Then divide both sides by -0.02 to get the answer $16,250.]

XAMPLE 3 Solve Equations with Negative Coefficients

TP Pose Purposeful Questions

Q: What does x represent? [Sample answer: x is the number of weeks until they have the same amount of money in their accounts.]

Q: In the first equation, why are there two terms on the right side that both include x? [Sample answer: Every week, Kris deposited both his allowance money and his money from dog walking, so each is multiplied by the number of weeks.]

Try It!

TP Elicit and Use Evidence of Student Thinking

Q: Why is it important to substitute your answer back into the original equation to check it? [Sample answer: You will probably not realize if you are making a mistake when solving the problem. Substituting the answer into the original equation will show if the answer is correct.]

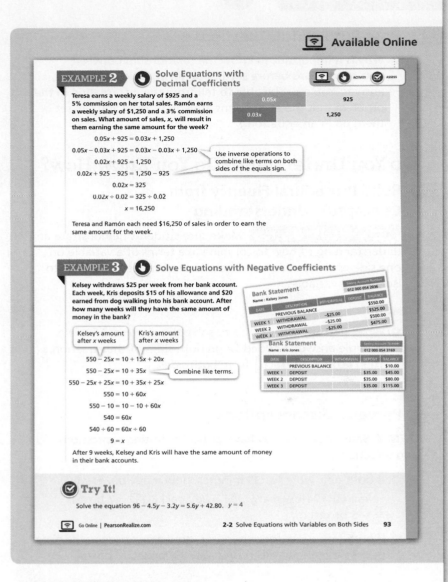

ADDITIONAL EXAMPLES

For additional examples go to PearsonRealize.com.

ELL English Language Learners

BEGINNING See Example 3.

English language learners may be unfamiliar with the vocabulary in this example. Have students relate withdrawal and deposit with the corresponding operations on the bank accounts.

Q: Look at the problem. How is a withdrawal represented in the equation? How is a deposit represented? [Sample answer: A withdrawal is shown as a negative coefficient of an x-term. A deposit is shown as a positive coefficient of an x-term.]

INTERMEDIATE See Example 3.

Have students reread the problem and summarize the known information and the question aloud. Ask students to share their summaries. Students should explain why Kelsey's and Kris's expressions are set equal to each other and how to solve for the variable.

ADVANCED See Example 3.

Have students reread the problem and then explain the steps taken to solve for the variable. Identify unknown vocabulary words and have students determine what they mean based on the context of the problem and the equation model. Have students edit each other's work to further shorten the summaries.

Q: What words were unknown and what is your definition, based on the problem context and equation model?

Q: How did you solve for the variable?

Have students share their suggestions.

Key Concept | Activity

STEP 2 | Develop: Visual Learning *continued*

KEY CONCEPT

ETP Pose Purposeful Questions

Q: Why is it important to know the relationship between two expressions before setting up an equation? [Sample answer: You must be able to tell from the information in the problem that the expressions are equal. Then you can set them up in an equation.]

Do You Understand/Do You Know How?

ETP Build Procedural Fluency from Conceptual Understanding

? Essential Question Make sure students demonstrate an understanding of how to combine like terms of a variable on one side of an equation and how to use inverse operations to isolate the variable.

ITEM 6

Q: What strategy did you use to solve this problem? Explain. [Sample answer: I added $\frac{2}{5}x$ on both sides of the equation. Then I could subtract $\frac{1}{3}$ from both sides.]

Prevent Misconceptions

ITEM 5 Some students may have difficulty writing expressions and equations.

Q: If both girls work for 35 minutes, how many boxes will Selma pack? How many will Trudy pack? [$\frac{35}{5}$ = 7 boxes, $\frac{35}{7}$ = 5 boxes]

Q: If both girls work for m minutes, how many boxes will Selma pack? How many will Trudy pack? [$\frac{m}{5}$ boxes, $\frac{m}{7}$ boxes]

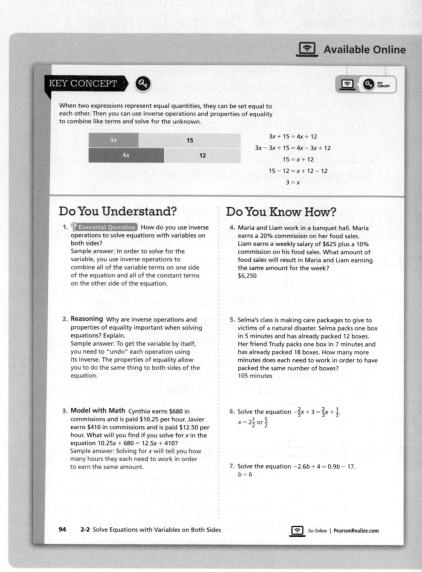

Available Online

KEY CONCEPT

When two expressions represent equal quantities, they can be set equal to each other. Then you can use inverse operations and properties of equality to combine like terms and solve for the unknown.

| $3x$ | 15 |
| $4x$ | 12 |

$3x + 15 = 4x + 12$
$3x - 3x + 15 = 4x - 3x + 12$
$15 = x + 12$
$15 - 12 = x + 12 - 12$
$3 = x$

Do You Understand?

1. **? Essential Question** How do you use inverse operations to solve equations with variables on both sides?
   Sample answer: In order to solve for the variable, you use inverse operations to combine all of the variable terms on one side of the equation and all of the constant terms on the other side of the equation.

2. **Reasoning** Why are inverse operations and properties of equality important when solving equations? Explain.
   Sample answer: To get the variable by itself, you need to "undo" each operation using its inverse. The properties of equality allow you to do the same thing to both sides of the equation.

3. **Model with Math** Cynthia earns $680 in commissions and is paid $10.25 per hour. Javier earns $410 in commissions and is paid $12.50 per hour. What will you find if you solve for x in the equation $10.25x + 680 = 12.5x + 410$?
   Sample answer: Solving for x will tell you how many hours they each need to work in order to earn the same amount.

Do You Know How?

4. Maria and Liam work in a banquet hall. Maria earns a 20% commission on her food sales. Liam earns a weekly salary of $625 plus a 10% commission on his food sales. What amount of food sales will result in Maria and Liam earning the same amount for the week?
   $6,250

5. Selma's class is making care packages to give to victims of a natural disaster. Selma packs one box in 5 minutes and has already packed 12 boxes. Her friend Trudy packs one box in 7 minutes and has already packed 18 boxes. How many more minutes does each need to work in order to have packed the same number of boxes?
   105 minutes

6. Solve the equation $-\frac{2}{5}x + 3 = \frac{2}{3}x + \frac{1}{3}$.
   $x = 2\frac{1}{2}$ or $\frac{5}{2}$

7. Solve the equation $-2.6b + 4 = 0.9b - 17$.
   $b = 6$

94 | 2-2 Solve Equations with Variables on Both Sides | Go Online | PearsonRealize.com

ADDITIONAL EXAMPLE 2

Help students interpret the problem situation and set up the equation.

Make sure students understand what the decimals mean in the context of the problem.

Q: What is another way the left side of the equation could be written? [Sample answer: $12.5x + 0.2 \cdot 12.5x$]

Q: How can you interpret the solution $x = 1.7$? [Sample answer: Tina doesn't sell fractions of items, so she must sell 2 items to pay for all of her costs.]

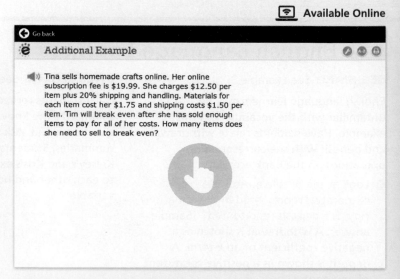

Available Online

Go back

Additional Example

Tina sells homemade crafts online. Her online subscription fee is $19.99. She charges $12.50 per item plus 20% shipping and handling. Materials for each item cost her $1.75 and shipping costs $1.50 per item. Tim will break even after she has sold enough items to pay for all of her costs. How many items does she need to sell to break even?

Answer: $x = 1.70$, so 2 items

Practice & Problem Solving

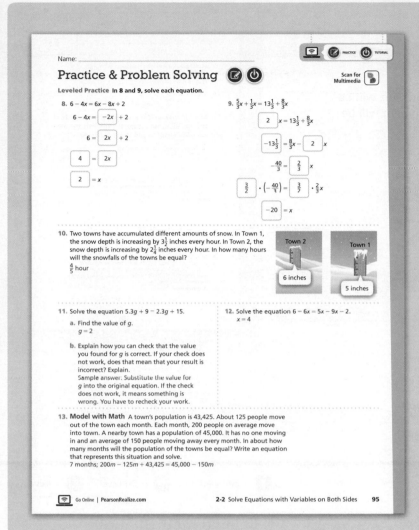

Name: _____

Practice & Problem Solving

Scan for Multimedia

Leveled Practice In **8** and **9**, solve each equation.

8. $6 - 4x = 6x - 8x + 2$

$6 - 4x = \boxed{-2x} + 2$

$6 = \boxed{2x} + 2$

$\boxed{4} = \boxed{2x}$

$\boxed{2} = x$

9. $\frac{5}{3}x + \frac{1}{3}x = 13\frac{1}{3} + \frac{8}{3}x$

$\boxed{2}x = 13\frac{1}{3} + \frac{8}{3}x$

$-13\frac{1}{3} = \frac{8}{3}x - \boxed{2}x$

$-\frac{40}{3} = \frac{2}{3}x$

$\frac{3}{2} \cdot \left(-\frac{40}{4}\right) = \frac{3}{7} \cdot \frac{2}{3}x$

$\boxed{-20} = x$

10. Two towns have accumulated different amounts of snow. In Town 1, the snow depth is increasing by $3\frac{1}{2}$ inches every hour. In Town 2, the snow depth is increasing by $2\frac{1}{4}$ inches every hour. In how many hours will the snowfalls of the towns be equal?

$\frac{4}{5}$ hour

Town 2 — 6 inches
Town 1 — 5 inches

11. Solve the equation $5.3g + 9 - 2.3g + 15$.
a. Find the value of g.
$g = 2$
b. Explain how you can check that the value you found for g is correct. If your check does not work, does that mean that your result is incorrect? Explain.
Sample answer: Substitute the value for g into the original equation. If the check does not work, it means something is wrong. You have to recheck your work.

12. Solve the equation $6 - 6x = 5x - 9x - 2$.
$x = 4$

13. **Model with Math** A town's population is 43,425. About 125 people move out of the town each month. Each month, 200 people on average move into town. A nearby town has a population of 45,000. It has no one moving in and an average of 150 people moving away every month. In about how many months will the population of the towns be equal? Write an equation that represents this situation and solve.
7 months; $200m - 125m + 43,425 = 45,000 - 150m$

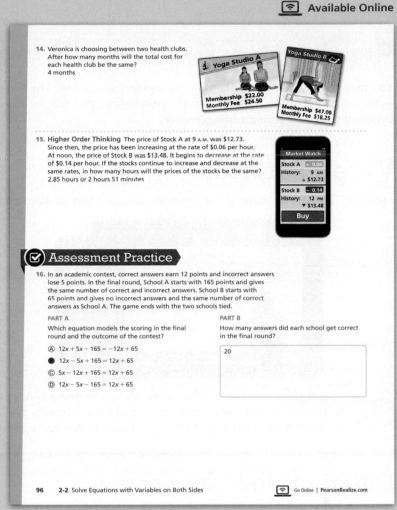

14. Veronica is choosing between two health clubs. After how many months will the total cost for each health club be the same?
4 months

Yoga Studio A — Membership Monthly Fee $22.00 $24.50
Yoga Studio B — Membership Monthly Fee $47.00 $18.25

15. **Higher Order Thinking** The price of Stock A at 9 A.M. was $12.73. Since then, the price has been increasing at the rate of $0.06 per hour. At noon, the price of Stock B was $13.48. It begins to decrease at the rate of $0.14 per hour. If the stocks continue to increase and decrease at the same rates, in how many hours will the prices of the stocks be the same?
2.85 hours or 2 hours 51 minutes

Market Watch
Stock A ▼ 0.06
History: 9 AM ▲ $12.73
Stock B ▼ 0.14
History: 12 PM ▼ $13.48
Buy

✅ Assessment Practice

16. In an academic contest, correct answers earn 12 points and incorrect answers lose 5 points. In the final round, School A starts with 165 points and gives the same number of correct and incorrect answers. School B starts with 65 points and gives no incorrect answers and the same number of correct answers as School A. The game ends with the two schools tied.

PART A
Which equation models the scoring in the final round and the outcome of the contest?

Ⓐ $12x + 5x - 165 = -12x + 65$

● $12x - 5x + 165 = 12x + 65$

Ⓒ $5x - 12x + 165 = 12x + 65$

Ⓓ $12x - 5x - 165 = 12x + 65$

PART B
How many answers did each school get correct in the final round?

20

You may opt to have students complete the automatically scored Practice & Problem Solving items online.

🔴 Error Intervention

ITEM 10 Some students are especially confused by mixed number coefficients in variable expressions and may make errors in simplification due to this confusion.

Q: Why are the expressions $6 + 3\frac{1}{2}h$ and $9\frac{1}{2}h$ not equal?
[Sample answer: The 6 is not being multiplied by the h, so you cannot combine these terms.]

Q: Could you rewrite the expression $6 + 3\frac{1}{2}h$ without any mixed numbers? Explain. [Sample answer: $6 + \frac{7}{2}h$. You can convert the mixed number to a fraction.]

🏆 Challenge

ITEM 15 Higher Order Thinking Some students can be challenged to understand the relationship between the price of the two stocks.

Q: What was the price of Stock A at noon? [$12.91]

Q: What time will the stocks be the same price? [2:51 P.M.]

Item Analysis

Example	Items	DOK
1	9	1
	10	2
2	11, 14	2
	15	3
3	8, 12	1
	13, 16	2

STEP 3 | Assess & Differentiate

Assess Tutorials Worksheets

☑ Lesson Quiz

Use the student scores on the Lesson Quiz to prescribe differentiated assignments.

I Intervention 0–3 Points **O** On-Level 4 Points **A** Advanced 5 Points

You may opt to have students take the Lesson Quiz online. The Lesson Quiz will be automatically scored and appropriate remediation, practice, or enrichment will be assigned based on student performance.

⏻ Video Tutorials

Students can access instructional tutorials using the **Virtual Nerd app**.

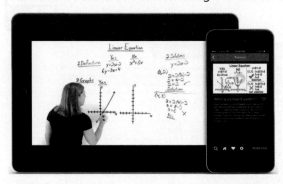

Students can also access the videos using the **BouncePages app** to scan exercise pages marked with this icon. Students can download both apps for free in their mobile devices' app store.

📶 Available Online

Name _____ Lesson Quiz 2-2

1. Moira solved a problem on the board. What error did Moira make and how can she correct it? Explain.

$$12x + 10 = 54 - 10x$$
$$12x + 10 - 10 = 54 - 10x - 10$$
$$12x = 44 - 10x$$
$$12x - 10x = 44 - 10x + 10x$$
$$2x = 44$$
$$x = 22$$

Sample answer: Moira added 10x to one side of the equation, but subtracted 10x from the other side. She needs to add 10x to each side.

2. Solve the equation $24 + 0.44x = 19 + 1.69x$.

● $x = 4$ ⓒ $x = 5$
ⓑ $x = 0.44$ ⓓ $x = 5.4$

3. A red candle is 8 inches tall and burns at a rate of $\frac{7}{10}$ inch per hour. A blue candle is 6 inches tall and burns at a rate of $\frac{1}{5}$ inch per hour. After how many hours will both candles be the same height?
4 hours

4. Solve the equation $75 - 3.5y - 4y = 4y + 6$.
$y = 6$

5. Naomi paints 16.5 square feet of a mural at a rate of 2 square feet per hour. Claire paints 7.5 square feet of the mural at a rate of 4 square feet per hour. If they continue at the same rates, how many more hours will it take for Naomi and Claire to paint an equal number of square feet?
4.5 hours

Q2-2

Differentiated Intervention

I = Intervention **O** = On-Level **A** = Advanced

Reteach to Build Understanding **I**

Provides scaffolded reteaching for the key lesson concepts.

Name _____ Reteach to Build Understanding 2-2

Rachel has saved $200 and spends $25 each week. Roy just started saving $15 per week. In how many weeks will Rachel and Roy have the same amount of money saved?

$200 - 25x = 15x$ Write an equation.
$200 - 25x + 25x = 15x + 25x$ Add 25x to both sides.
$200 = 40x$ Combine like terms.
$\frac{200}{40} = \frac{40x}{40}$ Divide both sides by 40.
$5 = x$ Simplify.

Rachel and Roy will have the same amount of money saved in 5 weeks.

Aldon and Jamal raised the same amount of money for the school fundraiser. Aldon donated $40 and sold 12 tickets for the school raffle. Jamal donated $25 and sold 15 tickets for the raffle. What was the cost of each raffle ticket?

1. Complete the bar diagram below.

Aldon $40 12x
Jamal $25 15x

2. What expression represents the total amount of money that Aldon raised?
40 + 12x

3. What expression represents the total amount of money that Jamal raised?
25 + 15x

4. Write an equation that shows that Aldon and Jamal raised the same amount of money.
40 + 12x = 25 + 15x

5. Solve your equation for x. What was the cost of each raffle ticket?
$5

On the Back!

6. Ray and Claudia are writing in journals. Ray has written 16 pages and he now writes 2 pages every day. Claudia has written only 2 pages, but she now writes 4 pages every day. In how many days will they have written the same number of pages?
7 days

R 2-2

Additional Vocabulary Support **I O**

Helps students develop and reinforce understanding of key terms and concepts.

Name _____ Additional Vocabulary Support 2-2

Use each of these words or phrases once to complete the sentences.

| coefficient | constant | equation | like terms |

1. A term that has no variable factor is a(n) **constant**.

2. In an expression, **like terms** have exactly the same variable factors.

3. A statement that two expressions are equal is a(n) **equation**.

4. When a term has a variable, the numerical factor is called the **coefficient**.

For 5–8, use the given equation to complete each sentence.

5. In the equation $0.5x - 8 = 1.5$, the decimal coefficient is **0.5**.

6. In the equation $\frac{3}{4}y + \frac{1}{2} = 3\frac{1}{4}$, the fractional coefficient is **$\frac{3}{4}$**.

7. In the equation $-2 - 6b = 32$, the negative coefficient is **-6**.

8. In the equation $5x + 9 = 3x$, **5x** and **3x** are like terms.

V 2-2

Build Mathematical Literacy **I**

Provides support for struggling readers to build mathematical literacy.

Name _____ Build Mathematical Literacy 2-2

Read the problem. Then answer the questions to identify the steps for solving the problem.

Toni and Nicky each earn a weekly salary plus commission selling eyeglass frames. Toni earns a weekly salary of $800 plus a 7% commission on her weekly sales. Nicky earns a weekly salary of $600 plus a 9% commission on her weekly sales. What number of eyeglass frames sold will result in Toni and Nicky earning the same amount for the week?

1. Circle the words that describe Toni's weekly earnings. Underline the words that describe Nicky's weekly earnings.
Check students' work.

2. What is the first step in writing an equation to solve the problem?
Sample answer: Define a variable to represent the amount of weekly sales for which Toni's and Nicky's total earnings will be the same.

3. Can you use the same variable to represent the unknown amount of sales for both Toni and Nicky? Explain.
Yes; The variable represents a single amount of weekly sales for which Toni's and Nicky's total earnings are the same.

4. Circle the expressions that represent Toni's total earnings and Nicky's total earnings for a week in which their weekly sales is x.

$600 + 9x$ and $800 + 7x$ (600 + 0.09x and 800 + 0.07x)
$600 \cdot 0.09 \cdot x$ and $800 \cdot 0.07 \cdot x$ $600 - 0.9x$ and $800 - 0.7x$

5. How can you use the two expressions from Exercise 4 to solve the problem? Explain.
Set the expressions equal to each other and solve for x. This will tell you the amount of weekly sales for which Toni's and Nicky's earnings will be the same.

M 2-2

Practice | Worksheets | Math Tools | Math Games

Additional Practice

You may opt to have students complete the automatically scored Additional Practice items online.

Item Analysis

Example	Items	DOK
1	2, 4, 11	2
2	1	1
2	6, 7, 8	2
3	3, 5, 10	2
3	9	3

 Available Online

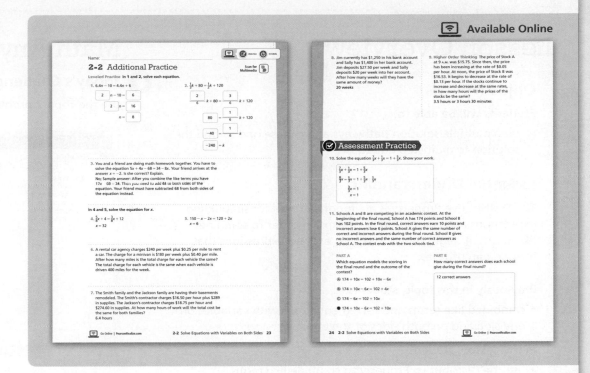

Differentiated Intervention

I = Intervention   **O** = On-Level   **A** = Advanced

Enrichment **O** **A**

Presents engaging problems and activities that extend the lesson concepts.

Math Tools and Games **I** **O** **A**

Offers additional activities and games to build understanding and fluency.

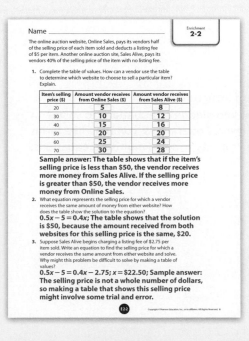

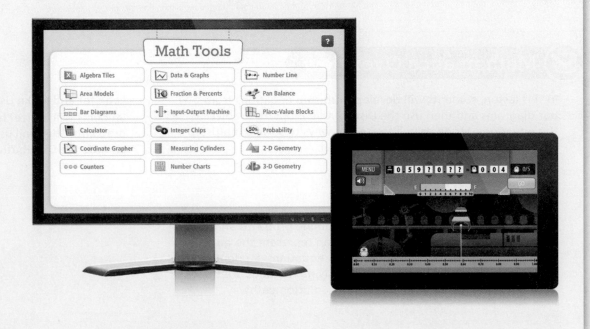

Lesson 2-3
Solve Multistep Equations

Lesson Overview

FOCUS

Objective

Students will be able to:

✔ plan multiple solution pathways and choose one to find the solution to multistep equations.

Essential Understanding

The Distributive Property is an important tool for simplifying expressions and combining like terms. In order to combine like terms, it might be necessary to expand expressions that include parentheses.

COHERENCE

Previously in this topic, students:

• combined like terms and solved equations with variables on one side and on both sides of the equation.

In this lesson, students:

• use the Distributive Property to combine like terms.

• solve multistep equations.

Later in this topic, students will:

• determine whether an equation with one variable has zero, one, or many solutions.

RIGOR

This lesson emphasizes a blend of **conceptual understanding** and **application**.

• Students will apply their knowledge of equation-solving methods as well as expand their knowledge to include using the Distributive Property to find the solution.

• Students will plan multiple approaches to solve a multistep equation based on a scenario.

Math Anytime

Today's Challenge

Use the Topic 2 problems any time during this topic.

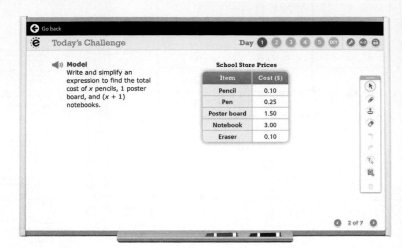

Mathematics Overview

In this lesson, students will develop multistep equations from bar diagrams and then use the Distributive Property to solve the equations. Students will strategize ways to solve a multistep equation based on a real-world situation.

Applying Math Practices

Reason Abstractly and Quantitatively
Throughout this lesson students will examine problems and determine their meaning so that they can represent the quantities and unknown quantities symbolically in equations. Students will understand when different equation-solving methods are the most beneficial for finding the simplest solution pathway.

Look for and Make Use of Structure
Students will utilize their knowledge of equations to solve problems. They will use inverse operations, combine like terms, and use the Distributive Property to solve multistep equations.

Solve & Discuss It!

Reason Abstractly and Quantitatively As students work through the *Solve & Discuss It*, listen and look for students who understand how the different rates of water flows affect the amount of water in the tank.

Before [WHOLE CLASS]

TP **1 Implement Tasks that Promote Reasoning and Problem Solving**

Q: What is a water storage tank and how much water does this tank hold? [Sample answer: A water storage tank holds water and then sends the water through pipes to the homes and businesses in the city. Each tank holds 1,000,000 gallons of water. Right now each is half full.]

2 Build Understanding

Q: How much water flows into each tank in an hour? Explain. [70,000 gallons per hour; Sample answer: There are two pipes. One has a flow of 25,000 gallons per hour and the other 45,000 gallons per hour.]

Q: How much water flows out of each tank? [60,000 gallons per hour]

During [SMALL GROUP]

TP **3 Support Productive Struggle in Learning Mathematics**

Q: What expression could you use to describe how the amount of water in one tank is changing? What does the variable represent? [Sample answer: $25,000x + 45,000x - 60,000x$; The variable stands for the time in hours.]

After [WHOLE CLASS]

TP **4 Facilitate Meaningful Mathematical Discourse**

Ask students to share their solutions. If needed, project Henry's and Kim's work and ask:

Q: How are Henry's and Kim's work different? [Sample answer: Henry solved the problem for one tank and then reasoned that all the tanks were filling at the same rate. Kim thought about all three tanks at once.]

5 Transition to Visual Learning

Q: How did the Distributive Property help Kim find the solution? [Sample answer: Kim was able to simplify her expression by multiplying the rates for one tank by the number of tanks.]

6 Extension for Early Finishers

Q: Suppose water leaves each tank at the rate of 50,000 gallons per hour. How long will it take to fill 1 tank? Explain. [25 hours to fill 1 tank. Sample answer: Each tank gains 20,000 gallons per hour so it will take 25 hours to fill one tank.]

Analyze Student Work

Available Online

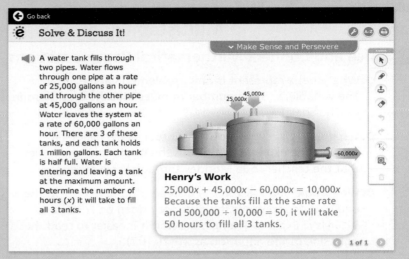

Go back

Solve & Discuss It!

∨ Make Sense and Persevere

A water tank fills through two pipes. Water flows through one pipe at a rate of 25,000 gallons an hour and through the other pipe at 45,000 gallons an hour. Water leaves the system at a rate of 60,000 gallons an hour. There are 3 of these tanks, and each tank holds 1 million gallons. Each tank is half full. Water is entering and leaving a tank at the maximum amount. Determine the number of hours (x) it will take to fill all 3 tanks.

45,000x
25,000x
–60,000x

Henry's Work
$25,000x + 45,000x - 60,000x = 10,000x$
Because the tanks fill at the same rate and $500,000 \div 10,000 = 50$, it will take 50 hours to fill all 3 tanks.

1 of 1

Henry combined like terms to find the hourly rate for one tank. Since all tanks were the same size, he reasoned that it would take the same amount of time for each tank to fill.

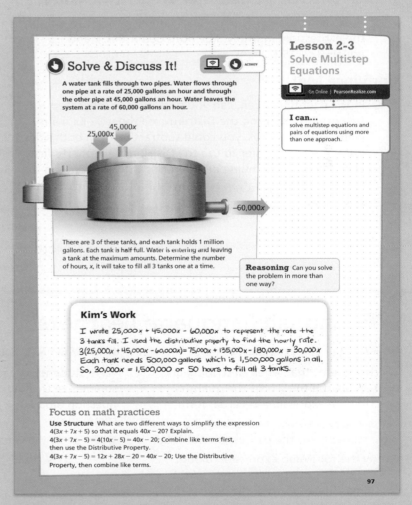

Solve & Discuss It!

ACTIVITY

A water tank fills through two pipes. Water flows through one pipe at a rate of 25,000 gallons an hour and through the other pipe at 45,000 gallons an hour. Water leaves the system at a rate of 60,000 gallons an hour.

45,000x
25,000x
–60,000x

There are 3 of these tanks, and each tank holds 1 million gallons. Each tank is half full. Water is entering and leaving a tank at the maximum amounts. Determine the number of hours, x, it will take to fill all 3 tanks one at a time.

Lesson 2-3
Solve Multistep Equations

Go Online | PearsonRealize.com

I can...
solve multistep equations and pairs of equations using more than one approach.

Reasoning Can you solve the problem in more than one way?

Kim's Work
I wrote $25,000x + 45,000x - 60,000x$ to represent the rate the 3 tanks fill. I used the distributive property to find the hourly rate.
$3(25,000x + 45,000x - 60,000x) = 75,000x + 135,000x - 180,000x = 30,000x$
Each tank needs 500,000 gallons which is 1,500,000 gallons in all. So, $30,000x = 1,500,000$ or 50 hours to fill all 3 tanks.

Focus on math practices
Use Structure What are two different ways to simplify the expression $4(3x + 7x - 5)$ so that it equals $40x - 20$? Explain.
$4(3x + 7x - 5) = 4(10x - 5) = 40x - 20$; Combine like terms first, then use the Distributive Property.
$4(3x + 7x - 5) = 12x + 28x - 20 = 40x - 20$; Use the Distributive Property, then combine like terms.

97

Kim used the Distributive Property to simplify her expression for the hourly rate of all three tanks. She used that rate to find out the time to fill the combined volume of the tanks.

STEP 2 | Develop: Visual Learning

Visual Learning · Assess

ETP Establish Mathematics Goals to Focus Learning

Engage students in a discussion about the *Essential Question*. Make sure students know how the Distributive Property works.

EXAMPLE 1 — Use the Distributive Property to Solve a Multistep Equation

ETP Use and Connect Mathematical Representations

Q: What does *x* represent in this problem? [Sample answer: The variable, *x*, is the number of miles that the teacher rode on Thursday.]

Q: What does the expression $4x + 3$ represent? [Sample answer: The expression $4x + 3$ is the total number of miles that the teacher rode Monday through Wednesday.]

Q: Why would you use $2(x + 7)$ instead of $x + 7 + x + 7$ in the equation to represent the distance ridden on Friday and Saturday? Explain. [Sample answer: It is easier to read the right side of the equation as $x + 2(x + 7)$.]

✓ Try It!

ETP Elicit and Use Evidence of Student Thinking

Q: How can you simplify $3(x - 5)$? [Sample answer: To simplify the expression, multiply 3 by both quantities, *x* and -5. This equals $3x - 15$.]

Convince Me!

Q: In the equation given, can you perform any other step first other than using the Distributive Property? Explain. [Sample answer: Yes, you could subtract 6x from both sides, but it might be easier to use the Distributive Property first. Then you could combine all the terms with variables on the left side of the equation before you subtracted 6x from both sides.]

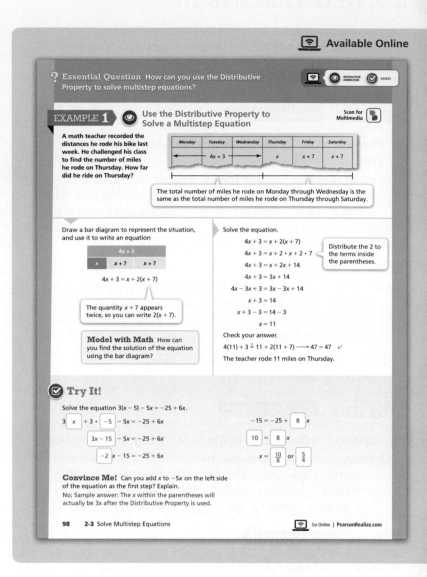

Students can access the *Visual Learning Animation Plus* by using the **BouncePages app** to scan this page. Students can download the app for free in their mobile devices' app store.

E L L English Language Learners

BEGINNING See Example 1.

Teach students that when describing an expression, use the words *the quantity* to describe the expression in verbal form.

Write the expressions on the board and have students say the expression out loud.

Q: Say the following expression aloud: $(x - 3)(x + 9)$. [The quantity *x* minus 3 times the quantity *x* plus 9.]

Q: Say the following expression aloud: $3(x - 5) + 4$. [3 times the quantity *x* minus 5, plus 4.]

INTERMEDIATE See Example 1.

Have students reread the problem and summarize the known information and the question aloud. Ask students to share their summaries.

Q: What do the expressions on each side of the equation represent?

Q: Why can the Monday–Wednesday expression be set equal to the sum of Thursday, Friday, and Saturday?

ADVANCED See Example 1.

Have students reread the problem and then explain the steps taken to solve for the variable. Identify unknown vocabulary words and try to determine what they mean based on the context of the problem and the equation model.

Q: What were the key vocabulary terms in the problem and in the steps you used to solve the problem?

Have students share their suggestions.

EXAMPLE 2 Distribute a Negative Coefficient to Solve Equations

ETP **Pose Purposeful Questions**

Q: Why might you want to use the Distributive Property first in these problems? Explain. [Sample answer: In Problem A you cannot work with the terms until you use the Distributive Property. In Problem B you can only combine the 3 and 25 until you use the Distributive Property.]

Q: What is the sign of the product when you multiply a positive and a negative number? [Negative]

Q: In Problem B, why would you divide both sides by -1 at the end of the problem? [Sample answer: You divide by -1 because you do not want to have a negative variable; by dividing by -1, the variable becomes positive and the value becomes negative.]

EXAMPLE 3 Use the Distributive Property on Both Sides of an Equation

ETP **Pose Purposeful Questions**

Q: Why is the Distributive Property the first step in solving the equation? [Sample answer: The expressions inside the parentheses cannot be simplified. You have to use the Distributive Property.]

Q: In the final step, why are both sides of the equation multiplied by -4? [Sample answer: In the previous step, $\frac{-x}{4} = \frac{-1}{4}x$. The reciprocal of the coefficient $\frac{-1}{4}$ is -4.]

Try It!

ETP **Elicit and Use Evidence of Student Thinking**

Q: What should be done first to solve this problem? [Sample answer: On each side there is a number multiplied by a quantity that cannot be simplified. The Distributive Property will let me write each side of the equation without parentheses so that I can combine like terms.]

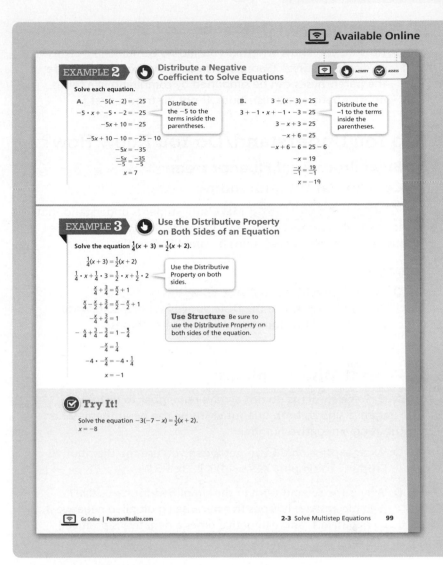

ADDITIONAL EXAMPLES

For additional examples go to PearsonRealize.com.

Response to Intervention

USE WITH EXAMPLE 3 Some students may need to review using the Distributive Property. Encourage students who are having trouble to draw arrows from the number being multiplied to each of the terms in the quantity in parentheses.

- **Use the Distributive Property.**

  Simplify.

  - $7(x - 5)$ $[7x - 35]$

  - $-\frac{2}{3}(6y + 18)$ $[-4y - 12]$

  - $-(3 - x)$ $[-3 + x]$

Enrichment

USE WITH EXAMPLE 3 Challenge students to find a different solution pathway to solve the problem.

- **Answer the following.**

- **Q:** Try multiplying both sides of the original equation by 4 as a first step. How does this change the process of solving the equation? [Sample answer: I would get the equation $x + 3 = 2(x + 2)$. Then I only have to use the Distributive Property on the right to get $x + 3 = 2x + 4$. I subtract x from both sides to get $3 = x + 4$, and then subtract 4 from both sides to get $x = -1$. I didn't have to use fractions after the first step.]

KEY CONCEPT

ETP Pose Purposeful Questions

Q: How do you know whether you should combine like terms or distribute first? [Sample answer: If the expression inside the parentheses can be simplified by combining like terms, do that before you distribute. If not, distribute first.]

Do You Understand/Do You Know How?

ETP Build Procedural Fluency from Conceptual Understanding

🔑 **Essential Question** Make sure students understand that they should use the Distributive Property first when quantities inside the parentheses cannot be simplified further.

ITEM 6

Q: What should be done first to solve this problem? [Sample answer: Use the Distributive Property to rewrite both sides of the equation without parentheses.]

🔄 Prevent Misconceptions

ITEM 5 Some students do not always remember to distribute the negative sign to both quantities inside the parentheses when distributing a negative number.

Q: What expression do you get when you use the Distributive Property to simplify $-3(x-1)$? $[-3x+3]$

Q: Why is the second term in the simplified form positive? [Sample answer: It is positive because I multiplied negative 3 by negative 1, and a negative times a negative is positive.]

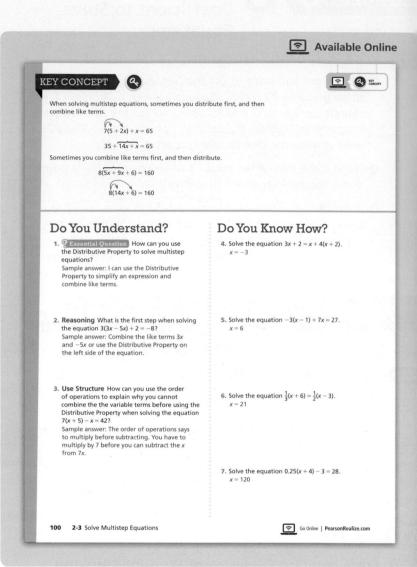

Available Online

KEY CONCEPT

When solving multistep equations, sometimes you distribute first, and then combine like terms.

$$7(5+2x)+x=65$$
$$35+14x+x=65$$

Sometimes you combine like terms first, and then distribute.

$$8(5x+9x+6)=160$$
$$8(14x+6)=160$$

Do You Understand?

1. 🔑 **Essential Question** How can you use the Distributive Property to solve multistep equations?
   Sample answer: I can use the Distributive Property to simplify an expression and combine like terms.

2. **Reasoning** What is the first step when solving the equation $3(3x-5x)+2=-8$?
   Sample answer: Combine the like terms $3x$ and $-5x$ or use the Distributive Property on the left side of the equation.

3. **Use Structure** How can you use the order of operations to explain why you cannot combine the the variable terms before using the Distributive Property when solving the equation $7(x+5)-x=42$?
   Sample answer: The order of operations says to multiply before subtracting. You have to multiply by 7 before you can subtract the x from $7x$.

Do You Know How?

4. Solve the equation $3x+2=x+4(x+2)$.
   $x=-3$

5. Solve the equation $-3(x-1)+7x=27$.
   $x=6$

6. Solve the equation $\frac{1}{3}(x+6)=\frac{1}{2}(x-3)$.
   $x=21$

7. Solve the equation $0.25(x+4)-3=28$.
   $x=120$

Go Online | PearsonRealize.com

ADDITIONAL EXAMPLE 3

Help students understand that they can change $\frac{1}{3}$ to $\frac{2}{6}$ before they use the Distributive Property. The coefficients of each variable will be fractions with a denominator of 6.

Make sure students understand that there are multiple ways to solve the problem, but they all result in the same answer.

Q: Why might you want to multiply the expression on the right side of the equation by $\frac{2}{6}$ instead of $\frac{1}{3}$? [Sample answer: It will be easier to work with the variable because both will have coefficients with fractions that are sixths. The constants will also be stated in terms of sixths.]

Q: The equation is now in the form $-\frac{7}{6}=\frac{x}{6}$. What can you do so you are only working with whole numbers? [Multiply each side by 6.]

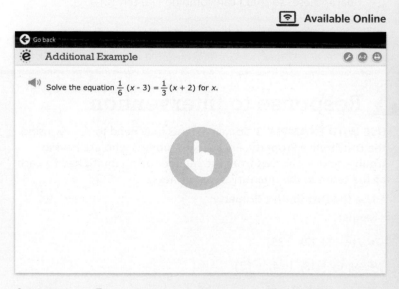

Available Online

← Go back

Additional Example

🔊 Solve the equation $\frac{1}{6}(x-3)=\frac{1}{3}(x+2)$ for x.

Answer: $x=-7$

Practice & Problem Solving

 Available Online

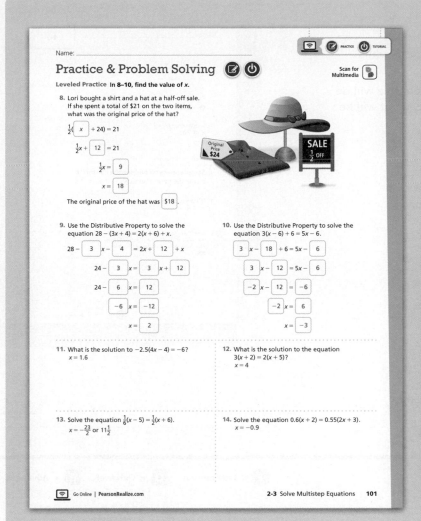

Name: _____

Practice & Problem Solving

Leveled Practice In **8–10**, find the value of x.

8. Lori bought a shirt and a hat at a half-off sale. If she spent a total of $21 on the two items, what was the original price of the hat?

$\frac{1}{2}(\boxed{x} + 24) = 21$

$\frac{1}{2}x + \boxed{12} = 21$

$\frac{1}{2}x = \boxed{9}$

$x = \boxed{18}$

The original price of the hat was $\boxed{\$18}$.

Original Price $24 — SALE ½ OFF

9. Use the Distributive Property to solve the equation $28 - (3x + 4) = 2(x + 6) + x$.

$28 - \boxed{3}x - \boxed{4} = 2x + \boxed{12} + x$

$24 - \boxed{3}x = \boxed{3}x + \boxed{12}$

$24 - \boxed{6}x = \boxed{12}$

$\boxed{-6}x = \boxed{-12}$

$x = \boxed{2}$

10. Use the Distributive Property to solve the equation $3(x - 6) + 6 = 5x - 6$.

$3\boxed{x} - \boxed{18} + 6 = 5x - \boxed{6}$

$3\boxed{x} - \boxed{12} = 5x - \boxed{6}$

$-2\boxed{x} - \boxed{12} = \boxed{-6}$

$-2\boxed{x} = \boxed{6}$

$x = \boxed{-3}$

11. What is the solution to $-2.5(4x - 4) = -6$?
$x = 1.6$

12. What is the solution to the equation $3(x + 2) = 2(x + 5)$?
$x = 4$

13. Solve the equation $\frac{1}{6}(x - 5) = \frac{1}{2}(x + 6)$.
$x = -\frac{23}{2}$ or $11\frac{1}{2}$

14. Solve the equation $0.6(x + 2) = 0.55(2x + 3)$.
$x = -0.9$

15. Solve the equation $4x - 2(x - 2) = -9 + 5x - 8$.
$x = 7$

16. Use the Distributive Property to solve the equation $2(m + 2) = 22$. Describe what it means to distribute the 2 to each term inside the parentheses.
$m = 9$; Sample answer: You have to multiply each term inside the parentheses by 2.

17. What is Peter's number?
30

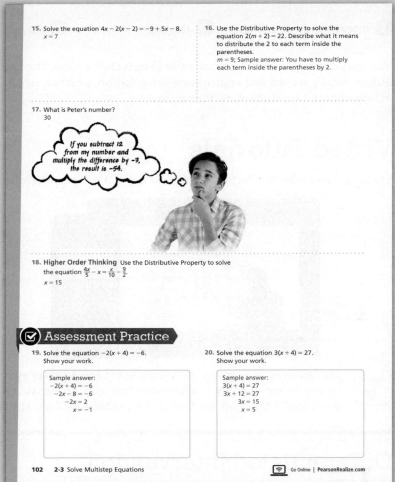

If you subtract 12 from my number and multiply the difference by -3, the result is -54.

18. **Higher Order Thinking** Use the Distributive Property to solve the equation $\frac{4x}{5} - x = \frac{x}{10} - \frac{9}{2}$.
$x = 15$

Assessment Practice

19. Solve the equation $-2(x + 4) = -6$. Show your work.

Sample answer:
$-2(x + 4) = -6$
$-2x - 8 = -6$
$-2x = 2$
$x = -1$

20. Solve the equation $3(x + 4) = 27$. Show your work.

Sample answer:
$3(x + 4) = 27$
$3x + 12 = 27$
$3x = 15$
$x = 5$

You may opt to have students complete the automatically scored Practice & Problem Solving items online.

Error Intervention

ITEM 9 Some students do not understand what it means to subtract a quantity in parentheses. Remind them that they are multiplying each item in the parentheses by -1.

Q: How would you simplify $28 - (3x + 4)$? [Sample answer: Multiply $3x$ and $+4$ by -1 to get $-3x - 4$. Then simplify $28 - 3x - 4$ as $24 - 3x$.]

English Language Learners

ITEM 17 Struggling English Language Learners may need to review some of the terms in the question including *difference*, *result*, and *subtract from*. It may also help to have them write separate expressions for each step in the problem statement.

Q: What expression shows "subtract 12 from the number"? [$x - 12$]

Q: What expression shows "multiply the difference of the unknown minus 12 by -3"? [$-3(x - 12)$]

Item Analysis

Example	Items	DOK
	8, 10, 20	1
1	16	2
	18	3
2	11, 15, 19	1
	17	2
3	9, 12, 13, 14	1

PearsonRealize.com

Assess   Tutorials   Worksheets

Lesson Quiz

 Use the student scores on the Lesson Quiz to prescribe differentiated assignments.

I Intervention 0–3 Points   **O** On-Level 4 Points   **A** Advanced 5 Points

You may opt to have students take the Lesson Quiz online. The Lesson Quiz will be automatically scored and appropriate remediation, practice, or enrichment will be assigned based on student performance.

Video Tutorials

Students can access instructional tutorials using the **Virtual Nerd app**.

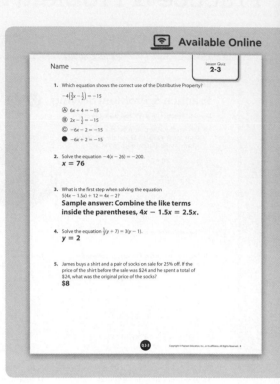

Students can also access the videos using the **BouncePages app** to scan exercise pages marked with this icon. Students can download both apps for free in their mobile devices' app store.

Lesson Quiz 2-3

Name _____

1. Which equation shows the correct use of the Distributive Property?
   $-4\left(\frac{3}{2}x - \frac{1}{2}\right) = -15$

   Ⓐ $6x + 4 = -15$
   Ⓑ $2x - \frac{1}{2} = -15$
   Ⓒ $-6x - 2 = -15$
   ⬤ $-6x + 2 = -15$

2. Solve the equation $-4(x - 26) = -200$.
   $x = 76$

3. What is the first step when solving the equation $5(4x - 1.5x) + 12 = 4x - 2$?
   Sample answer: Combine the like terms inside the parentheses, $4x - 1.5x = 2.5x$.

4. Solve the equation $\frac{1}{3}(y + 7) = 3(y - 1)$.
   $y = 2$

5. James buys a shirt and a pair of socks on sale for 25% off. If the price of the shirt before the sale was $24 and he spent a total of $24, what was the original price of the socks?
   $8

Differentiated Intervention

I = Intervention   **O** = On-Level   **A** = Advanced

Reteach to Build Understanding **I**

Provides scaffolded reteaching for the key lesson concepts.

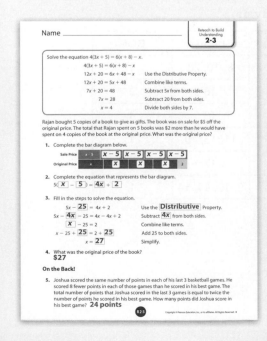

Additional Vocabulary Support **I** **O**

Helps students develop and reinforce understanding of key terms and concepts.

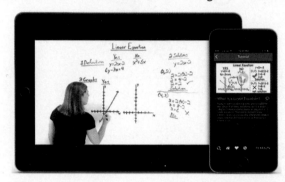

Build Mathematical Literacy **I**

Provides support for struggling readers to build mathematical literacy.

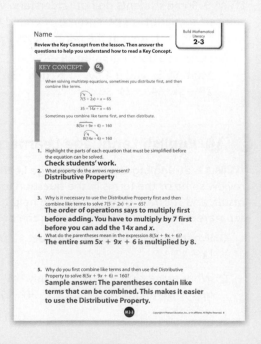

Additional Practice

You may opt to have students complete the automatically scored Additional Practice items online.

Item Analysis

Example	Items	DOK
1	1, 3, 10, 11	2
	9	3
2	6, 7, 8	2
3	2, 4, 5	2

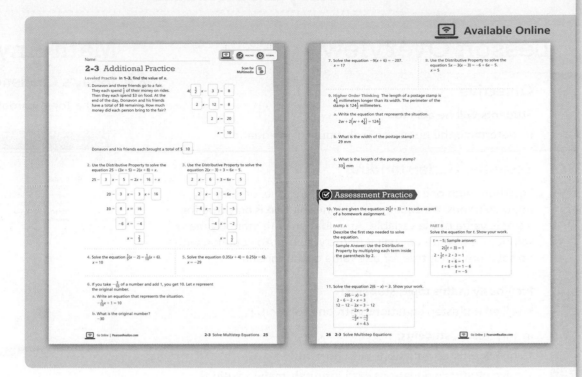

Differentiated Intervention

I = Intervention   **O** = On-Level   **A** = Advanced

Enrichment O A

Presents engaging problems and activities that extend the lesson concepts.

Math Tools and Games I O A

Offers additional activities and games to build understanding and fluency.

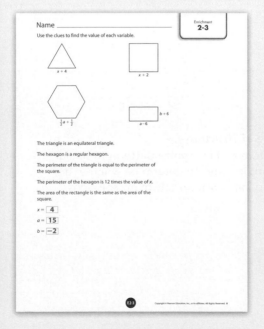

Lesson 2-4

Equations with No Solutions or Infinitely Many Solutions

Video   Activity

Lesson Overview

Objective

Students will be able to:

✔ determine the number of solutions to an equation.

Essential Understanding

Equations with one variable can have zero, one, or infinitely many solutions. An equation with one solution is only true for a single value of the variable. An equation with infinitely many solutions is true for any value of the variable. An equation with no solutions is not true for any value of the variable.

Previously in this topic, students:

• solved multistep equations with one solution.

In this lesson, students:

• solve multistep equations with no solution.

• solve multistep equations with infinitely many solutions.

• determine whether an equation with one variable has zero, one, or many solutions.

Later in this topic, students will:

• graph linear equations in two variables.

This lesson emphasizes a blend of **conceptual understanding** and **application**.

• Students will interpret the solution to an equation when the solution method results in a true or untrue statement showing that two numbers are equal. They will understand what it means for an equation to have no solutions or infinitely many solutions.

• Students will use equation-solving methods they have already learned in order to solve real-world problems with no solutions, one solution, or infinitely many solutions.

FOCUS

COHERENCE

RIGOR

Math Anytime

Today's Challenge

Use the Topic 2 problems any time during this topic.

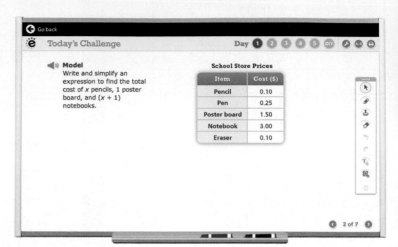

Mathematics Overview

In this lesson, students will understand the importance of using different approaches to simplify expressions with infinitely many, one, or no solution. Students will also interpret the result of finding many solutions or no solution to an equation based on a real-world situation.

Applying Math Practices

Reason Abstractly and Quantitatively
Students will solve an equation and use the resulting statement to identify the number of solutions for the equation.

Look for and Make Use of Structure
Students will see structure and recognize patterns in similar situations and equations in order to determine whether an equation will have zero, one, or infinitely many solutions.

STEP 1 | Develop: Problem-Based Learning

15-20 min

Activity

Solve & Discuss It!

Reason Abstractly and Quantitatively As students work through the *Solve & Discuss It*, listen and look for ways in which students reason about why the numbers will always come out the same, regardless of the twins' ages.

Before [WHOLE CLASS]

TP **1 Implement Tasks that Promote Reasoning and Problem Solving**

Q: What is the magician asking the twins to do? [Sample answer: He is asking them to perform operations on integers and suggesting he knows how their results compare.]

2 Build Understanding

Q: What value is unknown and must be represented by a variable? [The twins' ages are unknown.]

During [SMALL GROUP]

TP **3 Support Productive Struggle in Learning Mathematics**

Q: Jasmine's instructions say to multiply by 3 and add 6 and then multiply the sum by 2. What expression models this? [$2(3x + 6)$]

Q: How can you compare the expressions that Jasmine and James have after following the instructions? Explain. [Sample answer: Set the two expressions equal to each other because the Great Karlo predicts they will both get the same number.]

After [WHOLE CLASS]

TP **4 Facilitate Meaningful Mathematical Discourse**

Ask students to share their solutions. If necessary, show Angela's and Aaron's work to the class and ask:

Q: What do you notice about Aaron's simplified expressions? [Sample answer: They are the same expression.]

Q: Why is it OK to use the same variable for Jasmine's age and James's age? [Sample answer: Because Jasmine and James are twins, they are the same age.]

5 Transition to Visual Learning

Q: What does it mean if two expressions with one variable are equal? [Sample answer: Any value for the variable will make the equation true.]

6 Extension for Early Finishers

Q: Jasmine and James have a friend who is the same age as them. Can you think of a third set of instructions to give the friend that will result in another equivalent expression? Write the expression. [Sample answer: Add 2 to the friend's age, then multiply the sum by 6. $6(x + 2)$]

Analyze Student Work

[Available Online]

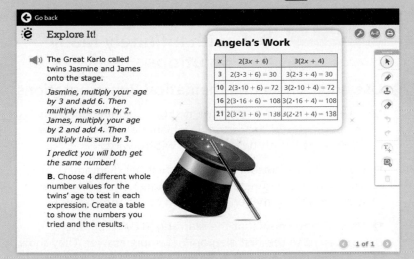

Angela substitutes the same value for the variable in Jasmine's expression and in James's expression and compares the results.

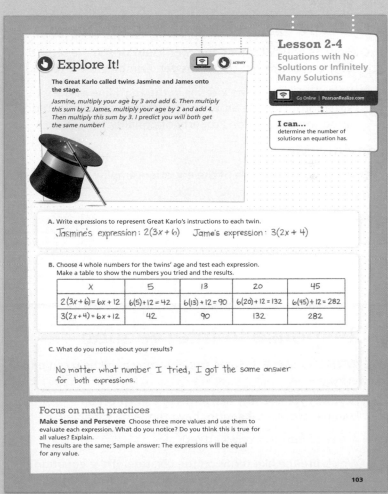

Aaron simplifies the expressions and finds that they are the same.

ETP **Establish Mathematics Goals to Focus Learning**

Engage students in a discussion about the *Essential Question*. Make sure students understand that the term *one-variable equation* means that there is only one variable used, but it can appear more than once within the equation.

EXAMPLE 1 **Solve an Equation with Infinitely Many Solutions**

ETP **Use and Connect Mathematical Representations**

Q: How does the top part of the first bar diagram represent the perimeter of the rectangle? [Sample answer: It shows adding the length twice and the width twice.]

Q: How does the bottom part of the first bar diagram represent the perimeter of the triangle? [Sample answer: It shows adding the length of each of the three sides.]

Q: How do you know that the rearranged bar diagrams are equivalent to the first diagram? [Sample answer: They show the same total number of x's and the same constants.]

 Try It!

ETP **Elicit and Use Evidence of Student Thinking**

Q: How do you determine the coefficient of x in the second line of the equation? [Sample answer: Combine the x-terms.]

Q: What happens to the x-terms in the third line of the equation? [Sample answers: The x-terms are eliminated using the Subtraction Property of Equality.]

Convince Me!

Q: What does each side of the equation simplify to if $x = -1$? [12]

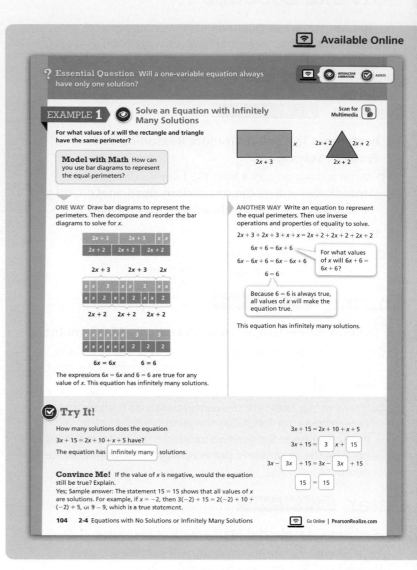

 Students can access the *Visual Learning Animation Plus* by using the **BouncePages app** to scan this page. Students can download the app for free in their mobile devices' app store.

RtI **Response to Intervention**

USE WITH EXAMPLE 1 Some students may need help combining like terms.

Q: How can you identify like terms in an expression? [Sample answer: Like terms have the same variable.]

Q: Are constants like terms? [Yes]

Q: Which are the like terms on the left side of the equation? [$2x$, $2x$, x, and x are like terms. 3 and 3 are like terms.]

E **Enrichment**

USE WITH EXAMPLE 1 Challenge students to create other figures, including a square, with the same perimeter as the rectangle and triangle.

Q: What should you do to the perimeter of the square to find the length of a side? [Divide by 4.]

Q: What expression gives the length of each side of the square? [$1.5x + 1.5$]

Q: Design another figure with the same perimeter. [Sample answer: A regular hexagon with side length $x + 1$]

EXAMPLE 2 Solve an Equation with One Solution

ETP Pose Purposeful Questions

Q: What does the expression $x + 1.2$ represent? [The number of hours Anna spent playing soccer each morning and afternoon]

Q: Can you make a generalization about equations with one solution? [Sample answer: If the variables cannot be eliminated, then the equation will have one solution.]

EXAMPLE 3 Solve an Equation with No Solutions

ETP Pose Purposeful Questions

Q: What does x represent? [Sample answer: The variable x represents the number of string colors used in each bracelet.]

Q: Can you make a generalization about equations with no solutions? [Sample answer: If all of the variables are eliminated and the remaining number statement is false, then the equation does not have a solution.]

Try It!

ETP Elicit and Use Evidence of Student Thinking

Q: What does the right side of the equation simplify to? [$4x + 3$]

Q: Compare this to the left side of the equation. What do you notice? [The x-terms have the same coefficient and can be eliminated using the Subtraction Property of Equality.]

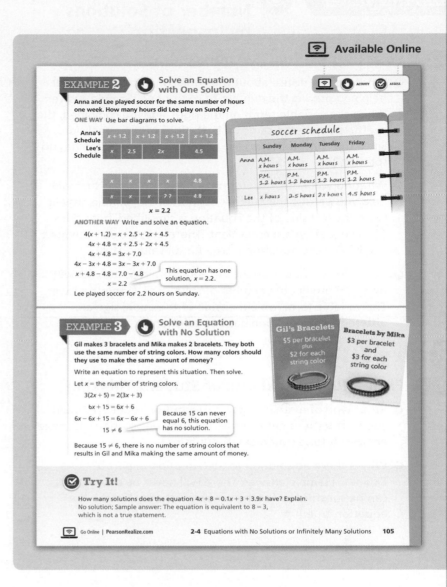

Available Online

EXAMPLE 2 Solve an Equation with One Solution

Anna and Lee played soccer for the same number of hours one week. How many hours did Lee play on Sunday?

ONE WAY Use bar diagrams to solve.

| Anna's Schedule | $x + 1.2$ | $x + 1.2$ | $x + 1.2$ | $x + 1.2$ |
| Lee's Schedule | x | 2.5 | $2x$ | 4.5 |

| x | x | x | x | 4.8 |
| x | x | ? ? | 4.8 |

$x = 2.2$

soccer schedule

	Sunday	Monday	Tuesday	Friday
Anna	A.M. x hours	A.M. x hours	A.M. x hours	A.M. x hours
	P.M. 1.2 hours	P.M. 1.2 hours	P.M. 1.2 hours	P.M. 1.2 hours
Lee	x hours	2.5 hours	$2x$ hours	4.5 hours

ANOTHER WAY Write and solve an equation.

$4(x + 1.2) = x + 2.5 + 2x + 4.5$
$4x + 4.8 = x + 2.5 + 2x + 4.5$
$4x + 4.8 = 3x + 7.0$
$4x - 3x + 4.8 = 3x - 3x + 7.0$
$x + 4.8 - 4.8 = 7.0 - 4.8$
$x = 2.2$

This equation has one solution, $x = 2.2$.

Lee played soccer for 2.2 hours on Sunday.

EXAMPLE 3 Solve an Equation with No Solution

Gil's Bracelets
$5 per bracelet plus $2 for each string color

Bracelets by Mika
$3 per bracelet and $3 for each string color

Gil makes 3 bracelets and Mika makes 2 bracelets. They both use the same number of string colors. How many colors should they use to make the same amount of money?

Write an equation to represent this situation. Then solve.

Let x = the number of string colors.

$3(2x + 5) = 2(3x + 3)$
$6x + 15 = 6x + 6$
$6x - 6x + 15 = 6x - 6x + 6$
$15 \neq 6$

Because 15 can never equal 6, this equation has no solution.

Because $15 \neq 6$, there is no number of string colors that results in Gil and Mika making the same amount of money.

Try It!

How many solutions does the equation $4x + 8 = 0.1x + 3 + 3.9x$ have? Explain.
No solution; Sample answer: The equation is equivalent to $8 = 3$, which is not a true statement.

Go Online | PearsonRealize.com   **2-4** Equations with No Solutions or Infinitely Many Solutions   **105**

BLL English Language Learners

BEGINNING Complete Example 2.

Help struggling English Language Learners work through the problem statement, diagrams, and solution. Students will use visual and contextual support to understand what the problem is asking and how the visual and algebraic models reflect the situation.

Q: What information does the table show? [Sample answer: The number of hours Anna and Lee played soccer on each of those four days.]

Q: Why is the value of x the answer to the problem? [Sample answer: It is the number of hours Lee played soccer on Sunday.]

INTERMEDIATE Complete Example 3.

Have students reread the problem and summarize the known information and the question aloud. Ask students to share their summaries. Have students edit each other's work for clarity, and help students use context to figure out the meanings of unknown words.

ADVANCED Complete Example 3.

Have students explain the steps taken to set up the visual and algebraic models of the problem. Have them also focus on the vocabulary that describes the bracelet and the cost to purchase each bracelet.

Q: Why does $6x + 15$ model the amount that Gil makes? [Sample answer: Because the cost of each bracelet is $5 plus $2 per string color, for a total of $5 + 2x$. Multiplying that by 3 results in $15 + 6x$.]

Q: Why is the result of the calculations $15 = 6$? [Sample answer: When $6x$ is subtracted from both sides of the equation, $15 = 6$ is the resulting statement.]

STEP **2** | Develop: Visual Learning *continued*

 EXAMPLE **4** **Determine the Number of Solutions by Inspection**

ETP **Pose Purposeful Questions**

Q: What do you notice about the equation in part a that will help you predict the number of solutions? [Sample answer: When the variable terms on the right side are combined, the coefficients are the same on both sides of the equal sign. Since the constant terms are not equal, the equation has no solution.]

Q: What do you notice about the equation in part b that will help you predict the number of solutions? [Sample answer: Once the left side of the equation is simplified, both sides of the equation are equivalent. Therefore, a true statement results and the equation is true for all values of *x*.]

Q: What do you notice about the equation in part c that will help you predict the number of solutions? [Sample answer: The variable terms on either side of the equal sign are different. The equation has one solution.]

 **Try It!**

ETP **Elicit and Use Evidence of Student Thinking**

Q: What type of mathematical statement or equation should you start with to get an equation with no solution? [Sample answer: A false statement or equation]

Q: Why is there no solution to the equation in part b? Explain. [Sample answer: There will never be a value that can be substituted for the variable *x* that will make the equation true.]

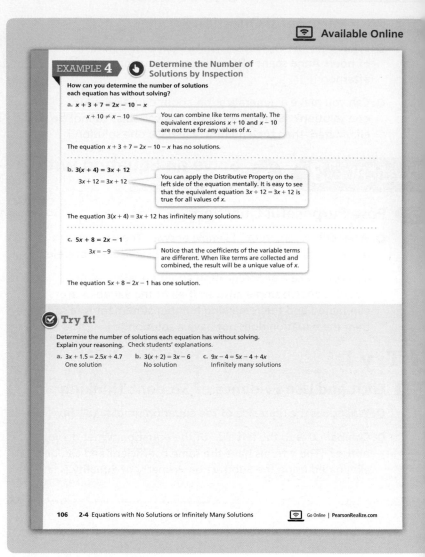

Available Online

EXAMPLE **4** Determine the Number of Solutions by Inspection

How can you determine the number of solutions each equation has without solving?

a. $x + 3 + 7 = 2x - 10 - x$
$x + 10 \neq x - 10$

You can combine like terms mentally. The equivalent expressions $x + 10$ and $x - 10$ are not true for any values of *x*.

The equation $x + 3 + 7 = 2x - 10 - x$ has no solutions.

b. $3(x + 4) = 3x + 12$
$3x + 12 = 3x + 12$

You can apply the Distributive Property on the left side of the equation mentally. It is easy to see that the equivalent equation $3x + 12 = 3x + 12$ is true for all values of *x*.

The equation $3(x + 4) = 3x + 12$ has infinitely many solutions.

c. $5x + 8 = 2x - 1$
$3x = -9$

Notice that the coefficients of the variable terms are different. When like terms are collected and combined, the result will be a unique value of *x*.

The equation $5x + 8 = 2x - 1$ has one solution.

Try It!

Determine the number of solutions each equation has without solving. Explain your reasoning. Check students' explanations.

a. $3x + 1.5 = 2.5x + 4.7$
One solution

b. $3(x + 2) = 3x - 6$
No solution

c. $9x - 4 = 5x - 4 + 4x$
Infinitely many solutions

 ADDITIONAL EXAMPLES

For additional examples go to PearsonRealize.com.

 Response to Intervention

USE WITH EXAMPLE 4 Some students may need help simplifying the equation in part b.

Q: Why does $3x - 2.5x$ simplify to $0.5x$? Use the Distributive Property to break down the steps. [$3x - 2.5x = (3 - 2.5)x = 0.5x$]

Q: Fill in the blank: Dividing by 0.5 is the same as multiplying by _____. [2]

E **Enrichment**

USE WITH EXAMPLE 4 Challenge students to create their own equations given the following instructions.

• Write this half of an equation on the board:
$$\frac{1}{2}x + 3 =$$

Q: Complete the equation so that it has no solution. [Sample answer: $\frac{1}{2}x + 1$]

Q: Complete the equation so that it has one solution. Write a real-world problem that your equation models. [$\frac{1}{2}x + 3 = x$; Sample answer: Dario spends $x on Saturday and 3 more than $\frac{1}{2}$ of that on Sunday. If he spent the same on both days, how much did he spend on each day?]

Q: Complete the equation so that it has infinitely many solutions. Use parentheses in your expression. [Sample answer: $\frac{1}{4}(2x + 12)$]

KEY CONCEPT

ETP Pose Purposeful Questions

Q: How can combining like terms on each side of the equal sign help you to determine the number of solutions to an equation? [Sample answer: Once all like terms have been combined, you can compare the variable and constant terms on each side of the equation to see if the variables can be eliminated and what number statement would result.]

Do You Understand/Do You Know How?

ETP Build Procedural Fluency from Conceptual Understanding

? Essential Question Make sure students understand what it means for an equation to have no solutions or infinitely many solutions.

ITEM 4

Q: Do you need to solve the equation fully in order to determine the number of solutions? [No; Sample answer: Once both sides of the equation are simplified, you can compare the coefficients and constants to determine the number of solutions.]

RtI Prevent Misconceptions

ITEM 6 Some students may not realize that it is acceptable to use the same variable to represent the number of apples and the number of peaches.

Q: What will the variable represent? Explain. [Sample answer: The variable represents the number of pieces of fruit each person bought. Each person bought the same number of pieces of fruit.]

Q: What will you have to do to represent the situation algebraically? [Sample answer: Write two expressions with the same variable and set them equal to each other.]

ADDITIONAL EXAMPLE 1

Help students apply the processes they already know to solve a problem with both fractions and decimals.

Make sure students understand how to use the bar diagrams to reason about the solution.

Q: How does rearranging the bar diagrams help you predict the solution? [Sample answer: You can see that the x terms and constant terms are the same, so there must be infinitely many solutions.]

Q: Does having fractions and decimals in the problem change the process for solving the equation? Explain. [No; Sample answer: You still use the Distributive Property first and then inverse operations to solve.]

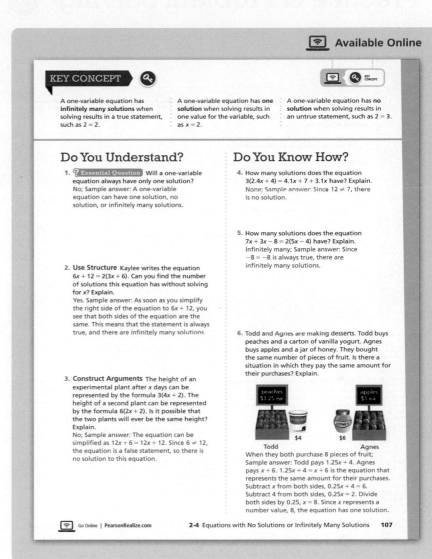

Available Online

KEY CONCEPT

A one-variable equation has **infinitely many solutions** when solving results in a true statement, such as $2 = 2$.

A one-variable equation has **one solution** when solving results in one value for the variable, such as $x = 2$.

A one-variable equation has **no solution** when solving results in an untrue statement, such as $2 = 3$.

Do You Understand?

1. **? Essential Question** Will a one-variable equation always have only one solution?
No; Sample answer: A one-variable equation can have one solution, no solution, or infinitely many solutions.

2. **Use Structure** Kaylee writes the equation $6x + 12 = 2(3x + 6)$. Can you find the number of solutions this equation has without solving for x? Explain.
Yes. Sample answer: As soon as you simplify the right side of the equation to $6x + 12$, you see that both sides of the equation are the same. This means that the statement is always true, and there are infinitely many solutions.

3. **Construct Arguments** The height of an experimental plant after x days can be represented by the formula $3(4x + 2)$. The height of a second plant can be represented by the formula $6(2x + 2)$. Is it possible that the two plants will ever be the same height? Explain.
No; Sample answer: The equation can be simplified as $12x + 6 = 12x + 12$. Since $6 \neq 12$, the equation is a false statement, so there is no solution to this equation.

Do You Know How?

4. How many solutions does the equation $3(2.4x + 4) = 4.1x + 7 + 3.1x$ have? Explain.
None; Sample answer: Since $12 \neq 7$, there is no solution.

5. How many solutions does the equation $7x + 3x - 8 = 2(5x - 4)$ have? Explain.
Infinitely many; Sample answer: Since $-8 = -8$ is always true, there are infinitely many solutions.

6. Todd and Agnes are making desserts. Todd buys peaches and a carton of vanilla yogurt. Agnes buys apples and a jar of honey. They bought the same number of pieces of fruit. Is there a situation in which they pay the same amount for their purchases? Explain.

peaches $1.25 ea. $4   apples $1 ea. $6
Todd   Agnes

When they both purchase 8 pieces of fruit; Sample answer: Todd pays $1.25x + 4$. Agnes pays $x + 6$. $1.25x + 4 = x + 6$ is the equation that represents the same amount for their purchases. Subtract x from both sides, $0.25x + 4 = 6$. Subtract 4 from both sides, $0.25x = 2$. Divide both sides by 0.25, $x = 8$. Since x represents a number value, 8, the equation has one solution.

Go Online | PearsonRealize.com   2-4 Equations with No Solutions or Infinitely Many Solutions   **107**

Available Online

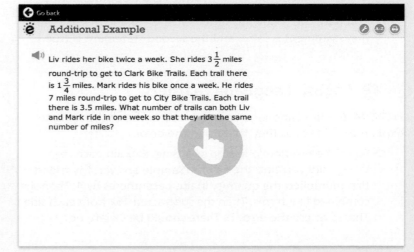

Go back

ë Additional Example

Liv rides her bike twice a week. She rides $3\frac{1}{2}$ miles round-trip to get to Clark Bike Trails. Each trail there is $1\frac{3}{4}$ miles. Mark rides his bike once a week. He rides 7 miles round-trip to get to City Bike Trails. Each trail there is 3.5 miles. What number of trails can both Liv and Mark ride in one week so that they ride the same number of miles?

Answer: For any number of trails that both Liv and Mark ride in one week, they always will ride the same number of miles.

Practice & Problem Solving

Available Online

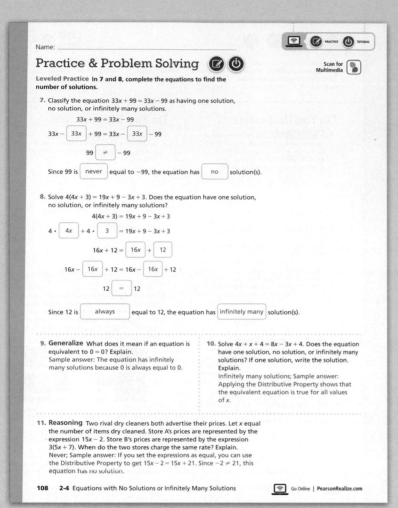

Name: _____

Practice & Problem Solving

Scan for Multimedia

Leveled Practice In 7 and 8, complete the equations to find the number of solutions.

7. Classify the equation $33x + 99 = 33x - 99$ as having one solution, no solution, or infinitely many solutions.

$$33x + 99 = 33x - 99$$

$$33x - \boxed{33x} + 99 = 33x - \boxed{33x} - 99$$

$$99 \boxed{\neq} -99$$

Since 99 is $\boxed{\text{never}}$ equal to −99, the equation has $\boxed{\text{no}}$ solution(s).

8. Solve $4(4x + 3) = 19x + 9 - 3x + 3$. Does the equation have one solution, no solution, or infinitely many solutions?

$$4(4x + 3) = 19x + 9 - 3x + 3$$

$$4 \cdot \boxed{4x} + 4 \cdot \boxed{3} = 19x + 9 - 3x + 3$$

$$16x + 12 = \boxed{16x} + \boxed{12}$$

$$16x - \boxed{16x} + 12 = 16x - \boxed{16x} + 12$$

$$12 \boxed{=} 12$$

Since 12 is $\boxed{\text{always}}$ equal to 12, the equation has $\boxed{\text{infinitely many}}$ solution(s).

9. Generalize What does it mean if an equation is equivalent to $0 = 0$? Explain.
Sample answer: The equation has infinitely many solutions because 0 is always equal to 0.

10. Solve $4x + x + 4 = 8x - 3x + 4$. Does the equation have one solution, no solution, or infinitely many solutions? If one solution, write the solution. Explain.
Infinitely many solutions; Sample answer: Applying the Distributive Property shows that the equivalent equation is true for all values of x.

11. Reasoning Two rival dry cleaners both advertise their prices. Let x equal the number of items dry cleaned. Store A's prices are represented by the expression $15x - 2$. Store B's prices are represented by the expression $3(5x + 7)$. When do the two stores charge the same rate? Explain.
Never; Sample answer: If you set the expressions as equal, you can use the Distributive Property to get $15x - 2 = 15x + 21$. Since $-2 \neq 21$, this equation has no solution.

108 2-4 Equations with No Solutions or Infinitely Many Solutions   Go Online | PearsonRealize.com

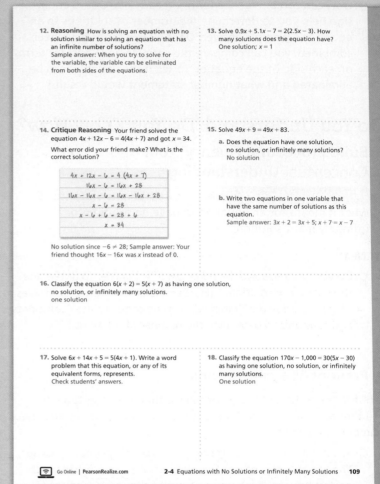

12. Reasoning How is solving an equation with no solution similar to solving an equation that has an infinite number of solutions?
Sample answer: When you try to solve for the variable, the variable can be eliminated from both sides of the equations.

13. Solve $0.9x + 5.1x - 7 = 2(2.5x - 3)$. How many solutions does the equation have?
One solution; $x = 1$

14. Critique Reasoning Your friend solved the equation $4x + 12x - 6 = 4(4x + 7)$ and got $x = 34$. What error did your friend make? What is the correct solution?

$$4x + 12x - 6 = 4(4x + 7)$$
$$16x - 6 = 16x + 28$$
$$16x - 16x - 6 = 16x - 16x + 28$$
$$x - 6 = 28$$
$$x - 6 + 6 = 28 + 6$$
$$x = 34$$

No solution since $-6 \neq 28$; Sample answer: Your friend thought $16x - 16x$ was x instead of 0.

15. Solve $49x + 9 = 49x + 83$.
a. Does the equation have one solution, no solution, or infinitely many solutions?
No solution
b. Write two equations in one variable that have the same number of solutions as this equation.
Sample answer: $3x + 2 = 3x + 5$; $x + 7 = x - 7$

16. Classify the equation $6(x + 2) = 5(x + 7)$ as having one solution, no solution, or infinitely many solutions.
one solution

17. Solve $6x + 14x + 5 = 5(4x + 1)$. Write a word problem that this equation, or any of its equivalent forms, represents.
Check students' answers.

18. Classify the equation $170x - 1,000 = 30(5x - 30)$ as having one solution, no solution, or infinitely many solutions.
One solution

Go Online | PearsonRealize.com   2-4 Equations with No Solutions or Infinitely Many Solutions 109

You may opt to have students complete the automatically scored Practice & Problem Solving items online.

Error Intervention

ITEM 9 Some students may struggle to understand that $0 = 0$ is a true statement.

Q: What happens if you add 1 to both sides of the equation $0 = 0$? [$0 = 0$ becomes $1 = 1$, which is a true statement.]

Q: Compare the following statements: $0 = 6$ and $0 = 0$. [The first statement is false, and the second statement is true.]

English Language Learners

ITEM 14 English Language Learners may find it challenging to explain their steps as they try to find the error.

Q: Solve the problem one step at a time. Explain each step. Where did you find the error? [Sample answer: My friend first multiplied the quantity in the parentheses by 4. Then she combined like terms. Then she subtracted $16x$ from each side. That is where the error is. There should be $0x$ left, not $1x$.]

Item Analysis

Example	Items	DOK
1	8, 20	1
	9, 10, 12, 17	3
2	16, 18	1
	13	2
	19	3
3	7, 21, 25	1
	11, 15	2
	14	3
4	24	1
	16, 18, 22, 23	2

Practice & Problem Solving

PearsonRealize.com

Practice   Tutorials   Math Tools

🏆 Challenge

ITEM 19 Higher Order Thinking Use this question to extend the problem and help students relate an equation with no solution to a real-world situation.

Q: Greta's gym charges a $135 membership fee plus $50 per month. Beck's gym charges a $100 membership fee plus $50 per month. Write an equation to find the number of months after which Greta and Beck will have paid the same amount. $[135 + 50x = 100 + 50x]$

Q: What is the solution to the equation? What does it mean in context of the problem? Explain. [The equation has no solution. It means that Beck and Greta will never have paid the same amount over time for their gym memberships. This is because their initial costs were different, but they pay the same amount each month.]

Item 20 How can you determine the number of solutions without fully solving the equation? [Sample answer: On the left side of the equation, use the Distributive Property; then compare the coefficients and constants on both sides of the equation to determine the number of solutions.]

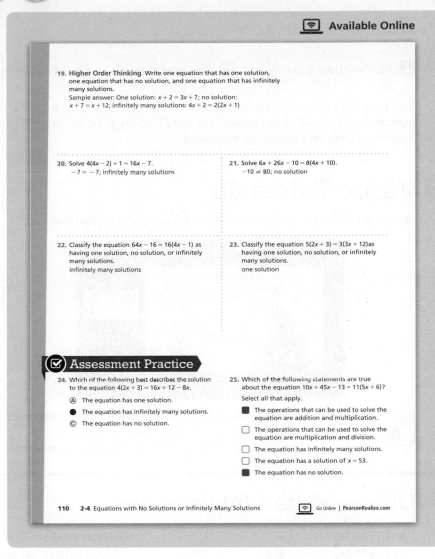

📶 Available Online

19. **Higher Order Thinking** Write one equation that has one solution, one equation that has no solution, and one equation that has infinitely many solutions.
Sample answer: One solution: $x + 2 = 3x + 7$; no solution: $x + 7 = x + 12$; infinitely many solutions: $4x + 2 = 2(2x + 1)$

20. Solve $4(4x - 2) + 1 = 16x - 7$.
$-7 = -7$; infinitely many solutions

21. Solve $6x + 26x - 10 = 8(4x + 10)$.
$-10 \neq 80$; no solution

22. Classify the equation $64x - 16 = 16(4x - 1)$ as having one solution, no solution, or infinitely many solutions.
infinitely many solutions

23. Classify the equation $5(2x + 3) = 3(3x + 12)$ as having one solution, no solution, or infinitely many solutions.
one solution

☑ Assessment Practice

24. Which of the following best describes the solution to the equation $4(2x + 3) = 16x + 12 - 8x$.
  Ⓐ The equation has one solution.
  ● The equation has infinitely many solutions.
  Ⓒ The equation has no solution.

25. Which of the following statements are true about the equation $10x + 45x - 13 = 11(5x + 6)$?
Select all that apply.
  ■ The operations that can be used to solve the equation are addition and multiplication.
  ☐ The operations that can be used to solve the equation are multiplication and division.
  ☐ The equation has infinitely many solutions.
  ☐ The equation has a solution of $x = 53$.
  ■ The equation has no solution.

PearsonRealize.com

Assess   Tutorials   Worksheets

Lesson Quiz

 Use the student scores on the Lesson Quiz to prescribe differentiated assignments.

I Intervention 0–3 Points   **O** On-Level 4 Points   **A** Advanced 5 Points

You may opt to have students take the Lesson Quiz online. The Lesson Quiz will be automatically scored and appropriate remediation, practice, or enrichment will be assigned based on student performance.

Video Tutorials

Students can access instructional tutorials using the **Virtual Nerd app**.

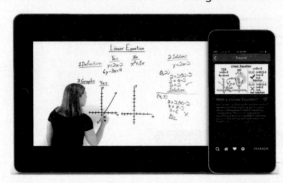

Students can also access the videos using the **BouncePages app** to scan exercise pages marked with this icon. Students can download both apps for free in their mobile devices' app store.

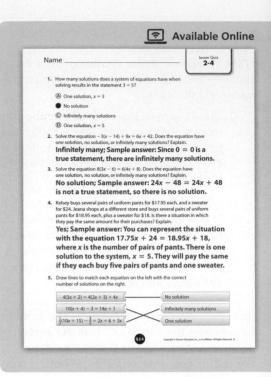

Available Online

Name _____   Lesson Quiz 2-4

1. How many solutions does a system of equations have when solving results in the statement $3 = 5$?
   (A) One solution, $x = 3$
   ● No solution
   (C) Infinitely many solutions
   (D) One solution, $x = 5$

2. Solve the equation $-3(x - 14) + 9x = 6x + 42$. Does the equation have one solution, no solution, or infinitely many solutions? Explain.
   Infinitely many; Sample answer: Since $0 = 0$ is a true statement, there are infinitely many solutions.

3. Solve the equation $8(3x - 6) = 6(4x + 8)$. Does the equation have one solution, no solution, or infinitely many solutions? Explain.
   No solution; Sample answer: $24x - 48 = 24x + 48$ is not a true statement, so there is no solution.

4. Kelsey buys several pairs of uniform pants for $17.95 each, and a sweater for $24. Jeana shops at a different store and buys several pairs of uniform pants for $18.95 each, plus a sweater for $18. Is there a situation in which they pay the same amount for their purchases? Explain.
   Yes; Sample answer: You can represent the situation with the equation $17.75x + 24 = 18.95x + 18$, where x is the number of pairs of pants. There is one solution to the system, $x = 5$. They will pay the same if they each buy five pairs of pants and one sweater.

5. Draw lines to match each equation on the left with the correct number of solutions on the right.

$4(3x + 2) = 4(2x + 3) + 4x$	—	No solution
$10(x + 4) - 3 = 14x + 1$	—	Infinitely many solutions
$\frac{1}{2}(10x + 15) - \frac{3}{2} = 2x + 6 + 3x$	—	One solution

---

Differentiated Intervention

I = Intervention   **O** = On-Level   **A** = Advanced

Reteach to Build Understanding **I**

Provides scaffolded reteaching for the key lesson concepts.

Additional Vocabulary Support **I** **O**

Helps students develop and reinforce understanding of key terms and concepts.

Build Mathematical Literacy **I**

Provides support for struggling readers to build mathematical literacy.

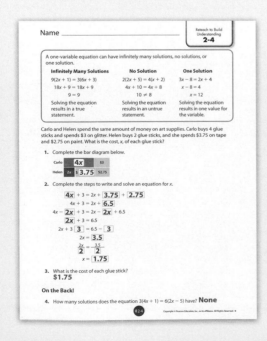

Name _____   Reteach to Build Understanding 2-4

A one-variable equation can have infinitely many solutions, no solutions, or one solution.

Infinitely Many Solutions	**No Solution**	**One Solution**
$9(2x + 1) = 3(6x + 3)$	$2(2x + 5) = 4(x + 2)$	$3x - 8 = 2x + 4$
$18x + 9 = 18x + 9$	$4x + 10 = 4x + 8$	$x - 8 = 4$
$9 = 9$	$10 \neq 8$	$x = 12$
Solving the equation results in a true statement.	Solving the equation results in an untrue statement.	Solving the equation results in one value for the variable.

Carlo and Helen spend the same amount of money on art supplies. Carlo buys 4 glue sticks and spends $3 on glitter. Helen buys 2 glue sticks, and she spends $3.75 on tape and $2.75 on paint. What is the cost, x, of each glue stick?

1. Complete the bar diagram below.

   Carlo | **4x** | $3
   Helen | 2x | $ **3.75** | $2.75

2. Complete the steps to write and solve an equation for x.

   $\boxed{4x} + 3 = 2x + \boxed{3.75} + \boxed{2.75}$
   $4x + 3 = 2x + \boxed{6.5}$
   $4x - \boxed{2x} + 3 = 2x - \boxed{2x} + 6.5$
   $\boxed{2x} + 3 = 6.5$
   $2x + 3 \boxed{3} = 6.5 - \boxed{3}$
   $2x = \boxed{3.5}$
   $\frac{2x}{2} = \frac{3.5}{2}$
   $x = \boxed{1.75}$

3. What is the cost of each glue stick?
   $1.75

On the Back!

4. How many solutions does the equation $3(4x + 1) = 6(2x - 5)$ have? **None**

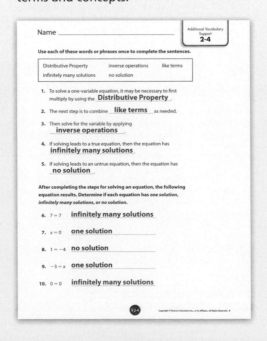

Name _____   Additional Vocabulary Support 2-4

Use each of these words or phrases once to complete the sentences.

| Distributive Property | inverse operations | like terms |
| infinitely many solutions | no solution | |

1. To solve a one-variable equation, it may be necessary to first multiply by using the **Distributive Property**.

2. The next step is to combine **like terms** as needed.

3. Then solve for the variable by applying **inverse operations**.

4. If solving leads to a true equation, then the equation has **infinitely many solutions**.

5. If solving leads to an untrue equation, then the equation has **no solution**.

After completing the steps for solving an equation, the following equation results. Determine if each equation has *one solution, infinitely many solutions,* or *no solution.*

6. $7 = 7$ **infinitely many solutions**

7. $x = 0$ **one solution**

8. $1 = -4$ **no solution**

9. $-3 = x$ **one solution**

10. $0 = 0$ **infinitely many solutions**

Name _____   Build Mathematical Literacy 2-4

Read the problem. Then answer the questions to help you understand how to solve the problem.

Classify each equation as having one solution, no solution, or infinitely many solutions.

$3x + 8 = 17$ $2x + 8 = 2(x + 4)$ $x + 4 = x - 4$

1. Highlight what you need to determine for each equation.
   Check students' work.

2. What does it mean for an equation to have no solution?
   There is no value for the variable that makes the equation true.

3. How can you tell when a one-variable equation has no solution?
   Sample answer: When solving the equation results in an untrue statement, such as $4 = -4$.

4. What does it mean for an equation to have infinitely many solutions?
   Any value substituted for the variable results in a true equation.

5. How can you tell when a one-variable equation has infinitely many solutions?
   Sample answer: When solving the equation results in a true statement, such as $3 = 3$.

6. Solving one of the equations results in $x = 3$. What can you conclude about the number of solutions for this equation?
   The equation has exactly one solution.

Additional Practice

You may opt to have students complete the automatically scored Additional Practice items online.

Item Analysis

Example	Items	DOK
1	3, 7, 8	2
	11a	3
2	2, 4, 5, 9	2
	11b	3
3	1, 6, 10, 13	2
	11c	3
4	12	2

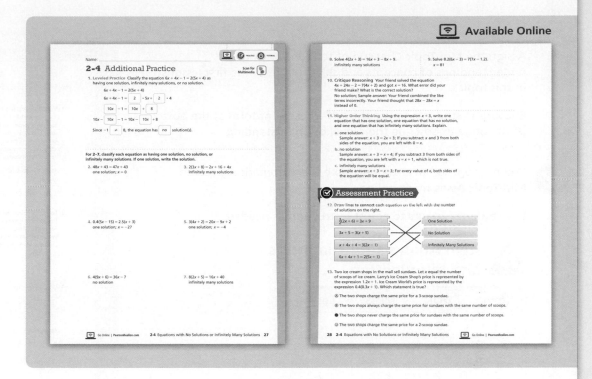

Differentiated Intervention

I = Intervention   **O** = On-Level   **A** = Advanced

Enrichment **O** **A**

Presents engaging problems and activities that extend the lesson concepts.

Math Tools and Games **I** **O** **A**

Offers additional activities and games to build understanding and fluency.

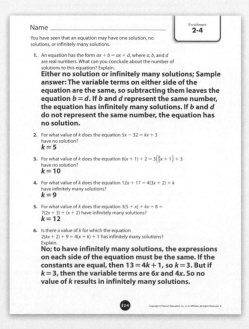

MID-TOPIC CHECKPOINT

Assess

PearsonRealize.co

Assign the Mid-Topic Checkpoint to monitor students' understandings of concepts and skills taught in the first lessons in this topic.

Encourage students to use the self-assessment form at the bottom of the page to describe their level of understanding.

 You may opt to have students take the automatically-scored Mid-Topic Assessment online.

Use students' results to adjust instruction as needed.

 ### Item Analysis for Diagnosis and Intervention

Item	DOK	MDIS	Lesson
1	3	K32	2-4
2	1	K29	2-1
3	2	K32	2-2
4	1	K32	2-4
5	1	K32	2-3
6	2	K30	2-3

📶 Available Onlin

Name: _____

MID-TOPIC CHECKPOINT
TOPIC 2

1. **Vocabulary** How can you determine the number of solutions for an equation? *Lesson 2-4*
   Sample answer: An equation in one variable has infinitely many solutions when solving results in a true statement. An equation in one variable has one solution when solving results in one value for the variable. An equation in one variable has no solution when solving results in an untrue statement.

2. Solve the equation $-\frac{2}{3}d - \frac{1}{4}d = -22$ for d. *Lesson 2-1*
   $d = 24$

3. Edy has $450 in her savings account. She deposits $40 each month. Juan has $975 in his checking account. He writes a check for $45 each month for his cell phone bill. He also writes a check for $20 each month for his water bill. After how many months will Edy and Juan have the same amount of money in their accounts? *Lesson 2-2*
   5 months

4. Which equation has infinitely many solutions? *Lesson 2-4*

   Ⓐ $\frac{3}{4}x + x - 5 = 10 + 2x$

   Ⓑ $3x - 2.7 = 2x + 2.7 + x$

   ● $9x + 4.5 - 2x = 2.3 + 7x + 2.2$

   Ⓓ $\frac{1}{5}x - 7 = \frac{3}{4} + 2x - 25\frac{3}{4}$

5. Solve the equation $-4(x - 1) + 6x = 34$ for x. *Lesson 2-3*
   $x = 15$

6. Hakeem subtracted 8 from a number, then multiplied the difference by 5. The result was 20. Write and solve an equation to find the number, x. *Lesson 2-3*
   $(x - 8) \cdot 5 = 20$; The number is 12.

How well did you do on the mid-topic checkpoint? Fill in the stars. ☆☆☆

📶 Go Online | PearsonRealize.com   **Topic 2** Analyze and Solve Linear Equations **111**

Mid-Topic Assessment Maste

Name _____

Topic 2
Mid-Topic Assessment

1. **Vocabulary** How can you tell when an equation in one variable has infinitely many solutions or no solution?
   Sample answer: When you solve for the variable, you will end up with a true statement, like 2 = 2, for an equation with infinitely many solutions, or a false statement, like 0 = 2, for an equation with no solution.

2. Solve the equation $-\frac{2}{3}e - \frac{1}{3}e = -24$.
   $e = 16$

3. Jaclyn has $120 saved and earns $40 each month in allowance. Pedro has $180 saved and earns $20 a month in allowance. If they both save their entire allowances, how long will it take before Jaclyn and Pedro have saved the same amount of money?
   3 months

4. Which equation has infinitely many solutions?
   Ⓐ $12 + 4x = 6x + 10 - 2x$
   ● $5x + 14 - 4x = 23 + x - 9$
   Ⓒ $x + 9 - 0.8x = 5.2x + 17 - 8$
   Ⓓ $4x - 2x = 20$

5. Solve the equation $-24 + 12d = 2(d - 3) + 22$.
   $d = 4$

6. Hilda adds 5 to a number, then multiplies the sum by −2. The result is 6. Write an equation to find the number, x. What is the number?
   $-2(x + 5) = 6$; **The number is −8.**

Mid-Topic Assessment **1 of 1**   Copyright © Pearson Education, Inc. or its affiliates. All Rights Reserved.

MID-TOPIC PERFORMANCE TASK

Assess students' ability to apply the concepts and skills in the first part of the topic using the Mid-Topic Performance Task, found in the Student's Edition or at PearsonRealize.com.

Item Analysis for Diagnosis and Intervention

Part	DOK	MDIS	Lesson
A	2	K30, K31	2-2, 2-3
B	2	K31	2-2
C	2	K31	2-2

Scoring Guide

Part	Points	Mid-Topic Performance Task
A	1	Correct answer
B	2	Correct answer and explanation
	1	Correct answer with partial explanation or mostly correct explanation
C	2	Correct answer and explanation
	1	Correct answer with partial explanation or mostly correct explanation

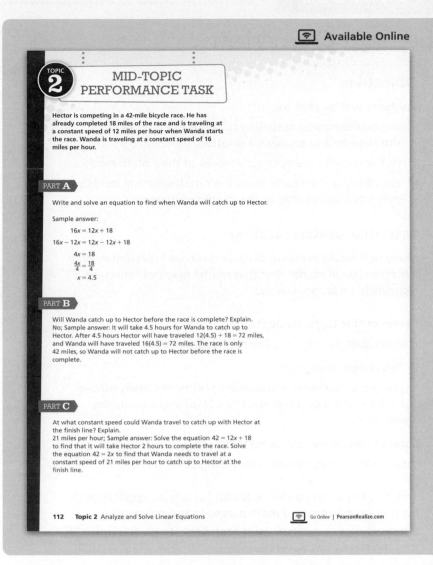

📶 Available Online

TOPIC 2 MID-TOPIC PERFORMANCE TASK

Hector is competing in a 42-mile bicycle race. He has already completed 18 miles of the race and is traveling at a constant speed of 12 miles per hour when Wanda starts the race. Wanda is traveling at a constant speed of 16 miles per hour.

PART A

Write and solve an equation to find when Wanda will catch up to Hector.

Sample answer:
$$16x = 12x + 18$$
$$16x - 12x = 12x - 12x + 18$$
$$4x = 18$$
$$\frac{4x}{4} = \frac{18}{4}$$
$$x = 4.5$$

PART B

Will Wanda catch up to Hector before the race is complete? Explain.
No; Sample answer: It will take 4.5 hours for Wanda to catch up to Hector. After 4.5 hours Hector will have traveled 12(4.5) + 18 = 72 miles, and Wanda will have traveled 16(4.5) = 72 miles. The race is only 42 miles, so Wanda will not catch up to Hector before the race is complete.

PART C

At what constant speed could Wanda travel to catch up with Hector at the finish line? Explain.
21 miles per hour; Sample answer: Solve the equation 42 = 12x + 18 to find that it will take Hector 2 hours to complete the race. Solve the equation 42 = 2x to find that Wanda needs to travel at a constant speed of 21 miles per hour to catch up to Hector at the finish line.

112 **Topic 2** Analyze and Solve Linear Equations 📶 Go Online | PearsonRealize.com

3-ACT MATH

PearsonRealize.com

Video Activity

3-Act Mathematical Modeling: Powering Down

Lesson Overview

FOCUS

Objectives

Students will be able to:

- ✔ use mathematical modeling to represent a problem situation and to propose a solution.
- ✔ test and verify the appropriateness of their math models.
- ✔ explain why the results from their mathematical models may not align exactly to the problem situation.

Essential Understanding

Many real-world problem situations can be represented with a mathematical model, but that model may not represent a real-world situation exactly.

COHERENCE

Earlier in this topic, students:

- solved different types of multi-step equations.

In this lesson, students:

- develop a mathematical model to represent and propose a solution to a problem situation involving a multi-step equation.

Later in this course, students will:

- refine their mathematical modeling skills.

RIGOR

This mathematical modeling lesson focuses on **application** of both **math content** and **math practices and processes**.

- Students draw on their understanding of equality concepts to develop a representative model.
- Students apply their mathematical model to test and validate its applicability to similar problem situations.

Math Anytime

Today's Challenge

Use the Topic 2 problems any time during this topic.

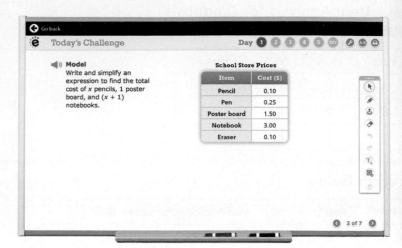

Mathematics Overview

In this lesson, students will develop and use a mathematical model to represent and propose a solution to a real-world problem involving a multi-step equation. Students will reinforce both their procedural skills and their understanding of equality concepts, while recognizing the limitations of some mathematical models for real-world situations.

Applying Math Practices

Model with Mathematics

The focus of this lesson is on mathematical modeling. Students identify variables and the relationship among variables, develop a model that represents the situation, and use the model to propose a solution. Students interpret their solutions and propose explanations for why their answers may not match the real-world answer.

As students carry out mathematical modeling, they will also engage in sense-making, abstract and quantitative reasoning, and mathematical communication and argumentation. In testing and validating their models, students look for patterns and structure.

PearsonRealize.com

Video

ACT 1 ▶ The Hook ▶

Students will be tasked with determining how much longer a smartphone's battery will last.

Play the Video and Brainstorm Questions

Have students complete **Question 1**. Encourage them to consider the situation and ask any questions that arise. Listen for interesting mathematical and non-mathematical questions. Ask students what makes each question interesting.

> **Q:** What questions do you have? [Sample questions: How much can he use his device before it loses power? How much power is left in the battery? How long has he been using the device so far?]

Pose the Main Question

After the question brainstorming, pose the Main Question students will be tasked with answering. Have students complete **Question 2**.

Main Question

> **Q:** What time will it be when the phone runs out of power?

Ask about Predictions

Have students complete **Questions 3–5**. You can survey the class for the range of predictions.

> **Q:** Why do you think your prediction is the answer to the Main Question?

> **Q:** Who had a similar prediction?

> **Q:** How many of you agree with that prediction?

> **Q:** Who has a different prediction?

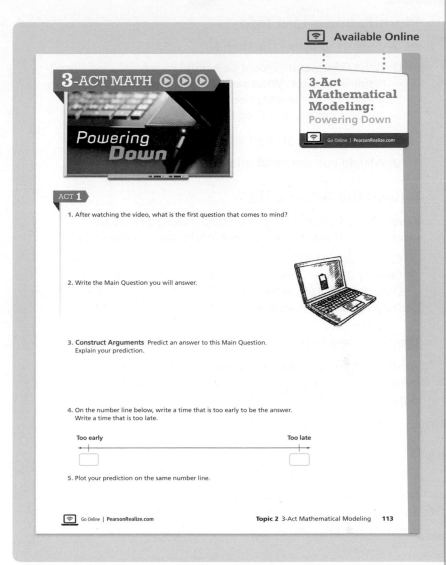

Available Online

3-ACT MATH ▶ ▶ ▶

3-Act Mathematical Modeling: Powering Down

Go Online | PearsonRealize.com

ACT 1

1. After watching the video, what is the first question that comes to mind?

2. Write the Main Question you will answer.

3. **Construct Arguments** Predict an answer to this Main Question. Explain your prediction.

4. On the number line below, write a time that is too early to be the answer. Write a time that is too late.

Too early   Too late

5. Plot your prediction on the same number line.

Go Online | PearsonRealize.com   Topic 2 3-Act Mathematical Modeling   113

3-Act Mathematical Modeling *continued*

Activity

ACT 2 ▶ The Model

Identify Important Info

Have students complete **Question 6**.

Q: What information would be helpful to solve the problem? [Sample answers: What percent the battery is at, how long the phone has already been used, what the unit rate of minutes per percent used is]

Q: How could you get that information?

Q: Why do you need that information?

Reveal the Information

Reveal the information provided below using the online interactivity. Have students record information in **Question 7**.

Current time: 3:42
Current battery: 20%
Data point 2: 16% at 3:57
Data point 3: 11% at 4:16

Develop a Model

As students answer **Questions 8 and 9**, look for inefficient methods that they are using and prompt them to think about organizing the information before making a model.

Q: What is the unit rate? [Sample answer: About 3.75 minutes per percent of battery]

Use the Model to Propose a Solution

After students answer **Questions 8 and 9**, facilitate a discussion about solution methods. If needed, project the possible student solutions (shown below).

⬚ **Available Online**

ACT 2

6. What information in this situation would be helpful to know? How would you use that information?

7. **Use Appropriate Tools** What tools can you use to get the information you need? Record the information as you find it.

8. **Model with Math** Represent the situation using the mathematical content, concepts, and skills from this topic. Use your representation to answer the Main Question.

9. What is your answer to the Main Question? Is it earlier or later than your prediction? Explain why.

114 **Topic 2** 3-Act Mathematical Modeling ⬚ Go Online | PearsonRealize.com

---

Possible Student Solutions

Tandy's Work

Time	Percent
3:42	20
3:57	16
4:16	11

$$\frac{15 \text{ minutes}}{4 \text{ percent}} = \frac{3.75 \text{ minutes}}{1 \text{ percent}} \qquad \frac{19 \text{ minutes}}{5 \text{ percent}} = \frac{3.8 \text{ minutes}}{1 \text{ percent}}$$

The unit rate is about 3.8 minutes per percent.
3.8 × 11 ≈ 42 minutes.
The battery will last until 4:58.

Tandy finds each unit rate using a table and then adds the remaining time.

Li's Work

Lost 9% in 34 minutes

$$\frac{34 \text{ minutes}}{9\%} = \frac{x \text{ minutes}}{11\%}$$

$$34 \cdot 11 = 9x$$
$$42 \approx x$$

Phone will be at 0% after 42 minutes
4:16 $\xrightarrow{42 \text{ minutes}}$ 4:58

Li uses the first and last data points to find a unit rate, and then writes and solves an equation to find the remaining time.

CT 3 The Solution and Sequel

Available Online

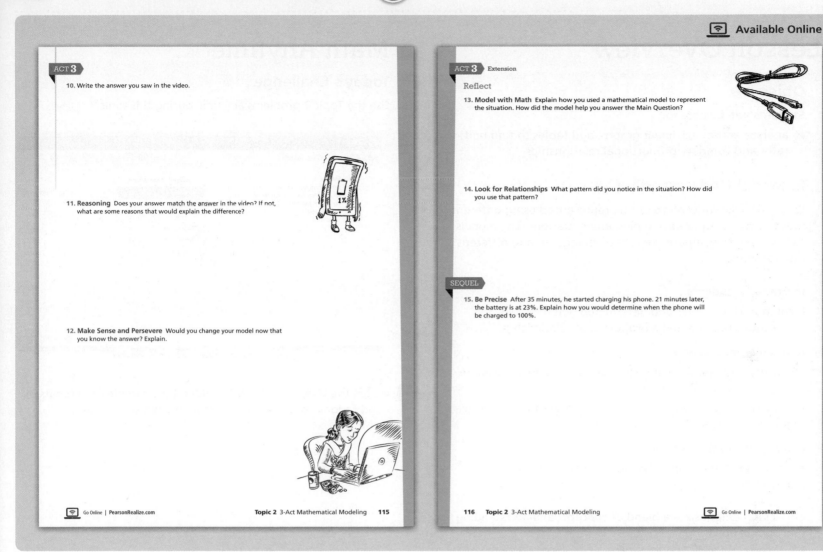

ACT 3

10. Write the answer you saw in the video.

11. **Reasoning** Does your answer match the answer in the video? If not, what are some reasons that would explain the difference?

12. **Make Sense and Persevere** Would you change your model now that you know the answer? Explain.

Go Online | PearsonRealize.com

Topic 2 3-Act Mathematical Modeling **115**

ACT 3 Extension

Reflect

13. **Model with Math** Explain how you used a mathematical model to represent the situation. How did the model help you answer the Main Question?

14. **Look for Relationships** What pattern did you notice in the situation? How did you use that pattern?

SEQUEL

15. **Be Precise** After 35 minutes, he started charging his phone. 21 minutes later, the battery is at 23%. Explain how you would determine when the phone will be charged to 100%.

116 **Topic 2** 3-Act Mathematical Modeling

Go Online | PearsonRealize.com

Use the Video to Reveal the Answer

The final part of the video shows the remaining time before the device powers down. Have students complete **Question 10**. Congratulate the students who were closest to the actual answer.

Main Question Answer
The phone lasts until 5:01.

Validate Conclusions

After students complete **Questions 11 and 12** encourage them to discuss possible sources of error inherent in using math to model real-world situations. Look for students to point out that their models are still useful even though they are not perfect.

Q: Why does your answer not match the answer in the video? [Sample answer: The rate the battery drains also depends on what you use the phone for.]

Q: How useful was your model at predicting the answer?

Q: How could your model better represent the situation?

Reflect on Thinking

Look for Relationships If time allows, have students complete **Questions 13 and 14** as an extension. Use this opportunity to discuss how students incorporate mathematical processes during the task.

Pose the Sequel

Be Precise Use **Question 15** to present a similar problem situation involving proportionality. You can assign to early finishers or as homework so students can test the usefulness of their models.

Q: After 35 minutes, he started charging his phone. 21 minutes later, the battery is at 23%. Explain how you would determine when the phone will be charged to 100% [Using their models and the answer in the video, look for student solutions around 90 minutes.]

Q: If he uses his smartphone while it is charging, will the battery percent increase or decrease? [increase]

Lesson 2-5

Compare Proportional Relationships

Lesson Overview

FOCUS

Objective

Students will be able to:

✔ analyze equations, linear graphs, and tables to find unit rates and compare proportional relationships.

Essential Understanding

Proportional relationships can be represented using different models, including graphs, tables, and equations. The models can be used to compare the rate of change among different relationships.

COHERENCE

In Grade 7, students:

• computed unit rates and determined whether two quantities represented a proportional relationship.

In this lesson, students:

• identify and calculate unit rates and use them to compare proportional relationships.

• compare proportional relationships represented with linear graphs, equations, ratios, and tables.

Later in this topic, students will:

• make the connection between proportional relationships and slope.

RIGOR

This lesson emphasizes a blend of **conceptual understanding** and **application**.

• Students will extend their understanding of proportional relationships and unit rates by finding and comparing rates of change between quantities from different representations.

• Students will apply their knowledge of ratios to compare proportional relationships in different forms.

Math Anytime

Today's Challenge

Use the Topic 2 problems any time during this topic.

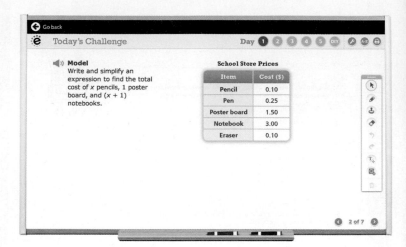

Watch the **Listen and Look For Video** for strategies and habits of mind to look for as students complete work on this lesson.

☑ Mathematics Overview

In this lesson, students will recognize that there are different models that can represent proportional relationships. They use various models to make comparisons between two different scenarios, and give verbal descriptions of the result.

Applying Math Practices

Make Sense and Persevere
Students will interpret and make sense of the quantities presented in real-world situations and identify the relationship between them. They will find and compute unit rates from different types of representations.

Construct Arguments
Students will compare proportional relationships and justify their conclusions. They will provide complete and clear explanations.

STEP 1 | Develop: Problem-Based Learning

15-20 min

Activity

Solve & Discuss It!

Construct Arguments As students work through the *Solve & Discuss It*, listen and look for ways in which students justify their reasoning, and incorporate them into the classroom discussion.

Before [WHOLE CLASS]

1 Implement Tasks that Promote Reasoning and Problem Solving

Q: What reasons might Mei Li for choosing one orchard over another? [Sample answer: She could choose the basket that costs less, or she could choose the basket with the lower price per pound of apples.]

2 Build Understanding

Q: How can you describe the price of each basket of apples? [Sample answer: You can use ratios to show the price of apples at each orchard. Annie's: $7.25 to 20 lb. Franklin's: $5.00 to 12 lb.]

During [SMALL GROUP]

3 Support Productive Struggle in Learning Mathematics

Q: Since the baskets are different sizes, how can you compare them to find the better deal? [Sample answer: Compare the unit rates or unit costs.]

Q: How would you find the unit rate or unit cost? [Sample answer: You could divide the price in dollars by the weight in pounds.]

After [WHOLE CLASS]

4 Facilitate Meaningful Mathematical Discourse

Ask students to share their solutions. If needed, project Anthony's and Zelda's work and ask:

Q: What is similar about Anthony's and Zelda's work? [Sample answer: They both find the price per pound of apples.]

Q: How did Anthony determine which orchard has the best price per pound? [Sample answer: He divides the total price by the number of pounds for each orchard and compares.]

5 Transition to Visual Learning

Q: For customers who pick their own apples, Annie's charges $0.30 per pound. If you were to graph this relationship, with pounds on the *x*-axis and dollars on the *y*-axis, what are some points that would be on the graph? [(1, 0.3), (2, 0.6), etc.]

6 Extension for Early Finishers

Q: What is the least common multiple of 12 and 20? [60]

Q: Why might using 60 pounds of apples be a good benchmark for comparing the two orchards? [Sample answer: 20 and 12 are both factors of 60, so you can compare the cost of 60 apples at both orchards by multiplying the price per basket by whole numbers.]

Analyze Student Work

Available Online

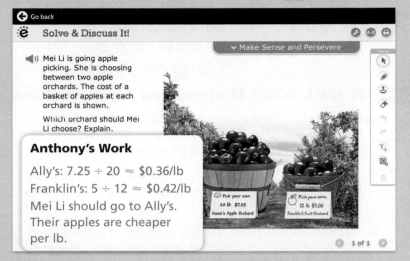

Anthony's Work

Ally's: 7.25 ÷ 20 ≈ $0.36/lb
Franklin's: 5 ÷ 12 ≈ $0.42/lb
Mei Li should go to Ally's. Their apples are cheaper per lb.

Anthony finds the price per pound of apples at each orchard and compares them to find the lowest price.

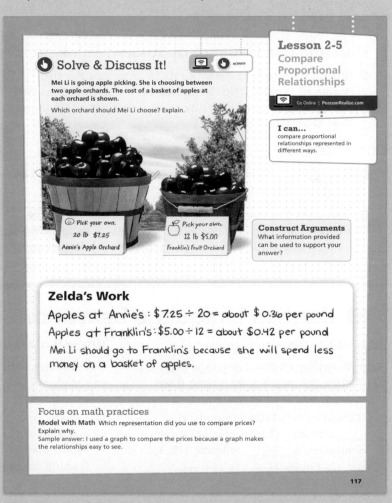

Lesson 2-5
Compare Proportional Relationships

Zelda's Work

Apples at Annie's : $7.25 ÷ 20 = about $0.36 per pound
Apples at Franklin's : $5.00 ÷ 12 = about $0.42 per pound
Mei Li should go to Franklin's because she will spend less money on a basket of apples.

Zelda also finds the price per pound of apples, but reasons that if Mei Li wants to spend less overall, then she should go to Franklin's Orchard.

STEP 2 | Develop: Visual Learning

ETP **Establish Mathematics Goals to Focus Learning**

Engage students in a discussion about the *Essential Question*. Make sure students understand that, in a proportional relationship, the quantities are related by the unit rate.

EXAMPLE 1 **Compare Proportional Relationships Represented by Tables and Graphs**

ETP **Use and Connect Mathematical Representations**

Q: How do you find the unit rate of the Cessna's speed? [Sample answer: Divide the distance by the time: 40 kilometers ÷ 5 minutes = 8 kilometers per 1 minute.]

Q: How do you find the unit rate of the Boeing 747? [Sample answer: Use two points on the graph. Divide the difference in distance by the difference in time.]

Q: Suppose another plane had the same graph as the Boeing 747. What could you conclude about this plane? [Sample answer: If the plane has the same graph as the Boeing 747, you can conclude that the plane travels at the same rate.]

 Try It!

ETP **Elicit and Use Evidence of Student Thinking**

Q: Do you have to find the unit rate in order to solve this problem? Explain. [No; Sample answer: You can compare the number of birds made by each person after 10 minutes, since that data is provided.]

Convince Me!

Q: Find the point that Josh's graph would go through with an x-value of 10. [(10, 25)]

Q: How does this point compare to Marlo's graph? [Sample answer: Marlo's graph passes through (10, 2), so Josh's graph is much steeper. Josh makes origami birds at a faster rate.]

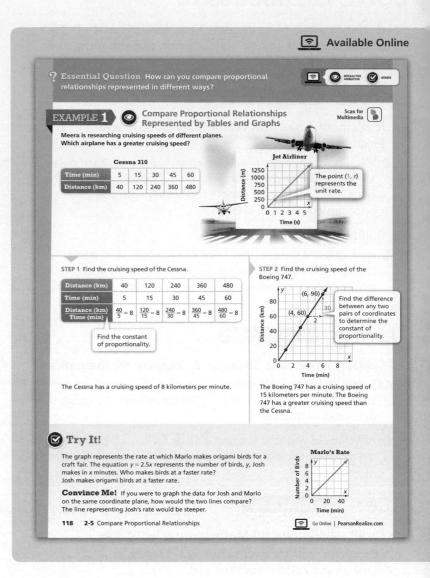

Students can access the *Visual Learning Animation Plus* by using the **BouncePages app** to scan this page. Students can download the app for free in their mobile devices' app store.

ELL English Language Learners

BEGINNING Use with Example 1.

Help struggling English Language Learners summarize the problem by having them complete the following sentences.

The Cessna travels 120 kilometers in _____ minutes. The Boeing 747 travels 15 kilometers in _____ minute. [15, 1]

Q: Which of those rates is a unit rate? [The Boeing's rate]

Q: If you graphed the Cessna's cruising speed and then compared both graphs, which would have the steeper graph? [The Boeing's graph would be steeper.]

INTERMEDIATE Use with Example 1.

Have students work in pairs to help them use academic language by retelling basic information represented in the diagram.

Q: Explain in your own words what the question is asking. [Sample answer: Which plane is flying at a greater cruising speed?]

Q: Graph the Cessna's cruising speed. Explain in your own words how you can answer the question from just looking at the graphs without making any computations. [Sample answer: The Boeing has a steeper graph, so it has a greater cruising speed.]

ADVANCED Use with Example 1.

Q: Explain what *constant rate* means in this problem. [Sample answer: Each plane's speed stays the same over time.]

Q: What do the unit rates mean in this problem? [Sample answer: The unit rates tell the speed of each plane in kilometers per minute.]

Q: How can you use the unit rates to solve the problem? [Sample answer: The plane with the larger unit rate is traveling at a faster cruising speed.]

EXAMPLE 2 Compare Proportional Relationships Represented by Graphs and Equations

TP Pose Purposeful Questions

Note that health points in a video game indicate how much life a player has remaining.

Q: To find Brianna's unit rate, you substituted 1 for x and found y. To find Daniel's unit rate, you found the y-value when the x-value is 1. Explain why using unit rates allows you to compare who earns points faster. [Sample answer: Since the unit rates use the same time increment, one minute, you can compare the number of points earned per minute.]

Q: If you graphed the line representing Brianna's score, would her line be steeper or less steep than Daniel's line? Explain. [Sample answer: Since her unit rate is less, her line is less steep.]

EXAMPLE 3 Compare Proportional Relationships Represented by Graphs and Verbal Descriptions

TP Pose Purposeful Questions

Q: To find the unit rate of the raisin cereal, how can you determine which quantity is the numerator and which is the denominator? [Sample answer: The question asked for the "cost per ounce," so cost is the numerator and weight in ounces is the denominator.]

Q: How does the point (1, 0.25) give the unit rate of the granola cereal per ounce? [Sample answer: It shows that the cost is $0.25 per 1 ounce of cereal.]

Try It!

ETP Elicit and Use Evidence of Student Thinking

Q: How can you find the unit rate for the United States' train? [Sample answer: Divide the distance in kilometers by time in hours to get the unit rate of kilometers per hour.]

Q: How can you find the unit rate for Japan's train? [Sample answer: Use the point (3, 1,000) to see that the unit rate is about 333 kilometers per hour.]

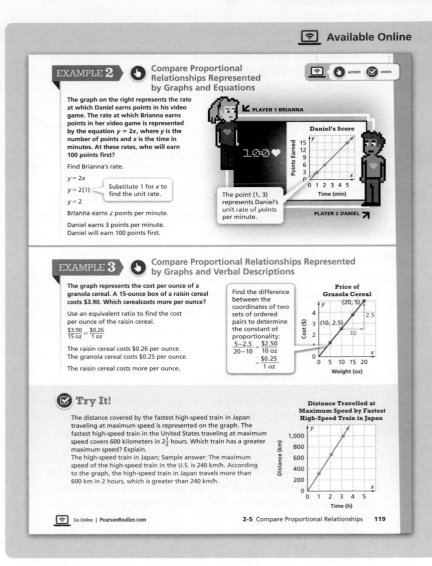

ADDITIONAL EXAMPLES

For additional examples go to PearsonRealize.com.

Response to Intervention

USE WITH EXAMPLE 3 Make sure students understand how to write ratios for each rate.

Q: How do you find the unit cost for the raisin cereal? [Sample answer: Divide the cost by the weight in ounces.]

Q: How could you find the unit cost for the granola cereal from this graph? Explain. [Sample answer: The point (4, 1) means that 4 ounces cost $1. You could divide 1 by 4 to get the unit cost per ounce.]

Enrichment

USE WITH EXAMPLE 2 Challenge students to write an equation using the unit rate.

• Answer the following questions.

Q: What equation could you write to find the time it would take Brianna to reach 60 points? [60 = 2x]

Q: What equation could you write to find the time it would take Daniel to reach 60 points? [60 = 3x]

STEP **2** | Develop: Visual Learning *continued*

Key Concept

Activity

KEY CONCEPT

ETP **Pose Purposeful Questions**

Q: Describe the connection between unit rates and steepness on a graph. [Sample answer: The steeper the line, the greater the unit rate.]

Do You Understand/Do You Know How?

ETP **Build Procedural Fluency from Conceptual Understanding**

? Essential Question Students should understand how to find the unit rate from a verbal description, a table, a linear graph, or an equation.

ITEM 4

Q: How do you find Amanda's unit rate? Pete's unit rate? [Sample answer: The point (4, 24) means that Amanda makes $24 in 4 hours, so divide 24 by 4. Pete makes $15 in 3 hours, so divide 15 by 3.]

Prevent Misconceptions

ITEM 5 It is not possible to find an exact unit rate from the given graph. Some students may need help finding another strategy to solve this problem.

Q: The problem asks at which store will Milo pay a lower rate for dog food. Do you have to know the exact unit rate to solve this problem? Explain. [No; Sample answer: You can graph the rate that Milo pays and compare the steepness of the graphs.]

Q: If Milo pays $3 per pound at Pat's, how much would he pay for 2 pounds? For 3 pounds? [$6, $9]

Q: Can you use one of those answers to solve the problem? [Yes; Sample answer: You can see on the graph that 3 lb of dog food at Mark's costs more than $10. Since 3 pounds costs only $9 at Pat's, Pat's has a lower rate.]

ADDITIONAL EXAMPLE **3**

Help students understand how to use graphs and verbal descriptions to determine unit rates and compare them.

Make sure students understand the relationship between unit rates and the steepness of a line on a graph.

Q: Why would you use the points chosen to find the unit rate? [Sample answer: Since these points are given on the graph, and other points do not lie on actual gridlines, you can use these points to calculate the unit rate easily.]

Q: If you graphed the unit rate represented on the sticker of Allen's new car, how would that line compare to the line that is graphed? Explain. [Sample answer: The line representing the unit rate on the sticker would be steeper.]

🛜 **Available Online**

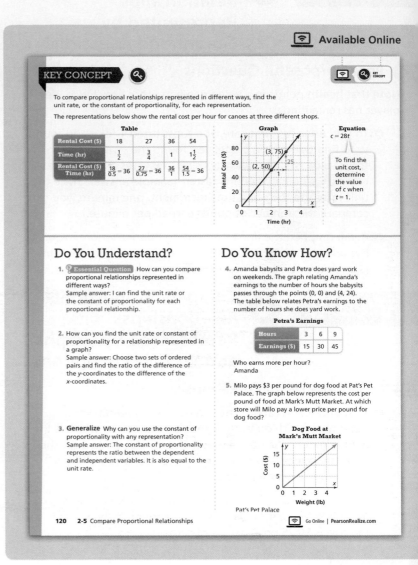

🛜 **Available Online**

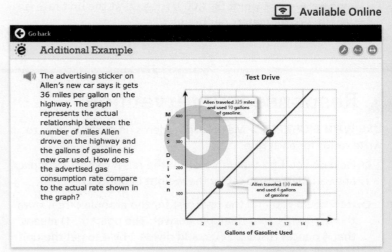

Answer: The advertised rate is greater than the actual rate.

Practice & Problem Solving

Available Online

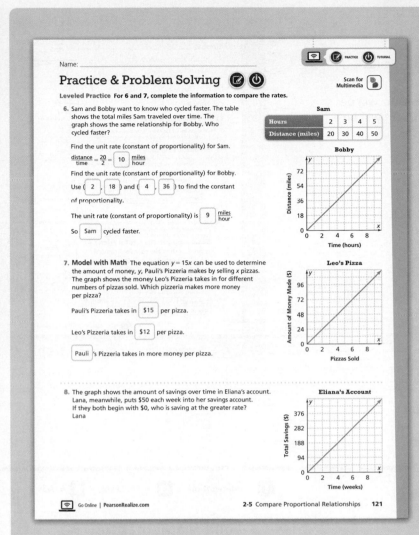

Name: _____

Practice & Problem Solving

Scan for Multimedia

Leveled Practice For 6 and 7, complete the information to compare the rates.

6. Sam and Bobby want to know who cycled faster. The table shows the total miles Sam traveled over time. The graph shows the same relationship for Bobby. Who cycled faster?

Sam

Hours	2	3	4	5
Distance (miles)	20	30	40	50

Find the unit rate (constant of proportionality) for Sam.

$\dfrac{\text{distance}}{\text{time}} = \dfrac{20}{2} = \boxed{10} \ \dfrac{\text{miles}}{\text{hour}}$

Find the unit rate (constant of proportionality) for Bobby.

Use (2 , 18) and (4 , 36) to find the constant of proportionality.

The unit rate (constant of proportionality) is $\boxed{9} \ \dfrac{\text{miles}}{\text{hour}}$.

So Sam cycled faster.

Bobby (graph: Distance (miles) vs Time (hours))

7. **Model with Math** The equation $y = 15x$ can be used to determine the amount of money, y, Pauli's Pizzeria makes by selling x pizzas. The graph shows the money Leo's Pizzeria takes in for different numbers of pizzas sold. Which pizzeria makes more money per pizza?

Pauli's Pizzeria takes in $15 per pizza.

Leo's Pizzeria takes in $12 per pizza.

Pauli 's Pizzeria takes in more money per pizza.

Leo's Pizza (graph: Amount of Money Made ($) vs Pizzas Sold)

8. The graph shows the amount of savings over time in Eliana's account. Lana, meanwhile, puts $50 each week into her savings account. If they both begin with $0, who is saving at the greater rate?

Lana

Eliana's Account (graph: Total Savings ($) vs Time (weeks))

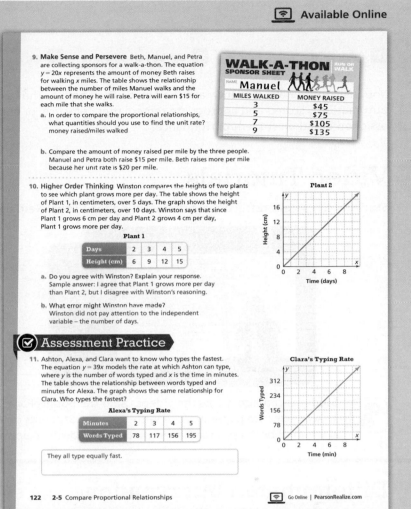

9. **Make Sense and Persevere** Beth, Manuel, and Petra are collecting sponsors for a walk-a-thon. The equation $y = 20x$ represents the amount of money Beth raises for walking x miles. The table shows the relationship between the number of miles Manuel walks and the amount of money he will raise. Petra will earn $15 for each mile that she walks.

WALK-A-THON SPONSOR SHEET

NAME **Manuel**

MILES WALKED	MONEY RAISED
3	$45
5	$75
7	$105
9	$135

a. In order to compare the proportional relationships, what quantities should you use to find the unit rate? money raised/miles walked

b. Compare the amount of money raised per mile by the three people. Manuel and Petra both raise $15 per mile. Beth raises more per mile because her unit rate is $20 per mile.

10. **Higher Order Thinking** Winston compares the heights of two plants to see which plant grows more per day. The table shows the height of Plant 1, in centimeters, over 5 days. The graph shows the height of Plant 2, in centimeters, over 10 days. Winston says that since Plant 1 grows 6 cm per day and Plant 2 grows 4 cm per day, Plant 1 grows more per day.

Plant 1

Days	2	3	4	5
Height (cm)	6	9	12	15

Plant 2 (graph: Height (cm) vs Time (days))

a. Do you agree with Winston? Explain your response. Sample answer: I agree that Plant 1 grows more per day than Plant 2, but I disagree with Winston's reasoning.

b. What error might Winston have made? Winston did not pay attention to the independent variable – the number of days.

Assessment Practice

11. Ashton, Alexa, and Clara want to know who types the fastest. The equation $y = 39x$ models the rate at which Ashton can type, where y is the number of words typed and x is the time in minutes. The table shows the relationship between words typed and minutes for Alexa. The graph shows the same relationship for Clara. Who types the fastest?

Alexa's Typing Rate

Minutes	2	3	4	5
Words Typed	78	117	156	195

Clara's Typing Rate (graph: Words Typed vs Time (min))

They all type equally fast.

You may opt to have students complete the automatically scored Practice & Problem Solving items online.

Error Intervention

ITEM 7 Some students may have difficulty plotting points on the coordinate plane.

Q: What y-value does the first horizontal line above zero represent? [12] What y-value does the horizontal line between 24 and 48 represent? [36]

Q: How do you plot the point (2, 30) on this graph? [Sample answer: From 0, move 2 grid lines to the right and $2\frac{1}{2}$ gridlines up to 30.]

Challenge

ITEM 8 Challenge advanced students to write equations that model each girl's earnings.

Q: What is the unit rate for Lana? [$50/week] For Eliana? [$47/week]

Q: Write an equation for Lana and for Eliana that represents how many weeks it will take each to earn $750. [Lana: $750 = 50x$; Eliana: $750 = 47x$]

Item Analysis

Example	Items	DOK
	6	1
1	9	2
	10	3
2	7	1
3	8	1
	11	2

PearsonRealize.com

Assess   Tutorials   Worksheets

Lesson Quiz

 Use the student scores on the Lesson Quiz to prescribe differentiated assignments.

I Intervention 0–3 Points   **O** On-Level 4 Points   **A** Advanced 5 Points

You may opt to have students take the Lesson Quiz online. The Lesson Quiz will be automatically scored and appropriate remediation, practice, or enrichment will be assigned based on student performance.

Video Tutorials

Students can access instructional tutorials using the **Virtual Nerd app**.

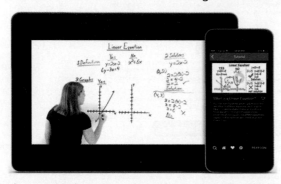

 Students can also access the videos using the **BouncePages app** to scan exercise pages marked with this icon. Students can download both apps for free in their mobile devices' app store.

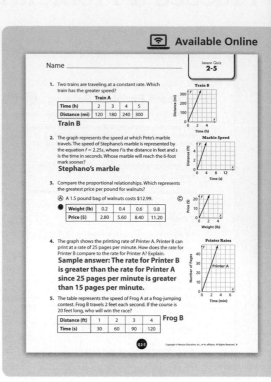

Differentiated Intervention

I = Intervention   **O** = On-Level   **A** = Advanced

Reteach to Build Understanding **I**

Provides scaffolded reteaching for the key lesson concepts.

Additional Vocabulary Support **I** **O**

Helps students develop and reinforce understanding of key terms and concepts.

Build Mathematical Literacy **I**

Provides support for struggling readers to build mathematical literacy.

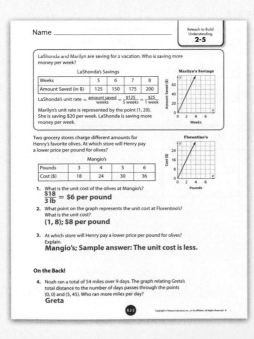

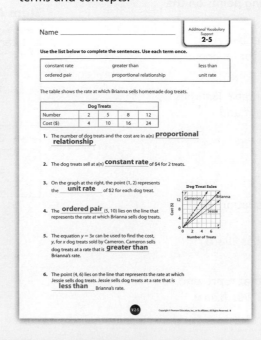

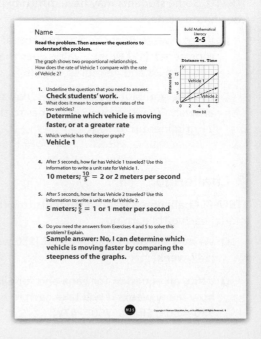

Practice Worksheets Math Tools Math Games

Additional Practice

You may opt to have students complete the automatically scored Additional Practice items online.

Item Analysis

Example	Items	DOK
1	1	1
1	4	2
2	2, 6	2
3	3	2
3	5	3

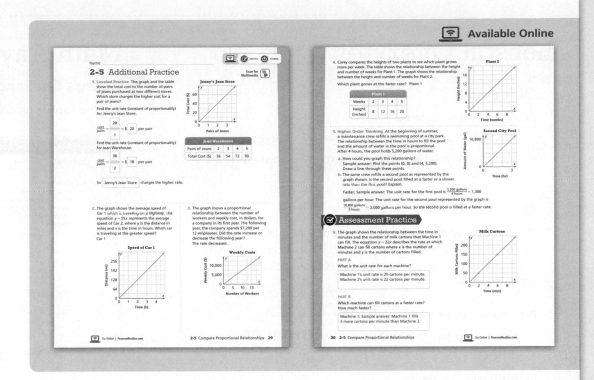

Available Online

Differentiated Intervention

I = Intervention   **O** = On-Level   **A** = Advanced

Enrichment O A

Presents engaging problems and activities that extend the lesson concepts.

Math Tools and Games I O A

Offers additional activities and games to build understanding and fluency.

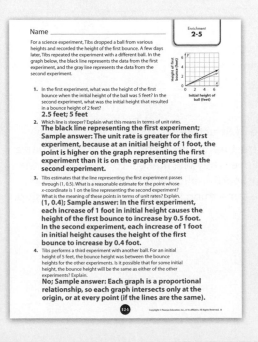

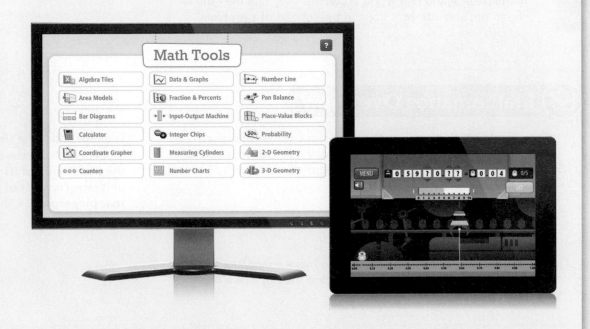

Activity

Lesson 2-6
Connect Proportional Relationships and Slope

FOCUS

Lesson Overview

Objective

Students will be able to:

✔ find the slope of a line using different strategies.

✔ interpret a slope in context and relate it to steepness on a graph.

Essential Understanding

Slope is a measure of the steepness of a line and is equal to the rate of change between quantities. In a proportional relationship, the slope is the same as the unit rate and the constant of proportionality.

COHERENCE

Previously in this topic, students:

• used models to represent proportional relationships.

• related the steepness of a line to its unit rate.

In this lesson, students:

• find the slope of a line from a graph.

• interpret slope in a real-world context.

Later in this topic, students:

• use slope to write linear equations.

RIGOR

This lesson emphasizes a blend of **conceptual understanding** and **application**.

• Students understand that the slope of a line is a measure of its rate of change and relate slope to steepness on a graph. They extend their understanding of unit rate and constant of proportionality to include slope.

• Students apply what they know about unit rates to solve mathematical and real-world problems. They find the ratio of rise to run and interpret slope in the context of a problem.

Math Anytime

Today's Challenge

Use the Topic 2 problems any time during this topic.

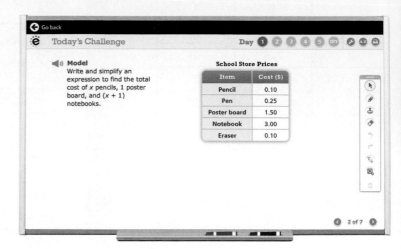

✓ Mathematics Overview

In this lesson, students will continue to work with proportional relationships as they review slope and how it is used to measure the steepness of a line. They also will use previous knowledge to find a unit rate for given scenarios.

Applying Math Practices

Reason Abstractly and Quantitatively
Students will use their reasoning skills to make connections regarding slope, unit rate, and how to find the slope of a line using two points.

Look for and Make Use of Structure
Students will use the structure of the graph of a line to recognize the significance of its slope. They will make a connection between unit rate, constant of proportionality, and slope to understand that they represent the same thing in a proportional relationship.

Solve & Discuss It!

Look for Relationships As students work through the *Solve & Discuss It*, listen and look for a variety of strategies students use and how they apply what they know about graphs and proportions to determine how much Rashida is paid per game.

Before [WHOLE CLASS]

TP **1 Implement Tasks that Promote Reasoning and Problem Solving**

Q: If you created a graph with the *x*-axis representing games and the *y*-axis representing dollars, what would be the units for the unit rate? [Dollars per game]

2 Build Understanding

Q: If (5, 98.5) were a point on the graph, what would it mean? [Sample answer: The point would mean that Rashida earns $98.50 for working 5 games.]

During [SMALL GROUP]

TP **3 Support Productive Struggle in Learning Mathematics**

Q: How would you find the unit rate? [Sample answer: Divide 98.50 by 5 to find the unit rate for 1 game.]

Q: How could you use the unit rate to find the amount Rashida earns in all? [Sample answer: Multiply the unit rate by the total number of games.]

After [WHOLE CLASS]

TP **4 Facilitate Meaningful Mathematical Discourse**

Ask students to share their solutions. If needed, project James's and Paige's work and ask:

Q: What strategy does James use to determine Rashida's earnings? [James solves a proportion to find the total amount Rashida earns.]

Q: How does James's strategy differ from Paige's? [Paige finds the unit rate using the ratio of 98.5 to 5 and then multiplies by the total number of games.]

5 Transition to Visual Learning

Q: For each game she works, how do Rashida's earnings change? [Sample answer: Her earnings increase by $19.70 for every game she works.]

Q: If this relationship were graphed, what would happen to the *y*-value each time the *x*-value increases by 1? [Sample answer: The *y*-value would increase by 19.70.]

6 Extension for Early Finishers

Q: As a returning referee next season, Rashida will earn $21.70 per game. How would a graph of next year's earnings compare to this year's graph? Explain. [Sample answer: The unit rate is greater, so the graph will be steeper.]

Analyze Student Work

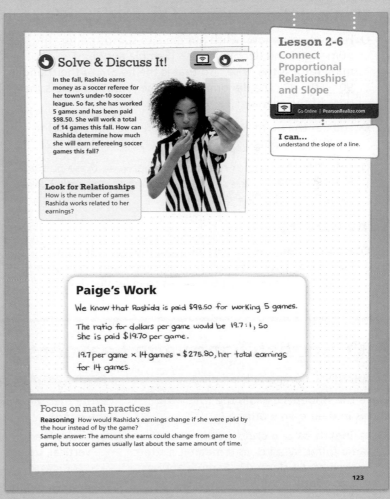

🖵 Available Online

← Go back

ë Solve & Discuss It!

⌄ Make Sense and Persevere

🔊 In the fall, Rashida earns money as a soccer referee for her town's under-10 soccer league. So far, she has worked 5 games and has been paid $98.50. She will work a total of 14 games this fall. How can Rashida determine how much she will earn refereeing soccer games this fall?

James's work

$\frac{98.5}{5} = \frac{x}{14} \cdot 14 \cdot \frac{98.5}{5} = \frac{x}{14} \cdot 14$

$x = 275.80$

Rashida will earn $275.80 for 14 games.

◁ 1 of 1 ▷

James uses a proportion to identify the total amount earned.

🕐 Solve & Discuss It! 🖥 🕐 ACTIVITY

In the fall, Rashida earns money as a soccer referee for her town's under-10 soccer league. So far, she has worked 5 games and has been paid $98.50. She will work a total of 14 games this fall. How can Rashida determine how much she will earn refereeing soccer games this fall?

Look for Relationships
How is the number of games Rashida works related to her earnings?

Lesson 2-6
Connect Proportional Relationships and Slope

🛜 Go Online | PearsonRealize.com

I can...
understand the slope of a line.

Paige's Work

We know that Rashida is paid $98.50 for working 5 games.

The ratio for dollars per game would be 19.7 : 1, so she is paid $19.70 per game.

19.7 per game × 14 games = $275.80, her total earnings for 14 games.

Focus on math practices

Reasoning How would Rashida's earnings change if she were paid by the hour instead of by the game?
Sample answer: The amount she earns could change from game to game, but soccer games usually last about the same amount of time.

123

Paige uses the 5 games and $98.50 to find the unit rate of dollars per game. She then multiplies this ratio by 14.

STEP 2 | Develop: Visual Learning

 Visual Learning | Assess

ETP Establish Mathematics Goals to Focus Learning

Engage students in a discussion about the *Essential Question*. Make sure they understand that slope is a rate of change between two quantities.

EXAMPLE 1 👁 Understand Slope

ETP Use and Connect Mathematical Representations

Q: Slope is equal to "rise over run." What is *rise* and what is *run*? [Sample answer: Rise is how much the graph goes up or down between points, and run is how far the graph goes right or left between points.]

Q: Why is the unit rate equivalent to $\frac{9}{12}$? [Sample answer: The graph contains the point (12, 9), and the unit rate on the graph of a proportional relationship is equal to $\frac{y}{x}$.]

Q: Explain what a slope of $\frac{3}{4}$ means in terms of rise and run. [Sample answer: A line rises 3 units for every 4 units it moves to the right.]

☑ Try It!

ETP Elicit and Use Evidence of Student Thinking

Q: How do you know which numbers to substitute for the numerator and denominator? [Sample answer: The numerator is the "rise," so that is the height of the triangle: $90 - 60 = 30$. The denominator is the "run," so that is the base of the triangle: $3 - 2 = 1$.]

Q: Look at the point (1, 30). What is the rise from (1, 30) to (3, 90)? [60] What is the run from (1, 30) to (3, 90)? [2]

Q: Calculate the ratio of rise over run between these points. Is it equivalent to the ratio found using the triangle? [Yes; Sample answer: $\frac{60}{2} = \frac{30}{1}$]

Convince Me!

Q: How can you use the axis labels to interpret the slope? [Sample answer: The vertical axis is *miles* and the horizontal is *days*, so rise over run translates to miles per day.]

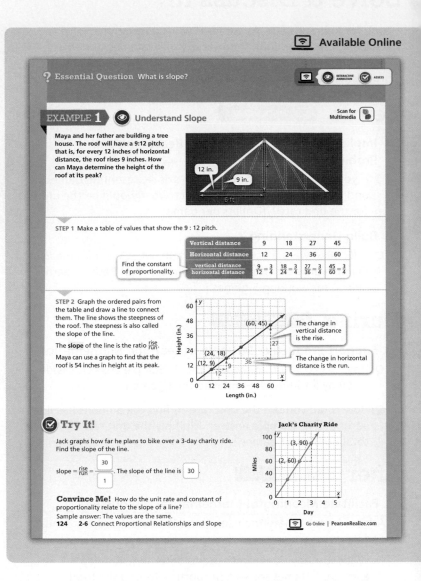

 Students can access the *Visual Learning Animation Plus* by using the **BouncePages app** to scan this page. Students can download the app for free in their mobile devices' app store.

🄴🄻🄻 English Language Learners

BEGINNING Complete Example 1.

Have the students explain the following terms in their own words.

Q: In English, *sloped* and *slanted* mean the same thing. What does it mean if a street or driveway is slanted? [Sample answer: It is not flat.]

Q: What does *constant* mean, and what does it tell you about the slope of a line? [Sample answer: *Constant* means that it does not change; it remains the same. The slope of a line is the same anywhere on the line.]

INTERMEDIATE Complete Example 1.

Write the following words and phrases on the board:

rise, left and right, run, horizontal, vertical, up and down

Ask students to work in pairs to sort the terms into two groups of related terms.

Then, write these terms on the board:

unit rate, slope, absolute value, constant of proportionality

Have the student pairs determine which term does not belong with the others, and explain their choice to the class.

ADVANCED Complete Example 1.

Have students work with a partner to relate the concept of slope to the given problem and graph.

Q: Explain what *rise over run* means. [Sample answer: The ratio of the change in vertical distance over the change in horizontal distance on a graph.]

Q: Fill in the blanks:

For every horizontal foot, the roof rises _____ inches. [9]

For every horizontal inch, the roof rises _____. [$\frac{3}{4}$ of an inch]

EXAMPLE 2 Find the Slope from Two Points

ETP Pose Purposeful Questions

Q: How could you write $-800 - (-400)$ in a simpler way? [Sample answer: $-800 + 400$ or $400 - 800$]

Q: What other two points could have been used to calculate the slope? [Sample answer: $(0, 0)$ and $(10, -800)$]

Q: Why do you think the slope is negative? [Sample answer: The line slants down from left to right.]

EXAMPLE 3 Interpret Slope

ETP Pose Purposeful Questions

Q: To move from one point to the next on the triangle, go over 2 and up 110. Is the slope equal to $\frac{110}{2}$? Explain. [No; Sample answer: The ratio $\frac{110}{2}$ can be expressed as the equivalent ratio $\frac{55}{1}$. This represents the slope, 55 miles in 1 hour.]

Q: How do the axis labels help to determine that the units for the slope are miles per hour? [Sample answer: The rise is the change in the y-values, which is miles. The run is the change in the x-values, which is the number of hours.]

Try It!

ETP Elicit and Use Evidence of Student Thinking

Q: Look at the ratio, $\frac{35}{25}$, that you wrote to represent the slope. What common factor can be factored out of the numerator and denominator? [5]

Q: Fill in the blanks: To make the purple frosting, the ratio of red to blue food coloring is _____ to _____. [7, 5]

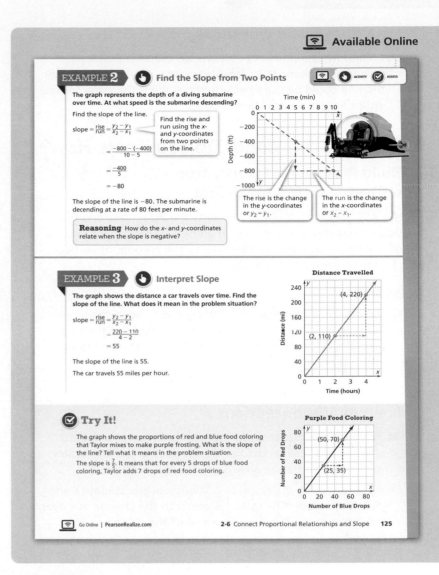

 ADDITIONAL EXAMPLES

For additional examples go to PearsonRealize.com.

Response to Intervention

USE WITH EXAMPLE 2 Demonstrate the importance of being precise when substituting values into the formula.

- Tell students that it doesn't matter which point is used for (x_1, y_1) and which is used for (x_2, y_2), but they must be consistent in the order in which x- and y-values are substituted.

  Q: Reverse the order in which the values are substituted. What ratio do you get? $\left[\frac{-400 - (-800)}{5 - 10}\right]$

  Q: Simplify the numerator and denominator of the ratio. $\left[\frac{400}{-5}\right]$ Divide the numerator and denominator by the common factor 5. $\left[\frac{80}{-1} \text{ or } -80\right]$

  Q: A student made a mistake in his calculations and found a slope of 80. How could the student use the graph to prove he made a mistake? [Sample answer: The line slopes downward from left to right. The slope should be a negative value.]

Enrichment

USE WITH EXAMPLE 3 TRY IT! Challenge students to use different strategies to solve the problem. Then, help them make a conceptual connection between graphs of proportional relationships and their slopes.

Q: Solve the problem using rise over run. [Sample answer: The line rises up 35 units and moves to the right 25 units, so $\frac{35}{25}$ is the rise over run. The slope simplifies to $\frac{7}{5}$.]

Q: Solve the problem by finding the ratio of y to x for the point $(70, 50)$. [The ratio is $\frac{70}{50} = \frac{7}{5}$.]

Q: The graph of a proportional relationship is a straight line through the origin. Explain why the slope of a proportional relationship is equal to $\frac{y}{x}$ for any point (x, y) on the line. [Sample answer: Because the line always contains the point $(0, 0)$, the slope is equal to $\frac{y - 0}{x - 0} = \frac{y}{x}$.]

KEY CONCEPT

ETP **Pose Purposeful Questions**

Q: Could any two points on the line be used for the slope formula? Explain. [Yes; Sample answer: Any two points on the line could be used because the slope is the same for the entire line. It is a constant ratio.]

Do You Understand/Do You Know How?

ETP **Build Procedural Fluency from Conceptual Understanding**

? **Essential Question** Students should understand that slope measures the steepness of a line and indicates a rate of change. The slope ratio is equal to the amount of vertical change to horizontal change.

ITEM 4

Q: Discuss some strategies for finding the slope of the line. [Sample answer: Calculate the rise over run, use the slope formula, or use the point (1, 3) to identify the unit rate, which is equal to the slope.]

RtI **Prevent Misconceptions**

ITEM 5 Make sure students understand that in a ratio that defines slope, the vertical change always goes in the numerator and the horizontal change always goes in the denominator.

Q: A student gave the slope as $\frac{3}{5}$. What was the student's error? [Sample answer: The ratio $\frac{3}{5}$ is equal to the change in x over the change in y. It is the reciprocal of the slope.]

🛜 Available Online

KEY CONCEPT

Slope is the measure of the steepness of a line. It represents the ratio of the rise (that is, the vertical distance) to the run (the horizontal distance) between two points on the line. In proportional relationships, slope is the same as the unit rate and constant of proportionality.

$$\text{slope} = \frac{\text{rise}}{\text{run}}$$

$$= \frac{\text{change in } y\text{-coordinates}}{\text{change in } x\text{-coordinates}}$$

$$= \frac{y_2 - y_1}{x_2 - x_1}$$

Theater Price

$\frac{\text{rise}}{\text{run}} = \frac{30}{2} = 15$. The slope of the line is 15.

rise: $75 - 45 = 30$

run: $5 - 3 = 2$

1 ticket costs $15. The constant of proportionality is 15.

Cost ($) / Number of Tickets

Do You Understand?

1. ? **Essential Question** What is slope?
   Sample answer: The slope of a line is the ratio of the rise to the run, or the change between two points on the line in y-coordinates divided by the change in x-coordinates.

2. **Reasoning** How is the slope related to a unit rate?
   Sample answer: The slope is a unit rate when written with a "run" of 1.

3. **Look for Relationships** Why is the slope between any two points on a straight line always the same?
   Sample answer: The rise and the run are in a proportional relationship. The ratio $\frac{\text{rise}}{\text{run}}$ will be the same for any two points on the line.

Do You Know How?

4. What is the slope of the line? 3

   Cost of Grapes
   Price ($) / Grapes (lb)

5. The scale of a model airplane is shown in the graph.
   a. Find the slope of the line using $\frac{y_2 - y_1}{x_2 - x_1}$. $\frac{5}{3}$
   b. What does the slope mean in the problem situation?
   Sample answer: The model is 3 cm for every 5 feet of the original airplane.

   Model Airplane
   Feet / Centimeters

ADDITIONAL EXAMPLE **3**

🛜 Available Online

Help students understand that there is more than one way to find the slope of the line in this problem.

Make sure students understand why the slope can be found using a single point.

Q: What would be the slope if you used the point (2, 30)? [Sample answer: It would still be 15 because $\frac{30}{2} = 15$.]

Q: Why can a single point be used to find the slope of this line? [Sample answer: The line goes through the origin, so (0, 0) is the second point. $\frac{90 - 0}{6 - 0}$ is the same as $\frac{90}{6} = \frac{15}{1}$ or 15.]

◀ Go back

ë **Additional Example**

🔊 The graph shows the cost of Hannah's piano lessons over time.

Find the slope of this line. Show two methods.

What does the slope mean in this situation?

Piano Lessons
Payment ($) / Number of Hours

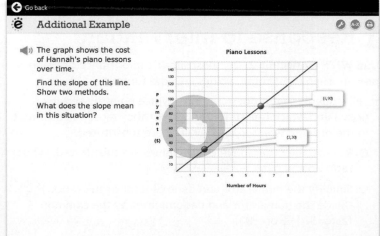

Answer: The slope of 15 represents the cost per hour for Hannah's piano lessons.

Practice & Problem Solving

Available Online

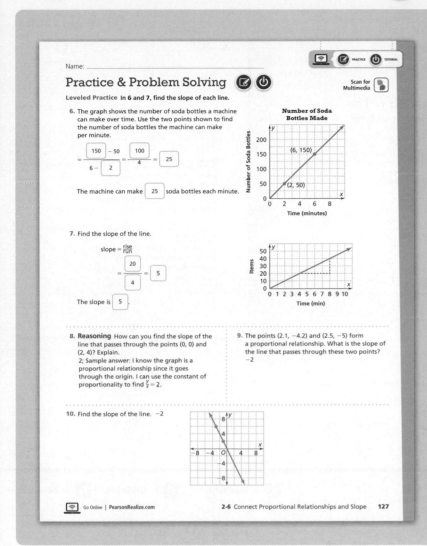

Name: _____

Practice & Problem Solving

Scan for Multimedia

Leveled Practice In 6 and 7, find the slope of each line.

6. The graph shows the number of soda bottles a machine can make over time. Use the two points shown to find the number of soda bottles the machine can make per minute.

$$= \frac{\boxed{150} - 50}{6 - \boxed{2}} = \frac{\boxed{100}}{\boxed{4}} = \boxed{25}$$

The machine can make $\boxed{25}$ soda bottles each minute.

Number of Soda Bottles Made

(6, 150)

(2, 50)

Time (minutes)

7. Find the slope of the line.

$$\text{slope} = \frac{\text{rise}}{\text{run}}$$

$$= \frac{\boxed{20}}{\boxed{4}} = \boxed{5}$$

The slope is $\boxed{5}$.

Items

Time (min)

8. **Reasoning** How can you find the slope of the line that passes through the points (0, 0) and (2, 4)? Explain.
2; Sample answer: I know the graph is a proportional relationship since it goes through the origin. I can use the constant of proportionality to find $\frac{y}{x} = 2$.

9. The points (2.1, −4.2) and (2.5, −5) form a proportional relationship. What is the slope of the line that passes through these two points? −2

10. Find the slope of the line. −2

11. The graph shows the number of Calories Natalia burned while running.
    a. What is the slope of the line? 10
    b. What does the slope tell you? Sample answer: Natalia burns 10 Calories per minute.

Calories Burned

Calories

Time (minutes)

12. **Critique Reasoning** A question on a test provides this graph and asks students to find the speed at which the car travels. Anna incorrectly says that the speed of the car is $\frac{1}{64}$ mile per hour.
    a. What is the speed of the car? 64 miles per hour
    b. What error might Anna have made? Sample answer: She found the change in the x-coordinates over the change in the y-coordinates.

Speed of a Car

Distance (miles)

Time (hours)

13. **Higher Order Thinking** You use a garden hose to fill a wading pool. If the water level rises 11 centimeters every 5 minutes and you record the data point of (10, y), what is the value of y? Use slope to justify your answer.

22 cm; slope $= \frac{\text{rise}}{\text{run}} = \frac{11}{5} = \frac{y}{10}$

Rises 11 cm every 5 min

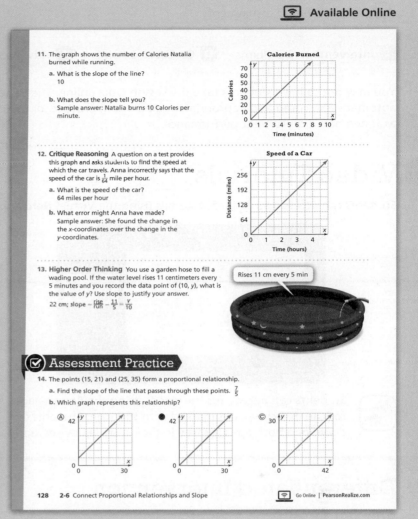

☑ Assessment Practice

14. The points (15, 21) and (25, 35) form a proportional relationship.
    a. Find the slope of the line that passes through these points. $\frac{7}{5}$
    b. Which graph represents this relationship?

    Ⓐ 42   ● 42   Ⓒ 30

    0   30   0   30   0   42

Error Intervention

ITEM 9 Students may have difficulty computing the slope with positive and negative decimals. Help them break the process into smaller steps.

Q: Represent the slope showing the change in y-values over the change in x-values. $\left[\frac{-5 - (-4.2)}{2.5 - 2.1}\right]$

Q: How can you write the expression in the numerator in an easier way? $[-5 + 4.2 \text{ or } 4.2 - 5]$

Q: Simplify the numerator and denominator. $\left[\frac{-0.8}{0.4}\right]$

Q: What do you notice about the relationship between the numerator and denominator? [Sample answer: The numerator is the opposite of twice the denominator.]

You may opt to have students complete the automatically scored Practice & Problem Solving items online.

Item Analysis

Example	Items	DOK
1	6, 10	1
2	7, 9	1
2	8, 14	2
3	11	2
3	12, 13	3

🏆 Challenge

ITEM 13 Higher Order Thinking Have students use their understanding of slope and equivalent ratios to find an unknown value in a mathematical context.

Q: A line passes through the point (2p, p). What is the slope of the line? Explain how you found the answer. [The slope is equal to the ratio $\frac{p}{2p}$, which is equivalent to $\frac{1}{2}$.]

STEP 3 | Assess & Differentiate

✓ Lesson Quiz

RtI Use the student scores on the Lesson Quiz to prescribe differentiated assignments.

I Intervention 0–3 Points   **O** On-Level 4 Points   **A** Advanced 5 Points

You may opt to have students take the Lesson Quiz online. The Lesson Quiz will be automatically scored and appropriate remediation, practice, or enrichment will be assigned based on student performance.

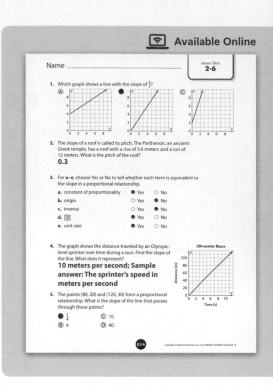

📶 Available Online

⏻ Video Tutorials

Students can access instructional tutorials using the **Virtual Nerd app**.

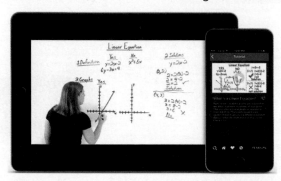

Students can also access the videos using the **BouncePages app** to scan exercise pages marked with this icon. Students can download both apps for free in their mobile devices' app store.

Differentiated Intervention

I = Intervention   **O** = On-Level   **A** = Advanced

Reteach to Build Understanding **I**

Provides scaffolded reteaching for the key lesson concepts.

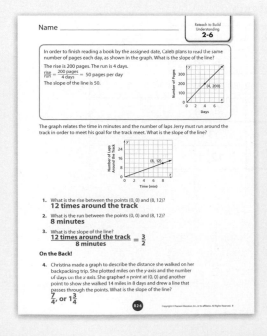

Additional Vocabulary Support **I** **O**

Helps students develop and reinforce understanding of key terms and concepts.

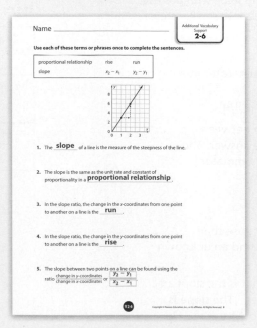

Build Mathematical Literacy **I**

Provides support for struggling readers to build mathematical literacy.

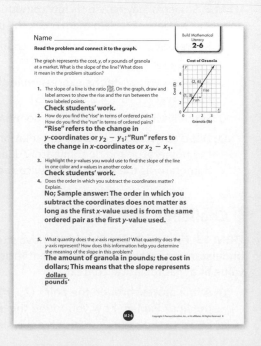

Additional Practice

You may opt to have students complete the automatically scored Additional Practice items online.

Item Analysis

Example	Items	DOK
1	1	1
1	8	2
2	2, 3, 4, 9	2
3	5, 6	2
3	7	3

📶 **Available Online**

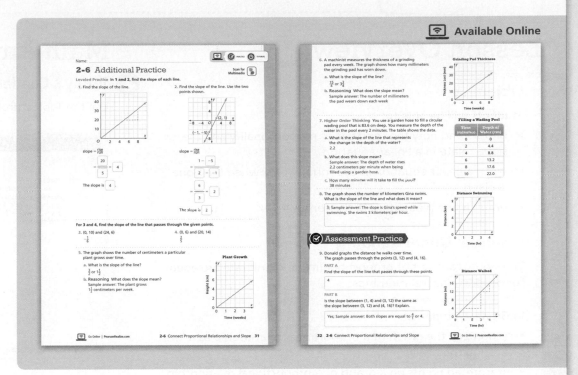

Differentiated Intervention

I = Intervention   **O** = On-Level   **A** = Advanced

Enrichment O A

Presents engaging problems and activities that extend the lesson concepts.

Math Tools and Games I O A

Offers additional activities and games to build understanding and fluency.

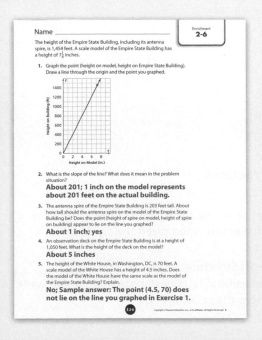

Lesson 2-7

Analyze Linear Equations: $y = mx$

Activity

Lesson Overview

FOCUS

Objective

Students will be able to:

✔ understand how the constant of proportionality and the slope relate in a linear equation.

✔ write a linear equation in the form $y = mx$ when the slope is given.

✔ graph a linear equation in the form $y = mx$.

Essential Understanding

The slope, constant of proportionality, and unit rate are equal for proportional relationships.

COHERENCE

In Grade 7, students:

• recognized the graph of a proportional relationship as a line through the origin.

• interpreted points on a graph of a proportional relationship and determined the constant of proportionality.

In this lesson, students:

• write a linear equation to describe a proportional relationship.

• graph a linear equation that describes a proportional relationship.

Later in this topic, students will:

• understand the y-intercept of a line.

• analyze linear equations of the form $y = mx + b$.

RIGOR

This lesson emphasizes a blend of **conceptual understanding** and **application**.

• Students understand the characteristics of a graph of a proportional relationship.

• Students apply their knowledge of proportional relationships to graph equations.

Math Anytime

Today's Challenge

Use the Topic 2 problems any time during this topic.

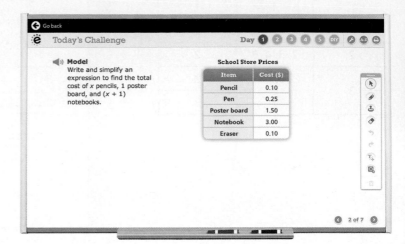

☑ Mathematics Overview

In this lesson, students will relate slope to proportional relationships as they review the equation for a line passing through the origin. They write equations in the form $y = mx$ to represent given scenarios. Students also analyze and solve linear equations by plotting and graphing their solutions.

Applying Math Practices

Model with Math

Students write an equation in the form $y = mx$ from a line on a graph or draw a line on a graph when given the equation.

Look for and Make Use of Structure

Students analyze a proportional relationship to graph it and write an equation that describes the relationship.

15-20 min

Activity

PearsonRealize.com

Explore It!

Model with Math As students work through the *Explore It*, listen and look for a variety of strategies students use that can be incorporated into the classroom discussion.

Before 👤 WHOLE CLASS

TP

1 Implement Tasks that Promote Reasoning and Problem Solving

Q: The car travels 100 meters per 4 seconds. What does this mean? [Sample answer: Every 4 seconds, the car travels a distance of 100 meters.]

2 Build Understanding

Q: Since the car travels at a constant speed, how far will it travel in 8 seconds? [200 meters]

During 👥 SMALL GROUP

TP

3 Support Productive Struggle in Learning Mathematics

Q: How could you use a graph to represent the distance the car will travel over time? [Sample answer: The time can be represented on the x-axis, while the distance can be represented on the y-axis. The graph will show all of the possible distances based upon different times.]

Q: What information from your representation helps you describe how far the car traveled and how long it took? [Sample answer: (0, 0) The car traveled 0 meters in 0 seconds; (2, 50) The car traveled 50 meters in 2 seconds.]

After 👤 WHOLE CLASS

TP

4 Facilitate Meaningful Mathematical Discourse

Ask students to share their solutions. If needed, project Nathan's and Lindsey's work and ask:

Q: What data does Nathan suggest the expression can provide that the table cannot? Explain. [The distance traveled for any amount of time; Sample answer: The table shows only data for specific amounts of time. However, the expression can be used to find the distance for any amount of time, even fractional amounts.]

Q: How might Lindsey have determined the equation for the distance the car will travel over time? [Sample answer: Since the car traveled 100 meters in 4 seconds, Lindsey could have started with the equation $4y = 100$. Then divide all terms y 4 so that y has a coefficient of 1. The final equation is $y = 25x$.]

5 Transition to Visual Learning

Q: Does it make a difference which points you choose along the line to compute the slope? Explain. [No; Sample answer: The slope is constant for the whole line.]

6 Extension for Early Finishers

Q: Can you predict how long it would take this car to travel 1 kilometer? Explain. [40 seconds; Sample answer: I used the equation $y = 25x$ with $y = 1,000$ and solved for x.]

Analyze Student Work

📶 Available Online

← Go back

ë · Explore It!

🔊 A group of college students developed a solar-powered car and entered it in a race. The car travels at a constant speed of 100 meters per 4 seconds.

C. Compare the representation and the expression. Which shows the distance traveled over time more clearly? Explain.

Nathan's work

The table shows the distance traveled over time more clearly because it lists several times and distances. However, the expression allows you to calculate the distance traveled after any amount of time.

◄ 1 of 1 ►

Nathan sees the value in the visual display of data in a table, but he also sees the value of using an expression to calculate distance for any time.

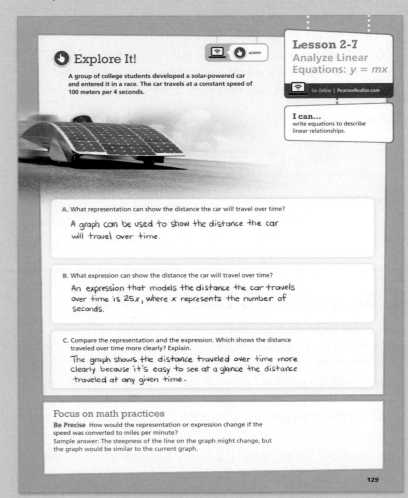

Explore It!

A group of college students developed a solar-powered car and entered it in a race. The car travels at a constant speed of 100 meters per 4 seconds.

Lesson 2-7
Analyze Linear Equations: $y = mx$

📶 Go Online | PearsonRealize.com

I can... write equations to describe linear relationships.

A. What representation can show the distance the car will travel over time?

A graph can be used to show the distance the car will travel over time.

B. What expression can show the distance the car will travel over time?

An expression that models the distance the car travels over time is $25x$, where x represents the number of seconds.

C. Compare the representation and the expression. Which shows the distance traveled over time more clearly? Explain.

The graph shows the distance traveled over time more clearly because it's easy to see at a glance the distance traveled at any given time.

Focus on math practices

Be Precise How would the representation or expression change if the speed was converted to miles per minute?
Sample answer: The steepness of the line on the graph might change, but the graph would be similar to the current graph.

129

Lindsey prefers the visual display of data in a graph.

STEP | Develop: Visual Learning

Visual Learning | Assess

Available Online

ETP **Establish Mathematics Goals to Focus Learning**

Engage students in a discussion about the *Essential Question*. Make sure they understand that the graph of a proportional relationship is always a line that passes through the origin.

EXAMPLE 1 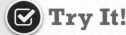 Relate Constant of Proportionality to Slope

ETP **Use and Connect Mathematical Representations**

Q: How can you find the cost of one foot of fencing? [Sample answer: Divide the cost by the number of feet of fence.]

Q: What does the point (15, 75) mean on the graph? [Sample answer: The *x*-value is the number of feet of fence and the *y*-value is the total cost. The point means that 15 feet of fence costs $75.]

Q: What does the value of 5 in the equation $y = 5x$ represent for the problem? [Sample answer: The value of 5 represents the slope or the cost of 1 foot of fence.]

 Try It!

ETP **Elicit and Use Evidence of Student Thinking**

Q: What about the graph tells you that it represents a proportional relationship with an equation of the form $y = kx$? [Sample answer: The graph passes through the origin.]

Q: Will you get the same value for the slope of the line if you choose a different pair of points? Give an example. [Yes; Sample answer: I used the points (2, 40) and (0, 0). $\frac{40 - 0}{2 - 0} = \frac{20}{1}$.]

Convince Me!

Q: For what types of relationships will the constant of proportionality, the unit rate, and the slope of the line all be equal? [a proportional relationship]

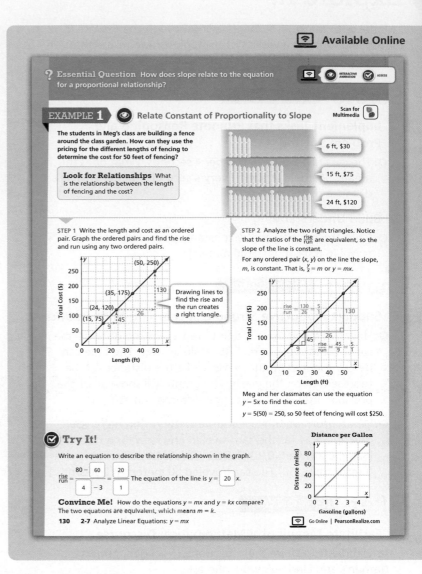

Students can access the *Visual Learning Animation Plus* by using the **BouncePages app** to scan this page. Students can download the app for free in their mobile devices' app store.

Response to Intervention

USE WITH EXAMPLE 2 Some students may need to review using the slope formula with negative integers and recognizing negative slope.

• Have students practice finding slope and describing graphs with negative slope.

Q: Find the slope of the line through (1, −250) and (4, −1000). [−250]

Q: Complete this sentence: If a line has a negative slope, the graph of the line slants _____ from left to right. [downward]

• Have students complete ordered pairs using the equation $y = -250x$, which has a negative slope.

Q: Find the *y*-value when $x = 10$. [$y = -2,500$]

Q: Find the *x*-value when $y = -25,000$. [$x = 100$]

Enrichment

USE WITH EXAMPLE 3 Challenge advanced students to compute slope using decimal values and then to write and graph a linear equation.

Q: What is the slope of the line through the points (1.6, 6.4) and (2.3, 9.2)? [4]

Q: What is the equation of the line? Sketch the graph. [Sample answer: $y = 4x$. Check students' graphs.]

EXAMPLE 2 Write a Linear Equation from Two Points

ETP Pose Purposeful Questions

Q: What is the constant of proportionality that relates the drone's distance and time? What is its unit rate? [−250; −250]

Q: Which variable in the equation $y = mx$ and $y = kx$ represents the slope? [m and k]

EXAMPLE 3 Graph an Equation of the Form $y = mx$

ETP Pose Purposeful Questions

Q: What information did you use to compute the slope? What is the slope? [Sample answer: There is 1 cup of raisins for every 2 cups of granola. The slope is $\frac{1}{2}$.]

Q: What two points would you pick to make this graph? Explain. [Sample answer: I would pick (0, 0) and (4, 2). The two points result in a line with a slope of $\frac{1}{2}$, and they are far enough apart that you can draw an accurate line.]

Try It!

ETP Elicit and Use Evidence of Student Thinking

Q: What is the slope of the line in problem a? Explain. [Sample answer: The slope is $\frac{2}{5}$, because the line goes through the points (0, 0) and (25, 10).]

Q: For the line $y = -3x$, if you increase the value of x by one, how does the value of y change? [Sample answer: The y-value will be three less than before.]

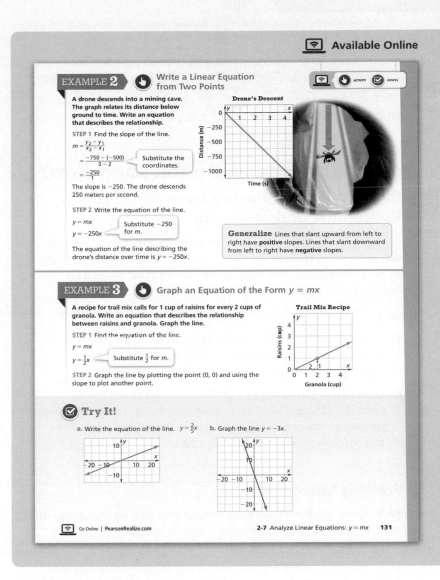

Available Online

EXAMPLE 2 Write a Linear Equation from Two Points

A drone descends into a mining cave. The graph relates its distance below ground to time. Write an equation that describes the relationship.

STEP 1 Find the slope of the line.

$m = \frac{y_2 - y_1}{x_2 - x_1}$

$= \frac{-750 - (-500)}{3 - 2}$ ← Substitute the coordinates.

$= \frac{-250}{1}$

The slope is −250. The drone descends 250 meters per second.

STEP 2 Write the equation of the line.

$y = mx$

$y = -250x$ ← Substitute −250 for m.

The equation of the line describing the drone's distance over time is $y = -250x$.

Drone's Descent

Generalize Lines that slant upward from left to right have **positive** slopes. Lines that slant downward from left to right have **negative** slopes.

EXAMPLE 3 Graph an Equation of the Form $y = mx$

A recipe for trail mix calls for 1 cup of raisins for every 2 cups of granola. Write an equation that describes the relationship between raisins and granola. Graph the line.

STEP 1 Find the equation of the line.

$y = mx$

$y = \frac{1}{2}x$ ← Substitute $\frac{1}{2}$ for m.

STEP 2 Graph the line by plotting the point (0, 0) and using the slope to plot another point.

Trail Mix Recipe

Try It!

a. Write the equation of the line. $y = \frac{2}{5}x$ b. Graph the line $y = -3x$.

Go Online | PearsonRealize.com

2-7 Analyze Linear Equations: $y = mx$ 131

ADDITIONAL EXAMPLES

For additional examples go to PearsonRealize.com.

ELL English Language Learners

BEGINNING Complete Example 2.

Have students work in groups. Have students identify the unit rate, slope, and the connection to the constant of proportionality.

Q: How do the terms unit rate and constant of proportionality relate to slope?

Q: How could you use a picture to explain the idea of slope to a friend?

Listen to student discussions and summarize various methods, modeling correct use of vocabulary terms.

INTERMEDIATE Complete Example 1.

Have students work in pairs. Listen for students who use content-area vocabulary and build academic language proficiency.

Q: How can you describe the slope of the line using words and numbers?

Q: How can you find the constant of proportionality using the graph?

ADVANCED Complete Example 3.

Have students work with a partner. Have them compare and contrast lines with a positive slope and lines with a negative slope. Encourage students to define the terms and show examples using both graphs and equations. Listen to student discussions and summarize various methods, modeling correct use of vocabulary terms.

STEP **2** | Develop: Visual Learning *continued*

KEY CONCEPT

ETP **Pose Purposeful Questions**

Q: What are some different forms for the equation describing a proportional relationship? [Sample answers: $y = mx$, $y = kx$ or $k = \frac{y}{x}$]

Q: What point is on the graph of every line with an equation of the form $y = mx$? [(0, 0)]

Do You Understand/Do You Know How?

ETP **Build Procedural Fluency from Conceptual Understanding**

? Essential Question Students should recognize several different ways to describe slope, such as rise over run, constant of proportionality, unit rate, or vertical change divided by horizontal change.

ITEM 4

Q: How would the constant of proportionality be different if the hiker was hiking downhill? [Sample answer: The constant of proportionality would be negative.]

Q: How could you check to see if the equation you found is correct? [Sample answer: I could substitute the coordinates of one of the points into my equation and make sure I get the corresponding point in the chart.]

Prevent Misconceptions

ITEM 5 Some students may have difficulty sketching the graph of an equation accurately. Encourage them to check their work by substituting a point on the graph into the equation.

Q: Find a point on the graph you drew. Do the coordinates of the point make a true statement when you substitute them in to the equation for the line? [Sample answer: (2, −1) is on the line. Yes, $(-1) = -\frac{1}{2}(2)$ is a true statement.]

ADDITIONAL EXAMPLE **2**

Help students transition to using slope to write a linear equation in this additional example.

Make sure students understand the relationship between the two points that could be used to find the slope and the given slope.

Q: Since the slope is a unit rate, what are two points that you know will be on the line? [(0, 0) and (1, −14)]

Q: Compare the steps for writing a linear equation in this additional example and Example 2. [Sample answer: In Example 2 there is an additional step of calculating the slope using two points. In this additional example, the slope is given, so you can just write the equation.]

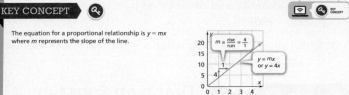

Available Online

KEY CONCEPT

The equation for a proportional relationship is $y = mx$ where m represents the slope of the line.

$m = \frac{rise}{run} = \frac{4}{1}$

$y = mx$ or $y = 4x$

Do You Understand?

1. **? Essential Question** How does slope relate to the equation for a proportional relationship? Sample answer: In a proportional relationship, the slope is the same as the constant of proportionality. The equation of a line $y = mx$ is the same as the equation for a proportional relationship $y = kx$.

2. **Look for Relationships** What do the graphs of lines in the form $y = mx$ have in common? How might they differ? Sample answer: They all pass through the origin. They may have slopes of different steepness and direction.

3. **Use Structure** The table below shows the distance a train traveled over time. How can you determine the equation that represents this relationship?

Time (s)	Distance (m)
2	25
4	50
6	75
8	100

Sample answer: I can find the ratio of meters to seconds between two pairs of values. This ratio is the constant of proportionality k, which is equal to the slope m. In this case, $m = 12.5$ so the equation is $y = 12.5x$.

Do You Know How?

4. The relationship between a hiker's elevation and time is shown in the graph.

Hiking Elevation

a. Find the constant of proportionality of the line. Then find the slope of the line. 30; 30

b. Write the equation of the line. $y = 30x$

5. Graph the equation $y = -\frac{1}{2}x$.

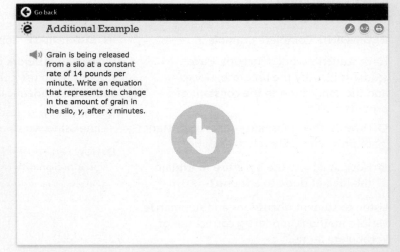

Available Online

◄ Go back

ë **Additional Example**

◄)) Grain is being released from a silo at a constant rate of 14 pounds per minute. Write an equation that represents the change in the amount of grain in the silo, y, after x minutes.

Answer: $y = -14x$

Practice & Problem Solving

📶 **Available Online**

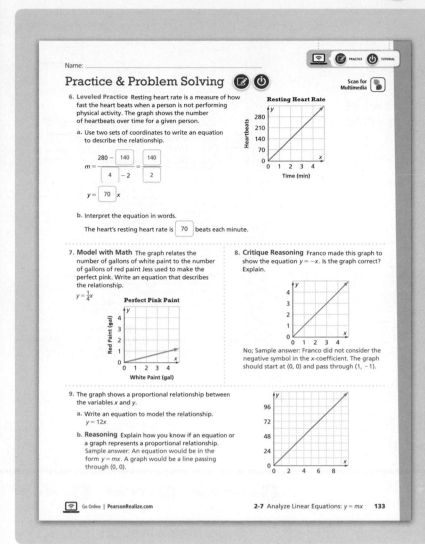

Name: _____

Practice & Problem Solving

Scan for Multimedia

6. Leveled Practice Resting heart rate is a measure of how fast the heart beats when a person is not performing physical activity. The graph shows the number of heartbeats over time for a given person.

Resting Heart Rate

a. Use two sets of coordinates to write an equation to describe the relationship.

$$m = \frac{280 - 140}{4 - 2} = \frac{140}{2}$$

$$y = 70 \, x$$

b. Interpret the equation in words.

The heart's resting heart rate is 70 beats each minute.

7. Model with Math The graph relates the number of gallons of white paint to the number of gallons of red paint Jess used to make the perfect pink. Write an equation that describes the relationship.

$y = \frac{1}{4}x$

Perfect Pink Paint

8. Critique Reasoning Franco made this graph to show the equation $y = -x$. Is the graph correct? Explain.

No; Sample answer: Franco did not consider the negative symbol in the x-coefficient. The graph should start at (0, 0) and pass through (1, −1).

9. The graph shows a proportional relationship between the variables x and y.

a. Write an equation to model the relationship.
$y = 12x$

b. **Reasoning** Explain how you know if an equation or a graph represents a proportional relationship. Sample answer: An equation would be in the form $y = mx$. A graph would be a line passing through (0, 0).

Go Online | PearsonRealize.com   2-7 Analyze Linear Equations: $y = mx$ **133**

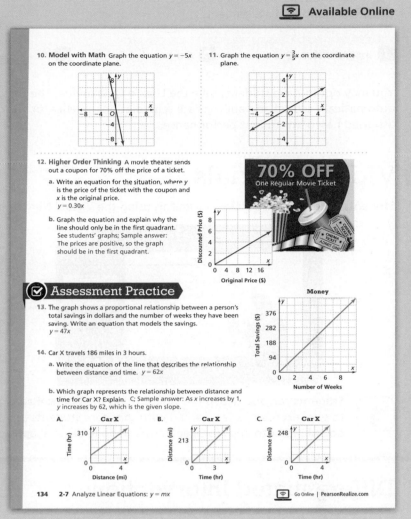

10. Model with Math Graph the equation $y = -5x$ on the coordinate plane.

11. Graph the equation $y = \frac{3}{2}x$ on the coordinate plane.

12. Higher Order Thinking A movie theater sends out a coupon for 70% off the price of a ticket.

70% OFF One Regular Movie Ticket

a. Write an equation for the situation, where y is the price of the ticket with the coupon and x is the original price.
$y = 0.30x$

b. Graph the equation and explain why the line should only be in the first quadrant. See students' graphs; Sample answer: The prices are positive, so the graph should be in the first quadrant.

☑ **Assessment Practice**

13. The graph shows a proportional relationship between a person's total savings in dollars and the number of weeks they have been saving. Write an equation that models the savings.
$y = 47x$

Money

14. Car X travels 186 miles in 3 hours.

a. Write the equation of the line that describes the relationship between distance and time. $y = 62x$

b. Which graph represents the relationship between distance and time for Car X? Explain. C; Sample answer: As x increases by 1, y increases by 62, which is the given slope.

A. **Car X**   B. **Car X**   C. **Car X**

134   2-7 Analyze Linear Equations: $y = mx$ Go Online | PearsonRealize.com

---

🔺 Error Intervention

ITEM 8 Critique Reasoning Some students may stumble using the correct words to describe Franco's error. Ask:

Q: What is the coefficient of x in the equation? [Sample answer: The coefficient is −1.]

Q: What should the graph of $y = -x$ look like? [Sample answer: It passes through the origin, (1, −1), and (2, −2) and slants downward from left to right.]

🏆 Challenge

ITEM 12 Higher Order Thinking Use this item to extend students' understanding of slope.

Q: Suppose the movie theater offers an additional 5% off the price of each ticket for each additional person. Write the equation to represent the cost for 2, 3, and 4 people. What is the slope for each ticket price? [$y = 0.35x$, $y = 0.4x$, $y = 0.45x$; 0.35, 0.4, 0.45]

You may opt to have students complete the automatically scored Practice & Problem Solving items online.

Item Analysis

Example	Items	DOK
1	13	1
	7	1
2	6	2
	9	3
	10, 11	1
3	12, 14	2
	8	3

PearsonRealize.com

Assess Tutorials Worksheets

Lesson Quiz

Use the student scores on the Lesson Quiz to prescribe differentiated assignments.

I Intervention 0–3 Points   **O** On-Level 4 Points   **A** Advanced 5 Points

You may opt to have students take the Lesson Quiz online. The Lesson Quiz will be automatically scored and appropriate remediation, practice, or enrichment will be assigned based on student performance.

Video Tutorials

Students can access instructional tutorials using the **Virtual Nerd app**.

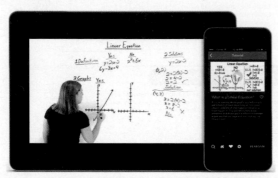

 Students can also access the videos using the **BouncePages app** to scan exercise pages marked with this icon. Students can download both apps for free in their mobile devices' app store.

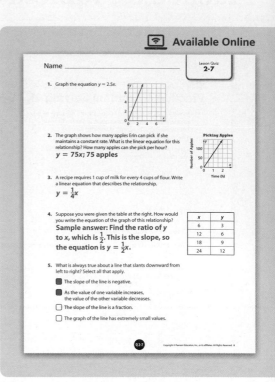

Available Online

Lesson Quiz 2-7

Name _____

1. Graph the equation $y = 2.5x$.

2. The graph shows how many apples Erin can pick if she maintains a constant rate. What is the linear equation for this relationship? How many apples can she pick per hour?
$y = 75x$; 75 apples

3. A recipe requires 1 cup of milk for every 4 cups of flour. Write a linear equation that describes the relationship.
$y = \frac{1}{4}x$

4. Suppose you were given the table at the right. How would you write the equation of the graph of this relationship?
Sample answer: Find the ratio of y to x, which is $\frac{1}{2}$. This is the slope, so the equation is $y = \frac{1}{2}x$.

x	y
6	3
12	6
18	9
24	12

5. What is always true about a line that slants downward from left to right? Select all that apply.
- ☑ The slope of the line is negative.
- ☑ As the value of one variable increases, the value of the other variable decreases.
- ☐ The slope of the line is a fraction.
- ☐ The graph of the line has extremely small values.

Differentiated Intervention

I = Intervention   **O** = On-Level   **A** = Advanced

Reteach to Build Understanding **I**

Provides scaffolded reteaching for the key lesson concepts.

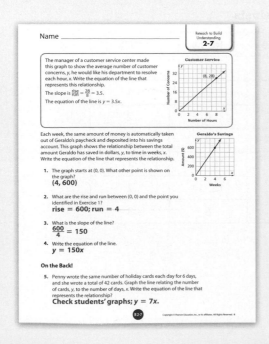

Name _____   **Reteach to Build Understanding 2-7**

The manager of a customer service center made this graph to show the average number of customer concerns, y, he would like his department to resolve each hour, x. Write the equation of the line that represents this relationship.
The slope is $\frac{28}{8} = 3.5$.
The equation of the line is $y = 3.5x$.

Each week, the same amount of money is automatically taken out of Geraldo's paycheck and deposited into his savings account. This graph shows the relationship between the total amount Geraldo has saved in dollars, y, to time in weeks, x. Write the equation of the line that represents the relationship.

1. The graph starts at (0, 0). What other point is shown on the graph?
(4, 600)

2. What are the rise and run between (0, 0) and the point you identified in Exercise 1?
rise = 600; run = 4

3. What is the slope of the line?
$\frac{600}{4} = 150$

4. Write the equation of the line.
$y = 150x$

On the Back!

5. Penny wrote the same number of holiday cards each day for 6 days, and she wrote a total of 42 cards. Graph the line relating the number of cards, y, to the number of days, x. Write the equation of the line that represents the relationship.
Check students' graphs; $y = 7x$.

Additional Vocabulary Support **I** **O**

Helps students develop and reinforce understanding of key terms and concepts.

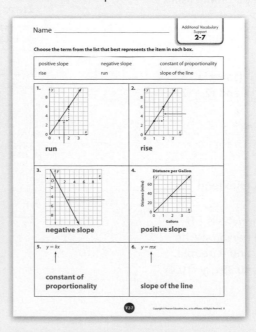

Name _____   **Additional Vocabulary Support 2-7**

Choose the term from the list that best represents the item in each box.

| positive slope | negative slope | constant of proportionality |
| rise | run | slope of the line |

1. run

2. rise

3. negative slope

4. positive slope

5. $y = kx$
constant of proportionality

6. $y = mx$
slope of the line

Build Mathematical Literacy **I**

Provides support for struggling readers to build mathematical literacy.

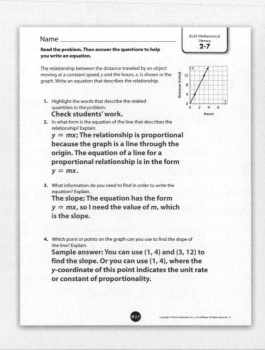

Name _____   **Build Mathematical Literacy 2-7**

Read the problem. Then answer the questions to help you write an equation.

The relationship between the distance traveled by an object moving at a constant speed, y and the hours, x, is shown in the graph. Write an equation that describes the relationship.

1. Highlight the words that describe the related quantities in the problem.
Check students' work.

2. In what form is the equation of the line that describes the relationship? Explain.
$y = mx$; **The relationship is proportional because the graph is a line through the origin. The equation of a line for a proportional relationship is in the form $y = mx$.**

3. What information do you need to find in order to write the equation? Explain.
The slope; The equation has the form $y = mx$, so I need the value of m, which is the slope.

4. Which point or points on the graph can you use to find the slope of the line? Explain.
Sample answer: You can use (1, 4) and (3, 12) to find the slope. Or you can use (1, 4), where the y-coordinate of this point indicates the unit rate or constant of proportionality.

Additional Practice

You may opt to have students complete the automatically scored Additional Practice items online.

Item Analysis

Example	Items	DOK
1	1, 4, 8	2
2	2, 6	2
	7	3
3	3, 5	2

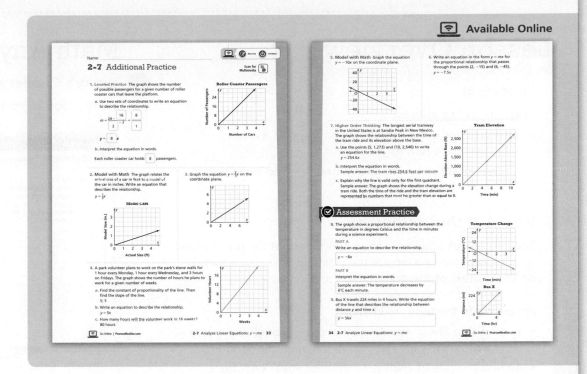

I = Intervention   **O** = On-Level   **A** = Advanced

Differentiated Intervention

Enrichment **O** **A**

Presents engaging problems and activities that extend the lesson concepts.

Math Tools and Games **I** **O** **A**

Offers additional activities and games to build understanding and fluency.

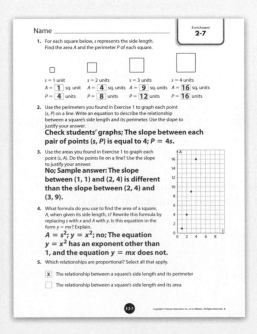

Lesson
2-8

Understand the *y*-intercept of a Line

Lesson Overview

Objective

Students will be able to:

✔ interpret and extend the table or graph of a linear relationship to find its *y*-intercept.

✔ analyze graphs in context to determine and explain the meaning of the *y*-intercept.

Essential Understanding

The *y*-intercept of a line is the *y*-coordinate of the point where the graph of the line crosses the *y*-axis. Its meaning depends on the context of the graph.

Previously in the topic, students:

- learned that linear equations that pass through the origin show a proportional relationship between the variables.
- studied the rate of change or slope of linear equations.

In this lesson, students will:

- extend their understanding of graphs to identify the *y*-intercept of a graph.
- demonstrate their understanding of the problem situation by explaining the meaning of the *y*-intercept in context.

Later in this topic, students will:

- interpret the graph of a line to produce an equation for the line in slope-intercept form.
- construct a graph of a linear function given an equation in slope-intercept form.

This lesson emphasizes a blend of **conceptual understanding** and **procedural skill and fluency**.

- Students will apply prior knowledge to create tables and graphs with precision to solve a variety of problems.
- Students will demonstrate understanding of the *y*-intercept in graphing and interpreting linear equations.

Math Anytime

Today's Challenge

Use the Topic 2 problems any time during this topic.

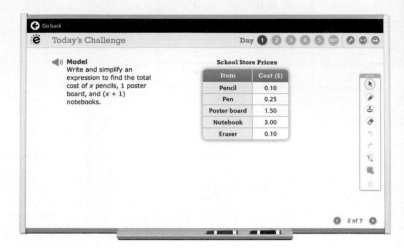

Mathematics Overview

In this lesson, students will analyze structures needed to create models and make sense of the *y*-intercept.

Applying Math Practices

Attend to Precision

Throughout the lesson, students will comprehend the relationship between the variables in the problem situation, and check the

accuracy of their work by relating the graphs and equations of linear functions to each other and the problem context.

STEP 1 | Develop: Problem-Based Learning

15-20 min

Activity

Solve & Discuss It

Use Structure As students work through the *Solve & Discuss It*, listen and look for students who recognize and use a pattern and demonstrate their understanding of the context by relating the pattern to a representation.

Before [WHOLE CLASS]

1 Implement Tasks that Promote Reasoning and Problem Solving

Q: If a horse is 5 years old, what is its equivalent age in human years? Explain. [2 years old; Sample answer: Because a horse ages 5 horse years for every 2 human years of its life.]

2 Build Understanding

Q: If you created a graph with Alex's age on the *x*-axis, what number might you count by? Explain. [2; Sample answer: Because the horse ages 5 years for every 2 human years.]

During [SMALL GROUP]

3 Support Productive Struggle in Learning Mathematics

Q: What pattern could you use to create a table of values for Alex's age and the horse's age? [Sample answer: Alex's age decreases by 2, and the horse's age decreases by 5.]

Q: On a graph, what does the point where the line crosses the *y*-axis represent? [Sample answer: It represents the solution. It represents when Alex was born, or 0 years old, and the corresponding age of the horse.]

After [WHOLE CLASS]

4 Facilitate Meaningful Mathematical Discourse

Ask students to share their solutions. If needed, project Kyle's and Dari's work and ask:

Q: Why was it helpful for Kyle to make Alex's age decrease by two years at a time rather than by one year? [Sample answer: If you use one year, then the horse's age would decrease by $2\frac{1}{2}$ years, and it might be harder to compute.]

Q: How is Dari's technique of stepping from one point to the next on the graph related to the slope of the line? [Sample answer: Dari goes left 2 and down 5. That means from one point to the next, the vertical change is −5, and the horizontal change is −2, so the slope would be $\frac{-5}{-2}$ or $\frac{5}{2}$.]

5 Transition to Visual Learning

Q: How is this graph different from the graphs showing proportional relationships? [Sample answer: This line does not pass through the origin.]

6 Extension for Early Finishers

Q: How old would Alex be if the horse lived to be 100 horse years old? Explain. [28 years old; Sample answer: The horse would age another 50 horse years to reach 100. 50 horse years is the same as 20 human years. In 20 years, Alex will be 28.]

Analyze Student Work

Available Online

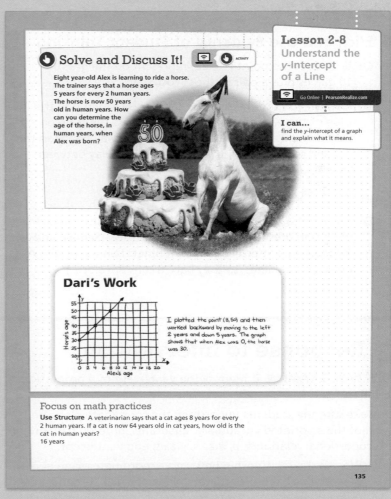

Kyle's work

30 horse years. I used the table and worked backward in steps of 2 human years and 5 horse years, until I reached 0, Alex's age when he was born.

Kyle uses a table and decreases Alex's age two years each row.

Solve and Discuss It!

Eight year-old Alex is learning to ride a horse. The trainer says that a horse ages 5 years for every 2 human years. The horse is now 50 years old in human years. How can you determine the age of the horse, in human years, when Alex was born?

Lesson 2-8
Understand the *y*-Intercept of a Line

Go Online | PearsonRealize.com

I can... find the *y*-intercept of a graph and explain what it means.

Dari's Work

I plotted the point (8, 50) and then worked backward by moving to the left 2 years and down 5 years. The graph shows that when Alex was 0, the horse was 30.

Focus on math practices

Use Structure A veterinarian says that a cat ages 8 years for every 2 human years. If a cat is now 64 years old in cat years, how old is the cat in human years? 16 years

135

Dari uses the information in the problem to step from one point to the next on the graph.

ETP Establish Mathematics Goals to Focus Learning

Engage students in a discussion about the *Essential Question*. Make sure students know that all lines have a constant slope, but some of them do not pass through the origin. The *y*-coordinate of the point where a line intersects the *y*-axis is called the *y*-intercept of the line.

 EXAMPLE **1**   Determine the *y*-Intercept of a Relationship

ETP Use and Connect Mathematical Representations

Q: What are the labels on the axes? Why are labels necessary? [Number of games and total cost; Sample answer: The labels are needed because number of games could be either axis.]

Q: What is the slope of the line? What does it represent? [The slope is 2 and represents the cost of each game.]

Q: Does the graph show a proportional relationship? Explain. [No; Sample answer: The graph does not go through the origin.]

☑ **Try It!**

ETP Elicit and Use Evidence of Student Thinking

Q: What does the point (10, 22) represent on the graph? [10 games plus a pair of shoes cost $22]

Q: How can you use the scale on the *y*-axis to help find the value of the *y*-intercept? [Sample answer: The scale on the *y*-axis is 2. Since the *y*-intercept is halfway between the first and second mark, the intercept is halfway between 2 and 4, or 3.]

Convince Me!

Q: How are the graphs of the lines on this page the same as the graph Dari drew about Alex and the horse? [Sample answer: The graphs all intersect at a point other than the origin. All the graphs are lines, so they have a constant slope.]

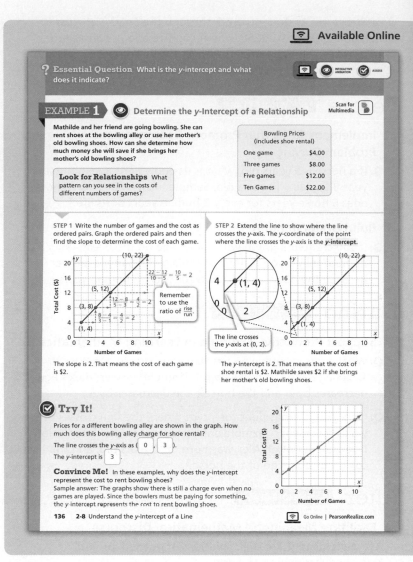

📶 **Available Online**

Students can access the *Visual Learning Animation Plus* by using the **BouncePages** app to scan this page. Students can download the app for free in their mobile devices' app store.

⚠️ Response to Intervention

USE WITH EXAMPLE 2 Identify the *y*-intercept of a proportional relationship.

• Make sure the students understand the coordinate plane and all of the associated vocabulary: quadrants, ordered pair, origin, proportional relationship, *x*-axis, *y*-axis, and *y*-intercept.

Q: What is the relationship between a coordinate plane and a number line? [The coordinate plane has two perpendicular number lines that cross to form perpendicular lines, which form four quadrants.]

Q: If a line goes through the point (0, 5), what is its *y*-intercept? [5]

Q: If a line goes through the point (0, 0), what is its *y*-intercept? [0]

🏆 Enrichment

USE WITH EXAMPLE 1 Encourage students to form hypotheses about the equation of a line that does not represent a proportional relationship.

Q: What equation represents the total cost for a person who rents shoes? [$y = 2x + 2$]

Q: What equation represents the total cost for a person who owns their own bowling shoes? [$y = 2x$]

Q: How would the graphs showing these two situations be the same? How would they be different? [Sample answer: They would both have the same slope, but the graph for the person who owns their shoes would intersect the origin.]

EXAMPLE 2 The y-Intercept of a Proportional Relationship

TP **Pose Purposeful Questions**

TP **Pose Purposeful Questions**

Q: How do you know the relationship is a proportional relationship? [Sample answer: It has a constant rate and intersects the origin.]

Q: Why does a y-intercept of a value other than 0 not make sense? [Sample answer: When the time is 0, there can be no parts manufactured.]

EXAMPLE 3 Identify the y-Intercept

TP **Pose Purposeful Questions**

Q: In what real-world situation would a line have a negative y-intercept? [Sample answer: The depth of a scuba diver compared to sea level.]

Q: Does a line with a negative y-intercept always have a negative slope? Explain. [No; Sample answer: The slope of the line does not affect the sign of the y-intercept.]

Try It!

TP **Elicit and Use Evidence of Student Thinking**

Q: How can you use the graph to tell if the y-intercept will be positive or negative? [Sample answer: If the y-intercept is above the origin, its value is positive. If the y-intercept is below the origin, its value is negative.]

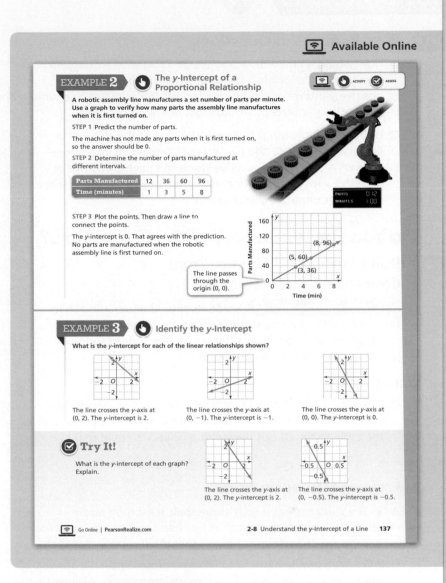

ADDITIONAL EXAMPLES

For additional examples go to PearsonRealize.com.

ELL English Language Learners

BEGINNING Use with Example 1.

Students need to build upon their knowledge of the vocabulary by listening, learning, and speaking the vocabulary words. Have the different levels of English speakers work together in small groups to build upon their comprehension.

Q: Look at the graph in the Try It section. Identify the parts of the graph associated with each word: x-axis, y-axis, coordinate plane, and y-intercept.

INTERMEDIATE Use with Example 2.

Ask students to review Example 2. Have them rewrite and illustrate the problem. After completing their illustrations, have them share their work and discuss how the illustration helped them understand the problem.

ADVANCED Use with Example 3.

Ask students to examine the graphs in Example 3 and list steps they could use to find the y-intercept. Have students work in pairs to compare their steps.

STEP **2** | Develop: Visual Learning *continued*

Key Concept   Activity

KEY CONCEPT

ETP ## Pose Purposeful Questions

Q: How would a line with a positive or a negative *y*-intercept compare to the origin? [Sample answer: A line with a positive *y*-intercept would cross above the origin. A line with a negative *y*-intercept would cross below the origin.]

Q: Is there a relationship between the sign of the slope of a line and the sign of the *y*-intercept? Explain. [No; Sample answer: A line with a positive slope can have a positive or negative *y*-intercept. A line with a negative slope can have a positive or negative *y*-intercept.]

Do You Understand/Do You Know How?

ETP ## Build Procedural Fluency from Conceptual Understanding

? Essential Question Students should understand that the *y*-intercept of a line is the *y*-coordinate of the point where the graph of the line crosses the *y*-axis and understand the meaning of the *y*-intercept in context.

ITEM 1

Q: If you didn't have a graph and only had a table, how would you find the *y*-intercept? [Sample answer: Use the pattern of the table to figure out the *y*-value when *x* is equal to 0.]

Prevent Misconceptions

ITEM 2 The students need to critique their reasoning and demonstrate an understanding that just because two relationships are proportional, that does not mean that the lines are identical.

Q: Is Chelsea's graph identical to Bradyn's graph? [Sample answer: Not necessarily. You would need more information. All lines with a proportional relationship pass through the origin, but that does not mean that the graphs are all the same.]

ADDITIONAL EXAMPLE **1**

Help students transition to interpreting points that are between grid lines in this additional example.

Make sure students understand the meaning of both coordinates of the *y*-intercept.

Q: What does the point halfway between 1 and 2 on the *y*-axis represent? [$1.50]

Q: Is there a situation where you might pay $0.50 for 0 ounces of frozen yogurt? [Sample answer: Yes, if you wanted a cup for water but no frozen yogurt.]

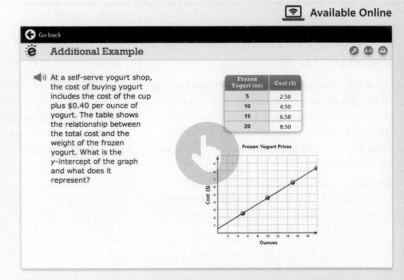

Answer: The *y*-intercept means the cost of the cup is $0.50.

📶 Available Online

KEY CONCEPT

The *y*-intercept is the *y*-coordinate of the point on a graph where the line crosses the *y*-axis.
When the line crosses through the origin, the *y*-intercept is 0.
When the line crosses above the origin, the *y*-intercept is positive.
When the line crosses below the origin, the *y*-intercept is negative.

The *y*-intercept is a positive number.

The *y*-intercept is always 0 for proportional relationships.

The *y*-intercept is a negative number.

Do You Understand?

1. **? Essential Question** What is the *y*-intercept and what does it indicate?
Sample answer: The *y*-intercept is the value of the *y*-coordinate where the line crosses the *y*-axis.

2. **Look for Relationships** Chelsea graphs a proportional relationship. Bradyn graphs a line that passes through the origin. What do you know about the *y*-intercept of each student's graph? Explain your answer.
Sample answer: Both of the graphs have a *y*-intercept of 0, and both represent proportional relationships. The graph of every proportional relationship crosses the *y*-axis at (0, 0).

3. **Generalize** When the *y*-intercept is positive, where does the line cross the *y*-axis on the graph? When it is negative?
Sample answer: When the *y*-intercept is positive, the line crosses the *y*-axis above the *x*-axis. When the *y*-intercept is negative, the line crosses the *y*-axis below the *x*-axis.

Do You Know How?

4. What is the *y*-intercept shown in the graph?
0

5. The graph shows the relationship between the remaining time of a movie and the amount of time since Kelly hit "play." What is the *y*-intercept of the graph and what does it represent?

Kelly's Movie

1.8; Sample answer: The movie had 1.8 hours remaining when Kelly hit "play."

📶 Available Online

⬅ Go back

ё   **Additional Example**

🔊 At a self-serve yogurt shop, the cost of buying yogurt includes the cost of the cup plus $0.40 per ounce of yogurt. The table shows the relationship between the total cost and the weight of the frozen yogurt. What is the *y*-intercept of the graph and what does it represent?

Frozen Yogurt (oz)	Cost ($)
5	2.50
10	4.50
15	6.50
20	8.50

Frozen Yogurt Prices

Practice & Problem Solving

📶 **Available Online**

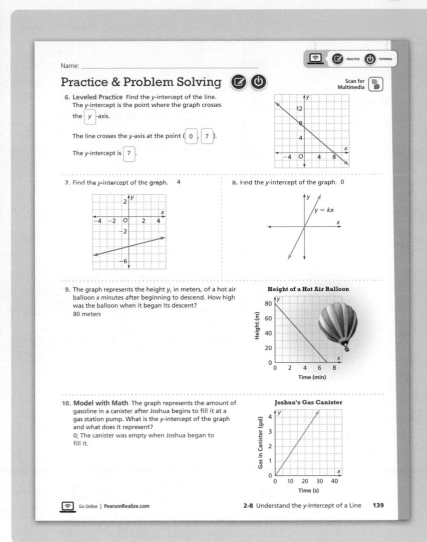

Name: _____

Practice & Problem Solving

Scan for Multimedia

6. Leveled Practice Find the *y*-intercept of the line. The *y*-intercept is the point where the graph crosses the [y]-axis.

The line crosses the *y*-axis at the point (0 , 7).

The *y*-intercept is 7 .

7. Find the *y*-intercept of the graph. 4

8. Find the *y*-intercept of the graph. 0

$y = kx$

9. The graph represents the height *y*, in meters, of a hot air balloon *x* minutes after beginning to descend. How high was the balloon when it began its descent?
80 meters

Height of a Hot Air Balloon

10. Model with Math The graph represents the amount of gasoline in a canister after Joshua begins to fill it at a gas station pump. What is the *y*-intercept of the graph and what does it represent?
0; The canister was empty when Joshua began to fill it.

Joshua's Gas Canister

Go Online | PearsonRealize.com
2-8 Understand the *y*-Intercept of a Line   **139**

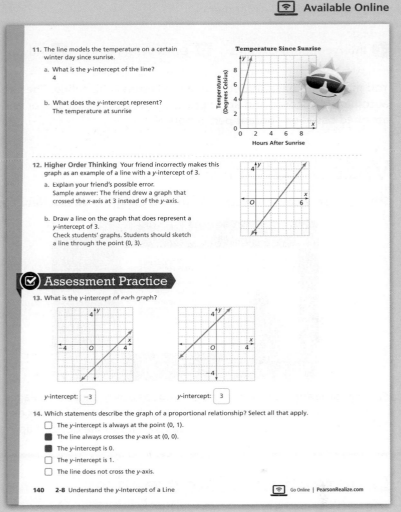

11. The line models the temperature on a certain winter day since sunrise.
a. What is the *y*-intercept of the line?
4
b. What does the *y*-intercept represent?
The temperature at sunrise

Temperature Since Sunrise

12. Higher Order Thinking Your friend incorrectly makes this graph as an example of a line with a *y*-intercept of 3.
a. Explain your friend's possible error.
Sample answer: The friend drew a graph that crossed the *x*-axis at 3 instead of the *y*-axis.
b. Draw a line on the graph that does represent a *y*-intercept of 3.
Check students' graphs. Students should sketch a line through the point (0, 3).

✓ **Assessment Practice**

13. What is the *y*-intercept of each graph?

y-intercept: −3   *y*-intercept: 3

14. Which statements describe the graph of a proportional relationship? Select all that apply.
☐ The *y*-intercept is always at the point (0, 1).
■ The line always crosses the *y*-axis at (0, 0).
■ The *y*-intercept is 0.
☐ The *y*-intercept is 1.
☐ The line does not cross the *y*-axis.

140 **2-8** Understand the *y*-Intercept of a Line   Go Online | PearsonRealize.com

---

You may opt to have students complete the automatically scored Practice & Problem Solving items online.

🔺 Error Intervention

ITEM 11 Students may have difficulty deciding whether the *y*-intercept is a point or a number.

Q: How are the coordinates of the point of the *y*-intercept and the value of the *y*-intercept different? [Sample answer: The coordinates give both the *x*- and *y*-value of the point where the graph crosses the *y*-axis but the *y*-intercept is just the *y*-value of that point.]

🅔🅛🅛 English Language Learners

ITEM 11 The wording of Item 11 might be confusing to English Language Learners.

Q: What information does this graph show? [Sample answer: The change in temperature over the course of one day, starting at sunrise.]

Q: How do you know that the *y*-intercept is equal to the temperature at sunrise? [Sample answer: The *x*-coordinate represents the time after sunrise. When *x* is 0, no time has passed since sunrise.]

Item Analysis

Example	Items	DOK
1	6, 9	1
	11	2
2	10, 14	2
3	7, 8, 13	1
	12	3

Lesson Quiz

Use the student scores on the Lesson Quiz to prescribe differentiated assignments.

I Intervention 0–3 Points   **O** On-Level 4 Points   **A** Advanced 5 Points

You may opt to have students take the Lesson Quiz online. The Lesson Quiz will be automatically scored and appropriate remediation, practice, or enrichment will be assigned based on student performance.

Video Tutorials

Students can access instructional tutorials using the **Virtual Nerd app**.

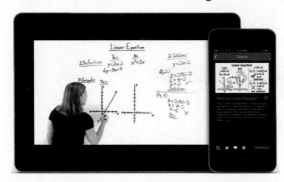

 Students can also access the videos using the **BouncePages app** to scan exercise pages marked with this icon. Students can download both apps for free in their mobile devices' app store.

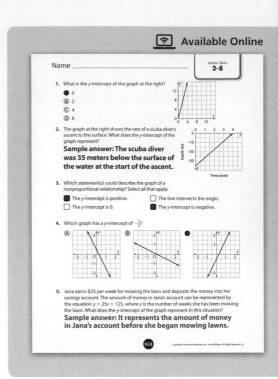
📶 **Available Online**

Differentiated Intervention

I = Intervention   **O** = On-Level   **A** = Advanced

Reteach to Build Understanding **I**

Provides scaffolded reteaching for the key lesson concepts.

Additional Vocabulary Support **I** **O**

Helps students develop and reinforce understanding of key terms and concepts.

Build Mathematical Literacy **I**

Provides support for struggling readers to build mathematical literacy.

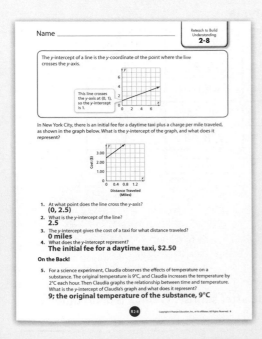

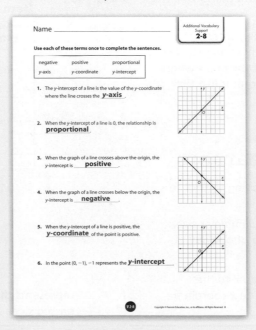

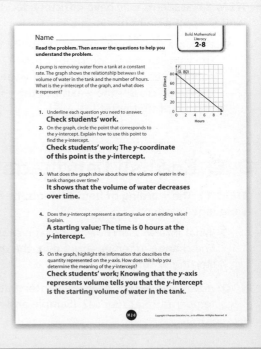

Additional Practice

You may opt to have students complete the automatically scored Additional Practice items online.

Item Analysis

Example	Items	DOK
1	2, 4	2
	6	3
2	3	1
	8	2
3	1, 5, 7	1

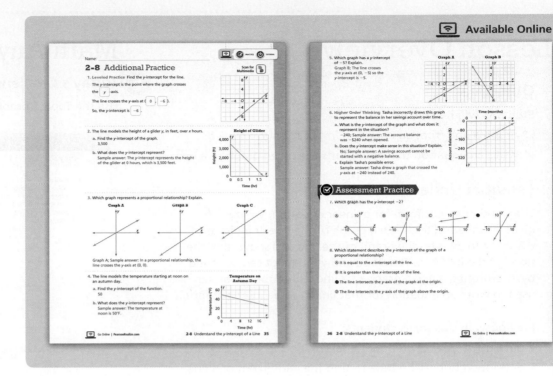

📶 **Available Online**

Differentiated Intervention

I = Intervention   **O** = On-Level   **A** = Advanced

Enrichment **O** **A**

Presents engaging problems and activities that extend the lesson concepts.

Math Tools and Games **I** **O** **A**

Offers additional activities and games to build understanding and fluency.

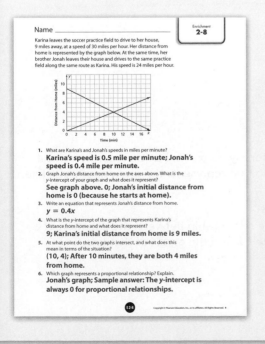

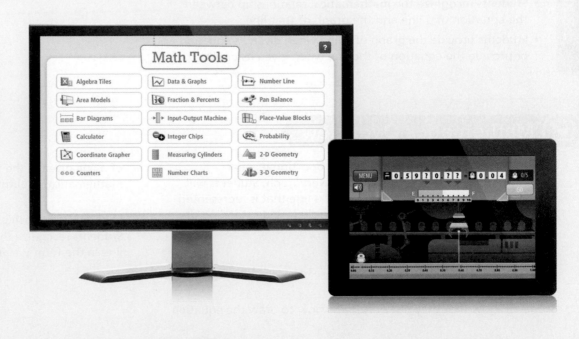

Video   Activity

Analyze Linear Equations:
$y = mx + b$

Lesson Overview

FOCUS

Objective

Students will be able to:

✔ graph a line from an equation in the form $y = mx + b$.

✔ write an equation that represents the given graph of a line.

Essential Understanding

The slope-intercept form for a linear equation, $y = mx + b$, gives information to sketch a graph of the line. It indicates the point $(0, b)$ is on the graph of the line and shows that the slope of the line is m. The slope and y-intercept can be found by interpreting a given graph of a line. This information can be used to write an equation for that line in slope-intercept form.

COHERENCE

Previously in this topic, students:

• developed fluency on how to determine the slope of a line.

• developed fluency on how to find the y-intercept of a line.

In this lesson, students:

• graph a line from an equation in the form $y = mx + b$.

• write an equation that represents the given graph of a line.

• learn that m and b from the slope-intercept equation will allow them to visualize a line before they draw the graph.

Later in Grade 8, students will:

• solve linear equations with rational coefficients, including equations whose solutions require expanding expressions using the Distributive Property and combining like terms.

RIGOR

This lesson emphasizes a blend of **conceptual understanding** and **procedural skill and fluency**.

• Students recognize the mathematical relationship between the equation of a line and the graph of that line.

• Students provide the graph of a line when given its equation or provide the equation of the line when given its graph.

Math Anytime

Today's Challenge

Use the Topic 2 problems any time during this topic.

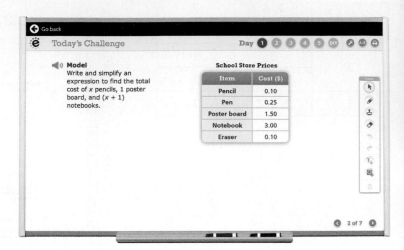

Watch the **Listen and Look For Video** for strategies and habits of mind to look for as students complete work on this lesson.

☑ Mathematics Overview

In this lesson, students will graph nonproportional linear equations, and write equations for a given graph. Students will also learn how to visualize the graph of a line that is represented by the slope-intercept equation by using their understanding of slope and y-intercept.

Applying Math Practices

Reason Abstractly and Quantitatively
Students show that they not only know how to draw the equation

of a line given in the form $y = mx + b$, but they can also give a mathematical equation that represents the given graph of a line.

Look for Relationships
Students recognize the relationship between the equation of a line in the form $y = mx + b$ and the graph of that line.

STEP 1 | Develop: Problem-Based Learning

15-20 min

Activity

Explain It!

Reason Abstractly As students work through the *Explain It*, listen and look for the variety of strategies students use to develop their graph of the line that represents the height of the tram.

Before [WHOLE CLASS]

1 Implement Tasks that Promote Reasoning and Problem Solving

Q: Based on the information given, what do you know about the graph of this line before you even draw it? [Sample answer: The slope of this line is positive because the tram's elevation is increasing during the trip.]

Q: What is the tram's elevation at the start of the trip? [2,080 feet]

2 Build Understanding

Q: What is the elevation of the tram in feet when it is 1 mile above sea level? [5,280 feet]

Q: What would have to change in order for the slope of this line to be negative? [Sample answer: The slope of the line would be negative if the tram were travelling *down* the mountain.]

During [SMALL GROUP]

3 Support Productive Struggle in Learning Mathematics

Q: What information from the problem tells you the slope of your graph? Explain. [Sample answer: The problem says the tram moves 800 vertical feet per minute. This is the slope because it tells how the elevation changes with time.]

After [WHOLE CLASS]

4 Facilitate Meaningful Mathematical Discourse

Ask students to share their solutions. If needed, project Zoe's and Max's work and ask:

Q: Do you think Zoe's or Max's method is more accurate? Explain. [Sample answer: Zoe's method wouldn't work if she didn't draw the correct graph. Max's method involves exact calculation instead of estimates.]

Q: Why did Max start by subtracting 5,280 − 2,080? [Sample answer: 5,280 feet is 1 mile above sea level, and 2,080 feet is the elevation at the start of the trip. Max found the distance the tram had to travel to get to 1 mile above sea level.]

5 Transition to Visual Learning

Q: How do we know the graph of the tram's elevation does not go through the origin? [Sample answer: The tram's elevation at time 0 is not 0 feet, it is 2,080 feet.]

6 Extension for Early Finishers

Q: How long does a round trip on the tram take? Explain. [18.8 minutes; Sample answer: The trip from 2,080 feet to 9,600 feet and back is 15,040 feet. I divided the distance by the speed to get 18.8 minutes.]

Analyze Student Work

Available Online

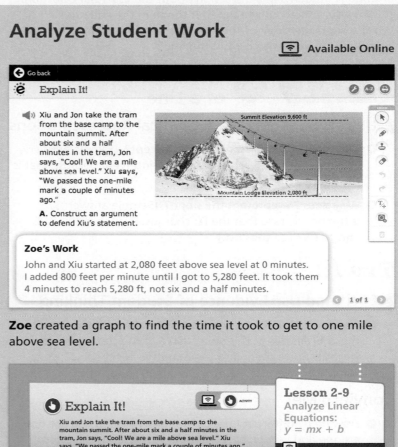

Zoe created a graph to find the time it took to get to one mile above sea level.

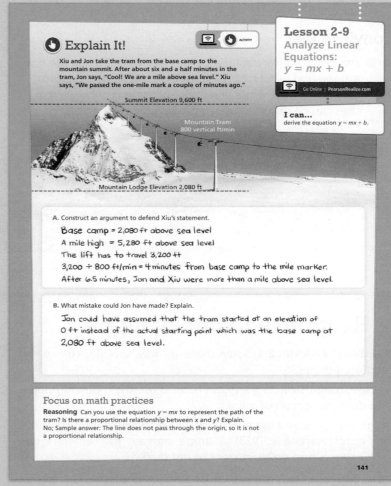

Max calculated the distance the tram had to travel to get to 1 mile above sea level and divided by the speed of the tram to find the time.

ETP **Establish Mathematics Goals to Focus Learning**

Engage students in a discussion about the *Essential Question*. Make sure they understand that the *m* in the equation represents the slope of the line, and that the *b* in the equation represents the *y*-intercept of the line.

EXAMPLE 1 **Write the Equation of a Line**

ETP **Use and Connect Mathematical Representations**

Q: Why does 125 represent the *y*-intercept? [Sample answer: We know that 125 represents the *y*-intercept because that is the charge when the time is zero.]

Q: Why does 75 represent the slope? [Sample answer: $75 is the hourly rate that the DJ charges. Every hour, *x*, adds another $75 to the cost.]

 Try It!

ETP **Elicit and Use Evidence of Student Thinking**

Q: The point (4, 5) looks like it is on the graph of the line. Do the coordinates of this point make a true statement when you substitute them into the equation for the line? [Yes; Sample answer: $(5) = \frac{3}{4}(4) + 2$ is a true statement.]

Convince Me!

Q: How many different lines can be drawn when you are given a slope and y-intercept? Explain. [One; Sample answer: Since the slope of the line is given, there is only one line that can be drawn through the given *y*-intercept.]

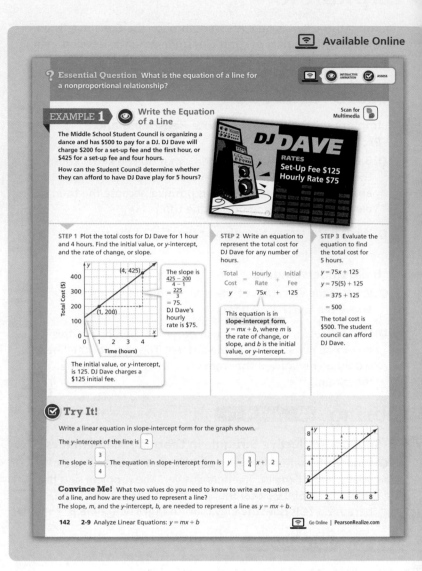

Students can access the *Visual Learning Animation Plus* by using the **BouncePages app** to scan this page. Students can download the app for free in their mobile devices' app store.

RtI **Response to Intervention**

USE WITH EXAMPLE 1 Some students may have difficulty with fractional slopes.

- Have students verbally explain how to use the following slopes to draw the graph of a line:

Q: How could you use a slope of $\frac{2}{5}$ to find another point on a graph starting at (0, 3)? [Sample answer: You can move up 2 spaces and right 5 spaces to get (5, 5).]

Q: How could you use a slope of $\frac{-4}{3}$ to find another point on a graph starting at (0, −2)? [Sample answer: You can move down 4 spaces and right 3 spaces to get (3, −6).]

Q: How could you use a slope of 5 to find another point on a graph starting at (0, 1)? [Sample answer: You can move up 5 spaces and right 1 space to get (1, 6).]

E **Enrichment**

USE WITH EXAMPLE 1 Challenge advanced students to display their understanding of the slope concept by explaining the slope of unusual graphs and equations.

- Have students answer the following questions.

Q: What is the slope of a horizontal line? Sketch a graph and explain your answer. [Sample answer: The slope of a horizontal line is 0. I drew a horizontal line through the points (0, 5) and (5, 5). I calculated the slope as $\frac{5-5}{5-0} = 0$.]

Q: What happens when you try to calculate the slope of a vertical line? Sketch a graph and explain your answer. [Sample answer: I drew a vertical line through the points (2, 0) and (2, 6). When I tried to calculate the slope, I got $\frac{6-0}{2-2}$, which is not defined. You can't divide by zero.]

XAMPLE 2 Write a Linear Equation Given Its Graph

TP Pose Purposeful Questions

Q: How can you find the *y*-intercept? Explain. [Sample answer: The graph gave us the point (0, −6), which is where the line crosses the *y*-axis, so the *y*-intercept is −6.]

Q: How can you find the slope of the line? Explain. [Sample answer: I used the two points (0, −6) and (3, 0) and the formula for slope to get $\frac{0-(-6)}{3-0} = \frac{6}{3} = 2$.]

XAMPLE 3 Graph a Given Linear Equation

TP Pose Purposeful Questions

Q: How do you use the information that *b* = 3 to plot a point on the graph? [Sample answer: The *y*-intercept is the *y*-coordinate of a point on the *y*-axis. Because it is on the *y*-axis, the *x*-coordinate must be 0. I can plot the point (0, 3).]

Q: How can you use the slope to find another point on the graph? [Sample answer: The slope is −4, so if I move down 4 and right 1, that gives me the point (1, −1).]

Try It!

TP Elicit and Use Evidence of Student Thinking

Q: What do you know about the slope of the first line? Explain. [Sample answer: You know that the slope of the line is negative because the line slants downward from left to right.]

Q: What do you know about the slope of the second line? Explain. [Sample answer: You know that the slope of the line is $\frac{1}{3}$ because the equation is given in slope-intercept form. In the given equation, *m* is $\frac{1}{3}$.]

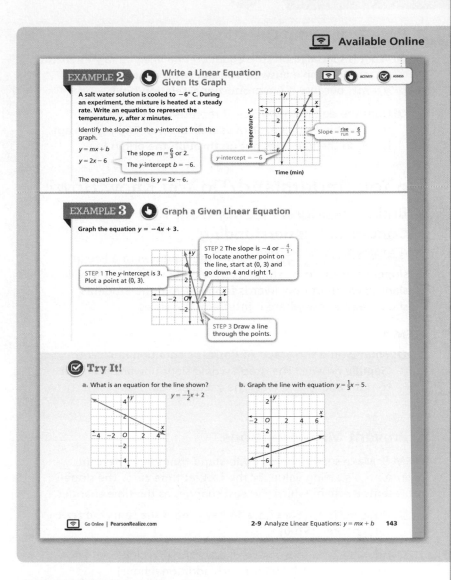

Available Online

ADDITIONAL EXAMPLES

For additional examples go to PearsonRealize.com.

ELL English Language Learners

BEGINNING Ask students to read Example 2.

Have students answer the following questions to ensure they understand the vocabulary used in the question.

Q: What does the word *cooled* mean in this question? [In this question, the word *cooled* means to reduce the mixture's temperature.]

Q: What does the word *heated* refer to? [The word *heated* means to raise the temperature of the mixture.]

INTERMEDIATE Ask students to read Example 1.

Help students develop fluency in academic language by working in pairs to answer the following questions.

Q: What number represents the value of the *y*-intercept? [The $125 set-up fee represents the *y*-intercept.]

Q: What number represents the slope? [The $75 per hour rate represents the slope.]

Encourage students to find points on the graph for a party that lasts 1 hour or 2 hours and to explain their calculations.

ADVANCED Ask students to review Example 1.

Have students read the problem and then rewrite it in their own words. Ask them to summarize the steps they took to solve the problem and answer questions from the group.

Have students work in small groups to share their revisions, discuss any errors, and streamline their version of the problem even more.

KEY CONCEPT

ETP **Pose Purposeful Questions**

Q: What is special about the equation of a line with a *y*-intercept of zero? [Sample answer: You can write the equation as $y = mx$, because it is a proportional relationship.]

Q: Does the equation $y = 5x - 3$ represent a proportional relationship? Explain. [No; Sample answer: The *y*-intercept is −3, so the line does not go through the origin.]

Do You Understand/Do You Know How?

ETP **Build Procedural Fluency from Conceptual Understanding**

 Essential Question Given the equation of a line in slope-intercept form, students should know whether it will slant upwards or downwards from left to right. Students should also know where it intersects the *y*-axis.

ITEM 4

Q: What would the graph of Chrissie's equation look like? [Sample answer: The graph would slant upward from left to right and would cross the *y*-axis at −5.]

⚠ **Prevent Misconceptions**

ITEM 5 Make sure students understand that the *y*-intercept represents a starting value, or the cost, at time zero. The slope represents a rate at which the cost changes as the time changes.

Q: How much will Fara have to pay even if she rents the tent for 0 hours? [$100]

Q: How much will Fara have to pay for each additional hour her party lasts? [$500 for each additional hour]

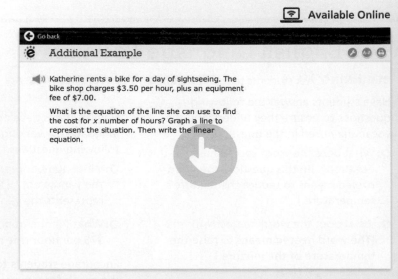

KEY CONCEPT

The equation of a line that represents a nonproportional relationship can be written in slope-intercept form, $y = mx + b$, where *m* is the slope of the line and *b* is the *y*-intercept.

Do You Understand?

1. **Essential Question** What is the equation of a line for a nonproportional relationship? Sample answer: The equation is $y = mx + b$, where *m* is the slope and *b* is the *y*-intercept.

2. **Use Structure** The donations by a restaurant to a certain charity, *y*, will be two-fifths of its profits, *x*, plus $50. How can you determine the equation in slope-intercept form that shows the relationship between *x* and *y* without graphing the line?
Sample answer: You can find the equation by using the information given. You know the slope, *m*, is $\frac{2}{5}$ and the *y*-intercept, *b*, is 50. So the equation of the line in slope-intercept form is $y = \frac{2}{5}x + 50$.

3. **Be Precise** Priya will graph a line with the equation $y = \frac{3}{4}x - 4$. She wants to know what the line will look like before she graphs the line. Describe the line Priya will draw, including the quadrants the line will pass through.
Sample answer: The graph has a positive slope, $\frac{3}{4}$, so it will move up from left to right. The *y*-intercept will be at −4, so the line will move up from Quadrant III through Quadrant IV to Quadrant I.

Do You Know How?

4. Chrissie says the equation of the line shown on the graph is $y = \frac{1}{2}x - 5$. George says that the equation of the line is $y = -\frac{1}{2}x + 5$. Which student is correct? Explain.

George; Sample answer: The slope is negative and the *y*-intercept is 5.

5. Fara wants to rent a tent for an outdoor celebration. The cost of the tent is $500 per hour, plus an additional $100 set-up fee.

a. Draw a line to show the relationship between the number of hours the tent is rented, *x*, and the total cost of the tent, *y*.

b. What is the equation of the line in slope-intercept form?
$y = 500x + 100$

144   2-9 Analyze Linear Equations: $y = mx + b$ Go Online | PearsonRealize.com

---

ADDITIONAL EXAMPLE **1**

Help students understand that there is more than one way to use the information to write the equation of the line.

Make sure students understand what each given value represents.

Q: What information given in the problem represents the slope of the line? [$3.50 per hour]

Q: What information given in the problem represents the *y*-intercept of the line? [$7.00 equipment fee]

Q: How can you use the given information to write the equation of the line without finding two points? [Sample answer: Since $m = 3.5$ and $b = 7$, you can use $y = mx + b$ to write the equation of the line: $y = 3.5x + 7$.]

Available Online

← Go back

Additional Example

🔊 Katherine rents a bike for a day of sightseeing. The bike shop charges $3.50 per hour, plus an equipment fee of $7.00.

What is the equation of the line she can use to find the cost for *x* number of hours? Graph a line to represent the situation. Then write the linear equation.

Answer: Check students' graphs. $y = 3.5x + 7$

Practice & Problem Solving

 Available Online

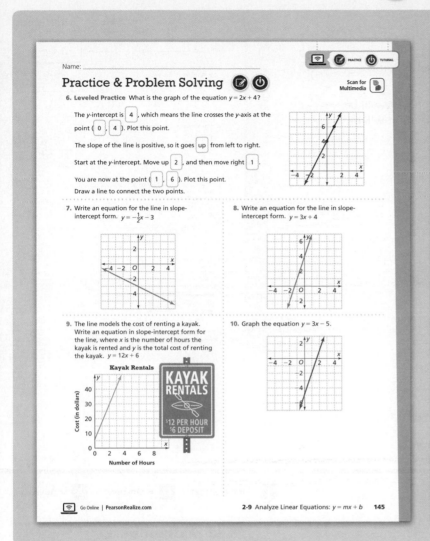

Name: _____

Practice & Problem Solving

Scan for Multimedia

6. Leveled Practice What is the graph of the equation $y = 2x + 4$?

The y-intercept is $\boxed{4}$, which means the line crosses the y-axis at the point ($\boxed{0}$, $\boxed{4}$). Plot this point.

The slope of the line is positive, so it goes $\boxed{up}$ from left to right.

Start at the y-intercept. Move up $\boxed{2}$, and then move right $\boxed{1}$.

You are now at the point ($\boxed{1}$, $\boxed{6}$). Plot this point.

Draw a line to connect the two points.

7. Write an equation for the line in slope-intercept form. $y = -\frac{1}{2}x - 3$

8. Write an equation for the line in slope-intercept form. $y = 3x + 4$

9. The line models the cost of renting a kayak. Write an equation in slope-intercept form for the line, where x is the number of hours the kayak is rented and y is the total cost of renting the kayak. $y = 12x + 6$

Kayak Rentals

KAYAK RENTALS
$12 PER HOUR
$6 DEPOSIT

10. Graph the equation $y = 3x - 5$.

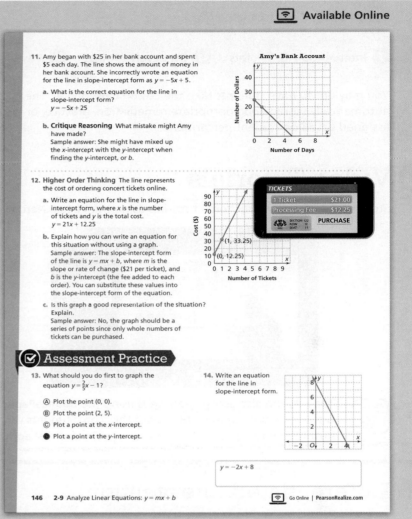

11. Amy began with $25 in her bank account and spent $5 each day. The line shows the amount of money in her bank account. She incorrectly wrote an equation for the line in slope-intercept form as $y = -5x + 5$.

a. What is the correct equation for the line in slope-intercept form?
$y = -5x + 25$

b. **Critique Reasoning** What mistake might Amy have made?
Sample answer: She might have mixed up the x-intercept with the y-intercept when finding the y-intercept, or b.

Amy's Bank Account

12. Higher Order Thinking The line represents the cost of ordering concert tickets online.

a. Write an equation for the line in slope-intercept form, where x is the number of tickets and y is the total cost.
$y = 21x + 12.25$

b. Explain how you can write an equation for this situation without using a graph.
Sample answer: The slope-intercept form of the line is $y = mx + b$, where m is the slope or rate of change ($21 per ticket), and b is the y-intercept (the fee added to each order). You can substitute these values into the slope-intercept form of the equation.

c. Is this graph a good representation of the situation? Explain.
Sample answer: No, the graph should be a series of points since only whole numbers of tickets can be purchased.

TICKETS
1 Ticket $21.00
Processing Fee $12.25
                  PURCHASE
SECTION 122 ROW H SEAT 11

✓ Assessment Practice

13. What should you do first to graph the equation $y = \frac{2}{5}x - 1$?

Ⓐ Plot the point (0, 0).
Ⓑ Plot the point (2, 5).
Ⓒ Plot a point at the x-intercept.
● Plot a point at the y-intercept.

14. Write an equation for the line in slope-intercept form.

$y = -2x + 8$

You may opt to have students complete the automatically scored Practice & Problem Solving items online.

⚠ Error Intervention

ITEM 7 Students may have difficulty finding the slope. Encourage students to find a second point on the line, looking for one with integer coordinates if possible.

Q: What are the coordinates of two points you can see on the graph? [Sample answer: (0, −3) and (4, −5)]

Q: Use your two points to calculate the slope. Does the sign of the slope you calculated make sense for the graph? [Sample answer: $\frac{-5-(-3)}{4-0} = \frac{-2}{4} = -\frac{1}{2}$. You expect a negative slope because the graph slants downwards from left to right, so the sign of the slope makes sense.]

Item Analysis

Example	Items	DOK
1	11, 12	3
2	7, 8, 9, 14	1
3	6, 10	1
	13	2

🏆 Challenge

ITEM 11 Critique Reasoning You can use this question to test the students' understanding of slope when hidden in a word problem.

Q: Why is the slope not equal to 25? [Sample answer: The slope is the rate at which the amount of money in her account changes each day. She only spends $5 a day.]

Lesson Quiz

 Use the student scores on the Lesson Quiz to prescribe differentiated assignments.

I Intervention 0–3 Points   **O** On-Level 4 Points   **A** Advanced 5 Points

You may opt to have students take the Lesson Quiz online. The Lesson Quiz will be automatically scored and appropriate remediation, practice, or enrichment will be assigned based on student performance.

Video Tutorials

Students can access instructional tutorials using the **Virtual Nerd app.**

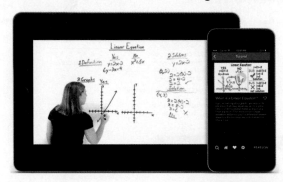

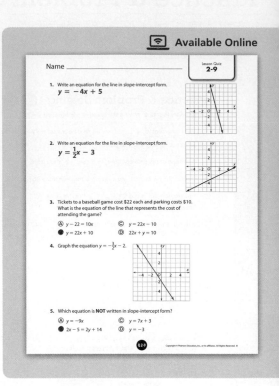

Students can also access the videos using the **BouncePages app** to scan exercise pages marked with this icon. Students can download both apps for free in their mobile devices' app store.

Differentiated Intervention

I = Intervention   **O** = On-Level   **A** = Advanced

Reteach to Build Understanding **I**

Provides scaffolded reteaching for the key lesson concepts.

Additional Vocabulary Support **I** **O**

Helps students develop and reinforce understanding of key terms and concepts.

Build Mathematical Literacy **I**

Provides support for struggling readers to build mathematical literacy.

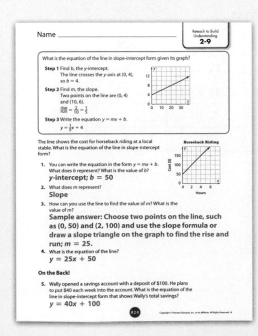

Additional Practice

You may opt to have students complete the automatically scored Additional Practice items online.

Item Analysis

Example	Items	DOK
1	3, 4	2
2	2, 5, 7	2
3	1	2
	6	3

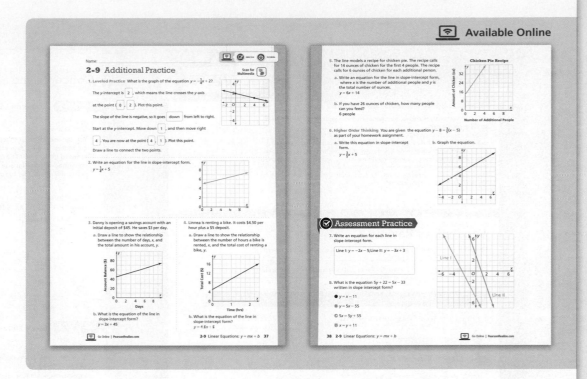

Differentiated Intervention

I = Intervention **O** = On-Level **A** = Advanced

Enrichment **O** **A**

Presents engaging problems and activities that extend the lesson concepts.

Math Tools and Games **I** **O** **A**

Offers additional activities and games to build understanding and fluency.

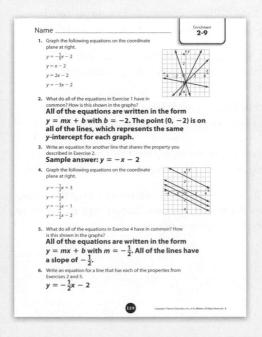

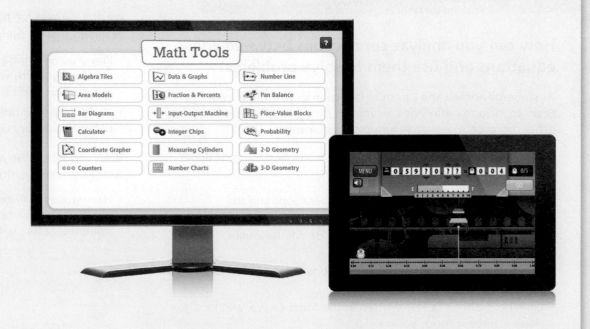

A-Z
Glossary

REVIEW | Analyze and Solve Linear Equations

Available Online

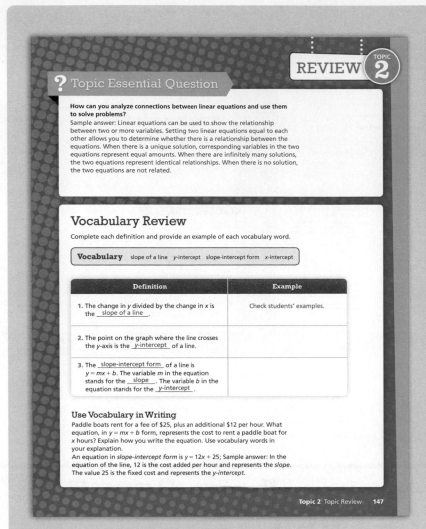

REVIEW TOPIC 2

? Topic Essential Question

How can you analyze connections between linear equations and use them to solve problems?
Sample answer: Linear equations can be used to show the relationship between two or more variables. Setting two linear equations equal to each other allows you to determine whether there is a relationship between the equations. When there is a unique solution, corresponding variables in the two equations represent equal amounts. When there are infinitely many solutions, the two equations represent identical relationships. When there is no solution, the two equations are not related.

Vocabulary Review

Complete each definition and provide an example of each vocabulary word.

Vocabulary slope of a line y-intercept slope-intercept form x-intercept

Definition	Example
1. The change in y divided by the change in x is the slope of a line .	Check students' examples.
2. The point on the graph where the line crosses the y-axis is the y-intercept of a line.	
3. The slope-intercept form of a line is y = mx + b. The variable m in the equation stands for the slope . The variable b in the equation stands for the y-intercept .	

Use Vocabulary in Writing

Paddle boats rent for a fee of $25, plus an additional $12 per hour. What equation, in y = mx + b form, represents the cost to rent a paddle boat for x hours? Explain how you write the equation. Use vocabulary words in your explanation.
An equation in *slope-intercept form* is y = 12x + 25; Sample answer: In the equation of the line, 12 is the cost added per hour and represents the *slope*. The value 25 is the fixed cost and represents the *y-intercept*.

Topic 2 Topic Review   **147**

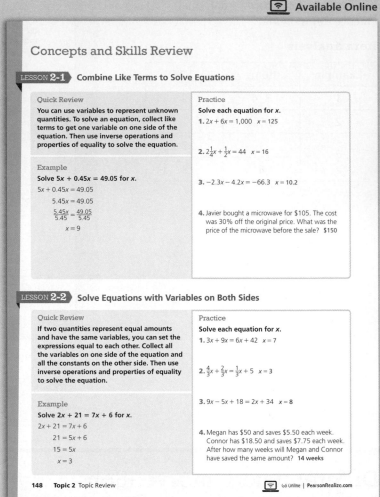

Concepts and Skills Review

LESSON 2-1 Combine Like Terms to Solve Equations

Quick Review
You can use variables to represent unknown quantities. To solve an equation, collect like terms to get one variable on one side of the equation. Then use inverse operations and properties of equality to solve the equation.

Example
Solve $5x + 0.45x = 49.05$ for x.
$$5x + 0.45x = 49.05$$
$$5.45x = 49.05$$
$$\frac{5.45x}{5.45} = \frac{49.05}{5.45}$$
$$x = 9$$

Practice
Solve each equation for x.
1. $2x + 6x = 1,000$ x = 125

2. $2\frac{1}{4}x + \frac{1}{2}x = 44$ x = 16

3. $-2.3x - 4.2x = -66.3$ x = 10.2

4. Javier bought a microwave for $105. The cost was 30% off the original price. What was the price of the microwave before the sale? $150

LESSON 2-2 Solve Equations with Variables on Both Sides

Quick Review
If two quantities represent equal amounts and have the same variables, you can set the expressions equal to each other. Collect all the variables on one side of the equation and all the constants on the other side. Then use inverse operations and properties of equality to solve the equation.

Example
Solve $2x + 21 = 7x + 6$ for x.
$$2x + 21 = 7x + 6$$
$$21 = 5x + 6$$
$$15 = 5x$$
$$x = 3$$

Practice
Solve each equation for x.
1. $3x + 9x = 6x + 42$ x = 7

2. $\frac{4}{3}x + \frac{2}{3}x = \frac{1}{3}x + 5$ x = 3

3. $9x - 5x + 18 = 2x + 34$ x = 8

4. Megan has $50 and saves $5.50 each week. Connor has $18.50 and saves $7.75 each week. After how many weeks will Megan and Connor have saved the same amount? 14 weeks

148   **Topic 2** Topic Review

Go Online | PearsonRealize.com

? Topic Essential Question

How can you analyze connections between linear equations and use them to solve problems?

As students answer the Essential Question in writing, encourage them to include definitions, examples, non-examples, models, and other representations that support their answers.

Be sure the following are made explicit while discussing students' answers.

- Combine like terms and use inverse operations and the Distributive Property to solve equations.

- Equations have none or one solution, or infinitely many solutions.

- The unit rate, or constant of proportionality can be used to compare proportional relationships.

- Linear equations can be written in the form $y = mx$ and in slope-intercept form, $y = mx + b$.

Vocabulary Review

ORAL LANGUAGE Before students complete the page, reinforce oral language by using one or more of the following activities.

- Play a game in which one student chooses one of the vocabulary words while the other students ask questions to get clues to guess the word.

- Draw a representation of each word. Have students use one of the vocabulary words to describe the drawings.

WRITING IN MATH After students complete the page, you can further reinforce writing in math by doing the following activity.

- Have students write a five-to-ten-sentence essay using the topic vocabulary. Provide assistance as needed. Encourage students to share their essay with the class or a partner.

Concepts and Skills Review

LESSON 2-3 Solve Multistep Equations

Quick Review
When solving multistep equations, sometimes the Distributive Property is used before you collect like terms. Sometimes like terms are collected, and then you use the Distributive Property.

Example
Solve $8x + 2 = 2x + 4(x + 3)$ for x.

First, distribute the 4. Then, combine like terms. Finally, use properties of equality to solve for x.

$8x + 2 = 2x + 4x + 12$
$8x + 2 = 6x + 12$
$\quad 8x = 6x + 10$
$\quad 2x = 10$
$\quad\; x = 5$

Practice
Solve each equation for x.

1. $4(x + 4) + 2x = 52$ $x = 6$

2. $8(2x + 3x + 2) = -4x + 124$ $x = 3$

3. Justin bought a calculator and a binder that were both 15% off the original price. The original price of the binder was $6.20. Justin spent a total of $107.27. What was the original price of the calculator? **$120**

LESSON 2-4 Equations with No Solutions or Infinitely Many Solutions

Quick Review
When solving an equation results in a statement that is always true, there are infinitely many solutions. When solving an equation produces a false statement, there are no solutions. When solving an equation gives one value for a variable, there is one solution.

Example
How many solutions does the equation $6x + 9 = 2x + 4 + 4x + 5$ have?

First, solve the equation.

$6x + 9 = 2x + 4 + 4x + 5$
$6x + 9 = 6x + 9$
$\quad\; 9 = 9$

Because $9 = 9$ is alwyas a true statement, the equation has infinitely many solutions.

Practice
How many solutions does each equation have?

1. $x + 5.5 + 8 = 5x \quad 13.5 - 4x$
   no solution

2. $4\left(\frac{1}{2}x + 3\right) = 3x + 12 - x$
   infinitely many solutions

3. $2(6x + 9 - 3x) = 5x + 21$
   one solution

4. The weight of Abe's dog can be found using the expression $2(x + 3)$, where x is the number of weeks. The weight of Karen's dog can be found using the expression $3(x + 1)$, where x is the number of weeks. Will the dogs ever be the same weight? Explain.
   Yes. Sample answer: Solving the equation $2(x + 3) = 3(x + 1)$ gives $x = 3$. So the dogs will be the same weight after 3 weeks.

LESSON 2-5 Compare Proportional Relationships

Quick Review
To compare proportional relationships, compare the rate of change or find the unit rate.

Example
The graph shows the rate at which Rob jogs. Emily's jogging rate is represented by the equation $y = 8x$, where x is the number of miles and y is the number of minutes. At these rates, who will finish an 8-mile race first?

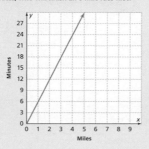

Emily's unit rate is $y = 8(1) = 8$ minutes per mile.

The point $(1, 6)$ represents Rob's unit rate of 6 minutes per mile.

Rob's unit rate is less than Emily's rate, so Rob will finish an 8-mile race first.

Practice
1. Two trains are traveling at a constant rate. Find the rate of each train. Which train is traveling at the faster rate?

   Train A

Time (h)	2	3	4	5	6
Distance (mi)	50	75	100	125	150

   Train A's unit rate: 25 mph; Train B's unit rate: 20 mph; Train A is traveling at a faster rate.

2. A 16-ounce bottle of water from Store A costs $1.28. The cost in dollars, y, of a bottle of water from Store B is represented by the equation $y = 0.07x$, where x is the number of ounces. What is the cost per ounce of water at each store? Which store's bottle of water costs less per ounce?
   Store A's unit rate: $0.08 per ounce; Store B's unit rate: $0.07 per ounce; Store B's bottle of water costs less per ounce.

📶 Available Online

LESSON 2-6 · Connect Proportional Relationships and Slope

Quick Review

The slope of a line in a proportional relationship is the same as the unit rate and the constant of proportionality.

Example

The graph shows the number of miles a person walked at a constant speed. Find the slope of the line.

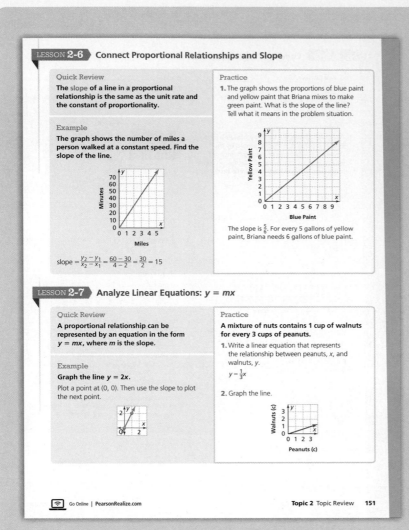

$$\text{slope} = \frac{y_2 - y_1}{x_2 - x_1} = \frac{60 - 30}{4 - 2} = \frac{30}{2} = 15$$

Practice

1. The graph shows the proportions of blue paint and yellow paint that Briana mixes to make green paint. What is the slope of the line? Tell what it means in the problem situation.

The slope is $\frac{5}{6}$. For every 5 gallons of yellow paint, Briana needs 6 gallons of blue paint.

LESSON 2-7 · Analyze Linear Equations: $y = mx$

Quick Review

A proportional relationship can be represented by an equation in the form $y = mx$, where m is the slope.

Example

Graph the line $y = 2x$.

Plot a point at (0, 0). Then use the slope to plot the next point.

Practice

A mixture of nuts contains 1 cup of walnuts for every 3 cups of peanuts.

1. Write a linear equation that represents the relationship between peanuts, x, and walnuts, y.

$$y = \frac{1}{3}x$$

2. Graph the line.

LESSON 2-8 · Understand the y-Intercept of a Line

Quick Review

The y-intercept is the y-coordinate of the point where a line crosses the y-axis. The y-intercept of a proportional relationship is 0.

Example

What is the y-intercept of the line?

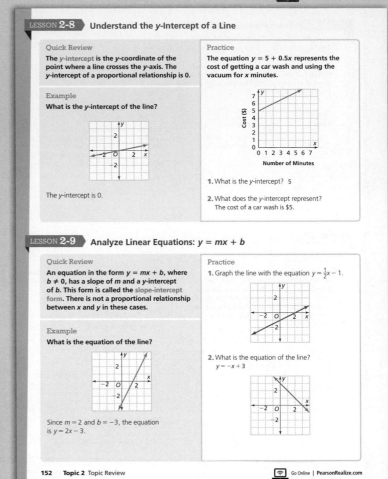

The y-intercept is 0.

Practice

The equation $y = 5 + 0.5x$ represents the cost of getting a car wash and using the vacuum for x minutes.

1. What is the y-intercept? 5

2. What does the y-intercept represent? The cost of a car wash is $5.

LESSON 2-9 · Analyze Linear Equations: $y = mx + b$

Quick Review

An equation in the form $y = mx + b$, where $b \neq 0$, has a slope of m and a y-intercept of b. This form is called the slope-intercept form. There is not a proportional relationship between x and y in these cases.

Example

What is the equation of the line?

Since $m = 2$ and $b = -3$, the equation is $y = 2x - 3$.

Practice

1. Graph the line with the equation $y = \frac{1}{2}x - 1$.

2. What is the equation of the line?
$$y = -x + 3$$

Fluency Practice

Pathfinder

Students practice fluently to solve two-step addition and subtraction equations as they complete a path-finding puzzle activity that reinforces mathematical practices.

Getting Started Students may work independently or with a partner. Go over the directions. Point out that there is only one solution path from START to FINISH.

Students should solve each equation to find the correct path. Encourage students to record their work on a separate sheet of paper.

As Students Do the Activity Remind students that each correctly solved equation is part of the solution path. If a path is not found, students need to check their work and correct as needed.

Some students may check all of the answers first and then shade in the path. Allow this strategy as it provides the same fluency practice.

Another Activity Have students work together to rearrange the blocks that result in a new path from START to FINISH. Ask them to record the new path on a separate sheet of paper.

Extra Challenge Create your own Pathfinder puzzle activity. Write a new equation and solution for each block and use grid paper to create the blocks. Then trade your activity with a partner and complete your partner's Pathfinder puzzle activity.

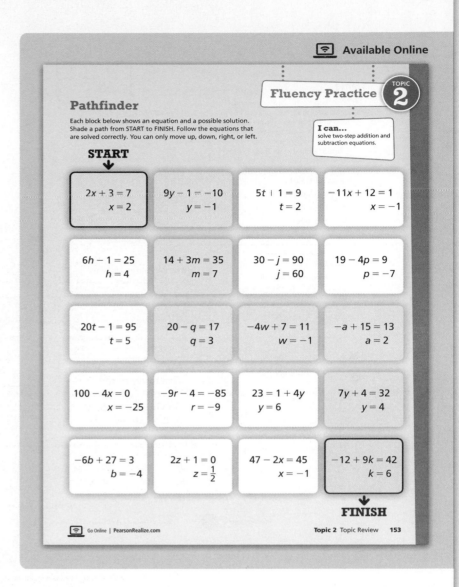

Available Online

Pathfinder

Fluency Practice TOPIC 2

Each block below shows an equation and a possible solution. Shade a path from START to FINISH. Follow the equations that are solved correctly. You can only move up, down, right, or left.

I can... solve two-step addition and subtraction equations.

START

$2x + 3 = 7$ $x = 2$	$9y - 1 = -10$ $y = -1$	$5t + 1 = 9$ $t = 2$	$-11x + 12 = 1$ $x = -1$
$6h - 1 = 25$ $h = 4$	$14 + 3m = 35$ $m = 7$	$30 - j = 90$ $j = 60$	$19 - 4p = 9$ $p = -7$
$20t - 1 = 95$ $t = 5$	$20 - q = 17$ $q = 3$	$-4w + 7 = 11$ $w = -1$	$-a + 15 = 13$ $a = 2$
$100 - 4x = 0$ $x = -25$	$-9r - 4 = -85$ $r = -9$	$23 = 1 + 4y$ $y = 6$	$7y + 4 = 32$ $y = 4$
$-6b + 27 = 3$ $b = -4$	$2z + 1 = 0$ $z = \frac{1}{2}$	$47 - 2x = 45$ $x = -1$	$-12 + 9k = 42$ $k = 6$

FINISH

TOPIC 2 Assessment

Assess

Available Online

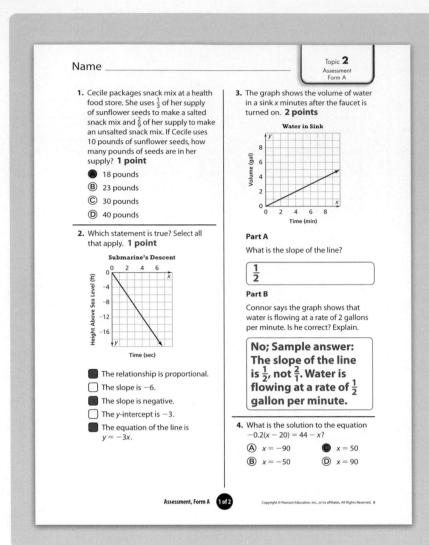

Name _____

Topic **2**
Assessment
Form A

1. Cecile packages snack mix at a health food store. She uses $\frac{1}{3}$ of her supply of sunflower seeds to make a salted snack mix and $\frac{2}{9}$ of her supply to make an unsalted snack mix. If Cecile uses 10 pounds of sunflower seeds, how many pounds of seeds are in her supply? **1 point**

Ⓐ 18 pounds
Ⓑ 23 pounds
Ⓒ 30 pounds
Ⓓ 40 pounds

2. Which statement is true? Select all that apply. **1 point**

Submarine's Descent

☑ The relationship is proportional.
☐ The slope is −6.
☑ The slope is negative.
☐ The y-intercept is −3.
☑ The equation of the line is $y = -3x$.

3. The graph shows the volume of water in a sink x minutes after the faucet is turned on. **2 points**

Water in Sink

Part A

What is the slope of the line?

$$\frac{1}{2}$$

Part B

Connor says the graph shows that water is flowing at a rate of 2 gallons per minute. Is he correct? Explain.

No; Sample answer: The slope of the line is $\frac{1}{2}$, not $\frac{2}{1}$. Water is flowing at a rate of $\frac{1}{2}$ gallon per minute.

4. What is the solution to the equation $-0.2(x - 20) = 44 - x$?

Ⓐ $x = -90$ Ⓒ $x = 50$
Ⓑ $x = -50$ Ⓓ $x = 90$

Assessment, Form A **1 of 2**   Copyright © Pearson Education, Inc., or its affiliates. All Rights Reserved. 8

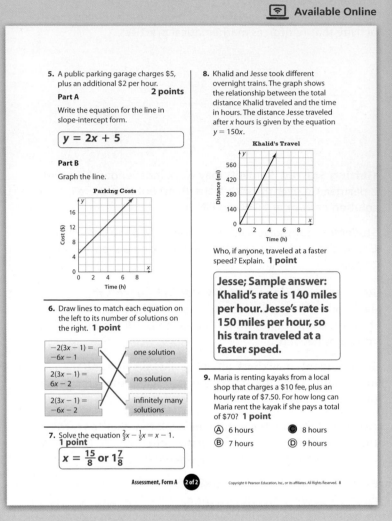

5. A public parking garage charges $5, plus an additional $2 per hour. **2 points**

Part A

Write the equation for the line in slope-intercept form.

$$y = 2x + 5$$

Part B

Graph the line.

Parking Costs

6. Draw lines to match each equation on the left to its number of solutions on the right. **1 point**

$-2(3x - 1) = -6x - 1$ → one solution
$2(3x - 1) = 6x - 2$ → no solution
$2(3x - 1) = -6x - 2$ → infinitely many solutions

7. Solve the equation $\frac{2}{3}x - \frac{1}{5}x = x - 1$. **1 point**

$$x = \frac{15}{8} \text{ or } 1\frac{7}{8}$$

8. Khalid and Jesse took different overnight trains. The graph shows the relationship between the total distance Khalid traveled and the time in hours. The distance Jesse traveled after x hours is given by the equation $y = 150x$.

Khalid's Travel

Who, if anyone, traveled at a faster speed? Explain. **1 point**

Jesse; Sample answer: Khalid's rate is 140 miles per hour. Jesse's rate is 150 miles per hour, so his train traveled at a faster speed.

9. Maria is renting kayaks from a local shop that charges a $10 fee, plus an hourly rate of $7.50. For how long can Maria rent the kayak if she pays a total of $70? **1 point**

Ⓐ 6 hours   Ⓒ 8 hours
Ⓑ 7 hours   Ⓓ 9 hours

Assessment, Form A **2 of 2**   Copyright © Pearson Education, Inc., or its affiliates. All Rights Reserved. 8

Assess students' understanding of the topic concepts and skills using the Topic Assessments found at PearsonRealize.com.

Use the Item Analysis Chart on the facing page to assign intervention to students based on their scores on the paper and pencil version of the Topic Assessments.

You may opt to have students take the Topic Assessment online at PearsonRealize.com. The online assessment is auto-scored, with differentiated intervention automatically assigned to students based on their scores.

You can use ExamView to generate additional Topic Assessments.

There are two versions of the Topic Assessment, Form A and Form B. These parallel versions assess the same content item for item. The Item Analysis chart on the next page can be used with both versions.

PearsonRealize.com
Assess

Available Online

Name _____

1. Adam works at a bakery. He uses $\frac{1}{8}$ of his flour supply to make bread and $\frac{3}{4}$ of his flour supply to make other baked goods. If Adam used 21 pounds of flour, how much flour did he have in his supply? **1 point**

Ⓐ 22 pounds

🅑 24 pounds

Ⓒ 34 pounds

Ⓓ 63 pounds

2. Which statement is true? Select all that apply. **1 point**

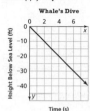

Whale's Dive

☑ The relationship is proportional.

☐ The slope is 5.

☐ The slope is positive.

☑ The y-intercept is 0.

☑ The equation of the line is $y = -5x$.

3. The graph shows the cost of buying beets at a farm stand. **2 points**

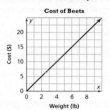

Cost of Beets

Part A

What is the slope of the line?

$$\frac{5}{2}$$

Part B

Abby says the graph shows that beets cost $0.40 per pound. Is she correct? Explain.

No; Sample answer: The slope of the line is $\frac{5}{2}$, not $\frac{2}{5}$. The unit price is $2.50 per pound.

4. What is the solution to the equation $-2.5(x - 4) = -3x + 4$? **1 point**

Ⓐ $x = -28$

🅑 $x = -12$

Ⓒ $x = 12$

Ⓓ $x = 28$

5. A taxi ride costs $4, plus an additional $3 per mile. **2 points**

Part A

Write the equation for the line in slope-intercept form.

$$y = 3x + 4$$

Part B

Graph the line.

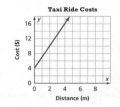

Taxi Ride Costs

6. Draw lines to match each equation on the left to its number of solutions on the right. **1 point**

$2(4x - 1) =$ $-8x - 2$		one solution
$2(4x - 1) =$ $=8x - 2$		no solution
$-2(4x - 1) =$ $-8x - 1$		infinitely many solutions

7. Solve the equation $\frac{1}{2}x + \frac{3}{4}x = 5 - 2.5x$. **1 point**

$$x = \frac{20}{15} \text{ or } 1\frac{1}{3}$$

8. Dominique and Ella are comparing whose jet traveled faster. The graph shows the relationship between the total distance Dominique traveled and the time in hours. The distance Ella traveled after x hours can be represented by the equation $y = 550x$.

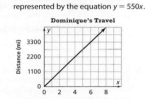

Dominique's Travel

Who, if anyone, traveled at a faster speed? Explain. **1 point**

No one; Sample answer: Dominique's rate is 550 miles per hour. Ella's rate is also 550 miles per hour. Both girls traveled at the same speed.

9. A music shop charges a deposit of $20, plus a monthly rate of $30 to rent an instrument. For how many months did Avi rent an instrument if he spent a total of $80? **1 point**

🅐 2 months

🅑 3 months

Ⓒ 4 months

Ⓓ 5 months

Item Analysis for Diagnosis and Intervention

Item	DOK	MDIS
1	2	K23, K29
2	2	K50, M33
3A	1	K50
3B	3	K50, M33
4	1	K11, K31
5A	1	K52
5B	1	K49

Item	DOK	MDIS
6	2	K32
7	2	K29, K32
8	3	M33, M34
9	2	K23

TOPIC 2 Performance Assessment

🖥 Available Online

Name _____

Students at Mendel Middle School are planning a fair for their school's fundraiser.

1. Liam volunteers to help plan the event. The first month, he volunteered for x hours. The next month, he volunteered for $1\frac{2}{3}$ times as many hours as he had the first month. If he volunteered for a total of 40 hours, how many hours did he volunteer during the first month? Write an equation to represent the situation and solve. **2 points**

> **15 hours; Sample answer:** $x + 1\frac{2}{3}x = 40$, $x = 15$

2. Maureen is in charge of renting a climbing wall. The equation $y = 170x$ represents the total cost of renting a climbing wall from Company A. The table shows the relationship between cost and rental time for Company B. The graph shows the relationship for Company C. Which company, if any, offers the best deal? Explain. **2 points**

Company B

Time (h)	2	3	4	5
Cost ($)	340	510	680	850

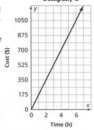

Company C

> **Company A and Company B; Sample answer:** You can compare the rates for each company. Company A charges $170 per hour, which is the slope of the equation. Company B charges $\frac{340}{2} = 170$, or $170 per hour, as shown by the proportions in the table. Company C charges $\frac{175}{1}$, or $175 per hour, which is the slope of the line. Company C costs more.

---

3. Liam makes a poster for the fair. Maureen looks at the poster and says that the price per ticket decreases the more tickets a customer buys. Liam disagrees.

> **Come to the Fair!**
> Admission Plus 5 tickets.......$15
> Admission Plus 10 tickets.....$25
> Admission Plus 20 tickets.....$45

Part A

The graph represents the relationship between the number of tickets bought and the price paid. Find the slope of the line using two different pairs of coordinate points. What does the slope mean about the price per ticket. Is Liam or Maureen correct? **2 points**

> **Liam; Sample answer:**
> slope $= \frac{45 - 25}{20 - 10} = \frac{20}{10} = 2$
> slope $= \frac{25 - 15}{10 - 5} = \frac{10}{5} = 2$
> **The slopes are the same. The price is $2 per ticket no matter how many tickets are bought.**

Fair Price

Part B

What is the y-intercept of the graph? Explain what it means in the problem situation. Then write the equation for the line. **2 points**

> **5; Sample answer: It shows the price of admission to the fair, $5;** $y = 2x + 5$.

4. Maureen proposes giving each student two free tickets, with the price represented by $2(x - 2) + 5$. Liam proposes giving students free admission, with the price represented by $2x$. What number of tickets would result in the same price for each student under either proposal? Explain. **2 points**

> **No amount of tickets; Sample answer: If you set the two expressions equal to each other and solve, you get an untrue statement, $0 = 1$.**

Assess students' ability to apply the topic concepts and skills using the Topic Performance Assessments found at PearsonRealize.com.

Item Analysis for Diagnosis and Intervention

Item	DOK	MDIS
1	2	K27, K29
2	3	M33, M34
3A	4	K50
3B	2	K52, N69
4	2	K31

Scoring Guide

Item	Points	Topic Performance Assessment (Form A)
1	2	Correct answer and equation
	1	Correct answer or equation
2	2	Correct answer and explanation
	1	Correct answer or explanation
3A	2	Two correct slopes and complete explanation
	1	Two correct slopes with little or no explanation; or One correct slope with complete explanation
3B	2	Correct y-intercept and explanation
	1	Correct y-intercept or explanation
4	2	Correct answer and explanation
	1	Correct answer or explanation

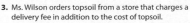 Available Online

---

Name _____

Ms. Wilson's science class decides to plant a community garden.

1. Trent builds planter beds using the dimensions as shown. He wants to determine whether the beds can be built with the same amount of plywood.

$x + 4$ | Vegetables | x

$x + 1$ | Flowers

Part A

Write an equation that Trent could use to represent equivalent perimeters. **1 point**

> **Sample answer:** $2(x + x + 4) = 4(x + 1)$

Part B

Will the perimeters be the same for any value of x? Explain. **2 points**

> No; Sample answer: When solving, the equation simplified to $8 = 4$. Since that statement is untrue, there is no solution. The two perimeters will never be equal.

2. Shana orders seed packets online. The equation $y = 1.22x$ represents the total cost, y, of buying x packets of seeds from Website A. The table shows the relationship between the cost and number of packets for Website B. The graph shows the relationship for Website C. If shipping is free and Shana wants to save money, from which website should she order the seeds? Explain. **2 points**

Website C

Cost ($)

3.75
2.50
1.25

0   2   4   6

Number of Packets

Website B

Number of Packets	2	3	4	5
Cost ($)	2.60	3.90	5.20	6.50

> Website A; Sample answer: Shana can compare the unit rates. Website A: $1.22 per packet (slope of the equation); Website B: $1.30 per packet (proportions in the table); Website C: $1.25 per packet (slope of the line). Website A is the least expensive.

---

3. Ms. Wilson orders topsoil from a store that charges a delivery fee in addition to the cost of topsoil.

Part A

Use the graph to find the slope and the y-intercept. What do they represent in this situation? **2 points**

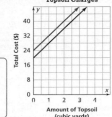

Topsoil Charges

Total Cost ($)

40
32
24
16
8
0

0   1   2   3   4

Amount of Topsoil (cubic yards)

> **Sample answer: The slope is 8; it means the topsoil costs $8 per cubic yard. The y-intercept is 20; it means the delivery fee is $20.**

Part B

When Ms. Wilson calls to place her order, the store informs her that the delivery fee has increased by $4, but the price of the topsoil remains the same. Write an equation and draw a line to represent the new situation on the graph above. Explain. **2 points**

> **Check students' graphs, $y = 8x + 24$; Sample answer: The cost per cubic yard is the same, so the slope is the same. The delivery fee is $4 more, so the y-intercept is now $24.**

4. Ms. Wilson mixes the topsoil with compost.

Part A

Soil Mixture Ratio

Amount of Compost (cubic yards)

6
4
2
0

0   2   4   6   8

Amount of Topsoil (cubic yards)

The graph shows the proportion of topsoil to compost. Write the equation of the line. **1 point**

> $y = \frac{1}{3}x$

Part B

What does the slope of the equation you wrote in Part A mean? **1 point**

> **Sample answer: It means that 1 yd³ of compost is needed for every 3 yd³ of topsoil.**

Assess students' ability to apply the topic concepts and skills using the Topic Performance Assessments found at PearsonRealize.com.

Item Analysis for Diagnosis and Intervention

Item	DOK	MDIS
1A	2	K30
1B	3	K32
2	3	M33, M34
3A	2	K21, K52
3B	4	K30
4A	2	K50
4B	2	K52

Scoring Guide

Item	Points	Topic Performance Assessment (Form B)
1A	1	Correct equation to represent situation
1B	2	Correct answer and explanation
	1	Correct answer or explanation
2	2	Correct answer and explanation
	1	Correct answer or explanation
3A	2	Correct slope, y-intercept, and valid interpretations
	1	Two correct answers with little or no explanation; or one correct answer with explanation
3B	2	Correct graph and explanation
	1	Correct graph or explanation
4A	1	Correct equation
4B	1	Correct explanation

CUMULATIVE/BENCHMARK ASSESSMENT

Available Online

Topics 1-2 Cumulative/Benchmark Assessment

Name _____

Topics **1-2**
Cumulative/
Benchmark Assessment

1. How would you write $0.\overline{7}$ as a fraction? **1 point**
Ⓐ $\frac{8}{9}$
Ⓑ $\frac{6}{9}$
● $\frac{7}{9}$
Ⓓ $\frac{7}{100}$

2. Cube A has a volume of 125 cubic inches. The edge lengths of Cube B measure 4.8 inches. Which cube is larger? Explain. **2 points**

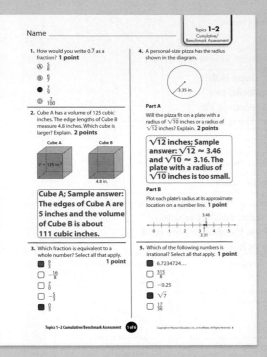

Cube A   Cube B

$V = 125$ in.³   4.8 in.

Cube A; Sample answer: The edges of Cube A are 5 inches and the volume of Cube B is about 111 cubic inches.

3. Which fraction is equivalent to a whole number? Select all that apply. **1 point**
■ $\frac{9}{3}$
☐ $-\frac{16}{8}$
☐ $\frac{7}{2}$
☐ $-\frac{5}{3}$
■ $\frac{8}{2}$

4. A personal-size pizza has the radius shown in the diagram.

3.35 in.

Part A
Will the pizza fit on a plate with a radius of $\sqrt{10}$ inches or a radius of $\sqrt{12}$ inches? Explain. **2 points**

$\sqrt{12}$ **inches; Sample answer:** $\sqrt{12} \approx 3.46$ **and** $\sqrt{10} \approx 3.16$**. The plate with a radius of** $\sqrt{10}$ **inches is too small.**

Part B
Plot each plate's radius at its approximate location on a number line. **1 point**

3.46
0 1 2 3 | 4 5
         3.31

5. Which of the following numbers is irrational? Select all that apply. **1 point**
☐ $6.7234724\ldots$
☐ $\frac{315}{8}$
☐ -0.25
■ $\sqrt{7}$
☐ $\frac{17}{36}$

---

6. A cube-shaped dog kennel is replaced by a larger kennel. The volume of the original kennel was 27 cubic feet. The volume of the new kennel is 64 cubic feet. How many feet were added to each edge length of the kennel? **1 point**
● 1 foot
Ⓑ 2 feet
Ⓒ 3 feet
Ⓓ 4 feet

7. Solve for x in the equation below.
1 point
$(x-2) = -\frac{1}{4}(x-8)$

$x = 3\frac{1}{5}$

8. A square has side lengths of $2x$ inches. An equilateral triangle has side lengths of $\left(2x + \frac{1}{3}\right)$ inches. If the square and the triangle have the same perimeter, what is the value of x?
1 point

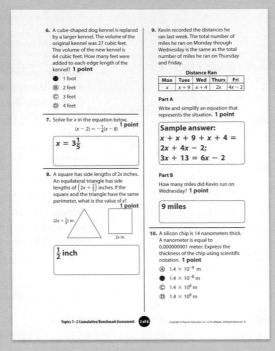

$\left(2x + \frac{1}{3}\right)$ in. $2x$ in.

$\frac{1}{2}$ inch

9. Kevin recorded the distances he ran last week. The total number of miles he ran on Monday through Wednesday is the same as the total number of miles he ran on Thursday and Friday.

Distance Ran

Mon	Tues	Wed	Thurs	Fri
x	$x+9$	$x+4$	$2x$	$4x-2$

Part A
Write and simplify an equation that represents the situation. **1 point**

Sample answer:
$x + x + 9 + x + 4 =$
$2x + 4x - 2;$
$3x + 13 = 6x - 2$

Part B
How many miles did Kevin run on Wednesday? **1 point**

9 miles

10. A silicon chip is 14 nanometers thick. A nanometer is equal to 0.000000001 meter. Express the thickness of the chip using scientific notation. **1 point**
Ⓐ 1.4×10^{-9} m
● 1.4×10^{-8} m
Ⓒ 1.4×10^{8} m
Ⓓ 1.4×10^{9} m

---

11. What is the area of the bulletin board?
1 point

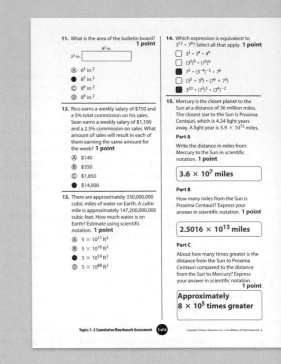

2^5 in. 4^3 in.

Ⓐ 6^3 in.²
Ⓑ 8^3 in.²
● 8^6 in.²
Ⓓ 8^9 in.²

12. Rico earns a weekly salary of $750 and a 5% total commission on his sales. Sean earns a weekly salary of $1,100 and a 2.5% commission on sales. What amount of sales will result in each of them earning the same amount for the week? **1 point**
Ⓐ $140
Ⓑ $350
Ⓒ $1,850
● $14,000

13. There are approximately 330,000,000 cubic miles of water on Earth. A cubic mile is approximately 147,200,000,000 cubic feet. How much water is on Earth? Estimate using scientific notation. **1 point**
Ⓐ 5×10^{17} ft³
Ⓑ 5×10^{18} ft³
● 5×10^{19} ft³
Ⓓ 5×10^{88} ft³

14. Which expression is equivalent to $3^{12} \cdot 7^9$? Select all that apply. **1 point**
☐ $3^3 \cdot 3^4 \cdot 4^9$
☐ $(3^3)^9 \cdot (7^3)^6$
■ $7^3 \cdot (3^{-4})^{-3} \cdot 7^6$
☐ $(3^2 \cdot 7^3)^6 \cdot (7^6 + 7^3)$
☐ $3^{20} \cdot (7^3)^3 \cdot (3^4)^{-2}$

15. Mercury is the closest planet to the Sun at a distance of 36 million miles. The closest star to the Sun is Proxima Centauri, which is 4.24 light years away. A light year is 5.9×10^{12} miles.

Part A
Write the distance in miles from Mercury to the Sun in scientific notation. **1 point**

3.6×10^7 miles

Part B
How many miles from the Sun is Proxima Centauri? Express your answer in scientific notation. **1 point**

2.5016×10^{13} miles

Part C
About how many times greater is the distance from the Sun to Proxima Centauri compared to the distance from the Sun to Mercury? Express your answer in scientific notation. **1 point**

Approximately
8×10^5 **times greater**

---

16. Draw lines to match each exponential number on the left to its equivalent on the right. **1 point**

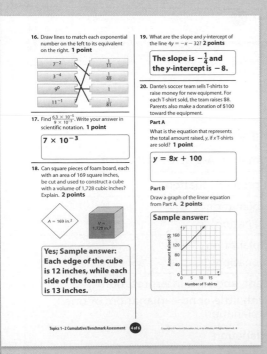

7^{-2} $\frac{1}{11}$
3^{-4} $\frac{1}{49}$
9^0 1
11^{-1} $\frac{1}{81}$

17. Find $\frac{6.3 \times 10^{-5}}{9 \times 10^{-3}}$. Write your answer in scientific notation. **1 point**

7×10^{-3}

18. Can square pieces of foam board, each with an area of 169 square inches, be cut and used to construct a cube with a volume of 1,728 cubic inches? Explain. **2 points**

$A = 169$ in.² $V = 1,728$ in.³

Yes; Sample answer: Each edge of the cube is 12 inches, while each side of the foam board is 13 inches.

19. What are the slope and y-intercept of the line $4y = -x - 32$? **2 points**

The slope is $-\frac{1}{4}$ **and the y-intercept is** -8**.**

20. Dante's soccer team sells T-shirts to raise money for new equipment. For each T-shirt sold, the team raises $8. Parents also make a donation of $100 toward the equipment.

Part A
What is the equation that represents the total amount raised, y, if x T-shirts are sold? **1 point**

$y = 8x + 100$

Part B
Draw a graph of the linear equation from Part A. **2 points**

Sample answer:

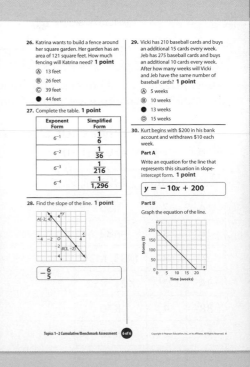

Amount Raised ($)
160
120
80
40
0   5   10   15
Number of T-shirts

---

21. How many solutions does the equation below have? **1 point**
$2x - 7 + 19 = 6x - 4x + 12$
Ⓐ No solution
Ⓑ 1 solution
Ⓒ 2 solutions
● Infinitely many solutions

22. Selena was comparing the flying speeds of different birds in science class.

Robin's Flight

Time (s)	2	3	4	5	6
Distance (m)	30	45	60	75	90

Blue Jay's Flight

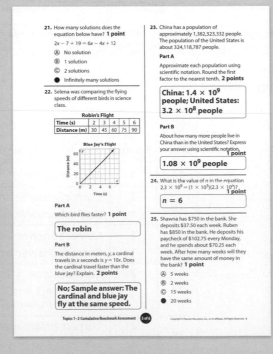

Distance (m)
60
40
20
0   2   4   6
Time (s)

Part A
Which bird flies faster? **1 point**

The robin

Part B
The distance in meters, y, a cardinal travels in x seconds is $y = 10x$. Does the cardinal travel faster than the blue jay? Explain. **2 points**

No; Sample answer: The cardinal and blue jay fly at the same speed.

23. China has a population of approximately 1,382,323,332 people. The population of the United States is about 324,118,787 people.

Part A
Approximate each population using scientific notation. Round the first factor to the nearest tenth. **2 points**

China: 1.4×10^9 **people; United States:** 3.2×10^8 **people**

Part B
About how many more people live in China than in the United States? Express your answer using scientific notation. **1 point**

1.08×10^9 **people**

24. What is the value of n in the equation $2.3 \times 10^9 = (1 \times 10^3)(2.3 \times 10^n)$? **1 point**

$n = 6$

25. Shawna has $750 in the bank. She deposits $37.50 each week. Ruben has $850 in the bank. He deposits his paycheck of $102.75 every Monday, and he spends about $70.25 each week. After how many weeks will they have the same amount of money in the bank? **1 point**
Ⓐ 5 weeks
Ⓑ 2 weeks
Ⓒ 15 weeks
● 20 weeks

---

26. Katrina wants to build a fence around her square garden. Her garden has an area of 121 square feet. How much fencing will Katrina need? **1 point**
Ⓐ 13 feet
Ⓑ 26 feet
Ⓒ 39 feet
● 44 feet

27. Complete the table. **1 point**

Exponent Form	Simplified Form
6^{-1}	$\frac{1}{6}$
6^{-2}	$\frac{1}{36}$
6^{-3}	$\frac{1}{216}$
6^{-4}	$\frac{1}{1,296}$

28. Find the slope of the line. **1 point**

A(-2, 4)
B(3, -2)

$-\frac{6}{5}$

29. Vicki has 210 baseball cards and buys an additional 15 cards every week. Jeb has 275 baseball cards and buys an additional 10 cards every week. After how many weeks will Vicki and Jeb have the same number of baseball cards? **1 point**
Ⓐ 5 weeks
Ⓑ 10 weeks
● 13 weeks
Ⓓ 15 weeks

30. Kurt begins with $200 in his bank account and withdraws $10 each week.

Part A
Write an equation for the line that represents this situation in slope-intercept form. **1 point**

$y = -10x + 200$

Part B
Graph the equation of the line.

Money ($)
200
150
100
50
0   5   10   15   20
Time (weeks)

Items 1–6, 10, 11, 13–18, 23, 24, 26, and 27 assess content taught in Topic 1. Items 7–9, 12, 19–22, 25, and 28–30 assess content taught in Topic 2.

Item Analysis for Topics 1–2 Benchmark Assessment

Item	DOK	MDIS
1	1	M22, M23
2	2	L82, N52
3	1	M9
4A	2	L80, L81
4B	1	L73
5	1	L80
6	2	L82, N52
7	1	K29, K32
8	2	K29, K32
9A	1	K32, K18
9B	1	K32
10	1	L84, L85
11	1	L83
12	2	K26, K30
13	2	L84, L85
14	1	L83
15A	1	L84, L85
15B	1	L84, L85
15C	3	L84, L85
16	1	L83

Item	DOK	MDIS
17	1	L84, L85
18	2	L81, L82
19	1	K50, K52
20A	1	K52
20B	1	K52
20C	1	K49
21	1	K32
22A	2	M32–M34
22B	1	M32–M34
23A	1	L84, L85
23B	2	L84, L85
24	1	L84, L85
25	1	K32, K26
26	1	L81
27	1	L83
28	1	K50
29	1	K32
30A	1	K52
30B	1	K49

You may opt to have students take the Cumulative/Benchmark Assessment online at PearsonRealize.com. The online assessment is auto-scored, with differentiated intervention automatically assigned to students based on their scores.

Scoring Guide

Item	Points	Benchmark Assessment	Item	Points	Benchmark Assessment
2	2 1	Correct answer and explanation Correct answer or explanation	19	2 1	Correct slope and y-intercept Correct slope or y-intercept
4A	2 1	Correct answer and explanation Correct answer or explanation	20B	2 1	Correct graph and labels Correct graph or labels
4B	2 1	Two correct answers correctly plotted on number line One correct answer correctly plotted on number line	22B	2 1	Correct answer and explanation Correct answer or explanation
18	2 1	Correct answer and explanation Correct answer or explanation	23A	2 1	Two correct answers Only one correct answer

TOPIC 3 — Use Functions to Model Relationships

Math Background Focus

Relations and Functions

- **The Concept of Function** In Lesson 3-1, students are introduced to relations and functions. They use arrow diagrams and tables to determine whether a relation is a function. They learn that a relation is a function if each input, or x-value, has exactly one output, or y-value.

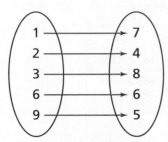

This relation is a function.

Input	Output
1	20
2	15
3	10
3	5
4	0

This relation is not a function.

In Lesson 3-2, students represent functions using graphs, in addition to tables and equations. They determine whether a function is linear or nonlinear using graphs and tables.

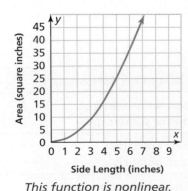

This function is nonlinear.

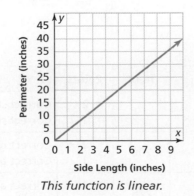

This function is linear.

Compare Properties of Functions

- **Properties of Functions** In Lesson 3-3, students compare functions in different representations by analyzing the properties of functions, specifically, initial value and constant rate of change. They relate initial value to the y-intercept in linear equations and the constant rate of change to the slope as they compare two linear functions in different representations.

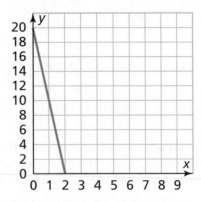

This function has a constant rate of change of -5.

This function has a constant rate of change of -10.

They also compare linear and nonlinear functions in different representations. Students come to understand that the graph of a linear function is a straight line because there is a constant rate of change while the graph of a nonlinear function is not because there is not a constant rate of change.

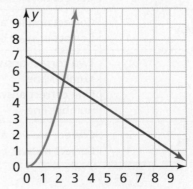

Construct Functions to Model Linear Relationships

- **Construct and Interpret Functions** In Lesson 3-4, students represent linear functions with equations in the form $y = mx + b$. They determine the rate of change and initial value from two ordered pairs or from a verbal description. They construct different representations of the relationship between variables and use the representations to construct a function. These representations include bar diagrams, graphs, tables, and equations in the form $y = mx + b$.

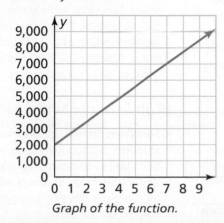

Graph of the function.

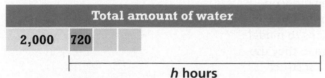

Total amount of water

| 2,000 | 720 | | |

h hours

Bar diagram representing the function.

$$y = 720h + 2,000$$

Equation in the form $y = mx + b$

Describe Behaviors of Functions Qualitatively

- **Intervals of Increase and Decrease** In Lesson 3-5, students describe the relationship between two quantities by looking at the behavior of the graph of the function in different intervals. They identify the intervals in a qualitative graph and describe the behavior of the function as increasing, decreasing, or constant. They recognize that when the slope of the line is positive, the function is increasing, and when the slope of the line is negative, the function is decreasing.

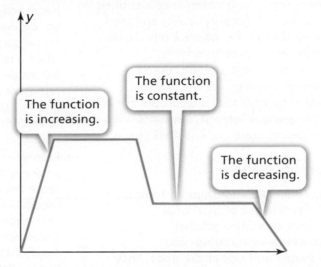

The function is increasing.

The function is constant.

The function is decreasing.

- **Sketches of Functions** In Lesson 3-6, students draw sketches of a graph for a function from a verbal description. Students analyze the relationship between the variables in the function, after which they sketch the graph of the function.

Danika rode a chair lift up to the top of the trail. She waited at the top for a few minutes before skiing down the trail.

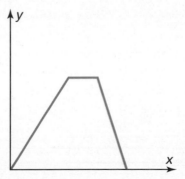

Math Background Coherence

Look Back

How does Topic 3 connect to what students learned earlier?

Grade 7

- **Proportional Reasoning** In Topic 2, students learned to reason about proportional relationships. They identified the constant of proportionality and used the equation $y = kx$, where k represents the constant of proportionality.

- **Percents** In Topic 3, students used the percent proportion and the percent equation to solve multistep problems involving simple interest, discounts, commissions, markups, and markdowns.

Earlier in Grade 8

- **Proportional Relationships** In Topic 2, students revisited proportional relationships as they graphed proportional relationships and interpreted unit rate as the slope. They compared two proportional relationships represented in different ways.

- **Linear Equations** Students studied slope by analyzing similar triangles. They derived the linear equation in the form $y = mx + b$, understanding that m represents the slope while b the y-intercept.

Topic 3

How is content connected within Topic 3?

- **Relations and Functions** In Lesson 3-1, students are introduced to two important concepts: relation and function. They learn that a function is a special kind of relation in which each input, or x-value has exactly one output, or y-value. They use different representations, specifically arrow diagrams and tables to determine when a relation is a function. In Lesson 3-2, students connect additional representations—bar diagrams and graphs—to functions as they continue to explore functions, both linear and nonlinear.

- **Properties of Functions** In Lesson 3-3, students compare functions in different representations by analyzing their properties: initial value and constant rate of change. In Lesson 3-4, they draw on their understanding of the properties of functions to construct functions to model linear relationships. Once again, they use different representations to construct functions: tables, graphs, and equations in the form $y = mx + b$.

- **Qualitative Graphs** In Lessons 3-5 and 3-6, students explore qualitative graphs that model relationships between quantities or variables. They first analyze qualitative graphs, identifying intervals in which the function is increasing, decreasing, or constant. Then, in Lesson 3-6, they sketch qualitative graphs that match verbal descriptions and interpret qualitative graphs to describe the situation they represent.

Look Ahead

How does Topic 3 connect to what students will learn later?

Later in Grade 8

- **Linear Associations** In Topic 4, students will connect linear equations and linear functions as they investigate bivariate data. They use their growing understanding of linear equations and linear functions as they explore linear associations in scatter plots.

High School Mathematics

- **Functions** In high school mathematics, students will study a range of functions, from linear, to quadratic, exponential, and logarithmic. Students will see that all functions have certain properties that help to define them.

Math Background Rigor

A rigorous curriculum emphasizes conceptual understanding, procedural skill and fluency, and applications.

Conceptual Understanding

- **Relations and Functions** Students build on their understanding of proportional relationships as they begin their study of functions. They internalize the definition of a relation and a function. Students explore different kinds of functions, linear and nonlinear, and are able to differentiate linear and nonlinear functions in tables and graphs.
- **Properties of Functions** Students build on their knowledge of the properties of linear equations—slope and initial value—as they study the properties of linear functions. Students come to understand that the properties of linear functions relate to the properties of linear equations: constant rate of change aligns to slope and initial value aligns to y-intercept. They are able to recognize a function as nonlinear because the graph of the function does not show a constant rate of change.
- **Linear Functions** Students learn that a linear function represents a relationship between two quantities. They understand that they can use different representations, such as tables, graphs, and equations, for a linear function. They come to relate the equation for a linear function to the linear equation $y = mx + b$.
- **Qualitative Graphs** Students learn that relationships between quantities can be shown in qualitative graphs, graphs that do not always have numerical values on the x- and y-axes. They come to understand the connection between qualitative graphs and the behavior of the function in different intervals.

Procedural Skill and Fluency

- **Differentiate Relations as Functions or Not Functions** In Lesson 3-1, students develop procedural skill in determining whether a relation is a function by using an arrow diagram or a table. Throughout Topic 3, students have frequent opportunities to develop fluency with identifying relations that are functions, and identifying functions that are linear and nonlinear.
- **Recognize Linear Relationships** Throughout Topic 3, students are expected to determine whether a given relationship represents a linear or nonlinear function. They use different representations, such as tables, graphs, and equations to make these determinations. They determine the properties of functions in different representations and are able to compare the functions based on their properties.
- **Qualitative Graphs** In Lessons 3-5 and 3-6, students develop proficiency with analyzing qualitative graphs to describe the behavior of a function in different intervals. They also practice constructing qualitative graphs based on verbal descriptions.

Applications

- **Functions that Model Linear Relationships** Throughout Topic 3, and especially in Lesson 3-4, students apply their understanding of linear functions as they construct linear functions to represent given real-world situations. They further apply their understanding of linear and nonlinear functions to determine whether a given representation accurately shows the behavior of two quantities.

Math Practices

The math practices and processes describe the behaviors and thinking habits that mathematically proficient students demonstrate when actively engaged in mathematics work. Opportunities for engagement in the practices and to develop expertise with these important behaviors and thinking habits exist throughout the topic and program. The focus below is on mathematical reasoning and explanation.

As students explore, construct, and analyze functions, look for these behaviors to assess students' proficiency with these mathematical practices.

Math Practices Within Topic 3 Lessons	
Model with mathematics.	**Reason abstractly and quantitatively.**
Mathematically proficient students:	Mathematically proficient students:
• Apply the mathematics they know to solve problems.	• Make sense of quantities and their relationships in problem situations.
• Identify key quantities in a problem situation and map their relationships using a range of tools.	• Are able to "decontextualize" quantities, that is, represent quantities symbolically.
• Make assumptions and approximations about the quantities and relationships in a problem situation.	• Are able to "contextualize" quantities, that is, explain what variables and symbols refer to in a real-world context.
• Analyze relationships mathematically to draw conclusions and construct models.	
• Interpret their mathematical results in the context of the situation, and propose improvements to the model as needed.	

Use these questioning strategies to help students compare, construct, and analyze functions and reason abstractly and quantitatively about them.

Q: What are the related quantities and what does each quantity represent in this situation?

Q: Which quantity is the input or *x*-value? Which quantity is the output or *y*-value?

Q: How can you represent the quantities mathematically?

Q: How can you use the graph of the function to write an equation in the form $y = mx + b$?

Q: How can you explain the relationship between the input values and the output values?

Q: What assumptions do you need to make about the relationship between the input values and output values?

Q: What conclusions can you draw about the relationship that you are modeling?

Q: Which representation best models the relationship?

Topic Readiness Assessment

Assess

Name _____

Topic **3**
Readiness Assessment

1. Which is the constant of proportionality for the relationship shown in the table?

x	y
3	2
6	4
9	6
12	8

● Ⓐ $\frac{2}{3}$
Ⓑ $\frac{3}{2}$
Ⓒ 2
Ⓓ 3

2. Which ordered pair is **NOT** a solution to the equation $y = 2x$?

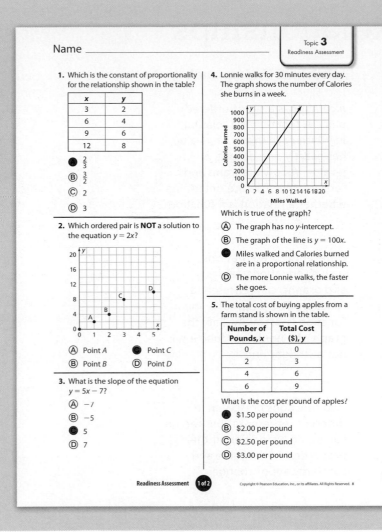

Ⓐ Point A
● Point C
Ⓑ Point B
Ⓓ Point D

3. What is the slope of the equation $y = 5x - 7$?

Ⓐ −7
● Ⓑ −5
● 5
Ⓓ 7

4. Lonnie walks for 30 minutes every day. The graph shows the number of Calories she burns in a week.

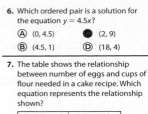

Miles Walked

Which is true of the graph?

Ⓐ The graph has no y-intercept.
Ⓑ The graph of the line is $y = 100x$.
● Miles walked and Calories burned are in a proportional relationship.
Ⓓ The more Lonnie walks, the faster she goes.

5. The total cost of buying apples from a farm stand is shown in the table.

Number of Pounds, x	Total Cost ($), y
0	0
2	3
4	6
6	9

What is the cost per pound of apples?

● $1.50 per pound
Ⓑ $2.00 per pound
Ⓒ $2.50 per pound
Ⓓ $3.00 per pound

6. Which ordered pair is a solution for the equation $y = 4.5x$?

Ⓐ (0, 4.5)
● (2, 9)
Ⓑ (4.5, 1)
Ⓓ (18, 4)

7. The table shows the relationship between number of eggs and cups of flour needed in a cake recipe. Which equation represents the relationship shown?

Number of Eggs, x	Cups of Flour, y
0	0
6	4
12	8
18	12

● $y = \frac{2}{3}x$
Ⓒ $y = 4x$
Ⓑ $y = \frac{3}{2}x$
Ⓓ $y = 6x$

8. A taxi driver charges a $2 fee plus an additional $4 per mile as shown by the graph.

Taxi Ride Cost

Distance (mi)

What is the cost of a 3-mile ride?

Ⓐ $1
Ⓒ $12
Ⓑ $10
● $14

9. Which equation describes a line with a slope of $\frac{2}{5}$ that passes through (0, 4)?

● $y = \frac{2}{5}x + 4$
Ⓑ $y = \frac{2}{5}x - 4$
Ⓒ $4y = 2x + 5$
Ⓓ $4y = 2x - 5$

10. What is the y-intercept of $y = -3x + 6$?

Ⓐ −6
Ⓒ 3
Ⓑ −3
● 6

11. Imani is training for a half marathon. The graph shows her distance during a 60-minute practice run.

Distance Imani Ran

Time (min)

Which statement is **NOT** supported by the graph?

Ⓐ The slope is $\frac{1}{12}$.
Ⓑ Imani ran at a constant rate.
Ⓒ Imani ran 5 miles in 1 hour.
● Imani ran 12 miles per minute.

12. Which ordered pair is a solution to the equation $y = -\frac{2}{3}x + 9$?

● $\left(-\frac{3}{2}, 10\right)$
Ⓒ $\left(-1, 10\frac{2}{3}\right)$
Ⓑ (0, 10)
Ⓓ $\left(\frac{2}{3}, 10\right)$

Copyright © Pearson Education, Inc., or its affiliates. All Rights Reserved. 8
Copyright © Pearson Education, Inc., or its affiliates. All Rights Reserved. 8

Assess students' understanding of prerequisite concepts and skills using the Topic Readiness Assessment found at PearsonRealize.com.

You may opt to have students take the automatically scored Topic Readiness Assessment online.

RtI **Item Analysis for Diagnosis and Remediation**

Item	DOK	MDIS
1	1	M32
2, 6, 12	2	K52
3, 9, 10	2	K50
4, 7	2	K51
5	2	M28
8	2	K49
11	2	K49

Topic Planner

Use Functions to Model Relationships

Lesson	Vocabulary	Objective	Essential Understanding
3-1 Understand Relations and Functions	relation, function	• Identify whether a relation is a function. • Interpret a function.	A relation is a set of ordered pairs. A function is a relation in which each input, or *x*-value, has exactly one output, or *y*-value. Arrow diagrams and tables can be used to determine whether a relation is a function.
3-2 Connect Representations of Functions	constant rate of change, initial value, linear function, nonlinear function	• Identify functions in different representations: equations, tables, and graphs. • Identify linear and nonlinear functions in different representations.	Different representations, such as equations, tables, and graphs, can represent a function. The graph of a linear function is a straight line; the graph of a nonlinear function is not a straight line.
3-3 Compare Linear and Nonlinear Functions	none	• Compare properties of linear functions in different representations. • Compare properties of linear and nonlinear functions in different representations.	Two functions presented in different representations can be compared by looking at their properties: initial value and constant rate of change.

Lesson Resources

Digital

Student's Edition

Additional Practice workbook

Print

Teaching Resources
- Reteach to Build Understanding
- Additional Vocabulary Support
- Build Mathematical Literacy
- Enrichment

Assessment Resources
- Lesson Quiz

Digital

Digital Lesson Courseware
- Today's Challenge
- Visual Learning Animation Plus
- Key Concept
- Additional Examples
- 3-Act Mathematical Modeling
- Online Practice powered by MathXL for School

- Virtual Nerd Video Tutorials
- Animated Glossary
- Digital Math Tools
- Online Math Games

Lesson Support for Teachers
- Listen and Look For PD Lesson Video

he suggested pacing for each lesson is 2 days for a 45-minute math class
nd 1 day for a 90-minute class.

Lesson	Vocabulary	Objective	Essential Understanding
3-Act Mathematical Modeling: Every Drop Counts	none	• Use mathematical modeling to represent a problem situation and to propose a solution. • Test and verify the appropriateness of their math models. • Explain why the results from their mathematical models may not align exactly to the problem situation.	Many real-world problem situations can be represented with a mathematical model, but that model may not represent a real-world situation exactly.
3-4 Construct Functions to Model Linear Relationships	none	• Construct a linear function to model a relationship using an equation in the form $y = mx + b$.	A function that represents a linear relationship between two quantities can be represented by an equation written in the form $y = mx + b$.
3-5 Intervals of Increase and Decrease	interval	• Describe qualitatively the behavior of a function by analyzing its graph. • Describe the graph of a function at each interval.	The relationship between two quantities can be represented in a qualitative graph that shows the behavior of the function in different intervals.
3-6 Sketch Functions from Verbal Descriptions	none	• Draw a qualitative graph of a function based on a verbal description. • Analyze and interpret the sketch of a graph of a function.	You can use what you know about the behavior of a function in different intervals to sketch a qualitative graph of a function.

Topic Resources

Digital

Print

Student's Edition
- Review What You Know
- Build Literacy in Mathematics
- Mid-Topic Checkpoint and Performance Task
- Topic Review
- Fluency Practice Activity
- STEM Project

Assessment Resources
- Topic Readiness Assessment
- Mid-Topic Assessment
- Topic Assessment
- Topic Performance Task

Digital

Topic Support for Students
- Math Practice Animations
- STEM Project
- 3-Act Mathematical Modeling Lesson

Topic Support for Teachers
- Topic Overview Video
- ExamView Test Generator

Use Functions to Model Relationships

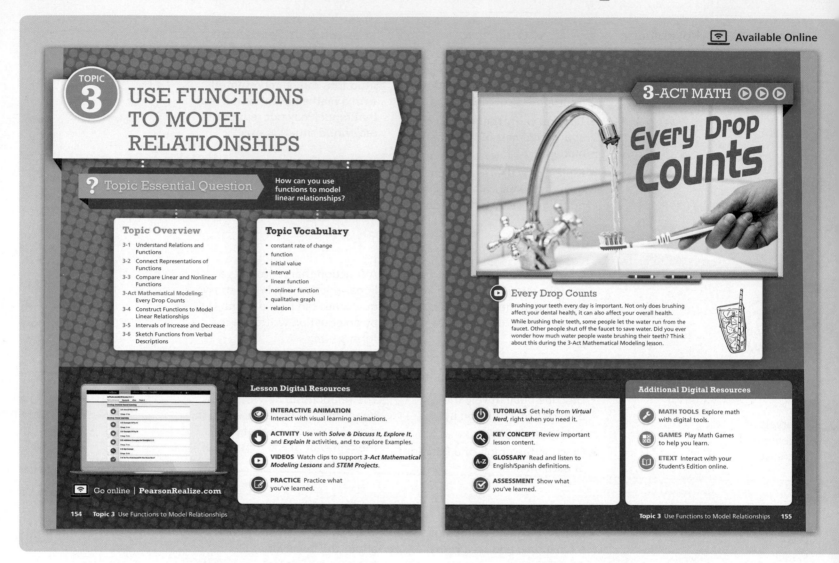

USE FUNCTIONS TO MODEL RELATIONSHIPS

Topic Essential Question

How can you use functions to model linear relationships?

Topic Overview

3-1 Understand Relations and Functions

3-2 Connect Representations of Functions

3-3 Compare Linear and Nonlinear Functions

3-Act Mathematical Modeling: Every Drop Counts

3-4 Construct Functions to Model Linear Relationships

3-5 Intervals of Increase and Decrease

3-6 Sketch Functions from Verbal Descriptions

Topic Vocabulary

- constant rate of change
- function
- initial value
- interval
- linear function
- nonlinear function
- qualitative graph
- relation

Lesson Digital Resources

INTERACTIVE ANIMATION Interact with visual learning animations.

ACTIVITY Use with *Solve & Discuss It, Explore It,* and *Explain It* activities, and to explore Examples.

VIDEOS Watch clips to support *3-Act Mathematical Modeling Lessons* and *STEM Projects*.

PRACTICE Practice what you've learned.

Go online | PearsonRealize.com

3-ACT MATH

Every Drop Counts

Every Drop Counts

Brushing your teeth every day is important. Not only does brushing affect your dental health, it can also affect your overall health.

While brushing their teeth, some people let the water run from the faucet. Other people shut off the faucet to save water. Did you ever wonder how much water people waste brushing their teeth? Think about this during the 3-Act Mathematical Modeling lesson.

Additional Digital Resources

TUTORIALS Get help from *Virtual Nerd*, right when you need it.

KEY CONCEPT Review important lesson content.

GLOSSARY Read and listen to English/Spanish definitions.

ASSESSMENT Show what you've learned.

MATH TOOLS Explore math with digital tools.

GAMES Play Math Games to help you learn.

ETEXT Interact with your Student's Edition online.

154 Topic 3 Use Functions to Model Relationships

Topic 3 Use Functions to Model Relationships 155

Available Online

Topic Essential Question

How can you use functions to model linear relationships?

Revisit the Topic Essential Question throughout the topic. See the Teacher's Edition for the Topic Review for notes about answering the question.

3-Act Mathematical Modeling

Have students read about the Mathematical Modeling lesson for this topic. You can use the preview for this lesson to get students interested in learning the content of the topic.

The Mathematical Modeling in 3 Acts lesson appears after Lesson 3-3.

Modeling Population Growth

Project Overview

In this project, students will continue their exploration of the science of demography, focusing on changes due to migration. Students will consider how migration to urban areas may change the growth of the population of the country.

What's the Math?

Students use population data to develop linear equations that model growth in urban areas. They use these to make predictions about future growth. They will also compare these equations with those they developed for general population growth in the last topic.

What's the Science?

Population studies analyze the relationships between economic, social, and biological processes that influence a population. Students will consider factors that may change their models for population growth. What factors differ between India and the United States?

What's the Engineering and Technology?

Students think like engineers as they gather, analyze, synthesize, and present data in clear and understandable ways. They recognize that resources vary between countries and consider how this impacts population growth.

Introduce the Project

Present the project by discussing causes and results of increasing urbanization. The questions below can be used to guide the discussion.

Q: What harmful effects might an increasing population in urban areas have on the environment? [Sample answers: Desertification as land is cleared for development, pollution, shortages of clean water]

Q: What are some of the advantages of migration to urban areas? [Sample answer: Increased job opportunities, better education, better health care and access to family planning resources, access to clean water]

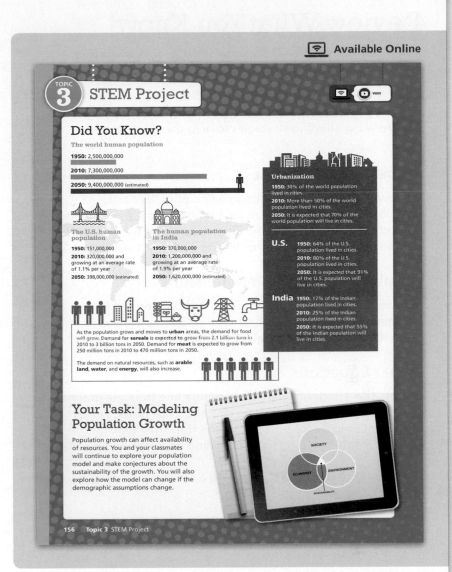

Q: Develop a linear model that presents the data on urbanization in India and the U.S. How does the model compare with those of population growth developed in the last topic? [Answers will vary.]

Q: What factors might affect the sustainability of growth indicated by your model? [Sample answers: Urban areas continue to offer more jobs and opportunities. Health and sanitation do not become degraded by an increase in population.]

You can launch this project any time during Topic 3.

 Show the Topic 3 STEM video to generate interest in the project.

Teacher resources that provide students with project details and support are available at PearsonRealize.com.

TOPIC 3 Get Ready!

Review What You Know!

Assign the Review What You Know in order to activate prior knowledge and practice prerequisite concepts and skills needed for success in the lessons in this topic.

Encourage students to work independently or with a partner. Use these questioning strategies to help them get started.

Slope and *y*-Intercept

Q: How can you find the slope of a line using two ordered pairs? [Sample answer: Set up a ratio of the rise over the run. Find the rise by finding the difference of the two *y*-values. Find the run by finding the difference of the two *x*-values.]

Graph Proportional Relationships

Q: How can you use the unit rate to find the slope of the line? [Sample answer: The unit rate is the same as the slope. So finding the unit rate gives you the slope.]

Linear Equations

Q: How can you derive the equation of a line from the graph of the line? [Sample answer: Find the slope of the line by determining the rise divided by the run. Then look for the *y*-intercept—the place where the line intercepts the *y*-axis.]

Item Analysis for Diagnosis and Intervention

Item	MDIS
1–4	K50, M33
5–7	K50
8	M34
9	K45

Vocabulary Review

You may choose to strengthen vocabulary with the following activity.

- Have students play a game with the vocabulary words. Give one student a vocabulary word and have him or her make a visual to illustrate the word. The student shows the visual to classmates who look to identify the word from the visual.

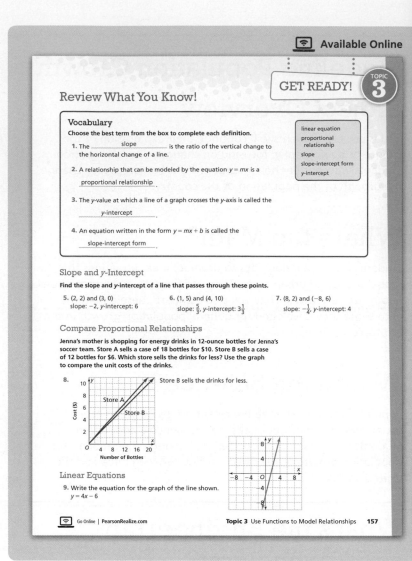

Build Vocabulary

Pre-reading Strategy: Graphic Organizer

Have students preview each term and complete the graphic organizer in order to build understanding of the math vocabulary in this topic.

Q: What does the graphic organizer tell you about a function? [Sample answer: It can have different representations.]

Q: What do you notice about each of the representations? [Sample answer: The equation is a proportional equation. In the arrow diagram, each number in the left oval is aligned to one number in the right oval.]

Have students offer observations on each of the representations. If no one mentions it, ask specifically about the x-values in the table, the form of the equation, and the direction of the parabola in the graph.

Tell students that throughout the topic, they will see these different representations and will learn how to determine whether the sets of numbers define a function.

Q: What text features help you identify new vocabulary terms in each lesson? [Sample answer: Highlighted Bold Terms, Examples, and Key Concept boxes]

As students progress through the topic, have them revisit this page and determine whether each representation is a function.

Extension for All Readers

Challenge students to use their completed graphic organizers to write a brief summary of the vocabulary terms they will encounter in this topic. Help students to develop strong mathematical communication skills by encouraging them to include examples, symbols, and diagrams in the summaries.

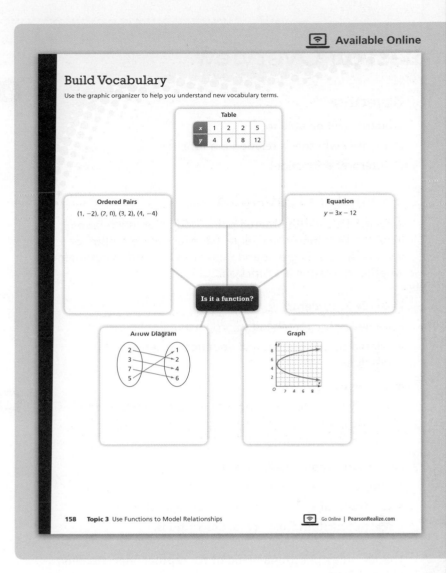

Lesson 3-1

Understand Relations and Functions

Lesson Overview

FOCUS

Objective

Students will be able to:

✔ identify whether a relation is a function.

✔ interpret a function.

Essential Understanding

A relation is a set of ordered pairs. A function is a relation in which each input, or *x*-value, has exactly one output, or *y*-value. Arrow diagrams and tables can be used to determine whether a relation is a function.

COHERENCE

In Grade 7, students:

• studied concepts related to proportional relationships.

• related tables, graphs, and equations when solving problems.

In this lesson, students:

• identify and interpret functions using diagrams and tables.

• recognize that a relation is a function if each input value has exactly one output value.

Later in this topic, students will:

• compare linear and nonlinear functions.

• construct functions to model linear relationships.

• sketch functions from verbal descriptions.

RIGOR

This lesson emphasizes a blend of **conceptual understanding** and **application**.

• Students reason about a relation and determine whether a relation is a function.

• Students apply their knowledge of linear relationships to interpret a function in real-world situations.

Math Anytime

Today's Challenge

Use the Topic 3 problems any time during this topic.

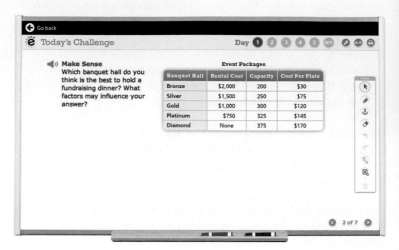

Watch the **Listen and Look For Video** for strategies and habits of mind to look for as students complete work on this lesson.

Mathematics Overview

In this lesson, students will be introduced to relations and functions. They will use arrow diagrams and tables to determine whether a relation is a function, such that each input has exactly one output.

Applying Math Practices

Construct Arguments and Critique Reasoning

Throughout this lesson, students support their contention that a relation is or is not a function with well-defended explanations.

Use Structure

Students have opportunities to recognize a pattern or relationship between input and output values of a function. They use the structure of a function to interpret a relation and solve problems.

Generalize

Students use reasoning to generalize whether a relation is a function. They understand when a relation is a function by recognizing that each input value has a unique output value.

STEP 1 | Develop: Problem-Based Learning

15-20 min

Activity

Solve & Discuss It!

Reasoning As students work through the *Solve & Discuss It,* listen and look for students who can articulate the difference between the two different relationships.

Before [WHOLE CLASS]

1 Implement Tasks that Promote Reasoning and Problem Solving

Q: How are these plans similar? How are they different? [Sample answer: Both plans set individual target goals to raise the $500. Jesse's plan focuses on tickets sold and Alexis' plan focuses on money raised.]

2 Build Understanding

Q: Would selling 50 tickets always raise $50? Explain your answer. [Sample answer: No; If a club member sold bunches of 6 or 25 tickets, he/she would not raise $50.]

Q: How many tickets would a club member need to sell to raise $50? [Sample answer: 50 tickets for individual tickets; up to 62 tickets for bunches.]

During [SMALL GROUP]

3 Support Productive Struggle in Learning Mathematics

Q: How can you determine whose plan allows the club to reach its fundraising goal? [Sample answer: Compare the different amounts raised by selling 50 tickets and the different number of tickets sold to raise $50.]

After [WHOLE CLASS]

4 Facilitate Meaningful Mathematical Discourse

Ask students to share their solutions. If needed, project Victor's and Hannah's work and ask:

Q: Which plan did Victor recommend? How did he defend his choice? [Sample answer: Alexis' plan; Victor reasons that selling 50 tickets doesn't necessarily mean raising $50.]

Q: How did Hannah explore the problem? [Sample answer: Hannah first looked at the amount of money club members might raise if they sold 50 tickets and decided that Alexis' plan is better.]

5 Transition to Visual Learning

Q: How does looking at the goals in each plan help you understand the relationship between ticket sales and money? [Sample answer: With Jesse's plan, club members sell the same number of tickets but may raise different amounts. With Alexis' plan, club members may need to sell a different number of tickets to raise the same amount of money.]

6 Extension for Early Finishers

Q: Can you propose a different plan that will allow club members to reach their fundraising goal? [Sample answer: Have only one price for tickets.]

Analyze Student Work

Available Online

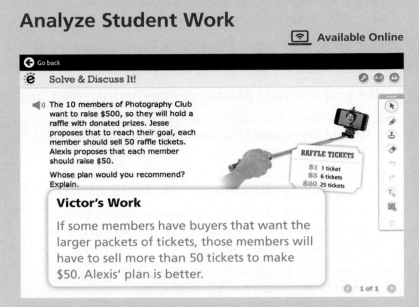

Victor's Work

If some members have buyers that want the larger packets of tickets, those members will have to sell more than 50 tickets to make $50. Alexis' plan is better.

Victor determines that to raise $50, some club members will have to sell more than 50 tickets, so he recommends Alexis' plan.

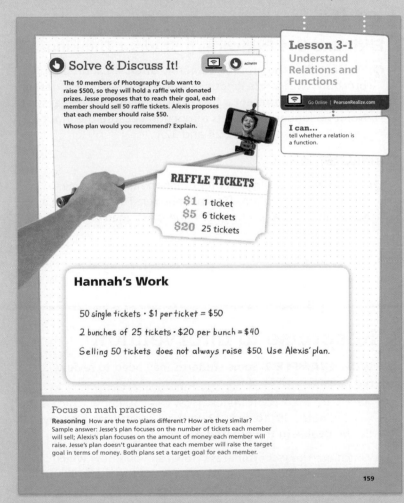

Hannah's Work

50 single tickets · $1 per ticket = $50

2 bunches of 25 tickets · $20 per bunch = $40

Selling 50 tickets does not always raise $50. Use Alexis' plan.

Hannah determines that selling 50 tickets will not always raise $50, so she recommends Alexis' plan.

STEP 2 | Develop: Visual Learning

ETP **Establish Mathematics Goals to Focus Learning**

Engage students in a discussion about the *Essential Question*. Remind them to be thinking about when a relation is a function throughout the Visual Learning.

 EXAMPLE 1 **Identify Functions with Arrow Diagrams**

ETP **Use and Connect Mathematical Representations**

Q: What is the question about the cost of shipping boxes? [Should Jonah expect that the cost of shipping a 15-pound box will be a unique cost?]

Q: What do you notice about the costs to ship packages? [Every package with a different weight has a different cost.]

Q: Does the cost to ship boxes of different weights increase at a constant rate? [Sample answer: No; the costs do not increase at a constant rate.]

Q: Would you expect that the cost to ship a 15-pound box be greater than or less than $10.03? Explain. [Sample answer: Greater than; Every other weight has a unique cost and the cost to ship increases with the weight of the box.]

Try It!

ETP **Elicit and Use Evidence of Student Thinking**

Q: Suppose that the printing company offers an additional brochure with a side length of 8 and an area of 32. Does the new relation represent a function? Explain. [Sample answer: No; it no longer represents a function because the input value 8 has two outputs, 24 and 32.]

Convince Me!

Q: How does the definition of a *function* help you solve this problem? Explain. [Sample answer: This relation is a function because each input value is assigned exactly one output value.]

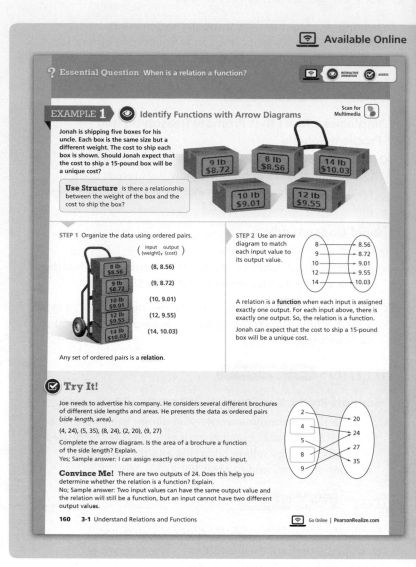

Available Online

Students can access the *Visual Learning Animation Plus* by using the **BouncePages app** to scan this page. Students can download the app for free in their mobile devices' app store.

Response to Intervention

USE WITH EXAMPLE 2 Some students may need to review ordered pairs.

Q: Which are the *x*-coordinates? How can you know which is the *x*-coordinate? [9, 10, 9, 8, 12, 8; the *x*-coordinate is always the first value in the ordered pair]

Q: Which are the *y*-coordinates? How can you know which is the *y*-coordinate? [54, 54, 61, 45, 65, 50; the *y*-coordinate is always the second value in the ordered pair]

Enrichment

USE WITH EXAMPLE 3 Challenge advanced students to determine whether the cost to park remains a function of time if the parking garage charges $30 for any amount of time parked over 5 hours.

Q: If the cost to park for more than 5 hours is a flat fee of $30, is the cost to park still a function of time? How can you tell? [Sample answer: Yes; The cost to park is still a function of the time in the parking lot. I can assign one output value (cost to park) for each input value (time).]

Q: Would Heather be able to determine within the hour how long a family was at the museum if they paid $30 to park? [Sample answer: No; A family paying $30 to park could have been at the museum for 6, 7, or even 8 hours.]

XAMPLE 2 — Use Tables to Identify Functions

TP Pose Purposeful Questions

Q: How can you determine whether a relation is a function when the data are presented in a table? [Sample answer: Check to see that each input has exactly one output value.]

Q: What other representations can you use to help determine whether a relation is a function? [Sample answer: Arrow diagram, ordered pairs]

Try It!

TP Elicit and Use Evidence of Student Thinking

Q: Do you think it will always be the case that the reverse of a relation that is a function is a function (or the reverse of a relation that is not a function is not a function)? [Sample answer: No, it all depends on the ordered pairs.]

EXAMPLE 3 — Interpreting Functions

TP Pose Purposeful Questions

Q: How does the sign help you determine whether the cost to park is a function of time? [Sample answer: You can use the sign to see that each input value is listed only once.]

Try It!

TP Elicit and Use Evidence of Student Thinking

Q: How long was the family at the museum if they paid $35 to park? Explain. [Sample answer: Up to 7 hours; As each hour increases, the cost to park increases by $5.00.]

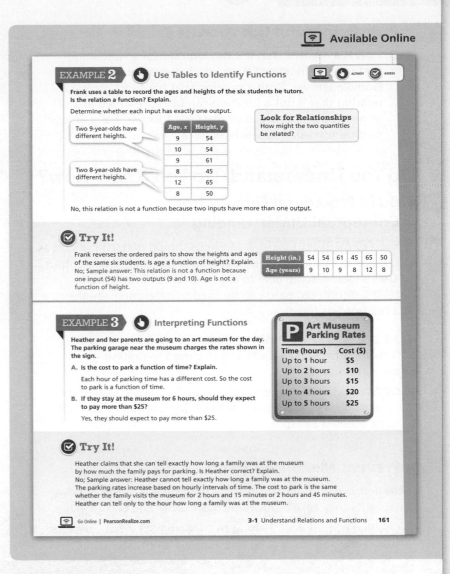

EXAMPLE 2 — Use Tables to Identify Functions

Frank uses a table to record the ages and heights of the six students he tutors. Is the relation a function? Explain.

Determine whether each input has exactly one output.

Two 9-year-olds have different heights.

Two 8-year-olds have different heights.

Age, x	Height, y
9	54
10	54
9	61
8	45
12	65
8	50

Look for Relationships
How might the two quantities be related?

No, this relation is not a function because two inputs have more than one output.

Try It!

Frank reverses the ordered pairs to show the heights and ages of the same six students. Is age a function of height? Explain.
No; Sample answer: This relation is not a function because one input (54) has two outputs (9 and 10). Age is not a function of height.

Height (in.)	54	54	61	45	65	50
Age (years)	9	10	9	8	12	8

EXAMPLE 3 — Interpreting Functions

Heather and her parents are going to an art museum for the day. The parking garage near the museum charges the rates shown in the sign.

A. Is the cost to park a function of time? Explain.

Each hour of parking time has a different cost. So the cost to park is a function of time.

B. If they stay at the museum for 6 hours, should they expect to pay more than $25?

Yes, they should expect to pay more than $25.

Art Museum Parking Rates

Time (hours)	Cost ($)
Up to 1 hour	$5
Up to 2 hours	$10
Up to 3 hours	$15
Up to 4 hours	$20
Up to 5 hours	$25

Try It!

Heather claims that she can tell exactly how long a family was at the museum by how much the family pays for parking. Is Heather correct? Explain.
No; Sample answer: Heather cannot tell exactly how long a family was at the museum. The parking rates increase based on hourly intervals of time. The cost to park is the same whether the family visits the museum for 2 hours and 15 minutes or 2 hours and 45 minutes. Heather can tell only to the hour how long a family was at the museum.

Go Online | PearsonRealize.com   3-1 Understand Relations and Functions   **161**

ADDITIONAL EXAMPLES

For additional examples go to PearsonRealize.com.

ELL English Language Learners

BEGINNING As students work through Examples 1–3, be sure to provide students additional practice with the key vocabulary terms, *relation* and *function*. Present additional relations as ordered pairs and do a think-aloud for students to follow:

This relation is a function because each input has exactly one output.

OR

This relation is not a function because at least one input has more than one output.

INTERMEDIATE As students work on the Try It for Example 2, clarify that the input and output are being reversed. Ask:

Q: What is the input in Example 2? [Age of students] What is the output? [Height of students]

Q: What is the input in the Try It for Example 2? [Height of students] What is the output? [Age of students]

ADVANCED As students work through Example 3, make sure that they see that the information in the sign is like a table. Ask:

Q: How is the information in the sign like a table? [Sample answers: There are two columns and some rows; The columns each have a heading.]

Q: Could the information be written as ordered pairs? If so, give an example. [Sample answer: Yes; (1, 5), (5, 25)]

Key Concept   Activity

STEP **2** | Develop: Visual Learning *continued*

KEY CONCEPT

ETP **Pose Purposeful Questions**

Q: How is a relation that is a function similar to a relation that is not a function? How are they different? Explain. [Sample answer: Both a relation that is a function and a relation that is not a function can be represented as a set of ordered pairs. A relation that is a function has a unique output or *y*-value for each input or *x*-value.]

Do You Understand/Do You Know How?

ETP **Build Procedural Fluency from Conceptual Understanding**

Essential Question Students should understand that a relation is a function when each input has exactly one output. They should also be able to explain how arrow diagrams, tables, or ordered pairs can be used to determine whether a relation is a function.

ITEM 2 Model with Math Students should understand that different mathematical models can be used to represent a real-world situation.

Q: What types of representations can be used to determine whether a relation is a function? [Arrow diagrams, tables, or ordered pairs]

Prevent Misconceptions

ITEM 4 If students answer that the relation is a function, have them verify that each input value has exactly one output value.

Q: What output does 20 map to? [40 and 50] What does that tell you about the relation? [That it is not a function]

Available Online

KEY CONCEPT

A relation is a function if each input corresponds to exactly one output. You can use an arrow diagram or a table to determine whether a relation is a function.

This relation is a function.

Each input corresponds to exactly one output.

1 → 2
3 → 7
8 → 14
5 → 9
7 → 21

This relation is not a function.

Input	Output
2	4
5	10
4	8
2	6

One input is assigned two different outputs.

Do You Understand?

1. **Essential Question** When is a relation a function?
Sample answer: A relation is a function when each input value has exactly one ouput value.

2. **Model with Math** How can you use different representations of a relation to determine whether the relation is a function?
Sample answer: In a table, look to see that each input value is listed only once; in an arrow diagram, see that each input value has only one arrow.

3. **Generalize** Is a relation always a function? Is a function always a relation? Explain.
Sample answer: A function is always a relation, but a relation is not always a function. A relation is a function only if for each input value there is exactly one output value.

Do You Know How?

4. Is the relation shown below a function? Explain.

5 → 10
10 → 20
15 → 30
20 → 40
20 → 50

No; Sample answer: There are two output values, 40 and 50, for the input value of 20.

5. Is the relation shown below a function? Explain.

Input	3	4	1	5	2
Output	4	6	2	8	5

Yes; Sample answer: There is exactly one output value for each input value.

6. Is the relation shown below a function? Explain.
(4, 16), (5, 25), (3, 9), (6, 36), (2, 4), (1, 1)
Yes; Sample answer: There is one output value for each input value.

162   3-1 Understand Relations and Functions   Go Online | PearsonRealize.com

---

ADDITIONAL EXAMPLE **1**

Make sure students understand that arrow diagrams and ordered pairs represent the same relation.

Q: How can you identify ordered pairs from an arrow diagram? [The numbers on the left represent the input values, or *x*-coordinates, and the numbers on the right represent the output values, or *y*-coordinates.]

Q: How do you determine whether a relation is a function when given an arrow diagram? [Sample answer: You can check to see whether there are any numbers on the left that have two arrows each pointing to a different number on the right. Or you can list the ordered pairs and check whether any of the ordered pairs have the same *x*-coordinate, or input value. If yes, check the *y*-coordinate, or output value, for these ordered pairs. If they are different, the relation is not a function.]

Available Online

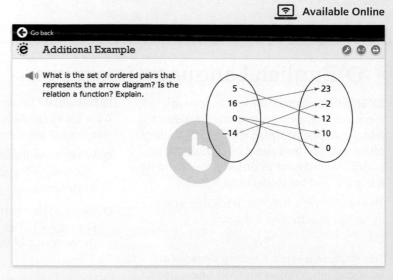

Answer: (5, 12), (16, 23), (0, 10), (0, 0), (−14, −2); the relation is not a function because the input 0 has two outputs, 10 and 0.

Practice & Problem Solving

Available Online

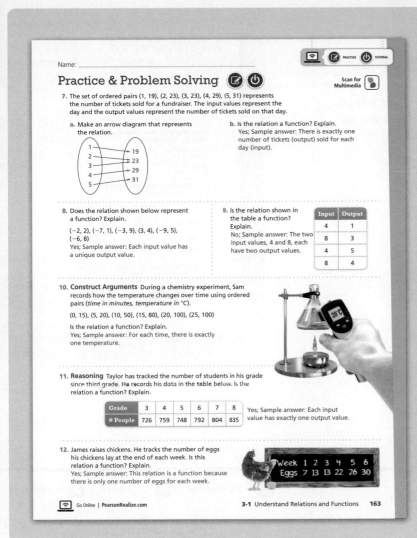

Name: _____

Practice & Problem Solving

Scan for Multimedia

7. The set of ordered pairs (1, 19), (2, 23), (3, 23), (4, 29), (5, 31) represents the number of tickets sold for a fundraiser. The input values represent the day and the output values represent the number of tickets sold on that day.

a. Make an arrow diagram that represents the relation.

1 → 19
2 → 23
3 → 29
4 → 31
5

b. Is the relation a function? Explain.
Yes; Sample answer: There is exactly one number of tickets (output) sold for each day (input).

8. Does the relation shown below represent a function? Explain.

(−2, 2), (−7, 1), (−3, 9), (3, 4), (−9, 5), (−6, 8)
Yes; Sample answer: Each input value has a unique output value.

9. Is the relation shown in the table a function? Explain.
No; Sample answer: The two input values, 4 and 8, each have two output values.

Input	Output
4	1
8	3
4	5
8	4

10. **Construct Arguments** During a chemistry experiment, Sam records how the temperature changes over time using ordered pairs (*time in minutes, temperature in °C*).

(0, 15), (5, 20), (10, 50), (15, 80), (20, 100), (25, 100)

Is the relation a function? Explain.
Yes; Sample answer: For each time, there is exactly one temperature.

11. **Reasoning** Taylor has tracked the number of students in his grade since third grade. He records his data in the table below. Is the relation a function? Explain.

Grade	3	4	5	6	7	8
# People	726	759	748	792	804	835

Yes; Sample answer: Each input value has exactly one output value.

12. James raises chickens. He tracks the number of eggs his chickens lay at the end of each week. Is this relation a function? Explain.
Yes; Sample answer: This relation is a function because there is only one number of eggs for each week.

Week	1	2	3	4	5	6
Eggs	7	13	13	22	26	30

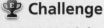 Go Online | PearsonRealize.com

3-1 Understand Relations and Functions 163

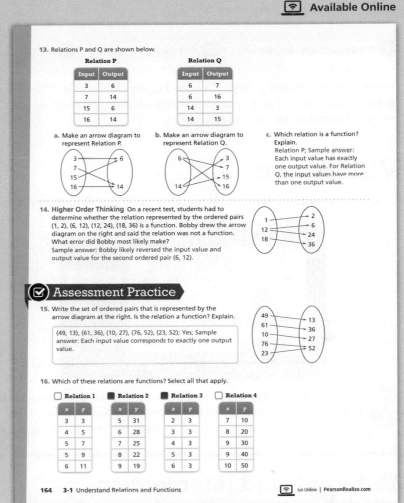

13. Relations P and Q are shown below.

Relation P

Input	Output
3	6
7	14
15	6
16	14

Relation Q

Input	Output
6	7
6	16
14	3
14	15

a. Make an arrow diagram to represent Relation P.

3 → 6
7
15 → 14
16

b. Make an arrow diagram to represent Relation Q.

6 → 3
→ 7
14 → 15
→ 16

c. Which relation is a function? Explain.
Relation P; Sample answer: Each input value has exactly one output value. For Relation Q, the input values have more than one output value.

14. **Higher Order Thinking** On a recent test, students had to determine whether the relation represented by the ordered pairs (1, 2), (6, 12), (12, 24), (18, 36) is a function. Bobby drew the arrow diagram on the right and said the relation was not a function. What error did Bobby most likely make?
Sample answer: Bobby likely reversed the input value and output value for the second ordered pair (6, 12).

1 → 2
12 → 6
18 → 24
→ 36

Assessment Practice

15. Write the set of ordered pairs that is represented by the arrow diagram at the right. Is the relation a function? Explain.

(49, 13), (61, 36), (10, 27), (76, 52), (23, 52); Yes; Sample answer: Each input value corresponds to exactly one output value.

49 → 13
61 → 36
10 → 27
76 → 52
23

16. Which of these relations are functions? Select all that apply.

☐ Relation 1   ■ Relation 2   ■ Relation 3   ☐ Relation 4

x	y
3	3
4	5
5	7
5	9
6	11

x	y
5	31
6	28
7	25
8	22
9	19

x	y
2	3
3	3
4	3
5	3
6	3

x	y
7	10
8	20
9	30
9	40
10	50

164 3-1 Understand Relations and Functions

 Go Online | PearsonRealize.com

Error Intervention

ITEM 11 Reasoning Confirm students' thinking around whether a relation is a function.

Q: How do you determine whether the relation between the grade and number of students is a function? [Sample answer: If each input value (grade) in the table has a unique output value (number of students), the relation is a function.]

Challenge

ITEM 14 Higher Order Thinking Use this item to extend students' understanding of functions.

Q: How can you tell that the relation shown by the ordered pairs is a function? [Sample answer: The inputs, or *x*-values, in the ordered pairs are all different.]

You may opt to have students complete the automatically scored Practice & Problem Solving items online.

Item Analysis

Example	Items	DOK
1	8, 10, 15	2
	7	3
2	9, 11, 16	2
	13	3
3	12	2
	14	3

Lesson Quiz

 Use the student scores on the Lesson Quiz to prescribe differentiated assignments.

I Intervention 0–3 Points   **O** On-Level 4 Points   **A** Advanced 5 Points

You may opt to have students take the Lesson Quiz online. The Lesson Quiz will be automatically scored and appropriate remediation, practice, or enrichment will be assigned based on student performance.

Video Tutorials

Students can access instructional tutorials using the **Virtual Nerd app**.

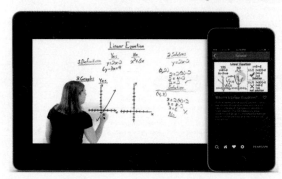

Students can also access the videos using the **BouncePages app** to scan exercise pages marked with this icon. Students can download both apps for free in their mobile devices' app store.

Available Online

Name _____ Lesson Quiz 3-1

1. For **a–d**, choose Yes or No to tell whether each relation represents a function.
   a. (1, 3), (2, 5), (2, 7), (4, 9)   ○ Yes   ● No
   b. (1, 3), (2, 5), (3, 7), (4, 9)   ● Yes   ○ No
   c. (1, 3), (1, 5), (1, 7), (1, 9)   ○ Yes   ● No
   d. (1, 3), (2, 3), (3, 3), (4, 3)   ● Yes   ○ No

2. Is the relation shown in the arrow diagram a function? Explain.
   Yes; Sample answer: Each input has only one output.

3. Is the relation shown in the table below a function? Explain.

Input	1	3	4	3
Output	1	9	16	27

   No; Sample answer: The input 3 has 2 outputs, 9 and 27.

4. The hourly cost to rent a paddleboard at the beach is shown. Is the cost a function of the rental time? Explain.

Time (hours)	1	2	3	4
Cost ($)	25	35	45	55

   Yes; Sample answer: Each input (number of hours) has a unique output (cost).

5. Lilly records the age, in years, and the height, in inches, of the starting players on the girls' middle school basketball team. She records them as ordered pairs (age, height): (11, 62), (12, 64), (13, 65), (13, 67), and (14, 68). Is this relation a function? Explain.
   No; Sample answer: There are 2 heights associated with the age 13.

Differentiated Intervention

I = Intervention   **O** = On-Level   **A** = Advanced

Reteach to Build Understanding **I**

Provides scaffolded reteaching for the key lesson concepts.

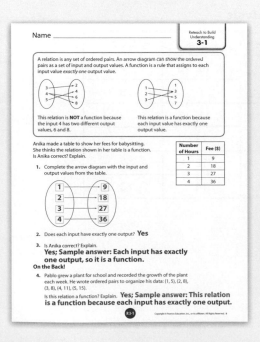

Additional Vocabulary Support **I** **O**

Helps students develop and reinforce understanding of key terms and concepts.

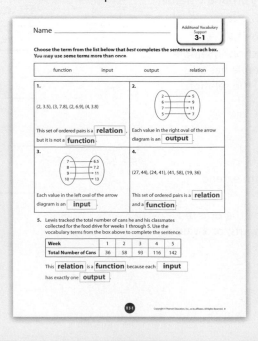

Build Mathematical Literacy **I**

Provides support for struggling readers to build mathematical literacy.

Practice Worksheets Math Tools Math Games

Additional Practice

You may opt to have students complete the automatically scored Additional Practice items online.

Item Analysis

Example	Items	DOK
	1	1
1	6, 8	2
	7	3
2	2, 4, 9	2
3	3, 5	2

Available Online

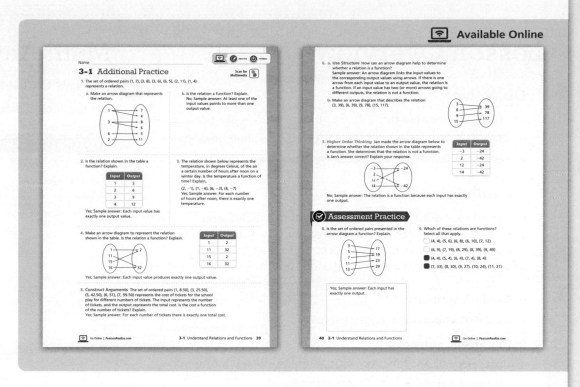

Differentiated Intervention

I = Intervention **O** = On-Level **A** = Advanced

Enrichment **O** **A**

Presents engaging problems and activities that extend the lesson concepts.

Math Tools and Games **I** **O** **A**

Offers additional activities and games to build understanding and fluency.

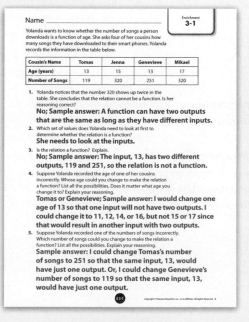

Lesson 3-2
Connect Representations of Functions

Lesson Overview

Objective

Students will be able to:

✔ identify functions by their equations, tables, and graphs.

✔ represent linear and non-linear functions with graphs.

Essential Understanding

Different representations, such as equations, tables, and graphs, can help determine that a relation is a function. The graph of a linear function is a straight line; the graph of a nonlinear function is not a straight line.

In Grade 7, students:

• graphed proportional relationships.

In this lesson, students:

• represent a linear function with an equation and a graph.

• represent a nonlinear function with a graph.

Later in this topic, students will:

• compare linear and nonlinear functions.

• construct functions to model linear relationships.

• sketch functions from verbal descriptions.

This lesson emphasizes a blend of **conceptual understanding** and **application**.

• Students deepen their understanding of functions as they explore graphs of linear and nonlinear functions.

• They apply this understanding to real-world examples and exercises.

Math Anytime

Today's Challenge

Use the Topic 3 problems any time during this topic.

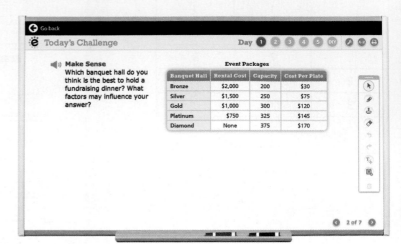

Watch the **Listen and Look For Video** for strategies and habits of mind to look for as students complete work on this lesson.

Mathematics Overview

In this lesson, students will represent functions using graphs, in addition to tables and equations. They also determine whether a function is linear or nonlinear, using graphs and tables.

Applying Math Practices

Construct Arguments

Throughout this lesson, students clearly and accurately explain when a graph shows a linear function and a nonlinear function. They describe the characteristics of a graph of linear and nonlinear functions.

Model with Math

Students use what they know about functions to model linear functions using graphs and equations.

Use Appropriate Tools Strategically

Students use grids to draw graphs of linear and nonlinear functions. They accurately draw the graphs and determine whether the graph of the function is linear or nonlinear.

Solve & Discuss It!

Make Sense As students work through the *Solve & Discuss It*, listen and look for students who understand the connection between the days and distance to estimate and determine the solution.

Before [WHOLE CLASS]

TP **1 Implement Tasks that Promote Reasoning and Problem Solving**

Q: How can you use the information presented in the table? [Sample answer: I can use the information to get an estimate of how many miles the whales travel in a given time period.]

2 Build Understanding

Q: What are the advantages of using average miles traveled per week? What are the advantages of using average miles traveled per day? [Sample answer: Using weekly averages gives larger, but more inexact numbers. Using daily averages gives more exact answers.]

During [SMALL GROUP]

TP **3 Support Productive Struggle in Learning Mathematics**

Q: What solution strategy are you planning to use? Explain. [Sample answer: Divide the total distance the whales will travel by the approximate daily distance.]

After [WHOLE CLASS]

TP **4 Facilitate Meaningful Mathematical Discourse**

Ask students to share their solutions. If needed, project Katie's and Vinny's work and ask:

Q: How did Katie approach the problem situation? Did you approach the problem in a similar way? [She used compatible numbers to compute both the daily distance a whale swims and the total time of the journey. Check students' responses.]

Q: How is Vinny's work different from Katie's? How different are their answers? [Sample answer: Vinny calculated the average daily distance the whales traveled rather than estimating. Their answers differ by 7 days.]

5 Transition to Visual Learning

Q: Is the relation between the distance traveled and the days a function? [Sample answer: Yes; Each day (input value) has exactly one amount (distance traveled, output value). The distance traveled is a function of the number of days.]

6 Extension for Early Finishers

Q: Investigate other animals that migrate. How long is their migration? On average how many miles do they travel each day during their migration? [Sample answer: Some species of caribou migrate 350–400 miles each season. They will travel between 15 and 30 miles each day.]

Analyze Student Work

[Available Online]

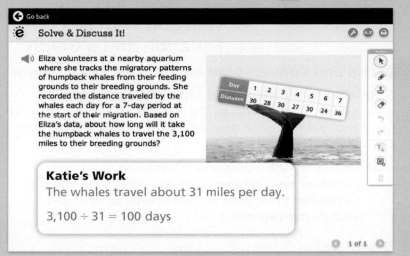

Go back

Solve & Discuss It!

Eliza volunteers at a nearby aquarium where she tracks the migratory patterns of humpback whales from their feeding grounds to their breeding grounds. She recorded the distance traveled by the whales each day for a 7-day period at the start of their migration. Based on Eliza's data, about how long will it take the humpback whales to travel the 3,100 miles to their breeding grounds?

Day	1	2	3	4	5	6	7
Distance	30	28	30	27	30	24	36

Katie's Work

The whales travel about 31 miles per day.

$3,100 \div 31 = 100$ days

1 of 1

Katie uses compatible numbers to determine the approximate number of days it will take the whales to reach their breeding grounds.

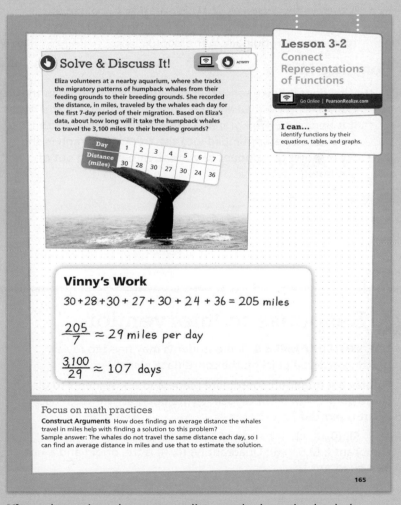

Solve & Discuss It!

Eliza volunteers at a nearby aquarium, where she tracks the migratory patterns of humpback whales from their feeding grounds to their breeding grounds. She recorded the distance, in miles, traveled by the whales each day for the first 7-day period of their migration. Based on Eliza's data, about how long will it take the humpback whales to travel the 3,100 miles to their breeding grounds?

Day	1	2	3	4	5	6	7
Distance (miles)	30	28	30	27	30	24	36

Lesson 3-2
Connect Representations of Functions

Go Online | PearsonRealize.com

I can...
identify functions by their equations, tables, and graphs.

Vinny's Work

$30 + 28 + 30 + 27 + 30 + 24 + 36 = 205$ miles

$\frac{205}{7} \approx 29$ miles per day

$\frac{3,100}{29} \approx 107$ days

Focus on math practices

Construct Arguments How does finding an average distance the whales travel in miles help with finding a solution to this problem?
Sample answer: The whales do not travel the same distance each day, so I can find an average distance in miles and use that to estimate the solution.

165

Vinny determines the average distance the humpback whales travel each day and then calculates how many days it would take the whales to travel the total distance.

STEP 2 | Develop: Visual Learning

Visual Learning | Assess

ETP **Establish Mathematics Goals to Focus Learning.**

Engage students in a discussion about the *Essential Question.* Ask them to be thinking about different representations they encounter in the lesson.

EXAMPLE 1 Represent a Linear Function with an Equation and a Graph

ETP **Use and Connect Mathematical Representations**

Q: Which quantity represents a constant rate of change? Explain. [Sample answer: The water being pumped from the pool. Each hour the same amount of water is pumped from the pool.]

Q: How does the bar diagram connect to the illustration? [The three bars represent three quantities: total water to be pumped in the pool, amount already pumped, and amount pumped each hour.]

☑ Try It!

ETP **Elicit and Use Evidence of Student Thinking**

Q: Why is the quantity 8,000 used instead of 10,000, which is used in the Example 1? [This situation is looking at the amount of water left in the pool, which is 8,000, not the total amount originally in the pool.]

Convince Me!

Q: Why does it make sense that the slope of the graph in the Example 1 is positive and the slope of the graph in the Try It is negative? [The graph in the example represents the amount of water pumped into the truck. The graph in the Try It shows the amount of water being pumped out of the pool.]

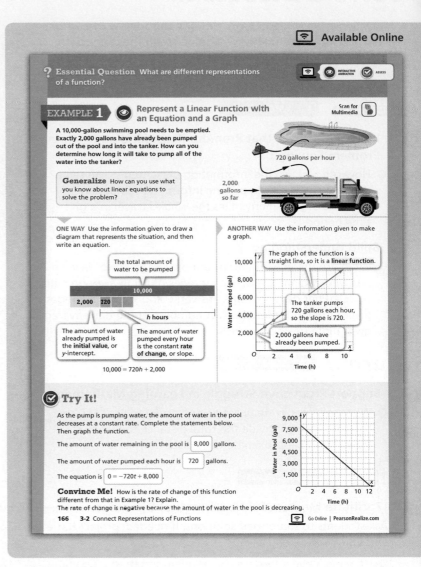

🛜 Available Online

? Essential Question What are different representations of a function?

EXAMPLE 1 Represent a Linear Function with an Equation and a Graph

Scan for Multimedia

A 10,000-gallon swimming pool needs to be emptied. Exactly 2,000 gallons have already been pumped out of the pool and into the tanker. How can you determine how long it will take to pump all of the water into the tanker?

720 gallons per hour

Generalize How can you use what you know about linear equations to solve the problem?

2,000 gallons so far

ONE WAY Use the information given to draw a diagram that represents the situation, and then write an equation.

The total amount of water to be pumped

2,000	720	

h hours

The amount of water already pumped is the **initial value**, or y-intercept.

The amount of water pumped every hour is the constant **rate of change**, or slope.

$10,000 = 720h + 2,000$

ANOTHER WAY Use the information given to make a graph.

The graph of the function is a straight line, so it is a **linear function**.

The tanker pumps 720 gallons each hour, so the slope is 720.

2,000 gallons have already been pumped.

Water Pumped (gal) — Time (h)

 Try It!

As the pump is pumping water, the amount of water in the pool decreases at a constant rate. Complete the statements below. Then graph the function.

The amount of water remaining in the pool is [8,000] gallons.

The amount of water pumped each hour is [720] gallons.

The equation is [$0 = -720t + 8,000$]

Water in Pool (gal) — Time (h)

Convince Me! How is the rate of change of this function different from that in Example 1? Explain. The rate of change is negative because the amount of water in the pool is decreasing.

166 3-2 Connect Representations of Functions

🛜 Go Online | PearsonRealize.com

 Students can access the *Visual Learning Animation Plus* by using the **BouncePages app** to scan this page. Students can download the app for free in their mobile devices' app store.

⚠ Response to Intervention

USE WITH EXAMPLE 1 Some students may need to review plotting ordered pairs on the coordinate plane.

Display a 4-quadrant coordinate plane and ask students to plot these points. Ask them to identify the quadrant in which each point is plotted.

$(-1, 5), (0, 0), (1, 14), (2.5, -6)$ [$(-1, 5)$: Quadrant II; $(1, 14)$: Quadrant I; $(2.5, -6)$: Quadrant IV; $(0, 0)$ is the origin and is not in a quadrant.]

🏆 Enrichment

USE WITH EXAMPLE 3 Challenge advanced students to draw two graphs, one that represents a linear function and one that represents a nonlinear function.

Q: What are the differences between the shapes of the two graphs? What are the similarities? [Sample answer: A linear function is a straight line. If a function is not a straight line, it is a nonlinear function. Both graphs are functions, so for each input value, there is exactly one output value.]

EXAMPLE 2 Represent a Nonlinear Function with a Graph

ETP Pose Purposeful Questions

Q: How can you determine whether a relation in the table is a function? [Sample answer: Check to see that each input (length) has only one output (area).]

Q: What do you notice about the shape of this graph? Is it a function? [Sample answer: The shape of this graph is not a straight line. It is still a function because each input value has exactly one output value.]

EXAMPLE 3 Identify Functions from Graphs

ETP Pose Purposeful Questions

Q: When is a graph a function? When is a graph not a function? [Sample answer: A graph is a function when for each input value, there is only one output value. A graph is not a function when there is more than one output value for an input value.]

Try It!

ETP Elicit and Use Evidence of Student Thinking

Q: What is one type of graph of a function? [Sample answer: The graph of a straight line]

Q: What are some examples of equations that represent a straight line? [Answers will vary. Sample answers: $y = 4x + 2$, $y = -3$, $y = -60x$]

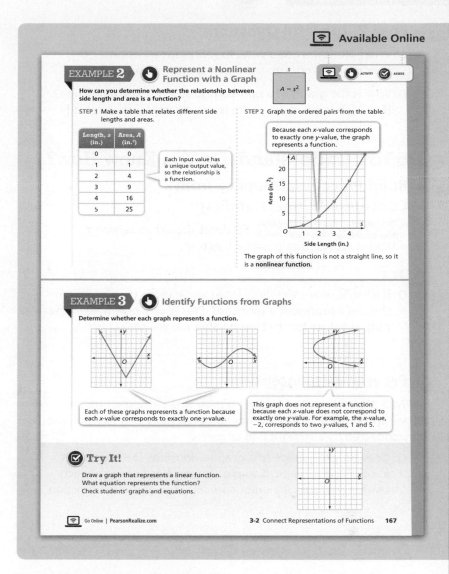

ADDITIONAL EXAMPLES

For additional examples go to PearsonRealize.com.

ELL English Language Learners

BEGINNING Confirm that students understand that the prefix *"non"* means *"not"* so that a nonlinear function is a function that is not a linear function. Have students compare the graph in Example 1 with that in Example 2.

Q: Which graph—the one in Example 1 or in Example 2—is a straight line? [The graph in Example 1 is a straight line.]

Q: Describe the graph in Example 2. [Sample answer: It is a curved line. It is not a straight line.]

INTERMEDIATE As students analyze each of the three graphs in Example 3, have them practice key vocabulary to describe each graph.

Q: Does the first graph show a linear or nonlinear function? Explain. [Sample answer: It shows a nonlinear function because the graph is not a single straight line.]

Q: Does the second graph show a linear or nonlinear function? Explain. [Sample answer: It shows a nonlinear function because the graph is not a straight line.]

ADVANCED Have students practice key vocabulary by analyzing the graph in Example 2 and the third graph in Example 3.

Q: How can you describe the graph in Example 2? [Sample answer: It is a curve.] Does the graph show a function? Explain. [Sample answer: Yes; Each x-value has just one y-value.]

Q: How can you describe the third graph in Example 3? [Sample answer: It is a curve.] Does the graph show a function? Explain. [Sample answer: No; The x-values have two y-values.]

STEP **2** | Develop: Visual Learning *continued*

KEY CONCEPT

ETP **Pose Purposeful Questions**

Q: What are some other ways to represent functions?
[Sample answer: Arrow diagrams, ordered pairs]

Q: Why is the graph of a non-vertical straight line a function?
[For each input value, there is exactly one output value.]

Do You Understand/Do You Know How?

ETP **Build Procedural Fluency from Conceptual Understanding**

? Essential Question Students should understand different representations of a function.

ITEM 1

Q: If a table shows the same input value more than once, can the table represent a function? [Yes it can, only if all of the output values for that input value are the same.]

 Prevent Misconceptions

ITEM 3 If students start by saying that only a straight line can represent a function, explain how ordered pairs of a function can be connected by a straight line or curve.

Q: Does only the shape of a graph determine if it represents a function? Explain. [Sample answer: No; As long as each *x*-value only has one unique *y*-value, the graph is a function.]

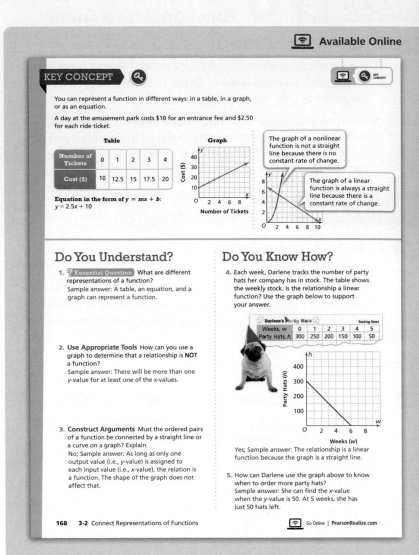

🖥 **Available Online**

KEY CONCEPT

You can represent a function in different ways: in a table, in a graph, or as an equation.

A day at the amusement park costs $10 for an entrance fee and $2.50 for each ride ticket.

Table

Number of Tickets	0	1	2	3	4
Cost ($)	10	12.5	15	17.5	20

Graph

Equation in the form of $y = mx + b$:
$y = 2.5x + 10$

The graph of a nonlinear function is not a straight line because there is no constant rate of change.

The graph of a linear function is always a straight line because there is a constant rate of change.

Do You Understand?

1. **? Essential Question** What are different representations of a function?
Sample answer: A table, an equation, and a graph can represent a function.

2. **Use Appropriate Tools** How can you use a graph to determine that a relationship is **NOT** a function?
Sample answer: There will be more than one *y*-value for at least one of the *x*-values.

3. **Construct Arguments** Must the ordered pairs of a function be connected by a straight line or a curve on a graph? Explain.
No; Sample answer: As long as only one output value (i.e., *y*-value) is assigned to each input value (i.e., *x*-value), the relation is a function. The shape of the graph does not affect that.

Do You Know How?

4. Each week, Darlene tracks the number of party hats her company has in stock. The table shows the weekly stock. Is the relationship a linear function? Use the graph below to support your answer.

Darlene's Party Hats — Tracking Sheet

Weeks, *w*	0	1	2	3	4	5
Party Hats, *h*	300	250	200	150	100	50

Yes; Sample answer: The relationship is a linear function because the graph is a straight line.

5. How can Darlene use the graph above to know when to order more party hats?
Sample answer: She can find the *x*-value when the *y*-value is 50. At 5 weeks, she has just 50 hats left.

168 **3-2** Connect Representations of Functions

Go Online | PearsonRealize.com

ADDITIONAL EXAMPLE **3**

🖥 **Available Online**

Help students recognize further the attributes of function graphs versus non-function graphs.

Make sure students understand that a graph is not always a representation of a function. For each *x*-value there must be a unique *y*-value when a graph represents a function.

Q: How can you confirm that the given graph is a function? [Sample answer: Check each point to make sure there is not another point with the same *x*-coordinate, but different *y*-coordinate.]

Q: What is one point from the list that would make the graph a non-function? Explain. [Sample answer: (2, −1); The points (2, 2) and (2, −1) have the same *x*-coordinate, but different *y*-coordinates.]

Q: What is a visual way to analyze a graph to determine whether a graph is a function? [Sample answer: Visualize vertical lines. If no two points are on the same vertical line, then the graph is a function.]

◀ Go back

ë **Additional Example**

🔊 The graph shown represents a function. Which of the following points can you add to the graph so that it still represents a function? Explain.

(2, −1), (−1, 4), (0, −3), (−3, 0)

Answer: (−1, 4) and (0, −3); neither of these points share an *x*-coordinate with any of the given points.

Practice & Problem Solving

Practice   Tutorials   Math Tools

📶 **Available Online**

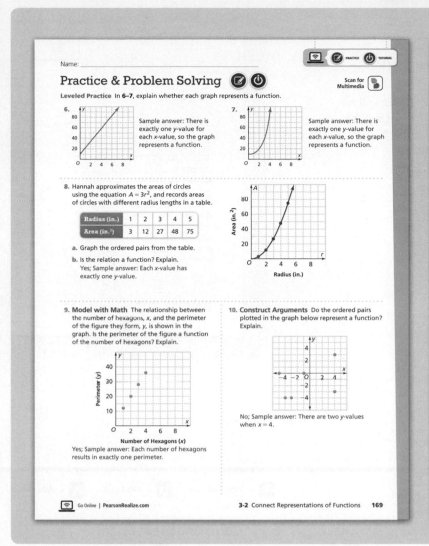

Name: _____

Practice & Problem Solving

Scan for Multimedia

Leveled Practice In **6–7**, explain whether each graph represents a function.

6.
Sample answer: There is exactly one y-value for each x-value, so the graph represents a function.

7.
Sample answer: There is exactly one y-value for each x-value, so the graph represents a function.

8. Hannah approximates the areas of circles using the equation $A = 3r^2$, and records areas of circles with different radius lengths in a table.

Radius (in.)	1	2	3	4	5
Area (in.²)	3	12	27	48	75

a. Graph the ordered pairs from the table.

b. Is the relation a function? Explain.
Yes; Sample answer: Each x-value has exactly one y-value.

9. Model with Math The relationship between the number of hexagons, x, and the perimeter of the figure they form, y, is shown in the graph. Is the perimeter of the figure a function of the number of hexagons? Explain.

Yes; Sample answer: Each number of hexagons results in exactly one perimeter.

10. Construct Arguments Do the ordered pairs plotted in the graph below represent a function? Explain.

No; Sample answer: There are two y-values when x = 4.

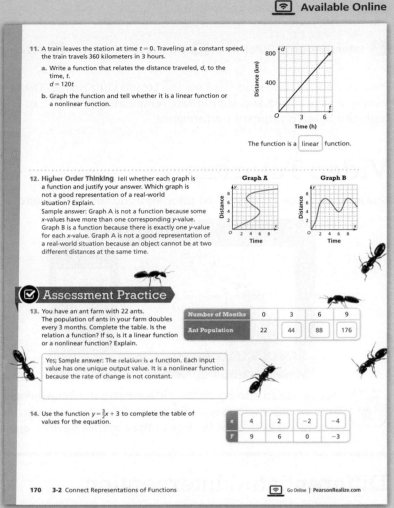

11. A train leaves the station at time $t = 0$. Traveling at a constant speed, the train travels 360 kilometers in 3 hours.

a. Write a function that relates the distance traveled, d, to the time, t.
$d = 120t$

b. Graph the function and tell whether it is a linear function or a nonlinear function.

The function is a [linear] function.

12. Higher Order Thinking Tell whether each graph is a function and justify your answer. Which graph is not a good representation of a real-world situation? Explain.
Sample answer: Graph A is not a function because some x-values have more than one corresponding y-value. Graph B is a function because there is exactly one y-value for each x-value. Graph A is not a good representation of a real-world situation because an object cannot be at two different distances at the same time.

Graph A

Graph B

✓ Assessment Practice

13. You have an ant farm with 22 ants. The population of ants in your farm doubles every 3 months. Complete the table. Is the relation a function? If so, is it a linear function or a nonlinear function? Explain.

Number of Months	0	3	6	9
Ant Population	22	44	88	176

Yes; Sample answer: The relation is a function. Each input value has one unique output value. It is a nonlinear function because the rate of change is not constant.

14. Use the function $y = \frac{3}{2}x + 3$ to complete the table of values for the equation.

x	4	2	−2	−4
y	9	6	0	−3

You may opt to have students complete the automatically scored Practice & Problem Solving items online.

🔺 Error Intervention

ITEM 10 Construct Arguments If students say that the relation is a function, review the definition of a function.

Q: What are the set of ordered pairs shown in the relation?
[{(−5, 0), (−4, −4), (−3, −4), (−1, 0), (4, −3), (4, −4)}]

Q: What do you notice about the set of ordered pairs that indicates the relation is not a function? [Sample answer: The x-value, 4, is listed twice, in (4, −3) and (4, −4).]

🏆 Challenge

ITEM 12 You can use this item to extend students' understanding of testing whether a graph is a function.

Q: What do you notice about the first graph that indicates the relation is not a function? [Sample answer: There is more than one y-value for certain x-values.]

Q: Is there one unique output value for each input value on the second graph? Explain. [Sample answer: Yes; Each x-value maps to exactly one y-value.]

Item Analysis

Example	Items	DOK
1	9	1
	12, 14	3
2	8	2
	13	3
3	6, 7, 10	2
	11	3

Lesson Quiz

Use the student scores on the Lesson Quiz to prescribe differentiated assignments.

I Intervention 0–3 Points   **O** On-Level 4 Points   **A** Advanced 5 Points

You may opt to have students take the Lesson Quiz online. The Lesson Quiz will be automatically scored and appropriate remediation, practice, or enrichment will be assigned based on student performance.

Video Tutorials

Students can access instructional tutorials using the Virtual Nerd app.

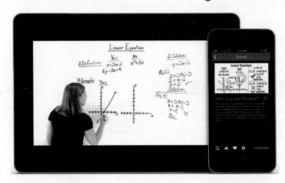

Students can also access the videos using the **BouncePages app** to scan exercise pages marked with this icon. Students can download both apps for free in their mobile devices' app store.

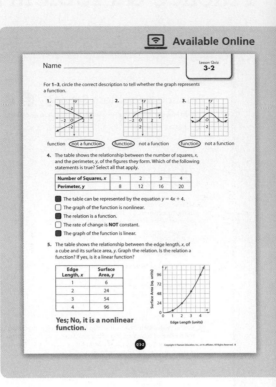

📶 Available Online

Name _____   Lesson Quiz **3-2**

For 1–3, circle the correct description to tell whether the graph represents a function.

1. function / **not a function**
2. **function** / not a function
3. **function** / not a function

4. The table shows the relationship between the number of squares, x, and the perimeter, y, of the figures they form. Which of the following statements is true? Select all that apply.

Number of Squares, x	1	2	3	4
Perimeter, y	8	12	16	20

- ■ The table can be represented by the equation y = 4x + 4.
- □ The graph of the function is nonlinear.
- ■ The relation is a function.
- □ The rate of change is **NOT** constant.
- ■ The graph of the function is linear.

5. The table shows the relationship between the edge length, x, of a cube and its surface area, y. Graph the relation. Is the relation a function? If yes, is it a linear function?

Edge Length, x	Surface Area, y
1	6
2	24
3	54
4	96

Yes; No, it is a nonlinear function.

Differentiated Intervention

I = Intervention   **O** = On-Level   **A** = Advanced

Reteach to Build Understanding **I**

Provides scaffolded reteaching for the key lesson concepts.

Additional Vocabulary Support **I** **O**

Helps students develop and reinforce understanding of key terms and concepts.

Build Mathematical Literacy **I**

Provides support for struggling readers to build mathematical literacy.

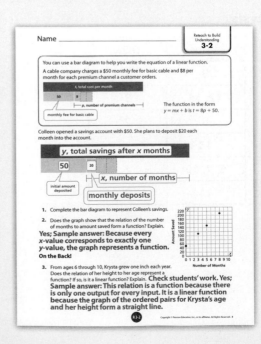

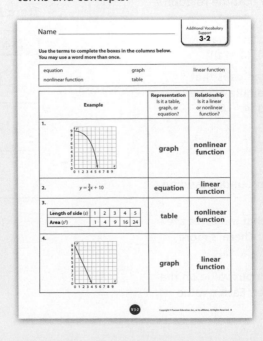

Name _____   Build Mathematical Literacy **3-2**

Read the word problem below. Then answer the questions to help determine the best way to solve the problem.

The table on the right shows the costs of different numbers of burritos at Tina's Taco Truck. Can the relationship between the number of burritos ordered and the total cost for the burritos be modeled by a linear function?

Number of Burritos	Cost ($)
2	8
3	12
4	16
6	24

1. Underline the question that you need to answer.
   Check students' work.

2. What two quantities are in the problem? Which of the two is the input and which is the output?
   The number of burritos ordered and the cost; the number of burritos is the input value and the cost is the output.

3. If you were to graph the information provided in the table, what would be the labels for the x- and y-axes?
   The x-axis would be the number of burritos; the y-axis would be the total cost.

4. What is a good first step to answer the question posed? Explain.
   Sample answer: Determine whether there is a constant rate of change between any two ordered pairs (number of burritos, cost).

5. Can the relationship between the number of burritos and the cost be modeled by a linear function? Explain.
   Yes; The two quantities, number of burritos ordered and total cost, have a constant rate of change of + 4, so the relationship can be modeled by a linear function.

Practice Worksheets Math Tools Math Games

Additional Practice

You may opt to have students complete the automatically scored Additional Practice items online.

Item Analysis

Example	Items	DOK
1	3, 4, 7	2
2	6	3
3	1, 2	2
	5	3

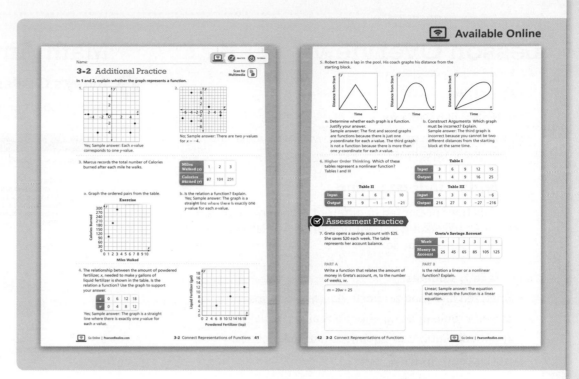

Available Online

Differentiated Intervention

I = Intervention   O = On-Level   A = Advanced

Enrichment O A

Presents engaging problems and activities that extend the lesson concepts.

Math Tools and Games I O A

Offers additional activities and games to build understanding and fluency.

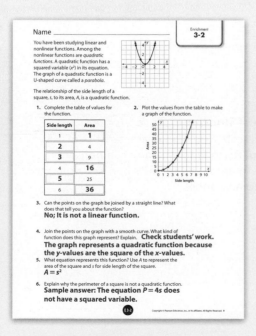

Video   Activity

Lesson 3-3

Compare Linear and Nonlinear Functions

Lesson Overview

FOCUS

Objective

Students will be able to:

✔ use different representations to compare linear and nonlinear functions.

Essential Understanding

Two functions presented in different representations can be compared by looking at their properties: initial value and constant rate of change.

COHERENCE

In Grade 7, students:

• analyzed and used proportional relationships.

• solved problems using equations and inequalities.

• graphed solutions of equations and inequalities.

In this lesson, students:

• compare properties of two linear functions.

• compare a linear and nonlinear function.

Later in this topic, students will:

• construct functions to model linear relationships.

• analyze intervals of increase and decrease.

• sketch functions from verbal descriptions.

RIGOR

This lesson emphasizes a blend of **conceptual understanding** and **application**.

• Students use representations, such as equations, tables, and graphs, to compare the properties of linear and nonlinear functions.

• Students apply their knowledge of functions to solve real-world problems using equations, tables, and graphs.

Math Anytime

Today's Challenge

Use the Topic 3 problems any time during this topic.

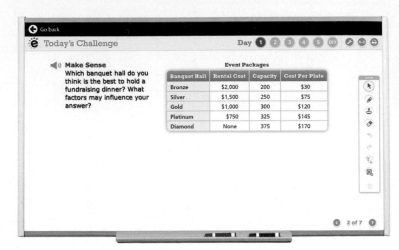

Watch the **Listen and Look For Video** for strategies and habits of mind to look for as students complete work on this lesson.

☑ Mathematics Overview

In this lesson, students will compare functions in different representations by analyzing their initial value and constant rate of change. They also will relate initial value to the *y*-intercept and the constant rate of change to the slope as they compare two linear functions in different representations. Students will relate a constant rate of change to a straight line graph, distinguishing a linear from a nonlinear function, whose graph is not a straight line.

Applying Math Practices

Reason Abstractly and Quantitatively
Students reason both abstractly and quantitatively about the properties of functions in order to compare these properties.

Look for and Make Use of Structure
Students analyze and describe common characteristics of functions and look for patterns when making comparisons. They analyze equations, graphs, and tables when describing the functions and making comparisons.

STEP 1 | Develop: Problem-Based Learning

15-20 min

Activity

Solve & Discuss It!

Model with Math As students work through the *Solve & Discuss It*, listen and look for students who propose interesting or unique ways to compare the two services.

Before [🖥 WHOLE CLASS]

ETP **1 Implement Tasks that Promote Reasoning and Problem Solving**

Q: What aspects about the video subscriptions should be considered when comparing the costs of the two services? [Sample answer: Total cost for different numbers of devices]

2 Build Understanding

Q: What representations would you use to model the two services? Explain. [Sample answer: A table because it can show the cost for different numbers of devices.]

During [👥 SMALL GROUP]

ETP **3 Support Productive Struggle in Learning Mathematics**

Q: How do the number of allowable devices affect the cost of each service? [Sample answer: One service charges for each device and the other service has a flat fee for a fixed number of devices, and charges for devices beyond that number.]

After [🖥 WHOLE CLASS]

ETP **4 Facilitate Meaningful Mathematical Discourse**

Ask students to share their solutions. If needed, project Elizabeth's and Zachary's work and ask:

Q: Whose representation, Zachary's or Elizabeth's, models the situation more clearly for you? Explain. [Sample answer: Zachary's tables model the situation more clearly. The cost for the number of devices is recorded on the chart.]

5 Transition to Visual Learning

Q: What do you notice about the cost for multiple devices for each service? [Sample answer: The costs for Movies4You represent a linear function. The costs for Family Stream represent a nonlinear function for 4 or fewer devices, and a linear function if you only consider the costs for more than 4 devices.]

6 Extension for Early Finishers

Q: If Movies4You ran a special where the cost for the first device is half off, for how many devices would Movies4You be a better deal? Explain. [Sample answer: Movies4You would be a better deal for up to 4 devices, and cost the same as Family Stream for 5 devices.]

Analyze Student Work

🖥 **Available Online**

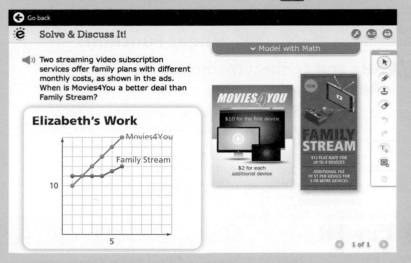

Elizabeth uses digital drawing tools to graph the cost of different numbers of devices for each service.

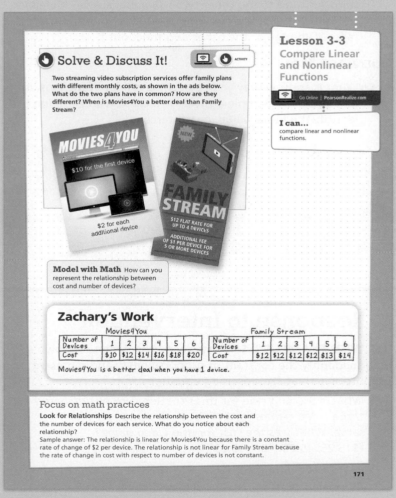

Lesson 3-3
Compare Linear and Nonlinear Functions

I can...
compare linear and nonlinear functions.

Solve & Discuss It!

Two streaming video subscription services offer family plans with different monthly costs, as shown in the ads below. What do the two plans have in common? How are they different? When is Movies4you a better deal than Family Stream?

Model with Math How can you represent the relationship between cost and number of devices?

Zachary's Work

Movies4You

Number of Devices	1	2	3	4	5	6
Cost	$10	$12	$14	$16	$18	$20

Family Stream

Number of Devices	1	2	3	4	5	6
Cost	$12	$12	$12	$12	$13	$14

Movies4You is a better deal when you have 1 device.

Focus on math practices

Look for Relationships Describe the relationship between the cost and the number of devices for each service. What do you notice about each relationship?

Sample answer: The relationship is linear for Movies4You because there is a constant rate of change of $2 per device. The relationship is not linear for Family Stream because the rate of change in cost with respect to number of devices is not constant.

171

Zachary uses tables to determine when the cost is lower for the Movies4You subscription than for Family Stream.

STEP 2 | Develop: Visual Learning

ETP **Establish Mathematics Goals to Focus Learning**

Engage students in a discussion about the *Essential Question*. Make sure they understand that there are different representations and properties of functions that can be used to make comparisons.

EXAMPLE 1 Compare Two Linear Functions

ETP **Use and Connect Mathematical Representations**

Q: What properties can be used to compare two functions? [Sample answer: You can use the initial value and the rate of change.]

Q: What does the constant rate of change for each model mean? [The number of tasks a robot can complete per minute.]

☑ Try It!

ETP **Elicit and Use Evidence of Student Thinking**

Q: How can you use the equation $y = 10.8w$ to compare the third function to the other two? [Sample answer: Compare the value of m in the equation $y = 10.8w$ to the constant rates of change of the other two functions.]

Convince Me!

Q: What is another way you can compare linear functions using an equation? [Sample answer: You can use an equation to identify the initial value, or y-intercept.]

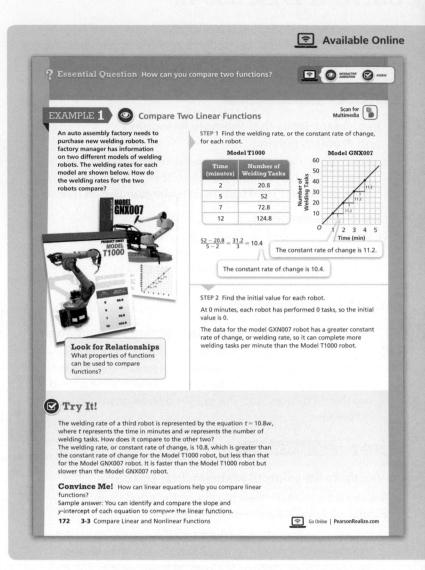

 Essential Question How can you compare two functions?

EXAMPLE 1 Compare Two Linear Functions

Scan for Multimedia

An auto assembly factory needs to purchase new welding robots. The factory manager has information on two different models of welding robots. The welding rates for each model are shown below. How do the welding rates for the two robots compare?

STEP 1 Find the welding rate, or the constant rate of change, for each robot.

Model T1000

Time (minutes)	Number of Welding Tasks
2	20.8
5	52
7	72.8
12	124.8

$$\frac{52 - 20.8}{5 - 2} = \frac{31.2}{3} = 10.4$$

Model GNX007

The constant rate of change is 11.2.

The constant rate of change is 10.4.

STEP 2 Find the initial value for each robot.

At 0 minutes, each robot has performed 0 tasks, so the initial value is 0.

The data for the model GXN007 robot has a greater constant rate of change, or welding rate, so it can complete more welding tasks per minute than the Model T1000 robot.

Look for Relationships
What properties of functions can be used to compare functions?

☑ Try It!

The welding rate of a third robot is represented by the equation $t = 10.8w$, where t represents the time in minutes and w represents the number of welding tasks. How does it compare to the other two?
The welding rate, or constant rate of change, is 10.8, which is greater than the constant rate of change for the Model T1000 robot, but less than that for the Model GNX007 robot. It is faster than the Model T1000 robot but slower than the Model GNX007 robot.

Convince Me! How can linear equations help you compare linear functions?
Sample answer: You can identify and compare the slope and y-intercept of each equation to compare the linear functions.

172   3-3 Compare Linear and Nonlinear Functions   Go Online | PearsonRealize.com

---

Students can access the *Visual Learning Animation Plus* by using the **BouncePages app** to scan this page. Students can download the app for free in their mobile devices' app store.

RtI Response to Intervention

USE WITH EXAMPLE 1 Some students may need to review how to identify the constant of proportionality and represent proportional relationships using equations.

Q: What is the unit rate for this situation: *Sidney purchased three video games for $45.75. Each game cost the same. What was the cost for one video game?* [$15.25; 45.75 ÷ 3 = 15.25]

Q: Write an equation to represent the total cost for the number of movie tickets purchased, where c represents the total cost, t represents the number of movie tickets purchased, and each movie ticket costs $9.75. What is the constant of proportionality? [$c = 9.75t$; 9.75]

E Enrichment

USE WITH EXAMPLE 2 Challenge advanced students to compare the two relationships using equations and graphs.

Q: What equation models the linear function represented in the table? [$y = 4x$ where x represents the side length and y represents the perimeter of the square.]

Q: What equation models the nonlinear function represented by the graph? [$y = x^2$ where x represents the side length and y represents the area of the square.]

Q: Graph the relationship represented in the table. How does this differ from the graph showing the relationship between the side lengths and area? [Check students' graphs. The graph of the relationship represented in the table is a straight line and is a linear function. The graph shown is not a straight line and is a nonlinear function.]

EXAMPLE 2 Compare a Linear and a Nonlinear Function

ETP Pose Purposeful Questions

Q: How can you determine whether the relationship in the table is a function? [Sample answer: Check to see that each input value (length) has exactly one output value (perimeter).]

Q: What are the similarities between the two relationships? Differences? [Sample answer: Both relationships are functions. One is a linear function, one is a nonlinear function.]

EXAMPLE 3 Compare Properties of Linear Functions

ETP Pose Purposeful Questions

Q: Which properties are being compared? [The initial value and constant rate of change]

Q: What does the initial value of a function equate to in a linear equation? [The y-intercept, or b]

Q: What does the constant rate of change of a function equate to in a linear equation? [The slope, or m]

Try It!

ETP Elicit and Use Evidence of Student Thinking

Q: What two properties can you compare? [Rate of change and initial value]

Q: What are the rates of change for each function? [The rate of change for Function 1 is 1.5; for Function 2 is 2.]

Q: What is the initial value for each function? [The initial value for Function 1 is −2; for Function 2 is −4.]

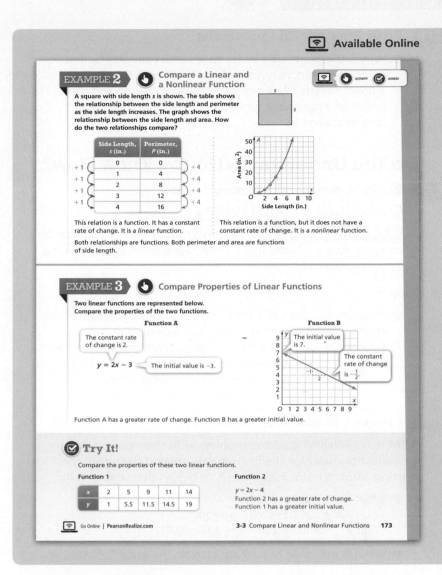

ADDITIONAL EXAMPLES

For additional examples go to PearsonRealize.com.

ELL English Language Learners

Students may struggle with understanding Example 1 due to the vocabulary demands of the problem situation

BEGINNING Have students look at Example 1 and identify the robots.

Q: What do you think these robots do?

Help students understand that these robots are welding robots that weld metal together.

Ask what factories produce.

Q: What kinds of products are made in factories?

INTERMEDIATE Have students discuss different kinds of robots that they may know about.

Q: What kinds of robots can you think of? [Sample answer: Robots in factories to help make different kinds of goods—electronics, cars, appliances]

Q: Why do businesses use robots? [Sample answer: They are more efficient than people. They can work without taking a break.]

ADVANCED Have students investigate other tasks that robots can do besides welding.

Q: What other jobs can robots do? [Sample answer: Painting, assembly]

Q: Are robots good for businesses? Are they good for people? [Sample answer: They are good for businesses, but not good for workers.]

Have students discuss their views on robots.

PearsonRealize.com

 Key Concept Activity

KEY CONCEPT

ETP **Pose Purposeful Questions**

Q: Why is the graph of a linear function a straight line and a nonlinear function not? [Sample answer: The graph of a linear function has a constant rate of change and the graph of a nonlinear function does not have a constant rate of change.]

Do You Understand/Do You Know How?

ETP **Build Procedural Fluency from Conceptual Understanding**

? Essential Question Students should understand how to compare two functions in different representations by looking at their properties.

ITEM 1

Q: How can you determine the constant rates of change of relationships presented in tables or as equations? [Sample answer: For data in a table, divide the difference of two y-values by the difference of the corresponding x-values. In an equation, look for the value of m.]

🔄 Prevent Misconceptions

ITEM 4 If students begin the problem with the incorrect starting amounts borrowed for the instruments, remind them that the starting amount is the initial value, or the y-value when x is 0.

Q: What is the value of y when x is 0 in the equation $y = -30x + 290$? Show your work. [290; $y = -30(0) + 290 = 0 + 290 = 290$]

Q: What is the value of y when x is 0 on the graph? [240]

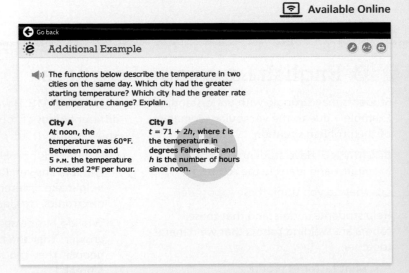

ADDITIONAL EXAMPLE **3** 👆

Remind students that functions can be represented by verbal descriptions, tables, graphs, or equations. Help them compare the properties of two linear functions represented by a verbal description and an equation.

Q: What are the initial value and constant rate of change described for City A? [The initial value is 60°F and the constant rate of change is 2°F per hour.]

Q: What are the initial value and constant rate of change described for City B? Explain. [Sample answer: The initial value is 71°F and the constant rate of change is 2°F per hour. The equation $t = 71 + 2h$, or $t = 2h + 71$, is in the form $y = mx + b$, where, 2 is the slope, and 71 is the y-intercept.]

🔊 Available Online

Go back

ē Additional Example

🔊) The functions below describe the temperature in two cities on the same day. Which city had the greater starting temperature? Which city had the greater rate of temperature change? Explain.

City A
At noon, the temperature was 60°F. Between noon and 5 P.M. the temperature increased 2°F per hour.

City B
$t = 71 + 2h$, where t is the temperature in degrees Fahrenheit and h is the number of hours since noon.

Answer: City B had the greater starting temperature, because $71 > 60$. The cities had the same rate of temperature change.

Practice   Tutorials   Math Tools

Practice & Problem Solving

🔊 **Available Online**

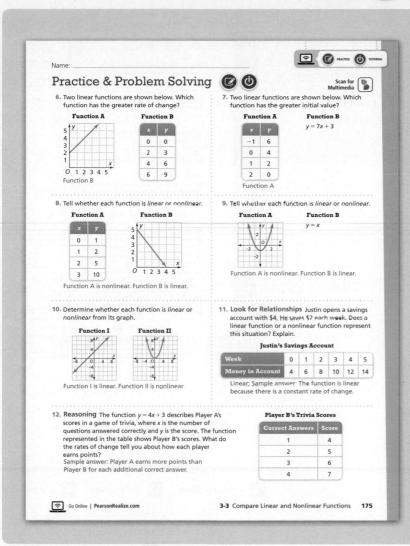

Name: _____

Practice & Problem Solving

Scan for Multimedia

6. Two linear functions are shown below. Which function has the greater rate of change?

Function A

Function B

x	y
0	0
2	3
4	6
6	9

Function B

7. Two linear functions are shown below. Which function has the greater initial value?

Function A

x	y
−1	6
0	4
1	2
2	0

Function B

$y = 7x + 3$

Function A

8. Tell whether each function is *linear* or *nonlinear*.

Function A

x	y
0	1
1	2
2	5
3	10

Function B

Function A is nonlinear. Function B is linear.

9. Tell whether each function is *linear* or *nonlinear*.

Function A

Function B

$y = x$

Function A is nonlinear. Function B is linear.

10. Determine whether each function is *linear* or *nonlinear* from its graph.

Function I   Function II

Function I is linear. Function II is nonlinear.

11. Look for Relationships Justin opens a savings account with $4. He saves $2 each week. Does a linear function or a nonlinear function represent this situation? Explain.

Justin's Savings Account

Week	0	1	2	3	4	5
Money in Account	4	6	8	10	12	14

Linear; Sample answer: The function is linear because there is a constant rate of change.

12. Reasoning The function $y = 4x + 3$ describes Player A's scores in a game of trivia, where x is the number of questions answered correctly and y is the score. The function represented in the table shows Player B's scores. What do the rates of change tell you about how each player earns points?
Sample answer: Player A earns more points than Player B for each additional correct answer.

Player B's Trivia Scores

Correct Answers	Score
1	4
2	5
3	6
4	7

Go Online | PearsonRealize.com

3-3 Compare Linear and Nonlinear Functions   **175**

---

13. Two athletes are training over a two-week period to increase the number of push-ups each can do consecutively. Athlete A can do 16 push-ups to start, and increases his total by 2 each day. Athlete B's progress is charted in the table. Compare the initial values for each. What does the initial value mean in this situation?
Sample answer: The initial value for Athlete A is greater. This means that Athlete A was able to do more push-ups than Athlete B when the training started.

Athlete B Push-up Progress

Day	Number of Push-ups
0	12
1	15
2	18
3	21

14. Higher Order Thinking The equation $y = 4x − 2$ and the table and graph shown at the right describe three different linear functions. Which function has the greatest rate of change? Which has the least? Explain.
The function in the table has the greatest rate of change;
The function in the graph has the least rate of change;
Sample answer: The slope of the function in the table is 5, the slope of the equation is 4, and the slope of the graph is −2.

x	y
1	5
2	10
3	15
4	20

✓ Assessment Practice

15. The students in the After-School Club ate 12 grapes per minute. After 9 minutes, there were 32 grapes remaining. The table shows the number of carrots remaining after different amounts of time. Which snack did the students eat at a faster rate? Explain.
Grapes; Sample answer: The constant rate of change for the grape function is −12, which means students ate 12 grapes per minute. The constant rate of change for the carrot function is −9, which means students ate 9 carrots per minute. The students ate the grapes at a faster rate.

Carrot Consumption

Time Elapsed	Carrots Remaining
6 minutes	136
8 minutes	118
9 minutes	109
11 minutes	91

16. The height of a burning candle can be modeled by a linear function. Candle A has an initial height of 201 millimeters, and its height decreases to 177 millimeters after 4 hours of burning. The height, h, in millimeters, of Candle B can be modeled by the function $h = 290 − 5t$, where t is the time in hours. Which of the following statements are true? Select all that apply.

☐ The initial height of Candle A is greater than the initial height of Candle B.

☑ The height of Candle A decreases at a faster rate than the height of Candle B.

☑ Candle B will burn out in 58 hours.

☐ After 10 hours, the height of Candle A is 110 millimeters.

☑ Candle A will burn out before Candle B.

176   3-3 Compare Linear and Nonlinear Functions

Go Online | PearsonRealize.com

Error Intervention

ITEM 12 Reasoning If students say that Player B gains more points than Player A, review the definition of rate of change.

Q: What is the rate of change for Player A? Player B?
[Player A: 4; Player B: 1]

Q: What does the rate of change mean in each situation?
[Sample answer: For each correct answer, Player A scores 4 points and Player B scores 1 point.]

🏆 Challenge

ITEM 14 Higher Order Thinking You can use this item to extend students' understanding of slope, or rate of change.

Q: For which representation can you determine the slope most easily? [Sample answer: The equation in the form $y = mx + b$; look for the value of m.]

You may opt to have students complete the automatically scored Practice & Problem Solving items online.

Item Analysis

Example	Items	DOK
1	6	2
	14, 15	3
2	8, 9, 10, 11	2
3	7, 13, 16	2
	12	3

Lesson Quiz

 Use the student scores on the Lesson Quiz to prescribe differentiated assignments.

I Intervention 0–2 Points   **O** On-Level 3 Points   **A** Advanced 4 Points

You may opt to have students take the Lesson Quiz online. The Lesson Quiz will be automatically scored and appropriate remediation, practice, or enrichment will be assigned based on student performance.

Video Tutorials

Students can access instructional tutorials using the **Virtual Nerd app**.

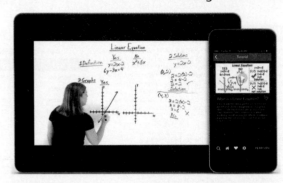

Students can also access the videos using the BouncePages app to scan exercise pages marked with this icon. Students can download both apps for free in their mobile devices' app store.

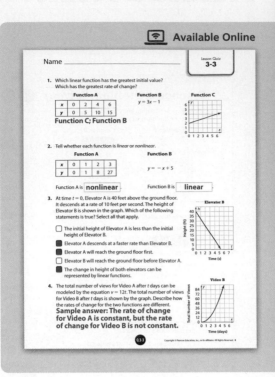

Differentiated Intervention

I = Intervention   **O** = On-Level   **A** = Advanced

Reteach to Build Understanding **I**

Provides scaffolded reteaching for the key lesson concepts.

Additional Vocabulary Support **I** **O**

Helps students develop and reinforce understanding of key terms and concepts.

Build Mathematical Literacy **I**

Provides support for struggling readers to build mathematical literacy.

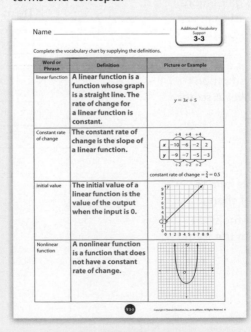

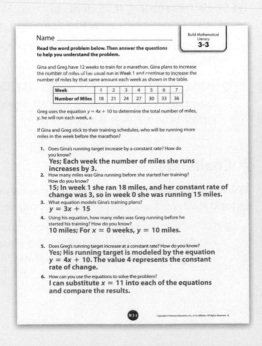

Practice Worksheets Math Tools Math Games

Additional Practice

You may opt to have students complete the automatically scored Additional Practice items online.

Item Analysis

Example	Items	DOK
1	1, 2, 5	2
2	3	1
	4	2
3	7, 8, 9	2
	6	3

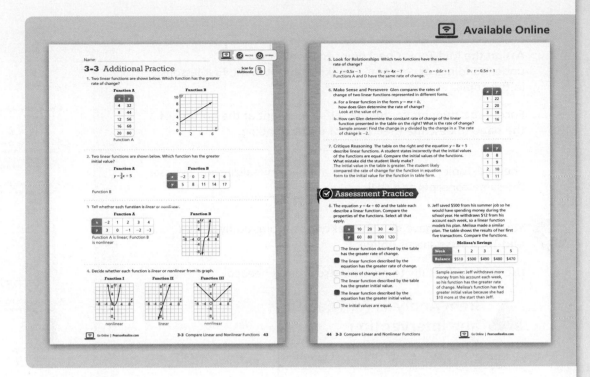

Available Online

Differentiated Intervention

I = Intervention   **O** = On-Level   **A** = Advanced

Enrichment **O** **A**

Presents engaging problems and activities that extend the lesson concepts.

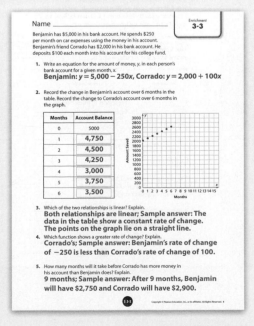

Math Tools and Games **I** **O** **A**

Offers additional activities and games to build understanding and fluency.

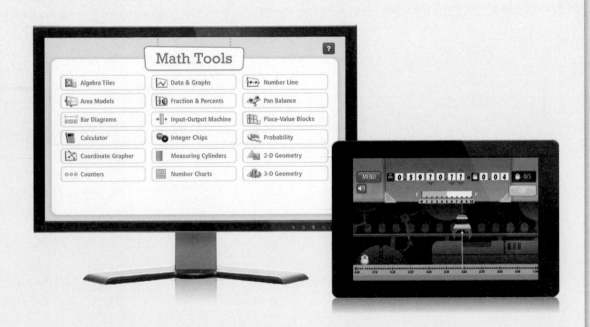

MID-TOPIC CHECKPOINT

Assess

Assign the Mid-Topic Checkpoint to monitor students' understandings of concepts and skills taught in the first lessons in this topic.

Encourage students to use the self-assessment at the bottom of the page to describe their level of understanding.

The Mid-Topic Assessment, found at PearsonRealize.com, assesses the same concepts and skills.

You may opt to have students take the automatically-scored Mid-Topic Assessment online.

Use students' results to adjust instruction as needed.

Item Analysis for Diagnosis and Intervention

Item	DOK	MDIS	Lesson
1	2	K51	3-1
2	1	K51	3-1
3	1	K50	3-3
4	1	K51	3-2
5	2	K52	3-3

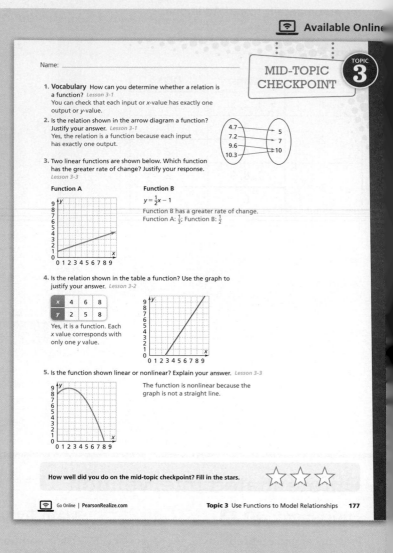

Available Online

Name: _____

MID-TOPIC CHECKPOINT
TOPIC 3

1. **Vocabulary** How can you determine whether a relation is a function? *Lesson 3-1*
You can check that each input or *x*-value has exactly one output or *y*-value.

2. Is the relation shown in the arrow diagram a function? Justify your answer. *Lesson 3-1*
Yes, the relation is a function because each input has exactly one output.

3. Two linear functions are shown below. Which function has the greater rate of change? Justify your response. *Lesson 3-3*

Function A

Function B
$y = \frac{1}{2}x - 1$
Function B has a greater rate of change.
Function A: $\frac{1}{3}$; Function B: $\frac{1}{2}$

4. Is the relation shown in the table a function? Use the graph to justify your answer. *Lesson 3-2*

| x | 4 | 6 | 8 |
| y | 2 | 5 | 8 |

Yes, it is a function. Each *x* value corresponds with only one *y* value.

5. Is the function shown linear or nonlinear? Explain your answer. *Lesson 3-3*
The function is nonlinear because the graph is not a straight line.

How well did you do on the mid-topic checkpoint? Fill in the stars. ☆☆☆

Go Online | PearsonRealize.com   **Topic 3** Use Functions to Model Relationships   **177**

Mid-Topic Assessment Master

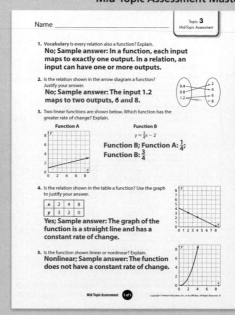

Name _____
Topic **3**
Mid-Topic Assessment

1. **Vocabulary** Is every relation also a function? Explain.
No; Sample answer: In a function, each input maps to exactly one output. In a relation, an input can have one or more outputs.

2. Is the relation shown in the arrow diagram a function? Justify your answer.
No; Sample answer: The input 1.2 maps to two outputs, 6 and 8.

3. Two linear functions are shown below. Which function has the greater rate of change? Explain.

Function A

Function B
$y = \frac{3}{4}x - 2$
Function B; Function A: $\frac{1}{4}$; Function B: $\frac{3}{4}$

4. Is the relation shown in the table a function? Use the graph to justify your answer.

| x | 2 | 4 | 8 |
| y | 3 | 2 | 0 |

Yes; Sample answer: The graph of the function is a straight line and has a constant rate of change.

5. Is the function shown linear or nonlinear? Explain.
Nonlinear; Sample answer: The function does not have a constant rate of change.

Mid-Topic Assessment 1 of 1

MID-TOPIC PERFORMANCE TASK

Assess students' ability to apply the concepts and skills in the first part of the topic using the Mid-Topic Performance Task, found in the Student's Edition or at PearsonRealize.com.

Item Analysis for Diagnosis and Intervention

Part	DOK	MDIS	Lesson
A	2	K52	3-1, 3-2
B	2	K51	3-2, 3-3
C	1	K50	3-2, 3-3
D	3	K51	3-3

Scoring Guide

Part	Points	Mid-Topic Performance Task (Student's Edition)
A	2	Correct answer and explanation
	1	Correct answer or explanation
B	2	Correct answer and explanation
	1	Correct answer with incorrect or incomplete explanation
C	2	Correct answer and explanation
	1	Correct answer with incorrect or incomplete explanation
D	2	Proposal with explanation
	1	Proposal with incomplete or missing explanation

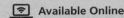 Available Online

TOPIC 3 MID-TOPIC PERFORMANCE TASK

Sarah, Gene, and Paul are proposing plans for a class fundraiser. Each presents his or her proposal for the amount of money raised, y, for x number of hours worked, in different ways.

Sarah's Proposal

Gene's Proposal

Hours Worked	Money Raised
5	42
10	77
15	112
20	147

Paul's Proposal

$y = 10x + 7$

PART A

Are each of the proposals represented by linear functions? Explain.
Yes, a straight line represents Sarah's proposal, so it is a linear function. Gene's proposal has a constant of rate of change, so it is a linear function. An equation in the form $y = mx + b$ represents Paul's proposal, so it is a linear function.

PART B

Does the class have any money in the account now? How can you tell?
Yes; the initial value of each function represents the amount of money the class already has or has earned. Each proposal shows that the class starts with $7.

PART C

Which fundraising proposal raises money at the fastest rate? Explain.
Sarah's proposal; Sample answer: The slope represents the amount of money earned per hour. Sarah's proposal earns $15 per hour, Gene's proposal earns $7 per hour, and Paul's proposal earns $10 per hour.

PART D

If Sarah and her classmates are hoping to raise $200, which proposal do you recommend that Sarah and her classmates choose? Explain why you recommend that proposal.
Sample answer: Assuming that Sarah's proposal is as easy as the others, the students should choose Sarah's proposal because they can earn the money in the fewest number of hours.

178   **Topic 3** Use Functions to Model Relationships   Go Online | PearsonRealize.com

3-Act MATH

3-Act Mathematical Modeling: Every Drop Counts

Lesson Overview

FOCUS

Objectives

Students will be able to:

✔ Use mathematical modeling to represent a problem situation and to propose a solution.

✔ Test and verify the appropriateness of their math models.

✔ Explain why the results from their mathematical models may not align exactly to the problem situation.

Essential Understanding

Many real-world problem situations can be represented with a mathematical model, but that model may not represent the real-world situation exactly.

COHERENCE

Earlier in this topic, students:

• identified and defined linear and nonlinear functions.

• compared properties of linear functions.

In this lesson, students:

• develop a mathematical model to represent and propose a solution to a problem situation involving linear functions.

Later in this course, students will:

• refine their mathematical modeling skills.

RIGOR

This mathematical modeling lesson focuses on application of both math content and math practices and processes.

• Students draw on their understanding of function concepts to develop a representative model.

• Students apply their mathematical model to test and validate its applicability to similar problem situations.

Math Anytime

Today's Challenge

Use the Topic 3 problems any time during this topic.

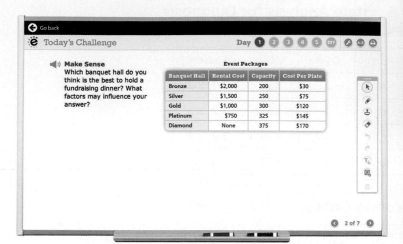

Mathematics Overview

In this lesson, students will develop and use a mathematical model to represent and propose a solution to a real-world problem involving a linear function. Students will reinforce both their procedural skills and their understanding of function concepts, while recognizing the limitations of some mathematical models for real-world situations.

Students interpret their solutions and propose explanations for why their answer may not match the real-world answer.

Students will also engage in sense-making, abstract and quantitative reasoning, and mathematical communication and argumentation. In testing and validating their models, students look for patterns in the structure of their models.

Applying Math Practices

Model with Math

To solve the problem situation presented, students identify variables and the relationship among variables, develop a model that represents the situation, and use the model to propose a solution.

Video

3-Act Mathematical Modeling

ACT 1 The Hook ▶

Students will be tasked with determining how much water a person wastes while brushing his teeth.

Play the Video and Brainstorm Questions

Have students complete **Question 1**. Encourage them to ask any question that comes to mind. Listen for interesting mathematical and non-mathematical questions. Ask students what makes each question interesting.

Q: What questions do you have? [Sample questions: How long do they brush for? Who did a better job brushing? How much water did they use?]

Pose the Main Question

After the question brainstorming, pose the Main Question students will be tasked with answering. Have students complete **Question 2**.

Main Question

Q: How much water was wasted?

Ask about Predictions

Have students complete **Questions 3–5**. You can survey the class for the range of predictions.

Q: Why do you think your prediction is the solution to the Main Question?

Q: Who had a similar prediction?

Q: How many of you agree with that prediction?

Q: Who has a different prediction?

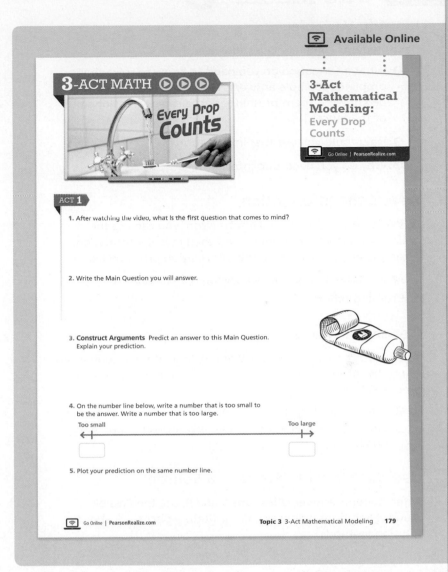

Available Online

3-ACT MATH ▶ ▶ ▶

Every Drop Counts

3-Act Mathematical Modeling: Every Drop Counts

Go Online | PearsonRealize.com

ACT 1

1. After watching the video, what is the first question that comes to mind?

2. Write the Main Question you will answer.

3. **Construct Arguments** Predict an answer to this Main Question. Explain your prediction.

4. On the number line below, write a number that is too small to be the answer. Write a number that is too large.

   Too small ←|———————————————————|→ Too large

   [   ]   [   ]

5. Plot your prediction on the same number line.

Go Online | PearsonRealize.com   Topic 3 3-Act Mathematical Modeling   **179**

Activity

3-Act Mathematical Modeling *continued*

ACT 2 The Model

Identify Variables

Have students complete **Questions 6** and **7**.

Q: What information do you need to know to solve the problem? [Sample answers: The information needed to be known is spent brushing, or the rate water flows out of the faucet.]

Q: How could you get that information?

Q: Why do you need that information?

Reveal the Information

As students identify needed information, you can use the online interactivity to estimate and then reveal information. Alternatively, you can share the information provided below.

Faucet rate: $1\frac{3}{4}$ cups, or 14 ounces, in 5 seconds

Brushing time: 01:25

Develop a Model

As students answer **Questions 8** and **9**, look at how students are using the information and prompt them to think about more precise solutions.

Q: What units do you think are most useful to describe the amount of water wasted? [Sample answers: cups, gallons, ounces]

Use the Model to Propose a Solution

After students answer **Questions 8** and **9**, use the Possible Student Solutions below as you facilitate a discussion about solution methods.

ACT 2

6. What information in this situation would be helpful to know? How would you use that information?

7. **Use Appropriate Tools** What tools can you use to get the information you need? Record the information as you find it.

8. **Model with Math** Represent the situation using the mathematical content, concepts, and skills from this topic. Use your representation to answer the Main Question.

9. What is your answer to the Main Question? Is it higher or lower than your prediction? Explain why.

180 **Topic 3** 3-Act Mathematical Modeling   Go Online | PearsonRealize.com

Available Online

Possible Student Solutions

Chloe's Work

$$\frac{1\frac{3}{4} \text{ cups}}{5 \text{ seconds}} = \frac{\frac{7}{20} \text{ cup}}{1 \text{ second}}$$

1:25 is 85 seconds

$$\frac{7}{20} \times 85 = 29.75 \text{ cups}$$

Chloe found the unit rate for the water flow from the faucet in cups per second and multiplied the rate by the number of seconds.

Jackson's Work

60 seconds + 25 seconds = 85 seconds

×17

$$\frac{14 \text{ ounces}}{5 \text{ seconds}} = \frac{238 \text{ ounces}}{85 \text{ seconds}}$$

×17

There's 128 ounces in a gallon.
He wasted almost 2 gallons.

Jackson used equivalent rates to find the number of ounces and then estimated the number of gallons.

ACT 3 ⏵ The Solution and Sequel ▶

⧠ **Available Online**

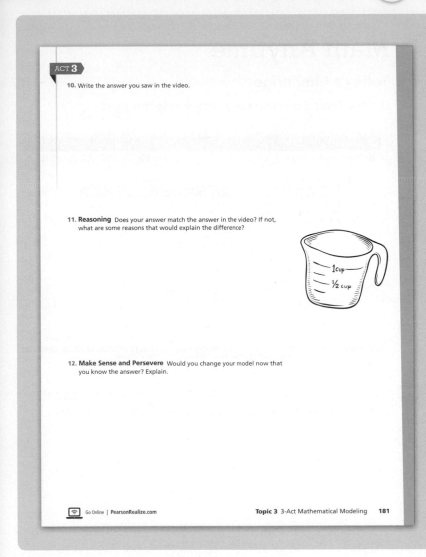

ACT 3

10. Write the answer you saw in the video.

11. Reasoning Does your answer match the answer in the video? If not, what are some reasons that would explain the difference?

12. Make Sense and Persevere Would you change your model now that you know the answer? Explain.

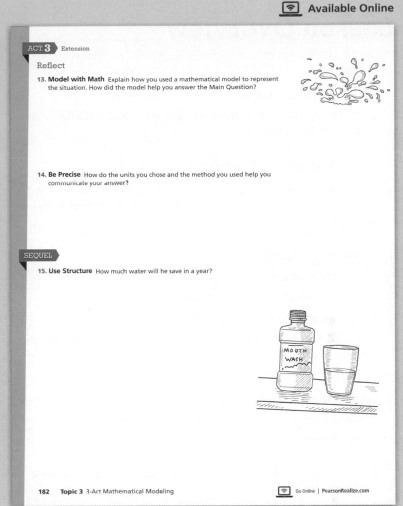

ACT 3 ⏵ Extension

Reflect

13. Model with Math Explain how you used a mathematical model to represent the situation. How did the model help you answer the Main Question?

14. Be Precise How do the units you chose and the method you used help you communicate your answer?

SEQUEL

15. Use Structure How much water will he save in a year?

Use the Video to Reveal the Answer

The final part of the video shows the amount of wasted water. Have students complete **Question 10**. Offer praise to the students who were closest to the actual answer.

Main Question Answer

230 ounces, or about 1.8 gallons

Validate Conclusions

After students complete **Questions 11 and 12**, encourage them to discuss possible sources of error inherent in using math to model real-world situations. Look for students to point out that their models are still useful even though they are not perfect.

Q: Why does your answer not match the answer in the video? [Sample answer: Some of the water at the beginning and end is not wasted.]

Q: How useful was your model at predicting the answer?

Q: How could your model better represent the situation?

Reflect on Thinking

Be Precise If time allows, have students complete **Questions 13 and 14** as an extension. Use this opportunity to discuss how students incorporate mathematical processes during the task.

Pose the Sequel

Use Structure Use **Question 15** to present a similar problem situation involving linear functions, so that they can test the usefulness of their models.

Q: If he turns the water off every time he brushes, how much water will he save in a year?

[Sample answer: If students assume he brushes twice a day, every day, they can use their models and the answer in the video to get an answer of around 1,300 gallons.]

Q: What other variables do you need to consider? [Sample answers: The other variables to consider are the number of times he brushes each day, or the typical amount of time he spends brushing.]

Lesson 3-4

Construct Functions to Model Linear Relationships

Lesson Overview

FOCUS

Objective

Students will be able to:

✔ write an equation in the form $y = mx + b$ to describe a linear function.

Essential Understanding

A function that represents a linear relationship between two quantities can be represented by an equation written in the form $y = mx + b$.

COHERENCE

In Grade 7, students:

• wrote and solved two-step equations.

• solved problems using equations and inequalities.

In this lesson, students:

• write a function in the form $y = mx + b$ from two values and from a graph.

• interpret a linear function from a representation.

Later in this topic, students will:

• analyze intervals of increase and decrease.

• sketch functions from verbal descriptions.

RIGOR

This lesson emphasizes a blend of **conceptual understanding** and **application**.

• Students understand that the equation $y = mx + b$ represents a linear function.

• Students use their knowledge of rate of change and initial value to write a linear function as an equation and interpret a function from a graph.

Math Anytime

Today's Challenge

Use the Topic 3 problems any time during this topic

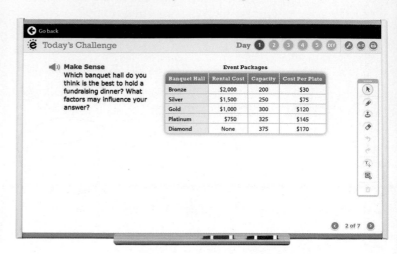

Watch the **Listen and Look For Video** for strategies and habits of mind to look for as students complete work on this lesson.

✅ Mathematics Overview

In this lesson, students will represent linear functions with equations in the form $y = mx + b$. They will determine the rate of change and initial value from two ordered pairs or from a verbal description. They also will construct different representations of the relationship between variables, and use the representations to construct a function. These representations will include bar diagrams, graphs, tables, and equations in the form $y = mx + b$.

Applying Math Practices

Make Sense and Persevere
Students use representations, such as graphs and equations, to make sense of problems.

Model with Math
Students model linear relationships using different representations, such as graphs and equations.

STEP 1 | Develop: Problem-Based Learning

15-20 min

Activity

Explore It!

Model with Math As students work through the Explore It, listen and look for students who understand the relationship between the two quantities and can represent this relationship on a graph.

Before [WHOLE CLASS]

TP 1 Implement Tasks that Promote Reasoning and Problem Solving

Q: What are the two quantities in this situation? [Weeks, money saved]

Q: What do you notice about the amount of money Erick plans to save each week? [Sample answer: He plans to save the same amount each week.]

2 Build Understanding

Q: What do you notice about the values you put in the table? [Sample answer: They increase at regular intervals.]

Q: What does the $120 that Erick has already saved represent in the function? [The initial value of the function]

During [SMALL GROUP]

TP 3 Support Productive Struggle in Mathematics

Q: How can you find the rate of change? [Sample answer: Use the difference in the output values (amount of money saved) divided by the difference in the input values (number of weeks)]

Q: How is the initial value represented on the graph? [The initial value is the *y*-intercept, or (0, 120).]

After [WHOLE CLASS]

TP 4 Facilitate Meaningful Mathematical Discourse

Ask students to share their solutions. If needed, project Seleniz's and Salome's work and ask:

Q: Do you agree with Salome's explanation? Explain. [Sample answer: Yes, I agree. The difference between the cost each week is 20. The table shows a constant rate of change.]

Q: Do you agree with Seleniz's explanation regarding the graph? Explain. [Sample answer: Yes; A non-vertical straight line represents a linear function.]

5 Transition to Visual Learning

Q: What other representations can we use to determine whether a relation is a function? Which representation is most useful for you? [Sample answer: Set of ordered pairs, table, graph, equation; responses will vary.]

6 Extension for Early Finishers

Q: Suppose in week 3 the amount of money Erick saved was $40 instead of $20. What would his balance in week 3 be now? Would this relationship still be a linear function? Explain. [$200; No; the rate of change is not constant, so the function would not be linear.]

Analyze Student Work

Available Online

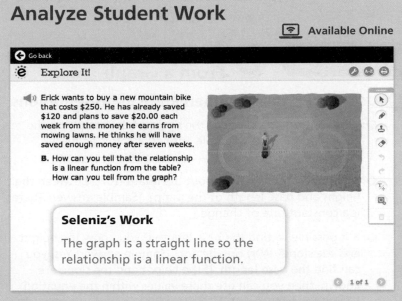

Erick wants to buy a new mountain bike that costs $250. He has already saved $120 and plans to save $20.00 each week from the money he earns from mowing lawns. He thinks he will have saved enough money after seven weeks.

B. How can you tell that the relationship is a linear function from the table? How can you tell from the graph?

Seleniz's Work

The graph is a straight line so the relationship is a linear function.

1 of 1

Seleniz determines that the relationship is a linear function because the graph of the function is a straight line.

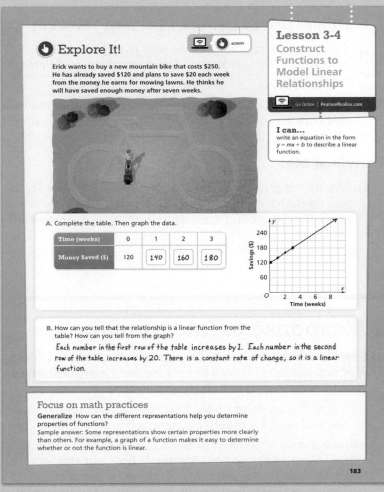

Explore It!

Lesson 3-4
Construct Functions to Model Linear Relationships

Erick wants to buy a new mountain bike that costs $250. He has already saved $120 and plans to save $20 each week from the money he earns for mowing lawns. He thinks he will have saved enough money after seven weeks.

I can... write an equation in the form $y = mx + b$ to describe a linear function.

A. Complete the table. Then graph the data.

Time (weeks)	0	1	2	3
Money Saved ($)	120	140	160	180

B. How can you tell that the relationship is a linear function from the table? How can you tell from the graph?

Each number in the first row of the table increases by 1. Each number in the second row of the table increases by 20. There is a constant rate of change, so it is a linear function.

Focus on math practices
Generalize How can the different representations help you determine properties of functions?
Sample answer: Some representations show certain properties more clearly than others. For example, a graph of a function makes it easy to determine whether or not the function is linear.

183

Salome determines that the relationship is a linear function because the values in the table have a constant rate of change.

ETP **Establish Mathematics Goals to Focus Learning**

Engage students in a discussion about the *Essential Question*. Review with students as needed the form of a linear equation, $y = mx + b$.

EXAMPLE 1 **Write a Function From a Graph**

ETP **Use and Connect Mathematical Representations**

Q: What do you notice about the shape of the ramp that the students will build? [Sample answer: It forms an incline. It has a slope.]

Q: What does that tell you about the relationship between the height and base length of the ramp? [Sample answer: There is a constant rate of change.]

Q: Is it possible to find the base length if you know the height and the slope? Why or why not. [Sample answer: Yes, you can find the base length. If the height and the slope are known, then you can use those values within the equation to find the base length.]

✓ Try It!

ETP **Elicit and Use Evidence of Student Thinking**

Q: How does the equation change now that the ramp has a 3 : 15 ratio? [Sample answer: The slope of the equation is now $\frac{3}{15}$ or $\frac{1}{5}$.]

Q: Will the height of the ramp now be taller or shorter than the height of the ramp in Example 1? [The height of the ramp will be shorter than the height of the ramp in Example 1.]

Convince Me!

Q: Why do the graphs of both functions (Example 1 and Try It) pass through the origin? Explain. [Sample answer: Both ramps start at ground level, which is (0, 0) on the graph.]

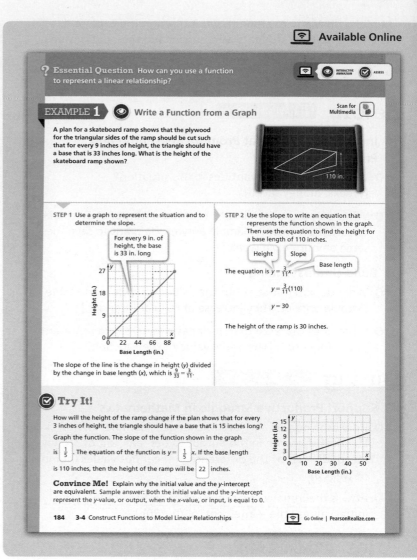

 Available Online

? Essential Question How can you use a function to represent a linear relationship?

EXAMPLE 1 Write a Function from a Graph

Scan for Multimedia

A plan for a skateboard ramp shows that the plywood for the triangular sides of the ramp should be cut such that for every 9 inches of height, the triangle should have a base that is 33 inches long. What is the height of the skateboard ramp shown?

110 in.

STEP 1 Use a graph to represent the situation and to determine the slope.

For every 9 in. of height, the base is 33 in. long

The slope of the line is the change in height (y) divided by the change in base length (x), which is $\frac{9}{33} = \frac{3}{11}$.

STEP 2 Use the slope to write an equation that represents the function shown in the graph. Then use the equation to find the height for a base length of 110 inches.

Height   Slope   Base length

The equation is $y = \frac{3}{11}x$.

$y = \frac{3}{11}(110)$

$y = 30$

The height of the ramp is 30 inches.

✓ Try It!

How will the height of the ramp change if the plan shows that for every 3 inches of height, the triangle should have a base that is 15 inches long? Graph the function. The slope of the function shown in the graph is $\boxed{\frac{1}{5}}$. The equation of the function is $y = \boxed{\frac{1}{5}}x$. If the base length is 110 inches, then the height of the ramp will be $\boxed{22}$ inches.

Convince Me! Explain why the initial value and the y-intercept are equivalent. Sample answer: Both the initial value and the y-intercept represent the y-value, or output, when the x-value, or input, is equal to 0.

184 3-4 Construct Functions to Model Linear Relationships

Go Online | PearsonRealize.com

 Students can access the *Visual Learning Animation Plus* by using the **BouncePages app** to scan this page. Students can download the app for free in their mobile devices' app store.

RtI **Response to Intervention**

USE WITH EXAMPLE 1 Some students may need to review that a set of ordered pairs is only a linear function if every ordered pair in the set lies on a non-vertical straight line.

• Make sure that students understand how to plot ordered pairs and can explain if the graph represents a linear function.

Q: Graph the set of ordered pairs {(0, 0), (2, 4), (3, 5), (4, 8)}. Do they fall on a straight line? Explain. [Check students' graphs. Sample Answer: No, you can only connect 3 out of the 4 points in a straight line. The ordered pair (3, 5) does not fall on the line.]

E **Enrichment**

USE WITH EXAMPLE 3 Challenge advanced students to use the equation that represents the graph of a function to analyze the situation and answer questions.

Q: What is the slope of the function $y = -1x + 10$ and what does it mean? [−1; Sample answer: The candle burns down at a constant rate of 1 inch an hour.]

Q: What do the variables x and y represent? [Sample answer: x: the number of hours; y: the height of the candle]

Q: What would the height of the candle be after it burned for 8 hours? Explain. [2 inches; Sample answer: $y = -1(8) + 10 = -8 + 10 = 2$]

XAMPLE 2 ▶ ● **Write a Function From Two Values**

ETP Pose Purposeful Questions

Q: What do the variables in the equation $y = mx + b$ represent? [m represents slope, b is the y-intercept, and x and y are input and output values.]

● Try It!

ETP Elicit and Use Evidence of Student Thinking

Q: What does the constant rate of change represent in this situation? Explain. [Sample answer: The amount of dog food Jin uses each week.]

Q: What does the initial value represent in this situation? Explain. [Sample answer: The amount of dog food Jin fed his dog in the first 2 weeks.]

EXAMPLE 3 ▶ ● **Interpret a Function From a Graph**

ETP Pose Purposeful Questions

Q: How do you know that $y = -x + 10$ represents a linear function? [Sample answer: $y = -1x + 10$ is the equation of a line that has a constant rate of change, -1, and an initial value, 10.]

Q: What does the ordered pair (5, 5) mean? [After 5 hours of burning, the candle has a height of 5 inches tall.]

Try It!

ETP Elicit and Use Evidence

Q: Including warm-up time, how long will it take to print 100 pages? Explain. [11 minutes; Sample answer: $y = 0.1(100) + 1 = 10 + 1 = 11$]

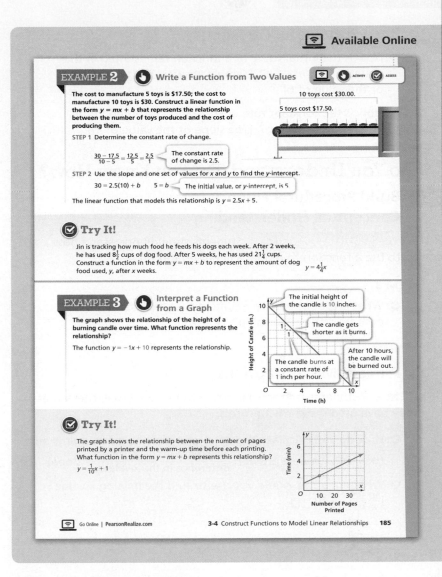

ADDITIONAL EXAMPLES ●

For additional examples go to PearsonRealize.com.

English Language Learners

Use with Example 2. Have students circle the following key words in the Example: function, constant rate of change, initial value.

BEGINNING Have students work with partners to look up the words in the digital glossary and define each word. Have them discuss each word and its definition with their partner. They can ask other students and their teacher for help if they are having trouble.

INTERMEDIATE Have students look up the words that they are unfamiliar with in the digital glossary and define each word. Have them discuss the word(s) and definition(s) with their classmates. Have them become familiar with these words so they can apply these terms throughout this lesson and future lessons.

Q: How are the constant rate of change and initial value represented in the equation of a linear function? [The equation is $y = mx + b$, where m is the constant rate of change and b is the initial value.]

ADVANCED Have students use index cards to write the key words on one side and the corresponding definition on the reverse side. Have them pair up with a partner to use the index cards to review these key words.

Q: Show a representation of a function. [Answers will vary. Sample answer: (0, 0), (5, 10), (10, 20)]

Key Concept Activity

STEP 2 | Develop: Visual Learning *continued*

KEY CONCEPT

ETP **Pose Purposeful Questions**

Q: How is the initial value of a function represented in the equation $y = mx + b$? [Sample answer: The y-intercept, or the value of b]

Q: How is the constant rate of change represented in the equation $y = mx + b$? [The slope or the value of m]

Do You Understand/Do You Know How?

ETP **Build Procedural Fluency from Conceptual Understanding**

? Essential Question Students should understand how to use a function to model a linear relationship.

ITEM 3

Q: What is the form of an equation that represents a proportional relationship? [$y = mx$]

⟳ Prevent Misconceptions

ITEM 2 If students find the value of x to be equal to 4, check that they have used the correct process.

Q: How do you calculate the slope of a line given two points on the line? [Sample answer: $\dfrac{\text{difference in the } y\text{-values}}{\text{difference in the } x\text{-values}} = \text{slope}$]

Q: What equation would you use to find the missing x-value? [$\dfrac{10 - 5}{x - 3} = -5$]

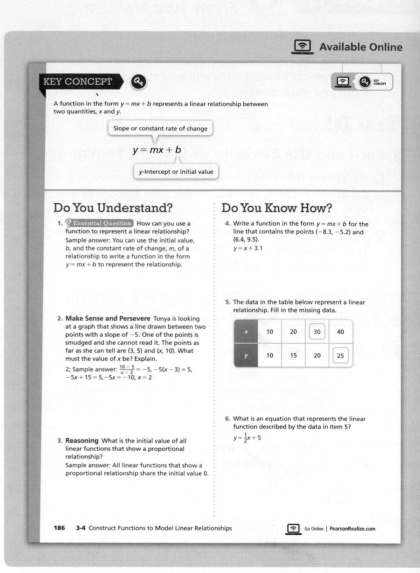

Available Online

KEY CONCEPT

A function in the form $y = mx + b$ represents a linear relationship between two quantities, x and y.

Slope or constant rate of change

$$y = mx + b$$

y-Intercept or initial value

Do You Understand?

1. **? Essential Question** How can you use a function to represent a linear relationship?
Sample answer: You can use the initial value, b, and the constant rate of change, m, of a relationship to write a function in the form $y = mx + b$ to represent the relationship.

2. **Make Sense and Persevere** Tonya is looking at a graph that shows a line drawn between two points with a slope of -5. One of the points is smudged and she cannot read it. The points as far as she can tell are (3, 5) and (x, 10). What must the value of x be? Explain.
2; Sample answer: $\frac{10 - 5}{x - 3} = -5, -5(x - 3) = 5,$ $-5x + 15 = 5, -5x = -10, x = 2$

3. **Reasoning** What is the initial value of all linear functions that show a proportional relationship?
Sample answer: All linear functions that show a proportional relationship share the initial value 0.

Do You Know How?

4. Write a function in the form $y = mx + b$ for the line that contains the points $(-8.3, -5.2)$ and (6.4, 9.5).
$y = x + 3.1$

5. The data in the table below represent a linear relationship. Fill in the missing data.

x	10	20	30	40
y	10	15	20	25

6. What is an equation that represents the linear function described by the data in Item 5?
$y = \frac{1}{2}x + 5$

186 **3-4** Construct Functions to Model Linear Relationships   Go Online | PearsonRealize.com

ADDITIONAL EXAMPLE 2

Available Online

Discuss with students that they can also write an equation of the form $y = mx + b$ from a description of a linear function.

Remind students that m represents the constant rate of change, or slope, and b represents the initial value, or y-intercept.

Q: At what height does the airplane start its descent? [30,000 feet]

Q: Is the rate of change in this situation positive or negative? Explain. [Negative; Sample answer: The plane is starting its descent, so the plane will be losing altitude.]

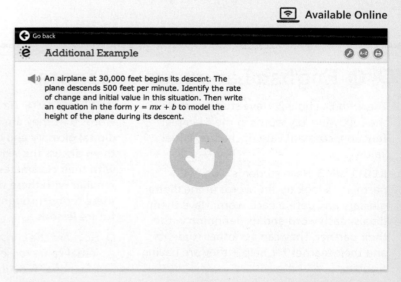

◁ Go back

ё Additional Example

🔊 An airplane at 30,000 feet begins its descent. The plane descends 500 feet per minute. Identify the rate of change and initial value in this situation. Then write an equation in the form $y = mx + b$ to model the height of the plane during its descent.

Answer: Rate of change: -500 ft/min; initial value: 30,000 ft; $y = -500x + 30,000$

Practice & Problem Solving

Available Online

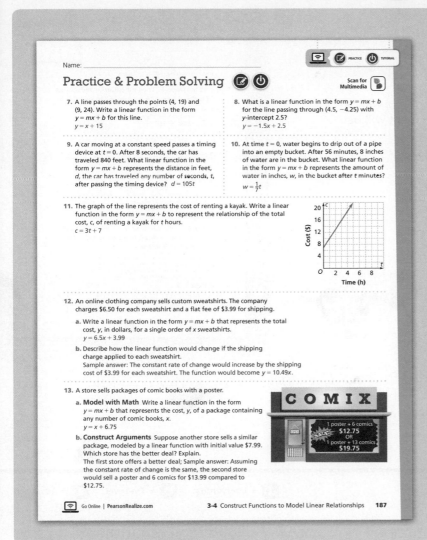

Name: _____

Practice & Problem Solving

Scan for Multimedia

7. A line passes through the points (4, 19) and (9, 24). Write a linear function in the form $y = mx + b$ for this line.
$y = x + 15$

8. What is a linear function in the form $y = mx + b$ for the line passing through (4.5, −4.25) with y-intercept 2.5?
$y = −1.5x + 2.5$

9. A car moving at a constant speed passes a timing device at $t = 0$. After 8 seconds, the car has traveled 840 feet. What linear function in the form $y = mx + b$ represents the distance in feet, d, the car has traveled any number of seconds, t, after passing the timing device? $d = 105t$

10. At time $t = 0$, water begins to drip out of a pipe into an empty bucket. After 56 minutes, 8 inches of water are in the bucket. What linear function in the form $y = mx + b$ represents the amount of water in inches, w, in the bucket after t minutes?
$w = \frac{1}{7}t$

11. The graph of the line represents the cost of renting a kayak. Write a linear function in the form $y = mx + b$ to represent the relationship of the total cost, c, of renting a kayak for t hours.
$c = 3t + 7$

12. An online clothing company sells custom sweatshirts. The company charges $6.50 for each sweatshirt and a flat fee of $3.99 for shipping.

a. Write a linear function in the form $y = mx + b$ that represents the total cost, y, in dollars, for a single order of x sweatshirts.
$y = 6.5x + 3.99$

b. Describe how the linear function would change if the shipping charge applied to each sweatshirt.
Sample answer: The constant rate of change would increase by the shipping cost of $3.99 for each sweatshirt. The function would become $y = 10.49x$.

13. A store sells packages of comic books with a poster.

a. **Model with Math** Write a linear function in the form $y = mx + b$ that represents the cost, y, of a package containing any number of comic books, x.
$y = x + 6.75$

b. **Construct Arguments** Suppose another store sells a similar package, modeled by a linear function with initial value $7.99. Which store has the better deal? Explain.
The first store offers a better deal; Sample answer: Assuming the constant rate of change is the same, the second store would sell a poster and 6 comics for $13.99 compared to $12.75.

COMIX

1 poster + 6 comics
$12.75
OR
1 poster + 13 comics
$19.75

Go Online | PearsonRealize.com

3-4 Construct Functions to Model Linear Relationships   **187**

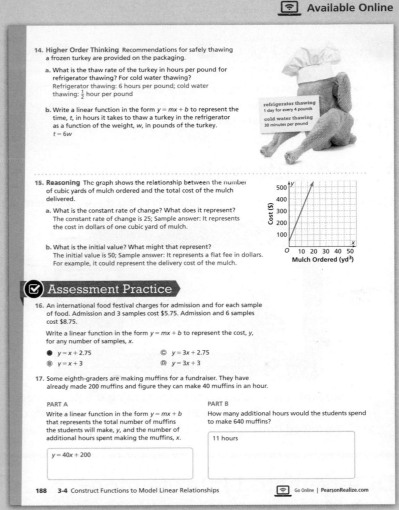

14. **Higher Order Thinking** Recommendations for safely thawing a frozen turkey are provided on the packaging.

a. What is the thaw rate of the turkey in hours per pound for refrigerator thawing? For cold water thawing?
Refrigerator thawing: 6 hours per pound; cold water thawing: $\frac{1}{2}$ hour per pound

b. Write a linear function in the form $y = mx + b$ to represent the time, t, in hours it takes to thaw a turkey in the refrigerator as a function of the weight, w, in pounds of the turkey.
$t = 6w$

refrigerator thawing
1 day for every 4 pounds

cold water thawing
30 minutes per pound

15. **Reasoning** The graph shows the relationship between the number of cubic yards of mulch ordered and the total cost of the mulch delivered.

a. What is the constant rate of change? What does it represent?
The constant rate of change is 25; Sample answer: It represents the cost in dollars of one cubic yard of mulch.

b. What is the initial value? What might that represent?
The initial value is 50; Sample answer: It represents a flat fee in dollars. For example, it could represent the delivery cost of the mulch.

Assessment Practice

16. An international food festival charges for admission and for each sample of food. Admission and 3 samples cost $5.75. Admission and 6 samples cost $8.75.

Write a linear function in the form $y = mx + b$ to represent the cost, y, for any number of samples, x.

● Ⓐ $y = x + 2.75$ Ⓒ $y = 3x + 2.75$
Ⓑ $y = x + 3$ Ⓓ $y = 3x + 3$

17. Some eighth-graders are making muffins for a fundraiser. They have already made 200 muffins and figure they can make 40 muffins in an hour.

PART A
Write a linear function in the form $y = mx + b$ that represents the total number of muffins the students will make, y, and the number of additional hours spent making the muffins, x.

$y = 40x + 200$

PART B
How many additional hours would the students spend to make 640 muffins?

11 hours

188   3-4 Construct Functions to Model Linear Relationships   Go Online | PearsonRealize.com

---

Error Intervention

ITEM 13 If students say that some comic books are $2.13 and others are $1.52, remind them that each total price given also includes the cost of a poster, and that each poster costs the same amount.

Q: What is the cost of the poster and what does this cost represent? [$6.75; the initial value]

Challenge

ITEM 14 Higher Order Thinking You can use this item to extend students' understanding of writing equations of linear functions from verbal descriptions.

Q: What is the rate of thawing a turkey in cold water in hours per pound? Explain. [0.5; Sample answer: 30 minutes = $\frac{1}{2}$ hour, 0.5 hours per pound]

Q: What equation can represent the time t in hours to thaw a turkey in cold water as a function of the weight in pounds w of the turkey? [Sample answer: $t = 0.5w$]

You may opt to have students complete the automatically scored Practice & Problem Solving items online.

Item Analysis

Example	Items	DOK
1	11	2
2	7, 8, 9, 10, 16, 17	2
	12, 13, 14	3
3	15	2

PearsonRealize.com

Assess   Tutorials   Worksheets

Lesson Quiz

RtI Use the student scores on the Lesson Quiz to prescribe differentiated assignments.

I Intervention 0–3 Points   **O** On-Level 5 Points   **A** Advanced 6 Points

You may opt to have students take the Lesson Quiz online. The Lesson Quiz will be automatically scored and appropriate remediation, practice, or enrichment will be assigned based on student performance.

Video Tutorials

Students can access instructional tutorials using the **Virtual Nerd app**.

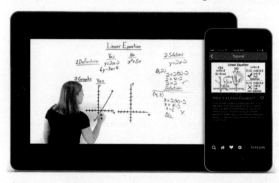

 Students can also access the videos using the BouncePages app to scan exercise pages marked with this icon. Students can download both apps for free in their mobile devices' app store.

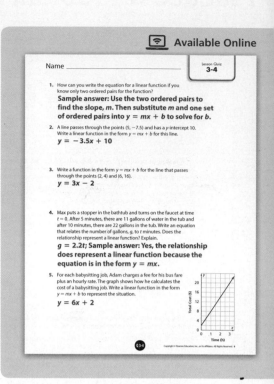

Available Online

Name _____   Lesson Quiz **3-4**

1. How can you write the equation for a linear function if you know only two ordered pairs for the function?
   Sample answer: Use the two ordered pairs to find the slope, m. Then substitute m and one set of ordered pairs into $y = mx + b$ to solve for b.

2. A line passes through the points (5, −7.5) and has a y-intercept 10. Write a linear function in the form $y = mx + b$ for this line.
   $y = -3.5x + 10$

3. Write a function in the form $y = mx + b$ for the line that passes through the points (2, 4) and (6, 16).
   $y = 3x - 2$

4. Max puts a stopper in the bathtub and turns on the faucet at time $t = 0$. After 5 minutes, there are 11 gallons of water in the tub and after 10 minutes, there are 22 gallons in the tub. Write an equation that relates the number of gallons, g, to t minutes. Does the relationship represent a linear function? Explain.
   $g = 2.2t$; **Sample answer: Yes, the relationship does represent a linear function because the equation is in the form $y = mx$.**

5. For each babysitting job, Adam charges a fee for his bus fare plus an hourly rate. The graph shows how he calculates the cost of a babysitting job. Write a linear function in the form $y = mx + b$ to represent the situation.
   $y = 6x + 2$

Differentiated Intervention

I = Intervention   **O** = On-Level   **A** = Advanced

Reteach to Build Understanding **I**

Provides scaffolded reteaching for the key lesson concepts

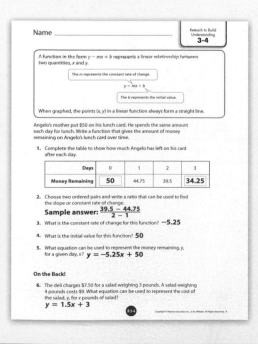

Name _____   Reteach to Build Understanding **3-4**

A function in the form $y = mx + b$ represents a linear relationship between two quantities, x and y.

The m represents the constant rate of change.

$y = mx + b$

The b represents the initial value.

When graphed, the points (x, y) in a linear function always form a straight line.

Angelo's mother put $50 on his lunch card. He spends the same amount each day for lunch. Write a function that gives the amount of money remaining on Angelo's lunch card over time.

1. Complete the table to show how much Angelo has left on his card after each day.

Days	0	1	2	3
Money Remaining	50	44.75	39.5	34.25

2. Choose two ordered pairs and write a ratio that can be used to find the slope or constant rate of change.
   Sample answer: $\frac{39.5 - 44.75}{2 - 1}$

3. What is the constant rate of change for this function? −5.25

4. What is the initial value for this function? 50

5. What equation can be used to represent the money remaining, y, for a given day, x? $y = -5.25x + 50$

On the Back!

6. The deli charges $7.50 for a salad weighing 3 pounds. A salad weighing 4 pounds costs $9. What equation can be used to represent the cost of the salad, y, for x pounds of salad?
   $y = 1.5x + 3$

Additional Vocabulary Support **I** **O**

Helps students develop and reinforce understanding of key terms and concepts.

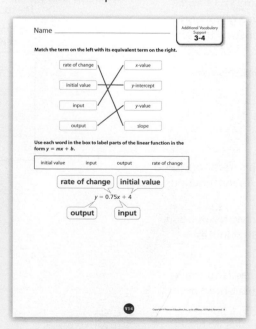

Name _____   Additional Vocabulary Support **3-4**

Match the term on the left with its equivalent term on the right.

rate of change — x-value
initial value — y-intercept
input — y-value
output — slope

Use each word in the box to label parts of the linear function in the form $y = mx + b$.

| initial value | input | output | rate of change |

rate of change   initial value
$y = 0.75x + 4$
output   input

Build Mathematical Literacy **I**

Provides support for struggling readers to build mathematical literacy.

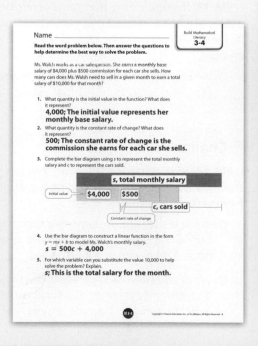

Name _____   Build Mathematical Literacy **3-4**

Read the word problem below. Then answer the questions to help determine the best way to solve the problem.

Ms. Walsh works as a car salesperson. She earns a monthly base salary of $4,000 plus $500 commission for each car she sells. How many cars does Ms. Walsh need to sell in a given month to earn a total salary of $10,000 for that month?

1. What quantity is the initial value in the function? What does it represent?
   4,000; The initial value represents her monthly base salary.

2. What quantity is the constant rate of change? What does it represent?
   500; The constant rate of change is the commission she earns for each car she sells.

3. Complete the bar diagram using s to represent the total monthly salary and c to represent the cars sold.

   s, total monthly salary
   Initial value | $4,000 | $500
   c, cars sold
   Constant rate of change

4. Use the bar diagram to construct a linear function in the form $y = mx + b$ to model Ms. Walsh's monthly salary.
   $s = 500c + 4,000$

5. For which variable can you substitute the value 10,000 to help solve the problem? Explain.
   s; This is the total salary for the month.

PearsonRealize.com

Practice | Worksheets | Math Tools | Math Games

Additional Practice

You may opt to have students complete the automatically scored Additional Practice items online.

Item Analysis

Example	Items	DOK
1	4, 5, 6, 7	2
2	8, 10, 11	2
3	1	1
	2, 3	2
	9	3

Available Online

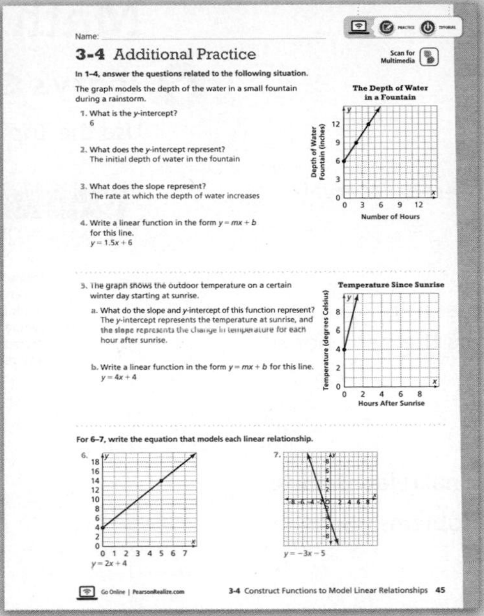
Name:

3-4 Additional Practice

Scan for Multimedia

In 1–4, answer the questions related to the following situation.

The graph models the depth of the water in a small fountain during a rainstorm.

1. What is the y-intercept?
   6
2. What does the y-intercept represent?
   The initial depth of water in the fountain
3. What does the slope represent?
   The rate at which the depth of water increases
4. Write a linear function in the form $y = mx + b$ for this line.
   $y = 1.5x + 6$

5. The graph shows the outdoor temperature on a certain winter day starting at sunrise.
   a. What do the slope and y-intercept of this function represent?
   The y-intercept represents the temperature at sunrise, and the slope represents the change in temperature for each hour after sunrise.
   b. Write a linear function in the form $y = mx + b$ for this line.
   $y = 4x + 4$

For 6–7, write the equation that models each linear relationship.

6. $y = 2x + 4$

7. $y = -3x - 5$

Go Online | PearsonRealize.com   3-4 Construct Functions to Model Linear Relationships 45

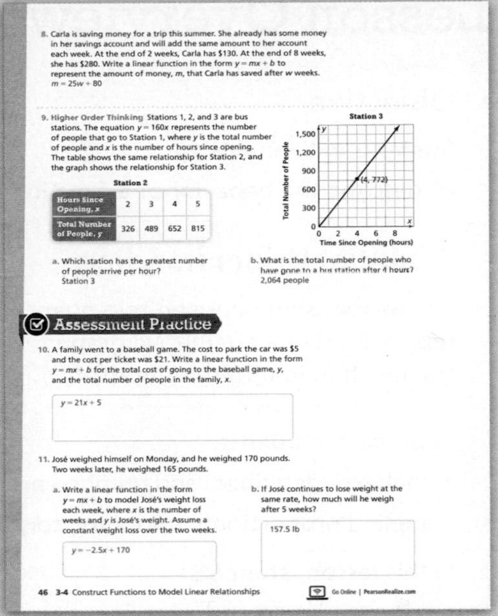
8. Carla is saving money for a trip this summer. She already has some money in her savings account and will add the same amount to her account each week. At the end of 2 weeks, Carla has $130. At the end of 8 weeks, she has $280. Write a linear function in the form $y = mx + b$ to represent the amount of money, m, that Carla has saved after w weeks.
   $m = 25w + 80$

9. **Higher Order Thinking** Stations 1, 2, and 3 are bus stations. The equation $y = 160x$ represents the number of people that go to Station 1, where y is the total number of people and x is the number of hours since opening. The table shows the same relationship for Station 2, and the graph shows the relationship for Station 3.

Station 2

Hours Since Opening, x	2	3	4	5
Total Number of People, y	326	489	652	815

   a. Which station has the greatest number of people arrive per hour?
   Station 3
   b. What is the total number of people who have gone to a bus station after 4 hours?
   2,064 people

Assessment Practice

10. A family went to a baseball game. The cost to park the car was $5 and the cost per ticket was $21. Write a linear function in the form $y = mx + b$ for the total cost of going to the baseball game, y, and the total number of people in the family, x.
    $y = 21x + 5$

11. José weighed himself on Monday, and he weighed 170 pounds. Two weeks later, he weighed 165 pounds.
    a. Write a linear function in the form $y = mx + b$ to model José's weight loss each week, where x is the number of weeks and y is José's weight. Assume a constant weight loss over the two weeks.
    $y = -2.5x + 170$
    b. If José continues to lose weight at the same rate, how much will he weigh after 5 weeks?
    157.5 lb

46 3-4 Construct Functions to Model Linear Relationships   Go Online | PearsonRealize.com

Differentiated Intervention

I = Intervention O = On-Level A = Advanced

Enrichment O A

Presents engaging problems and activities that extend the lesson concepts.

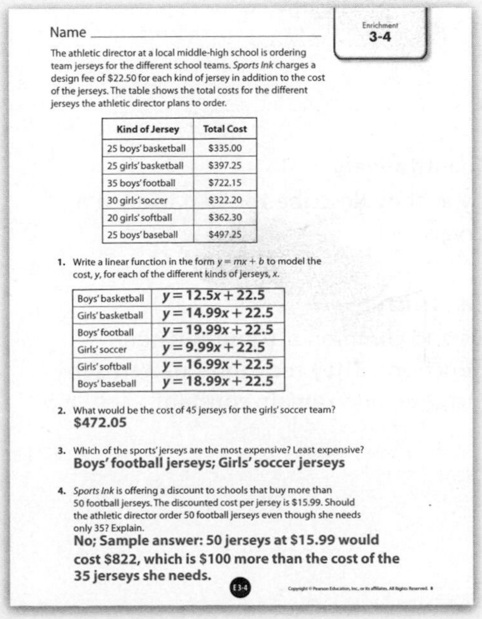
Name

Enrichment 3-4

The athletic director at a local middle-high school is ordering team jerseys for the different school teams. *Sports Ink* charges a design fee of $22.50 for each kind of jersey in addition to the cost of the jerseys. The table shows the total costs for the different jerseys the athletic director plans to order.

Kind of Jersey	Total Cost
25 boys' basketball	$335.00
25 girls' basketball	$397.25
35 boys' football	$722.15
30 girls' soccer	$322.20
20 girls' softball	$362.30
25 boys' baseball	$497.25

1. Write a linear function in the form $y = mx + b$ to model the cost, y, for each of the different kinds of jerseys, x.

Boys' basketball	$y = 12.5x + 22.5$
Girls' basketball	$y = 14.99x + 22.5$
Boys' football	$y = 19.99x + 22.5$
Girls' soccer	$y = 9.99x + 22.5$
Girls' softball	$y = 16.99x + 22.5$
Boys' baseball	$y = 18.99x + 22.5$

2. What would be the cost of 45 jerseys for the girls' soccer team?
   $472.05
3. Which of the sports' jerseys are the most expensive? Least expensive?
   Boys' football jerseys; Girls' soccer jerseys
4. *Sports Ink* is offering a discount to schools that buy more than 50 football jerseys. The discounted cost per jersey is $15.99. Should the athletic director order 50 football jerseys even though she needs only 35? Explain.
   No; Sample answer: 50 jerseys at $15.99 would cost $822, which is $100 more than the cost of the 35 jerseys she needs.

E 3-4

Copyright © Pearson Education, Inc., or its affiliates. All Rights Reserved.

Math Tools and Games I O A

Offers additional activities and games to build understanding and fluency.

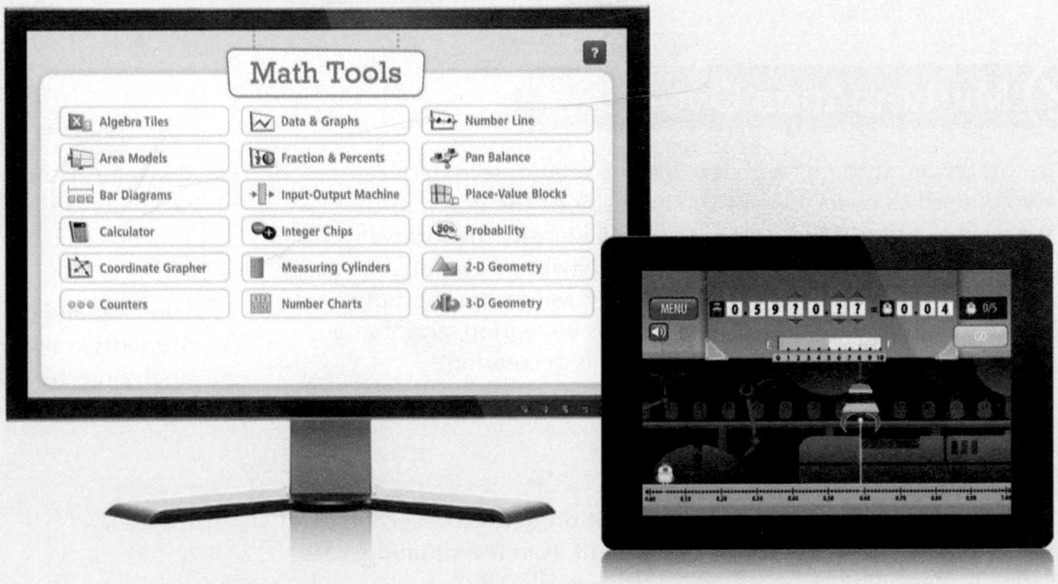

Video   Activity

Lesson 3-5

Intervals of Increase and Decrease

Lesson Overview

FOCUS

Objective

Students will be able to:

✔ describe the behavior of a function in different intervals.

Essential Understanding

The relationship between two quantities on a graph can be represented in a qualitative graph that shows the behavior of the function in different intervals.

COHERENCE

In Grade 7, students:

• analyzed, described, and graphed proportional relationships.

• applied proportional reasoning to solve problems.

In this lesson, students:

• interpret linear and nonlinear graphs.

• describe the relationship between two quantities.

Later in this topic, students will:

• sketch the graph of linear and nonlinear functions.

RIGOR

This lesson emphasizes a blend of **conceptual understanding** and **application.**

• Students understand that the relationship between two variables can be represented in a qualitative graph.

• Students apply this understanding to analyze and describe the relationship between two quantities.

Math Anytime

Today's Challenge

Use the Topic 3 problems any time during this topic.

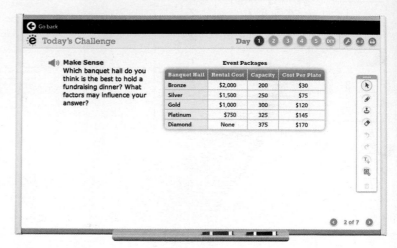

Watch the **Listen and Look For Video** for strategies and habits of mind to look for as students complete work on this lesson.

☑ Mathematics Overview

In this lesson, students will describe the relationship between two quantities by looking at the behavior of the graph of the function in different intervals. They will identify the intervals in a qualitative graph and describe the behavior of the function as increasing, decreasing, or constant. They will recognize that a positive slope means that the function is increasing, and that a negative slope means that the function is decreasing.

Applying Math Practices

Make Sense and Persevere

Students make sense of a problem situation to sketch a graph of the relationship between the two quantities in the situation.

Reason Abstractly and Quantitatively

Students reason abstractly as they describe the behavior of a function in different intervals.

Look For and Make Use of Structure

Students look for patterns and common attributes when analyzing the graphs of functions. They recognize patterns in intervals that increase, decrease, and remain constant.

Solve & Discuss It!

Reason Abstractly and Quantitatively As students work through the *Solve & Discuss It*, listen and look for students who understand the relationship between the two quantities and describe the relationship.

Before [WHOLE CLASS]

ETP 1 Implement Tasks that Promote Reasoning and Problem Solving

Q: How are the two routes different? [Sample answer: One route is hilly but a shorter distance, the other is flat and a longer distance.]

Q: What are the two relationships you're asked to consider? [Distance and time, speed and time]

2 Build Understanding

Q: What will likely happen to Martin's speed on the hill route? On the flat route? [Sample answer: Martin's speed on the hill route will decrease as he goes up the hill and increase as he goes down. His speed on the flat route can remain fairly constant.]

During [SMALL GROUP]

ETP 3 Support Productive Struggle in Learning Mathematics

Q: How could he travel the two distances in the same amount of time? [Sample answer: His rate of speed for the hill route would be less than for the longer flat route.]

Q: How would you describe his rate of speed during the duration of each trip? [Sample answer: For the shorter distance he had a constant rate of speed, then it decreased for a longer period of time as he went more slowly. It then increased for a short period of time, and then became constant again. For the longer trip it was constant.]

After [WHOLE CLASS]

ETP 4 Facilitate Meaningful Mathematical Discourse

Ask students to share their solutions. If needed, project Sally's and Joziah's work and ask:

Q: Which solution do you find more useful? Explain. [Sample answer: I find Joziah's solution more useful because it is more visual.]

5 Transition to Visual Learning

Q: What might a graph of the distance traveled over time while biking the hilly portion of the hill route look like? [Sample answer: A line with a shallow positive slope representing the uphill portion, changing to a steeper positive slope representing the downhill portion.]

6 Extension for Early Finishers

Q: Suppose that there is a tunnel that passes through the hill. Should Martin take that route? Explain. [Sample answer: Yes; Using the tunnel would be shorter. He wouldn't have to go up the hill or around the hill.]

Analyze Student Work

📶 Available Online

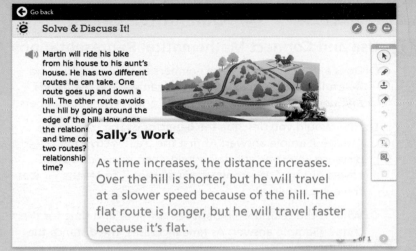

Sally's Work

As time increases, the distance increases. Over the hill is shorter, but he will travel at a slower speed because of the hill. The flat route is longer, but he will travel faster because it's flat.

Sally analyzes the given information for each route and interprets the relationships. Then she describes the results.

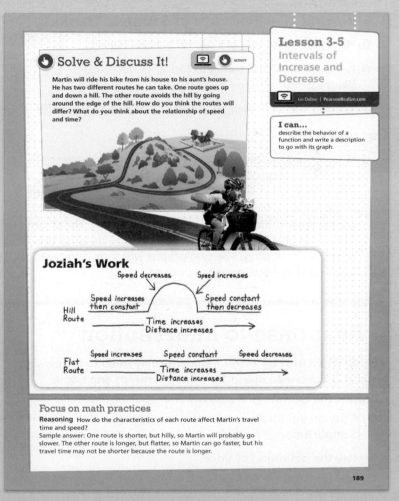

Joziah uses diagrams to analyze each situation and describe the relationships.

ETP ## Establish Mathematics Goals to Focus Learning

Engage students in a discussion about the *Essential Question*. Make sure they understand that they can use a qualitative graph to describe the relationship between two quantities.

 EXAMPLE 1 ◉ Interpret a Qualitative Graph

ETP ## Use and Connect Mathematical Representations

Q: Does a graph need to have numbers to be descriptive and helpful? [Sample answer: No; You can still see the trends and understand the behaviors on a graph without numbers.]

Q: How would you describe the behavior of the train in the graph? [Sample answer: At first the train is covering distance at a constant slow speed, then it speeds up and covers distance at a constant speed that is faster than it was traveling previously.]

Q: What is the relationship between distance and time for the train? [Sample answer: As time increases, the distance the train has traveled increases.]

✅ Try It!

ETP ## Elicit and Use Evidence of Student Thinking

Q: How many intervals are on the graph? [One]

Q: Is the speed of the train increasing or decreasing? [Decreasing]

Q: What is the train's speed at the end of the interval? [0]

Convince Me!

Q: How would the distance over time graph compare to the speed over time graph while the speed is decreasing? [Sample answer: The distance over time graph has a positive slope because the train is still increasing the distance it has traveled even though its speed has decreased. The speed over time graph will have a negative slope because the speed is decreasing. The two graphs will look different because they have opposite slopes.]

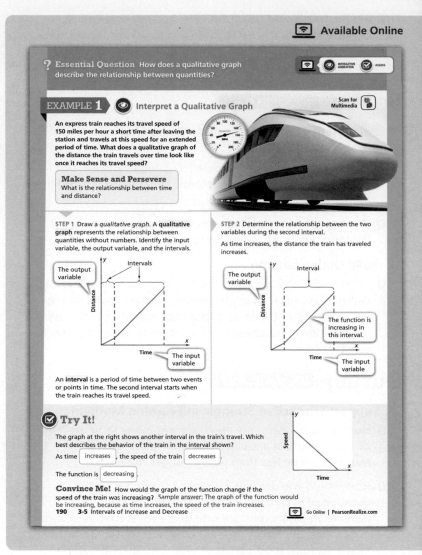

 Students can access the *Visual Learning Animation Plus* by using the **BouncePages** app to scan this page. Students can download the app for free in their mobile devices' app store.

 # Response to Intervention

USE WITH EXAMPLE 1 Some students may need to review the connection between proportional relationships and slope.

• Review the definition of *proportional relationships*.

Q: Write an equation representing a proportional relationship. [Sample answer: $y = \frac{1}{2}x$]

• Review the definition of *slope*.

Q: What is the slope of each of the following linear functions? $y = -7x - 4$, $y = 17x + 8$, $y = \frac{1}{3}x$ [-7, 17, $\frac{1}{3}$]

 # Enrichment

USE WITH EXAMPLE 3 Challenge advanced students to sketch a graph that represents the following scenario: Maxie rides the commuter rail from her house to work. It makes four stops along the way to pick up additional passengers.

Q: Sketch a graph of this scenario showing the relationship between distance and time. [Check students' graphs.]

Q: What is the minimum number of intervals the graph could have? [Nine]

Q: How many constant intervals? Explain. [Sample answer: Four; there are 4 times that the train stops to pick up passengers; therefore, the train is not moving any distance at those points.]

EXAMPLE 2 Interpret the Graph of a Nonlinear Function

ETP Pose Purposeful Questions

Q: How do you know that the graph is nonlinear? [Sample answer: The graph is not a straight line, so it cannot be the graph of a linear function.]

Q: Describe how the speed of the ball and time relate. [Sample answers: The speed of the ball is fast at first and slows down as it reaches its maximum height. Then the speed of the ball starts to increase as the ball descends to the ground.]

Try It!

ETP Elicit and Use Evidence of Student Thinking

Q: When is an interval on a graph constant? Explain. [Sample answer: As the *x*-values increase, the *y*-values remain the same.]

EXAMPLE 3 Describe the Relationship of Quantities

ETP Pose Purposeful Questions

Q: Is this function shown on the graph linear or nonlinear? Explain. [Sample answer: Nonlinear; The graph is not one continuous straight line.]

Q: What are the different behaviors represented on the graph? [Sample answer: At different intervals, the function increases, decreases, and remains constant.]

Try It!

ETP Elicit and Use Evidence of Student Thinking

Q: How would the scenario need to change if the *y*-value changed to speed instead of distance? [Sample answer: Jenny rides her bicycle faster and faster, then rides at a constant speed for a while. She speeds up again, then once again rides at a constant speed. She slows down to a stop.]

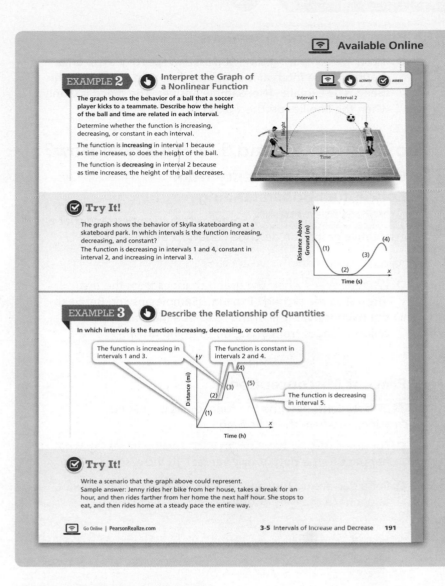

ADDITIONAL EXAMPLES

For additional examples go to PearsonRealize.com.

English Language Learners

BEGINNING Use with Example 1. Discuss the term *interval* with the students.

Q: What prefix is part of the word *interval*? [Inter]

Q: What does the prefix inter mean? [Between]

Q: How does knowing this help define interval? [An interval is a period of time between two points of time or events.]

INTERMEDIATE Have students work with partners. Have them draw a graph of a relationship that is increasing during an interval. Have them draw a graph of a relationship that is decreasing during an interval.

Q: Describe the slope of the graph that is increasing. [The slope is positive.]

Q: Describe the slope of the graph that is decreasing. [The slope is negative.]

ADVANCED Have students work with partners to draw a graph that shows the relationship between two quantities is increasing and one that shows the relationship is decreasing in an interval.

Q: What relationship might the graph with an increasing interval describe? [Sample answer: The speed of an airplane over time as it takes off.]

Q: What relationship might the graph with a decreasing interval describe? [Sample answer: The speed of an airplane over time as it makes a landing.]

KEY CONCEPT

ETP **Pose Purposeful Questions**

Q: If you are comparing time (*x*-axis) and speed (*y*-axis) on a graph and the interval is constant, does that mean that the speed is 0? Explain. [No; Sample answer: The speed is 0 only when the line lies on the *x*-axis.]

Do You Understand/Do You Know How?

ETP **Build Procedural Fluency from Conceptual Understanding**

? Essential Question Students should understand that a qualitative graph can describe behaviors of a function.

ITEM 4

Q: What happens when the graph changes from the first interval to the second? Explain. [Sample answer: Between the two intervals the graph reaches a maximum, so the object changes from going up to going down.]

RtI **Prevent Misconceptions**

ITEM 3 If students describe the function as increasing or decreasing, ask them the following:

Q: For an increasing function, as each *x*-value increases, what happens to the output or *y*-values? [It increases.]

Q: For a decreasing function, as each *x*-value increases, what happens to the output or *y*-values? [It decreases.]

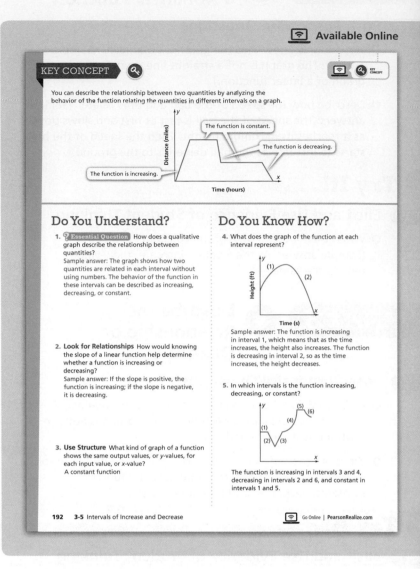

ADDITIONAL EXAMPLE 2

Remind students that a graph helps to identify intervals in which the function increases, decreases, or remains constant. A graph also helps to identify maximum and minimum values.

Help students understand that a maximum occurs between an increasing interval and a decreasing interval, and a minimum occurs between a decreasing interval and an increasing interval.

Q: How does a function behave in an increasing interval? [Sample answer: The graph looks like it is climbing up from the bottom left to the top right of the interval.]

Q: How does a function behave in a decreasing interval? [Sample answer: The graph looks like it is coming down from the top left to the bottom right of the interval.]

Q: How does a function behave at a maximum? At a minimum? [Sample answer: At a maximum, the graph hits the highest point. At a minimum, the graph hits the lowest point.]

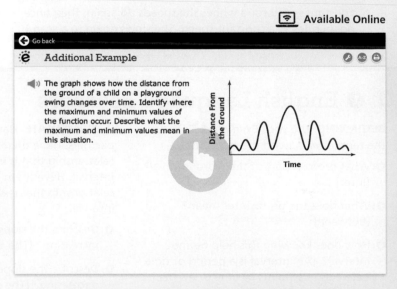

Answer: The maximum represents the highest point of the swing. The minimum represent the lowest point of the swing.

Practice | Tutorials | Math Tools

Practice & Problem Solving

Available Online

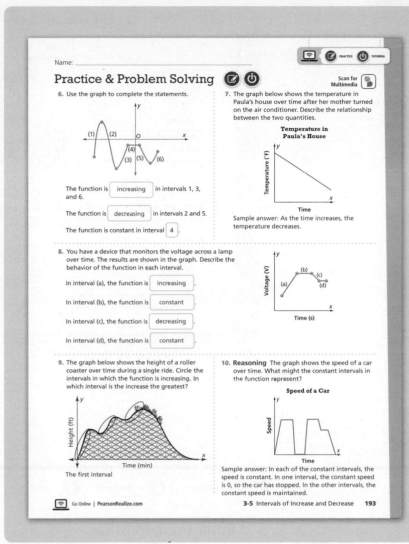

Name: _____

Practice & Problem Solving

Scan for Multimedia

6. Use the graph to complete the statements.

The function is [increasing] in intervals 1, 3, and 6.

The function is [decreasing] in intervals 2 and 5.

The function is constant in interval [4].

7. The graph below shows the temperature in Paula's house over time after her mother turned on the air conditioner. Describe the relationship between the two quantities.

Temperature in Paula's House

Sample answer: As the time increases, the temperature decreases.

8. You have a device that monitors the voltage across a lamp over time. The results are shown in the graph. Describe the behavior of the function in each interval.

In interval (a), the function is [increasing].

In interval (b), the function is [constant].

In interval (c), the function is [decreasing].

In interval (d), the function is [constant].

9. The graph below shows the height of a roller coaster over time during a single ride. Circle the intervals in which the function is increasing. In which interval is the increase the greatest?

The first interval

10. **Reasoning** The graph shows the speed of a car over time. What might the constant intervals in the function represent?

Speed of a Car

Sample answer: In each of the constant intervals, the speed is constant. In one interval, the constant speed is 0, so the car has stopped. In the other intervals, the constant speed is maintained.

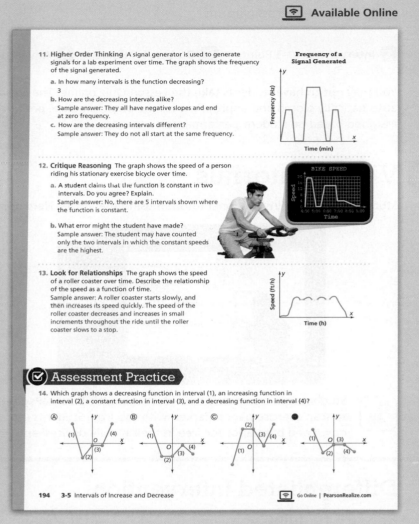

11. **Higher Order Thinking** A signal generator is used to generate signals for a lab experiment over time. The graph shows the frequency of the signal generated.

a. In how many intervals is the function decreasing?
   3

b. How are the decreasing intervals alike?
   Sample answer: They all have negative slopes and end at zero frequency.

c. How are the decreasing intervals different?
   Sample answer: They do not all start at the same frequency.

Frequency of a Signal Generated

12. **Critique Reasoning** The graph shows the speed of a person riding his stationary exercise bicycle over time.

a. A student claims that the function is constant in two intervals. Do you agree? Explain.
   Sample answer: No, there are 5 intervals shown where the function is constant.

b. What error might the student have made?
   Sample answer: The student may have counted only the two intervals in which the constant speeds are the highest.

13. **Look for Relationships** The graph shows the speed of a roller coaster over time. Describe the relationship of the speed as a function of time.
   Sample answer: A roller coaster starts slowly, and then increases its speed quickly. The speed of the roller coaster decreases and increases in small increments throughout the ride until the roller coaster slows to a stop.

✓ Assessment Practice

14. Which graph shows a decreasing function in interval (1), an increasing function in interval (2), a constant function in interval (3), and a decreasing function in interval (4)?

Ⓐ   Ⓑ   Ⓒ   ●

Go Online | PearsonRealize.com   3-5 Intervals of Increase and Decrease   193

194   3-5 Intervals of Increase and Decrease   Go Online | PearsonRealize.com

---

🏆 Challenge

ITEM 11 Higher Order Thinking You can use this item to extend students' understanding of intervals on a graph and what they represent.

Q: How many increasing intervals are on the graph? How are they alike? [3; Sample answer: They all have positive slopes and start at a frequency of 0.]

Q: Are there any constant intervals and what do they mean? [Yes; Sample answer: These five intervals represent the period of time when the frequency of the signal remains the same.]

🔴 Error Intervention

ITEM 12 Critique Reasoning Help students understand that there are more than two constant intervals in the graph. Review what a constant interval is and how it is represented on the graph.

Q: What is true of the y-values in a constant interval? [The y-values are all the same.]

You may opt to have students complete the automatically scored Practice & Problem Solving items online.

Item Analysis

Example	Items	DOK
1	7	1
2	9	1
	6	2
3	8, 14	1
	10, 11, 12, 13	2

PearsonRealize.com

Assess   Tutorials   Worksheets

☑ Lesson Quiz

Use the student scores on the Lesson Quiz to prescribe differentiated assignments.

I Intervention 0–3 Points   **O** On-Level 4 Points   **A** Advanced 5 Points

You may opt to have students take the Lesson Quiz online. The Lesson Quiz will be automatically scored and appropriate remediation, practice, or enrichment will be assigned based on student performance.

⏻ Video Tutorials

Students can access instructional tutorials using the **Virtual Nerd app**.

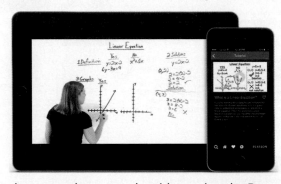

Students can also access the videos using the **BouncePages app** to scan exercise pages marked with this icon. Students can download both apps for free in their mobile devices' app store.

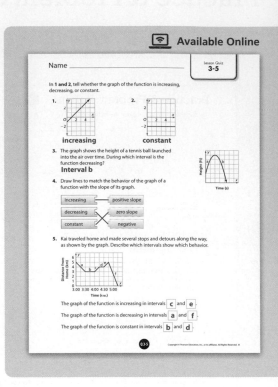

Differentiated Intervention

I = Intervention   **O** = On-Level   **A** = Advanced

Reteach to Build Understanding **I**

Provides scaffolded reteaching for the key lesson concepts.

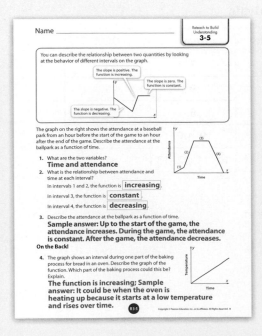

Additional Vocabulary Support **I** **O**

Helps students develop and reinforce understanding of key terms and concepts.

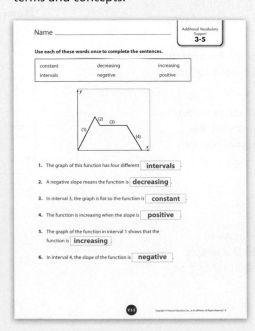

Build Mathematical Literacy **I**

Provides support for struggling readers to build mathematical literacy.

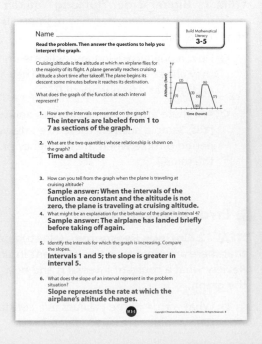

Additional Practice

You may opt to have students complete the automatically scored Additional Practice items online.

Item Analysis

Example	Items	DOK
1	2	2
	1	1
2	4, 6	2
3	3, 5, 8	2
	7	3

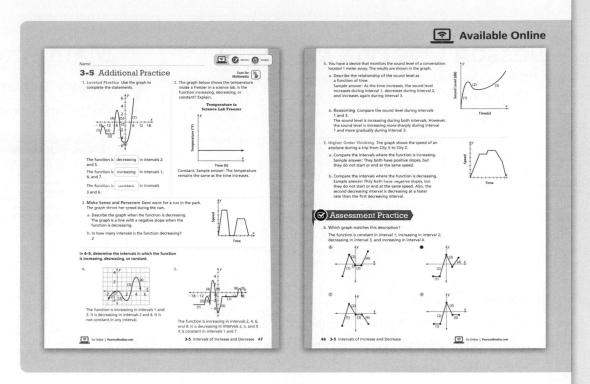

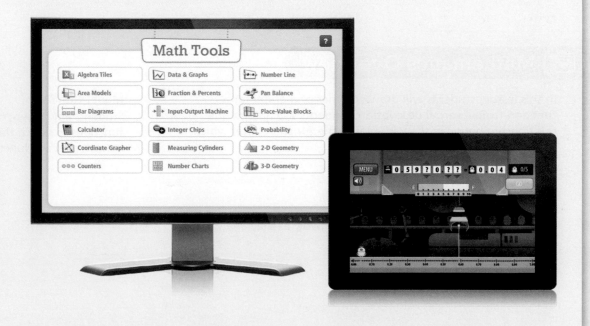

Differentiated Intervention

I = Intervention   **O** = On-Level   **A** = Advanced

Enrichment O A

Presents engaging problems and activities that extend the lesson concepts.

Math Tools and Games I O A

Offers additional activities and games to build understanding and fluency.

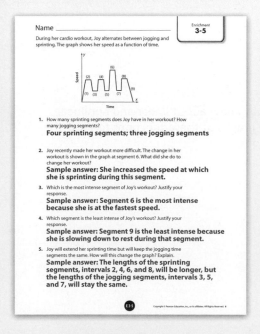

Lesson 3-6
Sketch Functions from Verbal Descriptions

Lesson Overview

<table>
<tr><td rowspan="2">FOCUS</td></tr>
<tr></tr>
</table>

Objectives

Students will be able to:

✔ draw a sketch of a graph for a function that has been described verbally.

✔ analyze and interpret the sketch of a graph of a function.

Essential Understanding

Understanding the behavior of a function in different intervals allows for a sketch of the qualitative graph of the function.

In Grade 7, students:

• graphed solutions of equations and inequalities.

• interpreted graphs of equations and inequalities

In this lesson, students:

• sketch the graphs of linear and nonlinear functions.

• analyze the sketches of linear and nonlinear functions.

Later in this grade, students will:

• analyze and solve systems of linear equations by graphing.

This lesson emphasizes a blend of **conceptual understanding** and **application**.

• Students understand that a qualitative graph can represent the relationship between two quantities in a function.

• Students apply this understanding as they sketch qualitative graphs of relationships.

(Left margin labels: FOCUS, COHERENCE, RIGOR)

Math Anytime

Today's Challenge

Use the Topic 3 problems any time during this topic.

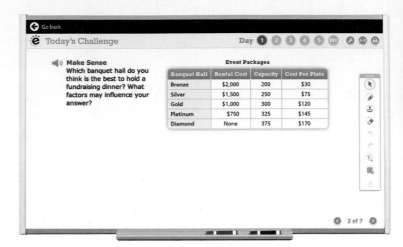

Watch the **Listen and Look For Video** for strategies and habits of mind to look for as students complete work on this lesson.

Mathematics Overview

In this lesson, students will draw sketches of a graph for a function from a verbal description. Students will analyze the relationship between the variables in the function, after which they sketch the graph of the function.

Applying Math Practices

Reason Abstractly and Quantitatively
Students reason abstractly and quantitatively as they analyze the relationship between two quantities.

Model with Math
Students apply what they know about linear and nonlinear functions to sketch the graphs of these functions to show the behaviors of the functions.

STEP 1 | Develop: Problem-Based Learning

15-20 min

Activity

Solve & Discuss It!

Construct Arguments As students work through the *Explain It*, listen and look for students who construct a valid argument to support their position.

Before [WHOLE CLASS]

ETP **1 Implement Tasks that Promote Reasoning and Problem Solving**

   Q: What is the graph showing? [Sample answer: Daily oil consumption in different countries]

2 Build Understanding

   Q: Describe the oil consumption in the United States from 2000 to 2011. [Sample answer: It has remained fairly steady, but decreased slightly overall.]

During [SMALL GROUP]

ETP **3 Support Productive Struggle in Learning Mathematics**

   Q: In which country or continent has the oil consumption increased the most? Explain. [China; the line on the graph shows the greatest increase.]

   Q: Compare the world consumption of oil to the US consumption of oil. What might explain the difference? [Sample answer: World consumption of oil has increased, but U.S. and European consumption has remained steady and even decreased slightly.]

After [WHOLE CLASS]

ETP **4 Facilitate Meaningful Mathematical Discourse**

   Ask students to share their solutions. If needed, project Cameron's and Nathaniel's work and ask:

   Q: Do you agree with Cameron's argument? Explain. [Sample answer: I agree with Cameron that U.S. consumption has decreased only a little, not a lot.]

5 Transition to Visual Learning

   Q: How does this graph help you understand the relationship between oil consumption and time? Explain. [Sample answer: The lines show the trends.]

6 Extension for Early Finishers

   Q: How would the cost of oil affect oil consumption in these countries? Explain. [Sample answer: If the cost of oil increases, oil consumption will likely go down as people will not be able to afford to consume as much oil. If the cost decreases, oil consumption will likely increase.]

Analyze Student Work

Available Online

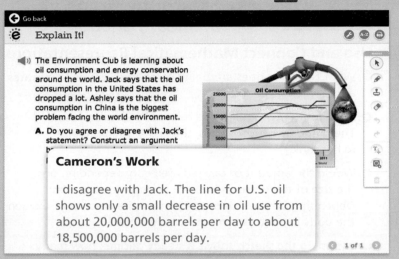

Cameron's Work

I disagree with Jack. The line for U.S. oil shows only a small decrease in oil use from about 20,000,000 barrels per day to about 18,500,000 barrels per day.

1 of 1

Cameron disagreed with Jack's statement. The line on the graph for U.S. oil consumption doesn't show a sharp decrease at any interval. It shows a slight decrease.

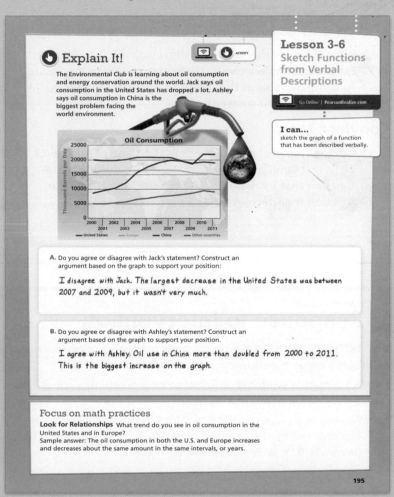

Nathaniel agreed with Ashley's statement. The graph shows that oil consumption in China increased consistently since 2000.

ETP **Establish Mathematics Goals to Focus Learning**

Engage students in a discussion about the *Essential Question*. Make sure they understand that the sketch of a graph will help show the relationship between two quantities of a function.

 EXAMPLE 1 Sketch the Graph of a Linear Function

ETP **Use and Connect Mathematical Representations**

Q: What two quantities are being compared? [Time in minutes and oxygen level in tank]

Q: How are the two quantities related? [Sample answer: The longer the diver swims, the less oxygen remains in her tank.]

Q: Would the amount of oxygen used vary depending on the size of the person? Explain. [Sample answer: Yes; Depending on the size of the person, the amount of oxygen the body needed per minute would differ.]

Q: Assuming the sketch shows a steady decline, how many minutes would the diver have underwater before the oxygen ran out? [44 minutes]

 Try It!

ETP **Elicit and Use Evidence of Student Thinking**

Q: What is the overall behavior shown on the sketch? Explain. [Sample answer: The sketch shows an increasing function because as the depth of the water increases, the water pressure increases.]

Convince Me!

Q: Are the slopes of these functions the same or different? Explain. [Sample answer: The slopes are different. The function that increases has a positive slope, while the function that decreases has a negative slope.]

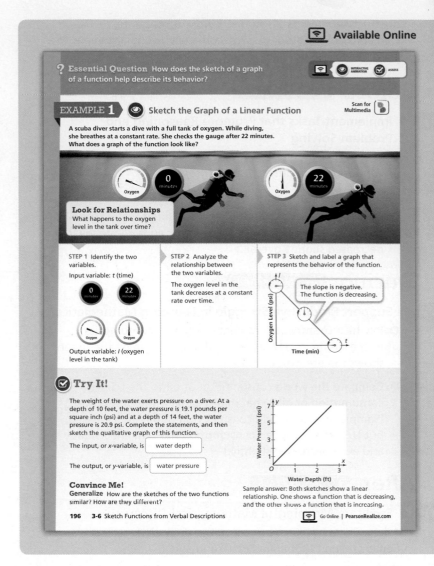

Available Online

? Essential Question How does the sketch of a graph of a function help describe its behavior?

EXAMPLE 1 Sketch the Graph of a Linear Function
Scan for Multimedia

A scuba diver starts a dive with a full tank of oxygen. While diving, she breathes at a constant rate. She checks the gauge after 22 minutes. What does a graph of the function look like?

Look for Relationships
What happens to the oxygen level in the tank over time?

STEP 1 Identify the two variables.
Input variable: *t* (time)
Output variable: *l* (oxygen level in the tank)

STEP 2 Analyze the relationship between the two variables.
The oxygen level in the tank decreases at a constant rate over time.

STEP 3 Sketch and label a graph that represents the behavior of the function.
The slope is negative. The function is decreasing.
Oxygen Level (psi) / Time (min)

Try It!

The weight of the water exerts pressure on a diver. At a depth of 10 feet, the water pressure is 19.1 pounds per square inch (psi) and at a depth of 14 feet, the water pressure is 20.9 psi. Complete the statements, and then sketch the qualitative graph of this function.

The input, or *x*-variable, is [water depth].

The output, or *y*-variable, is [water pressure].

Water Pressure (psi) / Water Depth (ft)

Convince Me!
Generalize How are the sketches of the two functions similar? How are they different?

Sample answer: Both sketches show a linear relationship. One shows a function that is decreasing, and the other shows a function that is increasing.

196 **3-6** Sketch Functions from Verbal Descriptions   Go Online | PearsonRealize.com

 Students can access the *Visual Learning Animation Plus* by using the **BouncePages app** to scan this page. Students can download the app for free in their mobile devices' app store.

 Response to Intervention

USE WITH EXAMPLE 1 Some students may need to review how to graph a linear function by plotting ordered pairs.

• Make sure that students understand how to identify the *x*-value and the *y*-value in an ordered pair.

Q: Name the *x*-values and the *y*-values in the linear function represented by the ordered pairs {(0, 4), (1, 6), (2, 8), (3, 10)}. [*x*-values: 0, 1, 2, 3; *y*-values: 4, 6, 8, 10]

• Make sure that students understand how to graph a set of ordered pairs representing a linear function on a coordinate plane.

Q: Graph the linear function represented by {(0, 4), (1, 6), (2, 8), (3, 10)} on a coordinate plane. [Check students' graphs.]

 Enrichment

USE WITH EXAMPLE 2 Challenge advanced students to write another description using words that could also be represented by the graph in Example 2.

Q: What could the *x*-axis represent? [Sample answer: Time]

Q: What could the *y*-axis represent? [Sample answer: Speed]

Q: Write a real-world situation that the graph in Example 2 could also represent using the variables identified above. [Sample answer: Monica rode her bike to the library. She picked up speed for a few minutes until she reached a good average speed and continued at that same speed for a few miles. Then she slowed down as she approached the library and came to a stop.]

EXAMPLE 2 Analyze the Sketch of a Nonlinear Function

ETP Pose Purposeful Questions

Q: What does the constant interval on the sketch represent? Explain. [Sample answer: The constant interval represents the time spent waiting or moving around at a constant altitude, before beginning the downhill descent.]

Q: What is Danika doing before and after the constant interval? [Sample answer: Before the constant interval, Danika is going up to the top of the ski run and after the constant interval, she is skiing down ski run.]

EXAMPLE 3 Sketch the Graph of a Nonlinear Function

ETP Pose Purposeful Questions

Q: How many intervals does the sketch show? Explain. [Sample answer: Three; The height of the javelin increases until it reaches its maximum height. It continues at this height for a short interval and then descends until it reaches the ground.]

Q: Can you sketch the graph without using ordered pairs? Explain. [Sample answer: Yes; You use the given information to make educated guesses on the height of the javelin from the time it was thrown to the time it hits the ground.]

☑ Try It!

ETP Elicit and Use Evidence of Student Thinking

Q: Why is the first increasing interval steeper than the second increasing interval on the sketch? Explain. [Sample answer: In the first increasing interval, Jackson rides his bike at a much faster rate than the second increasing interval, so the slope is steeper.]

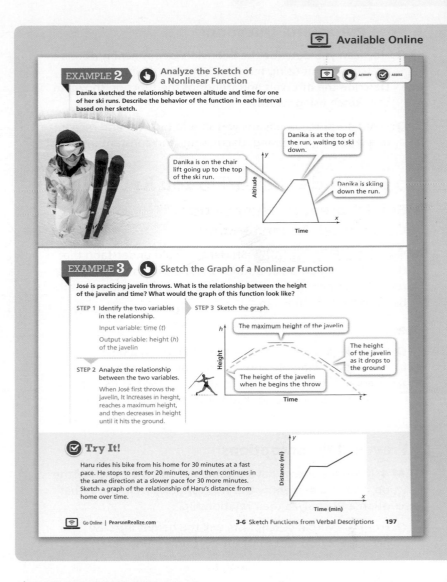

Available Online

EXAMPLE 2 Analyze the Sketch of a Nonlinear Function

Danika sketched the relationship between altitude and time for one of her ski runs. Describe the behavior of the function in each interval based on her sketch.

Danika is on the chair lift going up to the top of the ski run.

Danika is at the top of the run, waiting to ski down.

Danika is skiing down the run.

EXAMPLE 3 Sketch the Graph of a Nonlinear Function

José is practicing javelin throws. What is the relationship between the height of the javelin and time? What would the graph of this function look like?

STEP 1 Identify the two variables in the relationship.

Input variable: time (t)

Output variable: height (h) of the javelin

STEP 2 Analyze the relationship between the two variables.

When José first throws the javelin, It increases in height, reaches a maximum height, and then decreases in height until it hits the ground.

STEP 3 Sketch the graph.

The maximum height of the javelin

The height of the javelin as it drops to the ground

The height of the javelin when he begins the throw

☑ Try It!

Haru rides his bike from his home for 30 minutes at a fast pace. He stops to rest for 20 minutes, and then continues in the same direction at a slower pace for 30 more minutes. Sketch a graph of the relationship of Haru's distance from home over time.

Go Online | PearsonRealize.com   3-6 Sketch Functions from Verbal Descriptions 197

ADDITIONAL EXAMPLES

For additional examples go to PearsonRealize.com.

ELL English Language Learners

BEGINNING Complete Examples 2 and 3.

Q: How can you describe *intervals* in a graph?

Discuss with students the meaning of an interval. Have students work with partners to describe the sketch. Help students internalize key vocabulary by retelling information represented by the diagram.

Have partners work to complete the sentence: If the sketch of a graph goes up, the function is _____. If the sketch of a graph goes down, the function is _____.

INTERMEDIATE Complete Examples 2 and 3.

Have partners discuss and do the following.

Q: Describe the term *increasing interval* and sketch various examples.

Q: Describe the term *decreasing interval* and sketch various examples.

Q: Describe the term *constant interval* and sketch various examples.

Then have partners share their work with their classmates to internalize vocabulary supported by diagrams.

ADVANCED Complete Examples 2 and 3.

Have students work with partners to describe a real-world situation where there is a combination of two or more different intervals (increasing, decreasing, and/or constant). Students should use vocabulary correctly in their descriptions.

Then have partners sketch the graph of the real-world situation they described. Have them share their work with the class to internalize information represented by diagrams.

KEY CONCEPT

ETP **Pose Purposeful Questions**

Q: How can you describe the behaviors of a function from a sketch without using numbers? Explain. [Sample answer: Describe the intervals and trends of the function shown in the sketch using words.]

Q: What are some behaviors you should look for and recognize in a sketch? [Increasing, decreasing, and constant intervals]

Do You Understand/Do You Know How?

ETP **Build Procedural Fluency from Conceptual Understanding**

? Essential Question Students should understand that the sketch of a graph of a function is helpful in showing the relationship between the two variables and describing the behaviors of the function.

ITEM 3

Q: How can you tell from a sketch when a function is increasing? [Sample answer: Look at the graph at that interval. If the graph is a line segment, look at its slope. If the graph is a curve, look at the direction of the curve.]

⚠ **Prevent Misconceptions**

ITEM 4 If some students have trouble starting the sketch of the function, have them identify the two variables from the verbal description and analyze their relationship.

Q: From the verbal description, will the height increase, decrease, or remain constant over time? [Increase]

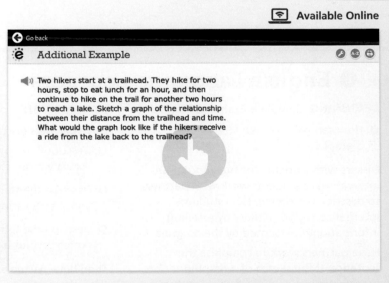

ADDITIONAL EXAMPLE 2 👆

Help students think about how the various intervals on a graph of a function compare as they sketch the graph from a verbal description.

Q: How can a sketch help you describe a function? Explain. [Sample answer: A sketch can show a graph's behavior during each interval and help you interpret each interval.]

Q: On the graph, how will the interval from the start of hiking to lunch compare with the interval during the lunch break? [Sample answer: The interval from the start of hiking to lunch will be linear (assuming they hike at a constant rate) with a positive slope. The interval during the lunch break will be linear with a zero slope (horizontal) and half the length of the first interval.]

Q: What would a decreasing interval on the graph of this function mean? Explain. [Sample answer: Since the graph is showing how the distance from the trailhead changes over time, a decreasing interval would mean that the hikers are getting closer to the trailhead rather than farther away.]

Answer: Check students' graphs; if the hikers receive a ride back to the trailhead the graph will end with a decreasing interval that is steeper than the increasing hiking intervals.

Practice & Problem Solving

Available Online

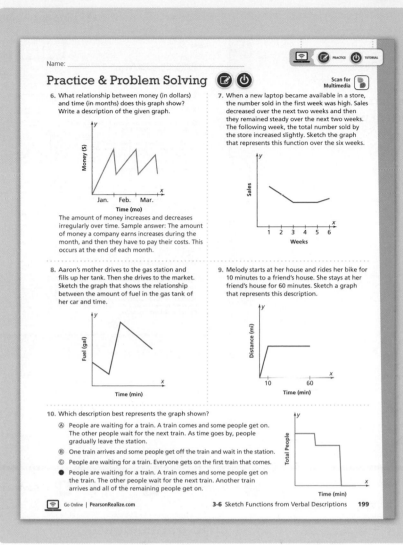

Name: _____

Practice & Problem Solving

Scan for Multimedia

6. What relationship between money (in dollars) and time (in months) does this graph show? Write a description of the given graph.

The amount of money increases and decreases irregularly over time. Sample answer: The amount of money a company earns increases during the month, and then they have to pay their costs. This occurs at the end of each month.

7. When a new laptop became available in a store, the number sold in the first week was high. Sales decreased over the next two weeks and then they remained steady over the next two weeks. The following week, the total number sold by the store increased slightly. Sketch the graph that represents this function over the six weeks.

8. Aaron's mother drives to the gas station and fills up her tank. Then she drives to the market. Sketch the graph that shows the relationship between the amount of fuel in the gas tank of her car and time.

9. Melody starts at her house and rides her bike for 10 minutes to a friend's house. She stays at her friend's house for 60 minutes. Sketch a graph that represents this description.

10. Which description best represents the graph shown?

Ⓐ People are waiting for a train. A train comes and some people get on. The other people wait for the next train. As time goes by, people gradually leave the station.

Ⓑ One train arrives and some people get off the train and wait in the station.

Ⓒ People are waiting for a train. Everyone gets on the first train that comes.

● People are waiting for a train. A train comes and some people get on the train. The other people wait for the next train. Another train arrives and all of the remaining people get on.

Go Online | PearsonRealize.com

3-6 Sketch Functions from Verbal Descriptions 199

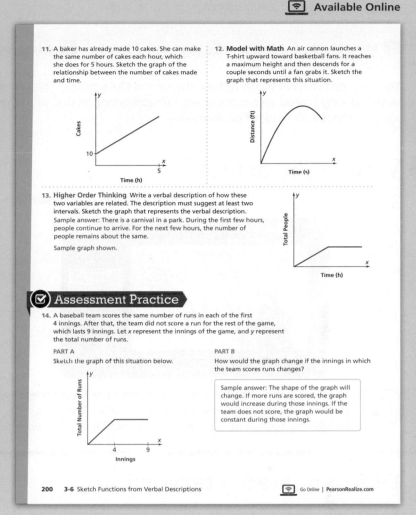

11. A baker has already made 10 cakes. She can make the same number of cakes each hour, which she does for 5 hours. Sketch the graph of the relationship between the number of cakes made and time.

12. **Model with Math** An air cannon launches a T-shirt upward toward basketball fans. It reaches a maximum height and then descends for a couple seconds until a fan grabs it. Sketch the graph that represents this situation.

13. **Higher Order Thinking** Write a verbal description of how these two variables are related. The description must suggest at least two intervals. Sketch the graph that represents the verbal description. Sample answer: There is a carnival in a park. During the first few hours, people continue to arrive. For the next few hours, the number of people remains about the same.

Sample graph shown.

☑ Assessment Practice

14. A baseball team scores the same number of runs in each of the first 4 innings. After that, the team did not score a run for the rest of the game, which lasts 9 innings. Let x represent the innings of the game, and y represent the total number of runs.

PART A
Sketch the graph of this situation below.

PART B
How would the graph change if the innings in which the team scores runs changes?

Sample answer: The shape of the graph will change. If more runs are scored, the graph would increase during those innings. If the team does not score, the graph would be constant during those innings.

200 3-6 Sketch Functions from Verbal Descriptions

Go Online | PearsonRealize.com

Error Intervention

ITEM 12 Model with Math If students confuse the input and output, review how to label the axes correctly.

Q: Which values or quantities represent the dependent variable? Explain. [Sample answer: The output (y-value) represents the dependent variable because the distance the T-shirt travels depends on the time.]

Challenge

ITEM 13 Higher Order Thinking You can use this item to extend students' understanding of using a verbal description to represent two variables in a real-world situation and to sketch the corresponding graph of the function.

Q: What are some real-world situations that you could use to represent an input variable and an output variable? [Sample answers: Distance and time, money and time, height and time]

Q: How would you sketch the graph without using numbers? [Sample answer: Look at the trends and behaviors in the verbal description and sketch the graph by estimating the values.]

You may opt to have students complete the automatically scored Practice & Problem Solving items online.

Item Analysis

Example	Items	DOK
1	11	2
2	6, 10	2
3	7, 8, 9, 12	2
	13, 14	3

PearsonRealize.com

Assess Tutorials Worksheets

Lesson Quiz

Use the student scores on the Lesson Quiz to prescribe differentiated assignments.

I Intervention 0–3 Points   **O** On-Level 4 Points   **A** Advanced 5 Points

You may opt to have students take the Lesson Quiz online. The Lesson Quiz will be automatically scored and appropriate remediation, practice, or enrichment will be assigned based on student performance.

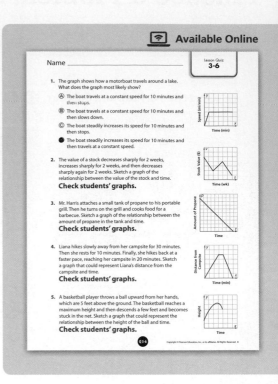

Video Tutorials

Students can access instructional tutorials using the **Virtual Nerd app**.

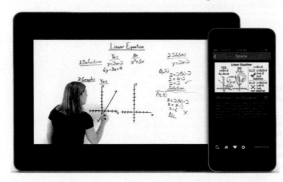

Students can also access the videos using the **BouncePages app** to scan exercise pages marked with this icon. Students can download both apps for free in their mobile devices' app store.

Differentiated Intervention

I = Intervention   **O** = On-Level   **A** = Advanced

Reteach to Build Understanding **I**

Provides scaffolded reteaching for the key lesson concepts.

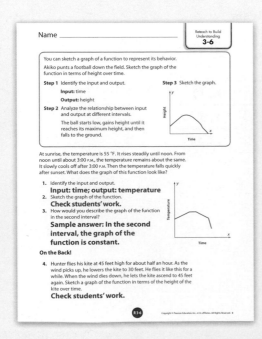

Additional Vocabulary Support **I** **O**

Helps students develop and reinforce understanding of key terms and concepts.

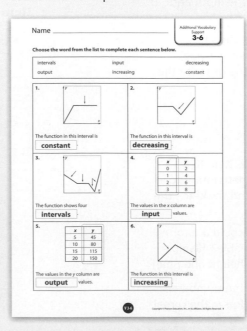

Build Mathematical Literacy **I**

Provides support for struggling readers to build mathematical literacy.

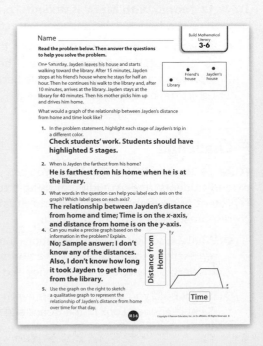

| Practice | Worksheets | Math Tools | Math Games |

Additional Practice

You may opt to have students complete the automatically scored Additional Practice items online.

Item Analysis

Example	Items	DOK
1	5, 6, 9	2
2	2, 3	2
	7	3
3	1	1
	4, 8	2

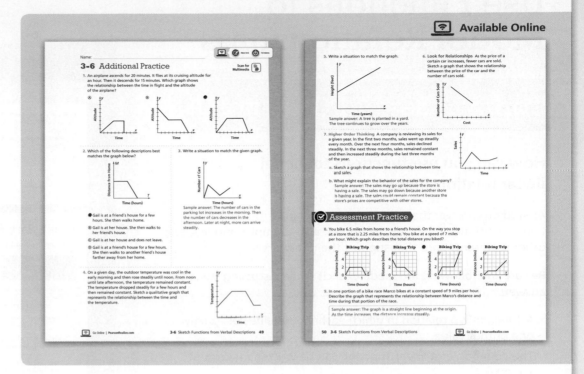

Differentiated Intervention

I = Intervention   **O** = On-Level   **A** = Advanced

Enrichment O A

Presents engaging problems and activities that extend the lesson concepts.

Math Tools and Games I O A

Offers additional activities and games to build understanding and fluency.

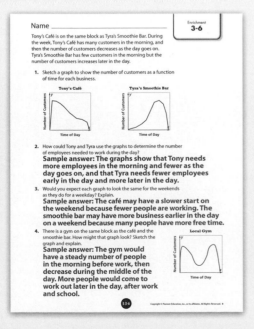

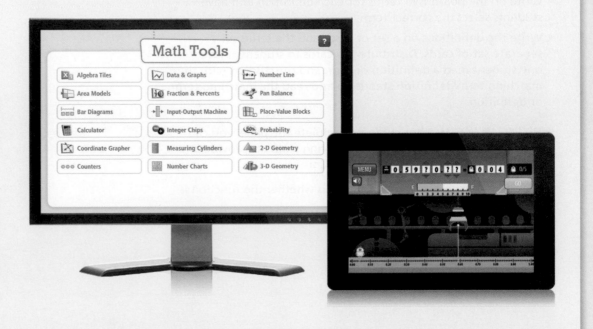

PearsonRealize.com

A-Z
Glossary

Use Functions to Model Relationships

? Topic Essential Question

How can you use functions to model linear relationships?

As students answer the **Essential Question** in writing, encourage them to include definitions, examples, non-examples, models, and other representations that support their answers.

Be sure the following are made explicit while discussing students' answers.

- A function is a relation in which each input value has exactly one output value.
- The equation of a linear function can be written in terms of $y = mx + b$.
- The initial value of a function is the y-intercept of its graph. The constant rate of change of a function is the slope of the line of the graph.
- A function that models a linear relationship has an initial value and a constant rate of change. A function that models a nonlinear relationship does not have a constant rate of change.

Vocabulary Review

ORAL LANGUAGE Before students complete the page, you can reinforce oral language by using one or more of the following activities.

- Write on the board two terms for each definition and have students select the correct term.
- Write the definitions on a set of cards and the terms on a separate set of cards. Distribute the cards to students. Have one student read a definition or term and the student with the matching term/definition stands up and read the matching term or definition.

WRITING IN MATH After students complete the page, you can further reinforce writing in math by having students provide a written response to the following question:

- How can a graph of a function tell you whether the function is linear or nonlinear?

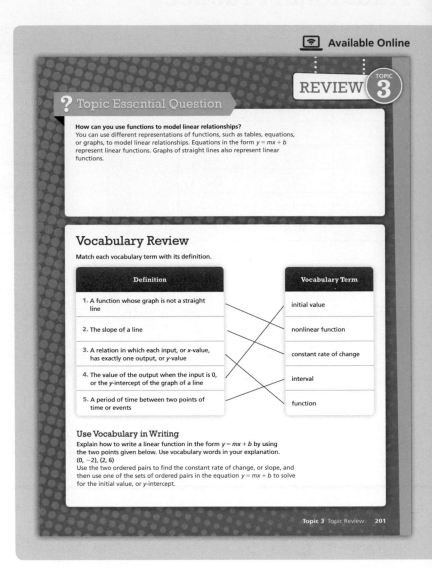

Available Online

REVIEW · TOPIC 3

? Topic Essential Question

How can you use functions to model linear relationships?
You can use different representations of functions, such as tables, equations, or graphs, to model linear relationships. Equations in the form $y = mx + b$ represent linear functions. Graphs of straight lines also represent linear functions.

Vocabulary Review

Match each vocabulary term with its definition.

Definition	Vocabulary Term
1. A function whose graph is not a straight line	initial value
2. The slope of a line	nonlinear function
3. A relation in which each input, or x-value, has exactly one output, or y-value	constant rate of change
4. The value of the output when the input is 0, or the y-intercept of the graph of a line	interval
5. A period of time between two points of time or events	function

Use Vocabulary in Writing
Explain how to write a linear function in the form $y = mx + b$ by using the two points given below. Use vocabulary words in your explanation.
$(0, -2), (2, 6)$
Use the two ordered pairs to find the constant rate of change, or slope, and then use one of the sets of ordered pairs in the equation $y = mx + b$ to solve for the initial value, or y-intercept.

Topic 3 Topic Review **201**

Concepts and Skills Review

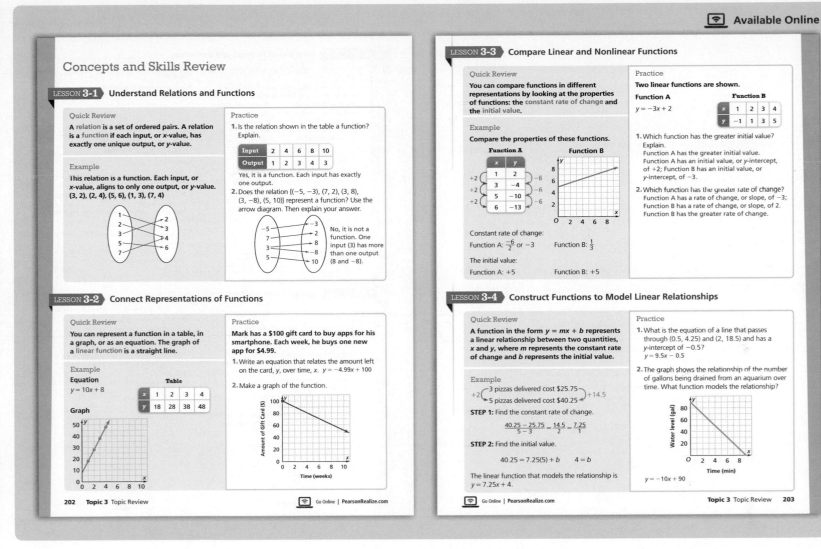

Concepts and Skills Review

LESSON 3-1 Understand Relations and Functions

Quick Review

A relation is a set of ordered pairs. A relation is a function if each input, or x-value, has exactly one unique output, or y-value.

Example

This relation is a function. Each input, or x-value, aligns to only one output, or y-value.
(3, 2), (2, 4), (5, 6), (1, 3), (7, 4)

Practice

1. Is the relation shown in the table a function? Explain.

Input	2	4	6	8	10
Output	1	2	3	4	3

Yes, it is a function. Each input has exactly one output.

2. Does the relation {(−5, −3), (7, 2), (3, 8), (3, −8), (5, 10)} represent a function? Use the arrow diagram. Then explain your answer.

No, it is not a function. One input (3) has more than one output (8 and −8).

LESSON 3-2 Connect Representations of Functions

Quick Review

You can represent a function in a table, in a graph, or as an equation. The graph of a linear function is a straight line.

Example

Equation
$y = 10x + 8$

Table

x	1	2	3	4
y	18	28	38	48

Graph

Practice

Mark has a $100 gift card to buy apps for his smartphone. Each week, he buys one new app for $4.99.

1. Write an equation that relates the amount left on the card, y, over time, x. $y = -4.99x + 100$

2. Make a graph of the function.

LESSON 3-3 Compare Linear and Nonlinear Functions

Quick Review

You can compare functions in different representations by looking at the properties of functions: the constant rate of change and the initial value.

Example

Compare the properties of these functions.

Function A

x	y
1	2
3	−4
5	−10
6	−13

Function B

Constant rate of change:
Function A: $\frac{-6}{2}$ or -3 Function B: $\frac{1}{3}$

The initial value:
Function A: +5   Function B: +5

Practice

Two linear functions are shown.

Function A
$y = -3x + 2$

Function B

x	1	2	3	4
y	−1	1	3	5

1. Which function has the greater initial value? Explain.
Function A has the greater initial value. Function A has an initial value, or y-intercept, of +2; Function B has an initial value, or y-intercept, of −3.

2. Which function has the greater rate of change?
Function A has a rate of change, or slope, of −3; Function B has a rate of change, or slope, of 2. Function B has the greater rate of change.

LESSON 3-4 Construct Functions to Model Linear Relationships

Quick Review

A function in the form $y = mx + b$ represents a linear relationship between two quantities, x and y, where m represents the constant rate of change and b represents the initial value.

Example

+2 ⟨ 3 pizzas delivered cost $25.75 / 5 pizzas delivered cost $40.25 ⟩ +14.5

STEP 1: Find the constant rate of change.
$$\frac{40.25 - 25.75}{5 - 3} = \frac{14.5}{2} = \frac{7.25}{1}$$

STEP 2: Find the initial value.
$$40.25 = 7.25(5) + b \qquad 4 = b$$

The linear function that models the relationship is $y = 7.25x + 4$.

Practice

1. What is the equation of a line that passes through (0.5, 4.25) and (2, 18.5) and has a y-intercept of −0.5?
$y = 9.5x - 0.5$

2. The graph shows the relationship of the number of gallons being drained from an aquarium over time. What function models the relationship?

$y = -10x + 90$

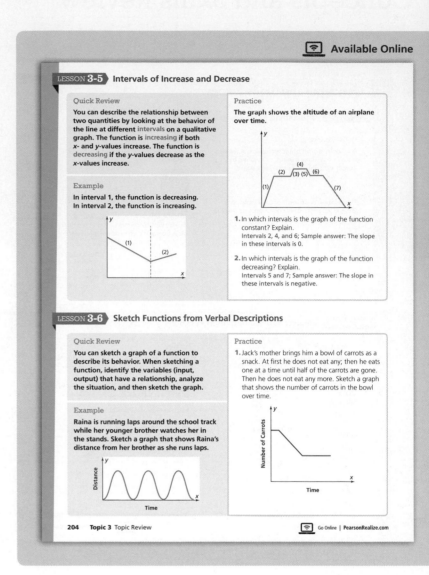

Available Online

LESSON 3-5 Intervals of Increase and Decrease

Quick Review

You can describe the relationship between two quantities by looking at the behavior of the line at different *intervals* on a qualitative graph. The function is *increasing* if both *x*- and *y*-values increase. The function is *decreasing* if the *y*-values decrease as the *x*-values increase.

Example

In interval 1, the function is decreasing.
In interval 2, the function is increasing.

Practice

The graph shows the altitude of an airplane over time.

1. In which intervals is the graph of the function constant? Explain.
   Intervals 2, 4, and 6; Sample answer: The slope in these intervals is 0.

2. In which intervals is the graph of the function decreasing? Explain.
   Intervals 5 and 7; Sample answer: The slope in these intervals is negative.

LESSON 3-6 Sketch Functions from Verbal Descriptions

Quick Review

You can sketch a graph of a function to describe its behavior. When sketching a function, identify the variables (input, output) that have a relationship, analyze the situation, and then sketch the graph.

Example

Raina is running laps around the school track while her younger brother watches her in the stands. Sketch a graph that shows Raina's distance from her brother as she runs laps.

Practice

1. Jack's mother brings him a bowl of carrots as a snack. At first he does not eat any; then he eats one at a time until half of the carrots are gone. Then he does not eat any more. Sketch a graph that shows the number of carrots in the bowl over time.

Fluency Practice

What's the Message?

Students maintain fluency with solving two-step linear equations in one variable.

Getting Started Remind students of the work they did last year with equivalent expressions and two-step equations. As needed, work through the first set of problems as a class.

As Students Do the Activity Remind students that one problem must have a solution with a greater value than the other, and that they are to circle the letter for the greater value.

Encourage students to solve each equation efficiently and accurately, checking each step in the process. Students should use the Properties of Equality in their steps; adding or subtracting, then multiplying or dividing.

Extra Challenge For each row, change the values in one equation that will lead to a change in which equation has the greater solution.

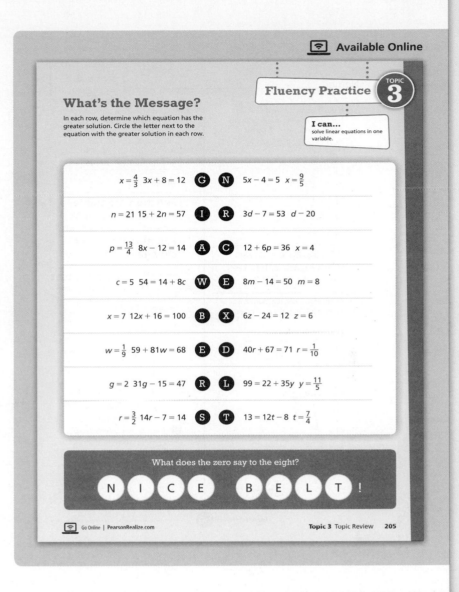

Available Online

Name _____

1. Is the relation shown below a function? Use the graph below to justify your answer. **1 point**

(0, 2), (2, 0), (2, 3), (3, 4), (6, 6)

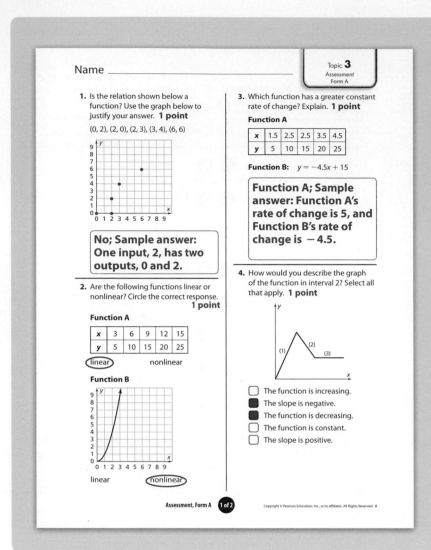

No; Sample answer: One input, 2, has two outputs, 0 and 2.

2. Are the following functions linear or nonlinear? Circle the correct response. **1 point**

Function A

x	3	6	9	12	15
y	5	10	15	20	25

(linear)   nonlinear

Function B

linear   (nonlinear)

3. Which function has a greater constant rate of change? Explain. **1 point**

Function A

x	1.5	2.5	2.5	3.5	4.5
y	5	10	15	20	25

Function B: $y = -4.5x + 15$

Function A; Sample answer: Function A's rate of change is 5, and Function B's rate of change is −4.5.

4. How would you describe the graph of the function in interval 2? Select all that apply. **1 point**

☐ The function is increasing.
■ The slope is negative.
■ The function is decreasing.
☐ The function is constant.
☐ The slope is positive.

5. The graph of a function is a line that passes through the coordinates (2, 11) and (8, 14). **2 points**

Part A

Which shows how to find the rate of change for the function?

Ⓐ $\frac{8-2}{14-11}$

● Ⓑ $\frac{14-11}{8-2}$

Ⓒ $\frac{14-8}{11-2}$

Ⓓ $\frac{11-2}{14-8}$

Part B

Write an equation in the form $y = mx + b$ for this function.

$y = \frac{1}{2}x + 10$

6. Natasha rides her bicycle to school. She rides slowly uphill for 5 minutes. Then she speeds up and rides at a consistent speed on a flat road for 15 minutes. The last 2 minutes of her ride, Natasha rides back downhill until she arrives at school. Sketch a graph of the behavior of the bike ride over time. **1 point**

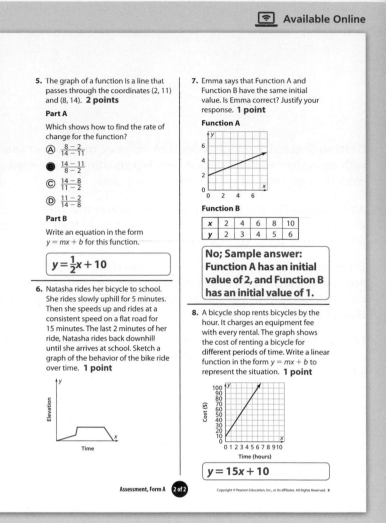

7. Emma says that Function A and Function B have the same initial value. Is Emma correct? Justify your response. **1 point**

Function A

Function B

x	2	4	6	8	10
y	2	3	4	5	6

No; Sample answer: Function A has an initial value of 2, and Function B has an initial value of 1.

8. A bicycle shop rents bicycles by the hour. It charges an equipment fee with every rental. The graph shows the cost of renting a bicycle for different periods of time. Write a linear function in the form $y = mx + b$ to represent the situation. **1 point**

$y = 15x + 10$

Assessment, Form A **1 of 2**   Copyright © Pearson Education, Inc., or its affiliates. All Rights Reserved. 8

Assessment, Form A **2 of 2**   Copyright © Pearson Education, Inc., or its affiliates. All Rights Reserved. 8

Assess students' understanding of the topic concepts and skills using the Topic Assessments found at PearsonRealize.com.

Use the Item Analysis Chart on the facing page to assign intervention to students based on their scores on the paper and pencil version of the Topic Assessments.

You may opt to have students take the Topic Assessment online at PearsonRealize.com. The online assessment is auto-scored, with differentiated intervention automatically assigned to students based on their scores.

You can use ExamView to generate additional Topic Assessments.

There are two versions of the Topic Assessment, Form A and Form B. These parallel versions assess the same content item for item. The Item Analysis Chart on the next page can be used with both versions.

🛜 Available Online

Name _____

Topic **3**
Assessment
Form B

1. Is the relation shown below a function? Use the graph below to justify your answer. **1 point**

(0, 3), (1, 4), (2, 3), (3, 0), (5, 4)

Yes; Sample answer: Each input value has exactly one output value.

2. Are the following functions linear or nonlinear? Circle the correct response. **1 point**

Function A

(linear)   nonlinear

Function B

x	1	2	3	4	5
y	1	8	27	64	125

linear   (nonlinear)

3. Which function has a greater constant rate of change? Explain. **1 point**

Function A: $y = 10x - 3$

Function B

x	1	2	3	4	5
y	20	15	10	5	0

Function A; Sample answer: Function A's rate of change is 10, and Function B's rate of change is − 5.

4. How would you describe the graph of the function in interval 2? **1 point**

Ⓐ The graph of the function is increasing.

Ⓑ The graph of the function is decreasing.

⬤ The graph of the function is constant.

Ⓓ The slope is positive.

5. The graph of a function is a line that passes through the points (0, 1) and (3, 10). **2 points**

Part A

Which shows how to find the rate of change for the function?

Ⓐ $\frac{0-3}{1-10}$

Ⓑ $\frac{3-1}{10-0}$

Ⓒ $\frac{10-3}{1-0}$

⬤ $\frac{10-1}{3-0}$

Part B

Write an equation in the form $y = mx + b$ for this function.

$y = 3x + 1$

6. A kite starts on the ground and slowly ascends into the sky. It flies at the same altitude for about 10 minutes and then quickly drops to the ground. Sketch a graph of the behavior of the kite over time. **1 point**

7. Raoul says that Function B has a greater initial value. Is Raoul correct? Justify your answer. **1 point**

Function A

Function B

x	0	2	4	6	8
y	3	6	9	12	15

Yes; Sample answer: Function A has an initial value of 0, and Function B has an initial value of 3.

8. A hot air balloon descends from an altitude of 2,000 feet at a constant rate of 90 feet per minute. The graph shows the altitude of the balloon over time. Write a linear function in the form $y = mx + b$ to represent the situation. **1 point**

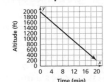

$y = -90x + 2000$

Item Analysis for Diagnosis and Intervention

Item	DOK	MDIS
1	2	K51
2A	1	K52
2B	1	K53
3	3	K51
4	2	K50, K51

Item	DOK	MDIS
5A	1	K49, K50
5B	2	K49
6	2	K54
7	2	K51
8	3	K52, K50

PearsonRealize.com

Available Online

---

Name _____

Topic **3**
Performance Assessment
Form A

Sophia and Hector are captains of their track and field team. As captains, they help their teammates train for the different events.

1. Sophia records the heights of the teammates competing in the high jump event and the heights of their best jumps.

Height of Teammate	5'4"	5'5"	5'5"	5'8"	5'10"
Highest Jump	4'4"	4'8"	5'	5'	4'10"

Is the height of a teammate's jump a function of his or her height? Explain. **2 points**

> **No; Sample answer: The relation is not a function because the input height of 5'5" has two outputs, 4'8" and 5'.**

2. Sophia and Aisha run a 10-kilometer course near their school. Aisha completes the course in 1 hour 10 minutes. Sophia runs at a steady pace as shown in the table below. Write each function as a linear equation where x is the number of kilometers and y is the number of minutes. Who runs faster? Explain. **2 points**

Distance (km)	1	2	3	4	5
Time (min)	5.5	11	16.5	22	27.5

> **Aisha: $y = 7x$; Sophia: $y = 5.5x$; Sample answer: Sophia runs faster. Looking at the slopes, Sophia runs 1 km in 5.5 minutes and Aisha runs 1 km in 7 minutes. Sophia covers the same distance in less time.**

3. Hector makes a graph to show the height of a shot put after it is thrown. Describe the behavior of the shot put based on the graph. **2 points**

Motion of Shot Put

> **Sample answer: The shot put rises as it moves horizontally until it reaches a maximum height, after which it begins to descend to the ground.**

---

4. Hector also runs. One of his training sessions is represented by the graph at the right.

Hector's Training Run

Part A

How would you describe Hector's training run based on the graph? **1 point**

> **Sample answer: Hector starts sprinting in a direction opposite from his home for 10 minutes. He runs at a slower pace for 10 minutes. Next, he stops and rests for 20 minutes. Then he spends 30 minutes jogging back home.**

Part B

During which interval is Hector running at the fastest speed? During which interval is he running at the slowest speed? Explain each answer. **1 point**

> **Interval 1; interval 4; Sample answer: In interval 1, the line has the steepest slope, which means Hector's speed is fastest. In interval 4, the line segment has the shallowest slope, which means his speed is slowest.**

5. Hector's friend Nick has a different training routine. He says, "I start by increasing my speed slowly over the first ten minutes. Then I run at a steady pace for 10 minutes. I decrease my speed over the next five minutes, and then I sprint as fast as I can for one more minute. After the sprint I slow down to a light jog before I stop." Sketch Nick's training run on the graph to the right. **1 point**

Nick's Training Run

Assess students' ability to apply the topic concepts and skills using the Topic Performance Assessments found at PearsonRealize.com.

Item Analysis for Diagnosis and Intervention

Item	DOK	MDIS
1	2	K51
2	3	K52
3	2	K51, K54
4A	2	K53
4B	2	K51
5	2	K54

Scoring Guide		
Item	Points	Topic Performance Assessment (Form A)
1	2	Correct answer and explanation
	1	Correct answer with incomplete or missing explanation
2	2	Correct functions and explanation
	1	Correct functions with incomplete or missing explanation
3	2	Correct description
	1	Partially correct description
4A	1	Correct description
4B	1	Correct rates of change for all intervals
5	1	Correct sketch

📶 Available Online

Name _____

The members of a middle school business club want to raise money to attend a conference for young entrepreneurs. So far, the club has raised $450. Members suggest a few new ideas.

1. Jenna suggests that the club hold a car wash. The club will need to spend $30 on cleaning supplies before making a profit.

Part A

Jenna presents her plan to the club using the table below. Make a graph of the data to show the relation. **1 point**

Number of Cars, x	Profit ($), y
0	−30
4	−10
8	10
12	30

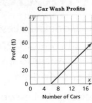
Car Wash Profits

Part B

Is the relation a function? If so, write an equation for the function. **1 point**

Yes; $y = 5x - 30$

2. Finn suggests that club members walk dogs for a fee. He proposes they offer 5 walks for $20 and 10 walks for $40 per dog. Write an equation to represent the amount earned, y, for x number of walks. Then graph the function. **2 points**

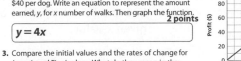
Dog-Walking Profits

$y = 4x$

3. Compare the initial values and the rates of change for Jenna's and Finn's plans. What do they mean in the problem situations? **2 points**

Sample answer: The initial value of −30 for Jenna's plan shows that the club members start $30 in debt, while Finn's plan starts with no debt. Jenna's plan raises $5 per car washed, and Finn's plan raises $4 per dog walked.

Copyright © Pearson Education, Inc., or its affiliates. All Rights Reserved. 8

4. Cole thinks they would make the most money if their club supervisor, Mr. Alvarez, invests the $450 they already raised in the stock market. He suggests buying the stock shown in the graph since the value is currently increasing. Do you agree with Cole? Describe what you see in the graph to support your reasoning. **2 points**

Stock's Value Over Time

Sample answer: I disagree. The stock is going up at the end, but the graph shows that the stock price increases and decreases irregularly over time. Investing in that stock could mean losing money.

5. The club members are able to attend the conference. On the way, the bus driver drives the speed limit for 2 hours when suddenly the bus breaks down. After half an hour, another bus arrives. Then they travel more slowly than the speed limit for 1 more hour.

Business Club's Travels

Part A

Sketch a graph to represent the bus trip over time. **1 point**

Sample graph:

Part B

Label the intervals on the graph. Describe the behavior of the function in each interval, and tell what it means in the problem situation. **2 points**

Sample answer: In interval a, the function increases, meaning a steady increase in distance traveled. In interval b, it is constant, meaning the bus did not travel when it was broken down. In interval c, it increases again, but not as steep as interval a since the bus is going at a slower speed.

Copyright © Pearson Education, Inc., or its affiliates. All Rights Reserved. 8

Item Analysis for Diagnosis and Intervention

Item	DOK	MDIS
1A	2	K48
1B	2	K48
2	2	K50, K51
3	3	K48, K50, K51
4	3	K51
5A	2	K54
5B	3	K53, K51

Scoring Guide		
Item	**Points**	**Topic Performance Assessment (Form B)**
1A	1	Correct graph
1B	1	Correct equation
2	2	Correct function and graph
	1	Correct function with incorrect graph or correct graph with incorrect function
3	2	Correct comparison of initial values and rates of change and explanation of meaning
	1	Correct comparison of initial values and rates of change with incomplete or inaccurate explanation of meaning
4	2	Reasonable answer and explanation
	1	Reasonable answer with incomplete or missing explanation
5A	1	Correct graph
5B	2	Correct labeling of intervals and description of behaviors
	1	Correct labeling of intervals with incorrect or incomplete description

TOPIC 4 Investigate Bivariate Data

Math Background Focus

Paired Data

- **Scatter Plots** In Lesson 4-1, students will construct and interpret scatter plots that show the relationship between two sets of data. Scatter plots give a visual representation of the relationship between the two quantities being measured. Students decide whether the data have a positive or negative association, or no association at all.

- **Linear Associations** In Lesson 4-2, students extend their work with scatter plots to begin drawing trend lines to represent the relationship that exists between the quantities. The students will use trend lines to decide whether the paired data show a linear association, a nonlinear association, or no association.

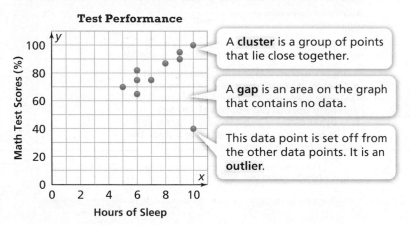

Test Performance

A **cluster** is a group of points that lie close together.

A **gap** is an area on the graph that contains no data.

This data point is set off from the other data points. It is an **outlier**.

The scatter plot shows a positive association between hours of sleep and math test scores.

Linear Associations and Models

- **Linear Models** In Lessons 4-2 and 4-3, students work with scatter plots and trend lines. When the data appear to have a linear association, students will sketch trend lines and write equations for them.

- **Predictions** In Lesson 4-3, students will also learn how to make predictions for the data using the equation of a trend line as a linear model of the relationship between the paired data.

Scatter plots can be used to make predictions about current or future trends.

Look for the corresponding y-value for a given x-value.

Find the equation of the trend line and find the y-value of a given x-value.

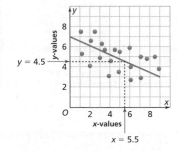

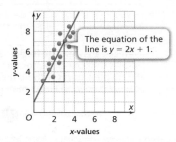

The equation of the line is $y = 2x + 1$.

Two-Way Frequency Tables

- **Frequency Tables** In Lesson 4-4, students will organize data into a two-way frequency table. The table will allow them to make comparisons against total data points and other sub-categories that will allow them to make informed conjectures.

- **Relative Frequency Tables** In Lesson 4-5, students will extend their work with two-way frequency tables to create two-way relative frequency tables that assist them with making comparisons and conjectures about the data in question.

Which type of textbook do you prefer?		
	Digital	**Print**
Students	42	28
Teachers	6	24

These data are **categorical data**. Categorical data consist of data that fall into categories. They do not have an inherent order, like numerical data.

Math Background Coherence

Students learn best when concepts are connected throughout the curriculum. This coherence is achieved within topics, across topics, across domains, and across grade levels.

Look Back

How does Topic 4 connect to what students learned earlier?

Grade 7

- **Collecting and Displaying Data** In Grade 7, students learned to collect data by randomly sampling a population in order to obtain a representative sample. They also reviewed and extended their fluency with various data displays including dot plots, bar graphs, and box-and-whisker plots.
- **Making Inferences from Data** In Grade 7, students computed measures of center and variability and used these measures to informally compare two populations.

Earlier in Grade 8

- **Linear Equations** In Topic 2, students learned to analyze and graph linear equations, finding the slope and *y*-intercept of a line by examining its graph. They will use this work to find the equations of trend lines for linear data.

Topic 4

How is content connected within Topic 4?

- **Paired Data** In Lessons 4-1 and 4-2, students construct and analyze scatter plots of paired data from two measured quantities. They examine the plots to determine what type of association may be present between the two quantities, whether positive or negative, linear or nonlinear, or perhaps no association at all.
- **Linear Associations and Models** In Lessons 4-2 and 4-3, students use trend lines to further explore data that appear to have a linear association. They find the equations of trend lines that closely fit data sets and use these as linear models in order to make predictions about the data.
- **Frequency Tables** In Lessons 4-4 and 4-5, students create and analyze two-way frequency and two-way relative frequency tables for paired categorical data. They learn to examine these tables and draw inferences about possible associations between the two data sets.

Book Type		Grade		
		7th	8th	Total
	E-books	$\frac{85}{207} \cdot 100 \approx 41.1\%$	$\frac{125}{197} \cdot 100 \approx 63.5\%$	52%
	Audio	58.9%	36.5%	48%
	Total	100%	100%	100%

The data you need to compare are in two different columns. Divide each frequency by the column total, not the table total.

Look Ahead

How does Topic 4 connect to what students will learn later?

High School

- **Data Analysis** In high school, students will extend their understanding of statistics to include fitting appropriate measurement data to a normal distribution in order to estimate population percentages.
- **Bivariate Data Associations** In high school, students will continue to create and analyze scatter plots, continuing to use trend lines. They will develop measures to evaluate how well a trend line fits their data and will extend their possible models to include exponential and quadratic associations.
- **Frequency Tables** In high school, students will continue their work with two-way frequency and two-way relative frequency tables for categorical data to understand joint, marginal, and conditional relative frequencies.

Math Background Rigor

A rigorous curriculum emphasizes conceptual understanding, procedural skill and fluency, and applications.

Conceptual Understanding

- **Paired Data** Topic 4 allows students to explore the idea that two sets of data may show a relationship to each other. In Lessons 4-1 and 4-2, students create scatter plots for numerous sets of paired measurement data and examine the plots for evidence of an association. Students categorize the associations between the paired data as positive, negative, linear, nonlinear, or no association at all.
- **Linear Associations and Models** Lessons 4-2 and 4-3 extend the examination of bivariate data that show a linear association. Students sketch and find equations for trend lines and use these lines as models to make predictions for the data.
- **Two-Way Frequency Tables** In Lessons 4-4 and 4-5, students work with paired sets of categorical data, using frequency tables to compare two sets of data. Students use the two-way frequency and two-way relative frequency tables to make evidence-based conjectures about the data.

Procedural Skill and Fluency

- **Scatter plots** Students practice graphing points by making scatter plots in Lessons 4-1 through 4-3. They also review the idea of slope by determining whether their data appear to have a positive or negative association.
- **Linear Associations and Models** Students find equations for the trend lines that model data with a linear association in Lessons 4-2 and 4-3. By using the equation of a trend line as a linear model, students can make predictions about their data.

The scatter plot shows a hiker's elevation above sea level over time. The equation of the trend line shown is $y = 8.77x + 686$. To the nearest whole number, predict what the hiker's elevation will be after 145 minutes.

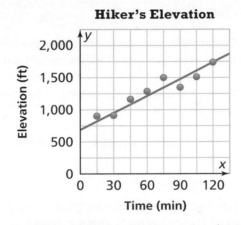

- **Two-Way Frequency Tables** In Lessons 4-4 and 4-5, students construct two-way frequency and two-way relative frequency tables for sets of paired categorical data. They use logic and computational skill to fill in blanks for both types of table. They draw inferences about the data by comparing fractions and percents.

Applications

- **Investigate Bivariate Data** Throughout Topic 4, students work with and analyze bivariate data using various tools such as scatter plots, trend lines, two-way frequency tables, and two-way relative frequency tables. The lessons in this topic show students how these tools can assist them in analyzing real-world data to draw inferences and make predictions.

Math Practices

The math practices and processes describe the behaviors and thinking habits that mathematically proficient students demonstrate when actively engaged in mathematics work. Opportunities for engagement in the practices and to develop expertise with these important behaviors and thinking habits exist throughout the topic and program. Here we focus on mathematical reasoning and explaining.

As students solve problems involving bivariate data, look for these behaviors to assess and identify students who demonstrate proficiency with mathematical reasoning and explaining.

Math Practices Within Topic 4 Lessons	
Make sense of problems and persevere in solving them.	**Look for and make use of structure.**
Mathematically proficient students:	Mathematically proficient students:
• Construct scatter plots and use them to interpret the relationship between two sets of measurement data.	• Recognize the constant slope of a linear association and determine whether it is positive or negative.
• Draw trend lines and determine the type of association that exists between the paired data in question.	• Interpret the meaning of the *y*-intercept and slope of a trend line in the context of the data.
• Make predictions using the equation of a trend line.	• Use the structure of the equation of a line in the form $y = mx + b$ to identify an appropriate trend line for a set of bivariate data.
• Organize data in a two-way frequency table and make comparisons of and conjectures about the data.	• Make sense of the structure of a frequency table through the Associative and Commutative Properties of Addition.
• Create two-way relative frequency tables from a two-way frequency table and make comparisons of and conjectures about the data.	• Justify their logic in drawing conclusions by calling on evidence in their data displays.

Help students become more proficient with mathematical reasoning and explanation.

If students do not display facility in investigating bivariate data using scatter plots, two-way frequency tables, and two-way relative frequency tables, then use these questioning strategies to help them develop reasoning and explanation skills as they solve problems throughout the topic.

Q: How can you recognize whether a scatter plot shows a linear association or not?

Q: How do you find the equation of a trend line from its graph?

Q: What is the purpose of a trend line?

Q: What are the advantages and disadvantages of using a two-way relative frequency table rather than a two-way frequency table?

Q: How would you describe a set of data that shows no relationship at all?

Q: What does the slope of the trend line tell you about the data?

Q: How does a two-way frequency table help to make comparisons and informed conjectures about paired data?

Q: How do you use a two-way frequency table to make a two-way relative frequency table?

Topic Readiness Assessment

Assess

Name _____

Topic **4**
Readiness Assessment

1. Which point is located at (2, −5)?

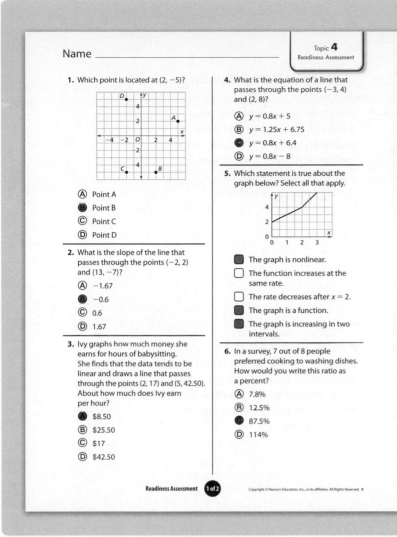

- Ⓐ Point A
- Ⓑ Point B
- Ⓒ Point C
- Ⓓ Point D

2. What is the slope of the line that passes through the points (−2, 2) and (13, −7)?

- Ⓐ −1.67
- Ⓑ −0.6
- Ⓒ 0.6
- Ⓓ 1.67

3. Ivy graphs how much money she earns for hours of babysitting. She finds that the data tends to be linear and draws a line that passes through the points (2, 17) and (5, 42.50). About how much does Ivy earn per hour?

- Ⓐ $8.50
- Ⓑ $25.50
- Ⓒ $17
- Ⓓ $42.50

4. What is the equation of a line that passes through the points (−3, 4) and (2, 8)?

- Ⓐ $y = 0.8x + 5$
- Ⓑ $y = 1.25x + 6.75$
- Ⓒ $y = 0.8x + 6.4$
- Ⓓ $y = 0.8x − 8$

5. Which statement is true about the graph below? Select all that apply.

- ▣ The graph is nonlinear.
- ☐ The function increases at the same rate.
- ☐ The rate decreases after x = 2.
- ▣ The graph is a function.
- ▣ The graph is increasing in two intervals.

6. In a survey, 7 out of 8 people preferred cooking to washing dishes. How would you write this ratio as a percent?

- Ⓐ 7.8%
- Ⓑ 12.5%
- Ⓒ 87.5%
- Ⓓ 114%

7. Find the equation of the line shown below.

- Ⓐ $y = −0.2x + 2$
- Ⓑ $y = −5x + 2$
- Ⓒ $y = 0.2x + 5$
- Ⓓ $y = 5x + 2$

8. A taxi company charges the rates shown in the following table.

Distance (mi)	Fare ($)
6	13.50
15	33.75
22	49.50

What would the company charge for a 10-mile ride?

- Ⓐ $15.80
- Ⓑ $18.10
- Ⓒ $19.00
- Ⓓ $22.50

9. Which statement is true?

- Ⓐ If a relationship is non-linear, it is not a function.
- Ⓑ A graph of a curve is linear.
- Ⓒ A graph that shows a constant rate of change is linear.
- Ⓓ A non-linear relationship has a constant slope.

10. Describe what is happening in the graph below.

- Ⓐ The function is steady, and then it increases.
- Ⓑ The function decreases sharply, and then it stays the same.
- Ⓒ The function increases a little, and then it decreases sharply.
- Ⓓ The function stays constant, and then it decreases sharply.

11. A water tank fills as shown in the graph below.

What is the slope of the line?

- Ⓐ $\frac{1}{3}$
- Ⓑ $\frac{2}{3}$
- Ⓒ $\frac{3}{2}$
- Ⓓ 3

 Copyright © Pearson Education, Inc., or its affiliates. All Rights Reserved. 8

 Copyright © Pearson Education, Inc., or its affiliates. All Rights Reserved. 8

Assess students' understanding of prerequisite concepts and skills using the Topic Readiness Assessment found at PearsonRealize.com.

 You may opt to have students take the Topic Readiness Assessment online.

RtI Item Analysis for Diagnosis and Remediation

Item	DOK	MDIS
1	1	K46
2	1	K50
3	1	K50
4	2	K50, K52
5	1	K51
6	1	K51
7	1	K50, K52
8	2	K50, K52
9	1	K52
10	2	K51
11	3	K50

Investigate Bivariate Data

Lesson	Vocabulary	Objective	Essential Understanding
4-1 Construct and Interpret Scatter Plots	cluster gap measurement data negative association outlier positive association scatter plot	• Construct a scatter plot graph to model paired data. • Utilize a scatter plot to identify and interpret the relationship between paired data.	A scatter plot is a graph on a coordinate plane that uses points to show the relationship between paired data. These points visually display any clusters, gaps, or outliers.
4-2 Analyze Linear Associations	trend line	• Recognize whether the paired data has a linear association, a nonlinear association, or no association. • Draw a trend line to determine whether a linear association is positive or negative and strong or weak.	A trend line on a scatter plot approximates the linear association between the paired data. Scatter plots can show a linear or nonlinear association, or no association.
4-3 Use Linear Models to Make Predictions	none	• Use the slope and y-intercept of a trend line to make a prediction. • Make a prediction when no equation is given by drawing trend lines and writing the equation of the linear model.	Trend lines in linear models can help with making predictions about a set of data. By determining the equation of a linear model, predictions of an outcome can be made.

Lesson Resources

Digital

Student's Edition

Additional Practice Workbook

Teaching Resources
- Reteach to Build Understanding
- Additional Vocabulary Support
- Build Mathematical Literacy
- Enrichment

Assessment Resources
- Lesson Quiz

Digital

Digital Lesson Courseware
- Today's Challenge
- Visual Learning Animation Plus
- Key Concept
- Additional Examples
- 3-Act Mathematical Modeling
- Online Practice powered by MathXL for School

- Virtual Nerd Video Tutorials
- Animated Glossary
- Digital Math Tools
- Online Math Games

Lesson Support for Teachers
- Listen and Look For PD Lesson Video

The suggested pacing for each lesson is 2 days for a 45-minute math class and 1 day for a 90-minute class.

Lesson	Vocabulary	Objective	Essential Understanding
4-4 Interpret Two-Way Frequency Tables	categorical data	• Organize paired categorical data into a two-way frequency table. • Compare and make conjectures about data displayed in a two-way frequency table.	Data can be displayed in a two-way frequency table, making it easier to analyze. Individual data categories can be compared to all the data. Individual data can also be compared to sub-categories to make evidence-based conjectures.
4-5 Interpret Two-Way Relative Frequency Tables	relative frequency table	• Construct two-way frequency tables and two-way relative frequency tables. • Compare and make conjectures about data displayed in a two-way relative frequency table.	Data can be organized in a two-way frequency table and then used to create a two-way relative frequency table. Relative frequency can be determined for the rows and the columns as well as for the whole table.
3-Act Mathematical Modeling: Reach Out	none	• Use mathematical modeling to represent a problem situation and to propose a solution. • Test and verify the appropriateness of their math models. • Explain why the results from their mathematical models may not align exactly with the problem situation.	Many real-world problem situations can be represented with a mathematical model, but that model may not represent a real-world situation exactly.

Topic Resources

Digital

Print

Student's Edition
- Review What You Know
- Build Literacy in Mathematics
- Mid-Topic Checkpoint and Performance Task
- Topic Review
- Fluency Practice Activity
- STEM Project

Assessment Resources
- Topic Readiness Assessment
- Mid-Topic Assessment
- Topic Assessment
- Topic Performance Task

Digital

Topic Support for Students
- Math Practice Animations
- STEM Project
- 3-Act Mathematical Modeling Lesson

Topic Support for Teachers
- Topic Overview Video
- ExamView Test Generator

Investigate Bivariate Data

Available Online

Topic Essential Question

How can you represent the relationship between paired data and use the representation to make predictions?

Revisit the Topic Essential Question throughout the topic. See the Teacher's Edition for the Topic Review for notes about answering the questions.

3-Act Mathematical Modeling

Have students read about the Math Modeling lesson for this topic. You can use the preview for this lesson to get students interested in learning the content of the topic.

The Mathematical Modeling in 3 Acts lesson appears after Lesson 4-5.

STEM Project

How Many Fish?

Project Overview

In this project students learn a sampling technique for estimating a population count when other more direct counting methods are not possible.

What's the Math?

Students use proportional relationships to determine the total number of organisms in a population. They calculate the ratio of tagged organisms caught the second time to the total number re-caught. This ratio is compared to the ratio of the total number of organisms tagged to the total population of that organism.

What's the Science?

Tag-and-Release studies are commonly used in ecology to estimate an animal population's size when monitoring wildlife. A portion of the population is captured, tagged, and released. Later, another portion is captured and the number of tagged individuals within the sample is counted. Tag-and-Release studies are common for fish and whales, but are also used for other organisms, including salamanders, snails, birds, and foxes.

What's the Engineering and Technology?

Students think like engineers as they gather, analyze, synthesize, and present data in clear and understandable ways. They determine the number of organisms in a population when it is not possible to actually count them.

Introduce the Project

Present the project by having students research Tag-and-Release studies on various organisms.

Q: Describe a Tag-and-Release study you read about.
[Answers will vary.]

Q: Why is a Tag-and-Release study a good method for counting the organisms in a population? [Sample answer: It uses proportional relationships to determine the unknown quantity. By establishing a ratio of the number of tagged organisms caught to the total caught in the second capture, you can make a good estimate for the total number in the population.]

Q: How many bass are in the lake described in the problem?
[Let x = total bass population. $\frac{30}{200} = \frac{500}{x}$ so x = 3,333 bass]

Available Online

TOPIC
4 STEM Project

Did You Know?

A fishery biologist collects data on fish, such as the size and health of the fish population in a particular body of water.

Largemouth bass and smallmouth bass are the most popular game fish in North America.

Biologists often use tagging studies to estimate fish population, as well as to estimate catch and harvest rates.

The average lifespan of a bass is about 16 years, but some have lived more than 20 years.

Research suggests that bass can see red better than any other color on the spectrum.

Your Task: How Many Fish?

Suppose a fishery biologist takes 500 bass from a lake, tags them, and then releases them back into the water. Several days later, the biologist nets a sample of 200 bass, of which 30 are tagged. How many bass are in the lake? You and your classmates will explore how the biologist can use sampling to describe patterns and to make generalizations about the entire population.

208   **Topic 4** STEM Project

Q: Design a Tag-and-Release study a team could do. How will you "tag" the organisms without causing any harm?
[Answers will vary.]

You can launch this project any time during Topic 4.

 Show the Topic 4 STEM video to generate interest in the project.

Teacher resources that provide students with project details and support are available at PearsonRealize.com.

Get Ready!

Review What You Know!

Assign the Review What You Know to activate prior knowledge and practice the prerequisite skills needed for success in this topic.

Encourage students to work independently or with a partner. Use these questioning strategies to help them get started.

Graphing Points

Q: When given a pair of coordinates, which coordinate represents the x-coordinate, and which represents the y-coordinate? [Sample answer: The x-coordinate is always the first number listed in the pair, and the y-coordinate is always the second number listed in the pair.]

Q: How would you describe the x-axis and y-axis of a coordinate plane? [Sample answer: The x-axis is the horizontal line passing through the origin. The y-axis is the vertical line passing through the origin.]

Finding Slope

Q: How do you find the slope of a line between two points? [Sample answer: Find the rise over the run, which is the change in the y-coordinates over the change in the x-coordinates.]

Q: What does a line with a negative slope look like? [Sample answer: The line will slant downward from left to right.]

Writing Fractions as Percents

Q: When is it useful to convert a fraction into a percent? [Sample answer: Percents are easier to compare than fractions, and it can be easier to visualize their size.]

 You may choose to provide additional practice for students who need more help.

Item Analysis for Diagnosis and Remediation

Item	MDIS
1	K50
2	M27
3	K46
4	K46
5–8	K48
9–11	K50
12	M38

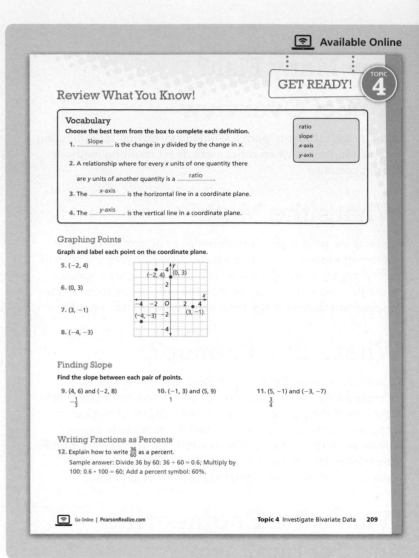

Vocabulary Review

You may choose to strengthen vocabulary with the following activity.

- Have the students write as many descriptive sentences as they can for each of the review vocabulary words. Then have a classroom discussion in which you share as many unique ideas as you can to develop complete definitions.

Build Vocabulary

Pre-reading Strategy: Graphic Organizer

Have the students preview each term and complete the graphic organizer by inserting each term's definition and an example of such in the appropriate fields in order to build understanding of the new math vocabulary in this topic.

Q: Why might you add information to your definitions after you study the lesson that introduces this vocabulary? [Sample answer: Sometimes you learn something new or make a connection that helps you understand more about what the word means when you see it in context.]

Q: Why could it be easier to understand vocabulary terms when you can see examples? [Sample answer: Examples can be easier to remember because they might be more visual.]

Make sure to encourage students to review and add to both the definitions and the examples for each term in this organizer as they study this topic.

Q: Why is it important to understand vocabulary terms in mathematics? [Sample answer: If you understand the vocabulary, then you understand instructions and questions better, and know what to do when solving problems.]

As students progress through the topic, encourage them to take the time to thoroughly complete this organizer. They should include the best visuals and graphics that they can find so they have an excellent tool to use for review or study of this topic.

Extension for All Readers

Challenge the students to use their completed graphic organizers to write their own practice exams. Then have the students take a partner's exam to see how well they do.

📶 **Available Online**

Build Vocabulary

Use the graphic organizer to help you understand new vocabulary terms.
Use words or a sketch to show an example.

Term	Definition	Example
measurement data	Sample answer: Data that give measures and are numerical	Sample answer: Number of miles run
scatter plot	Sample answer: A scatter plot is a graph that uses points to display the relationship between two different sets of data. Each point can be represented by an ordered pair.	Check students' work.
cluster	Sample answer: A group of points that lie close together	Sample answer: This data set shows a cluster around 5. <1, 2, 3, 4, 4, 5, 5, 5, 6, 6, 7, 8>
gap	Sample answer: An area on a graph that contains no data points	Sample answer: This data set shows a gap between 3 and 5. <1, 1, 1, 2, 5, 5, 6, 6, 7, 8>
outlier	Sample answer: A piece of data that does not seem to fit with the rest of the data set	Sample answer: In this data set, 10 is an outlier. {1, 2, 2, 3, 4, 4, 5, 5, 10}
trend line	Sample answer: A line on a scatter plot, drawn near the points, that approximates the association between paired data	Check students' work.
categorical data	Sample answer: Data that fall into categories and are not numerical	Sample answer: Favorite type of pet
relative frequency table	Sample answer: This table shows the ratio of the number of data in each category to the total number of data items. The ratio can be expressed as a fraction, decimal, or percent.	Sample answer: 33% of pet owners

210 Topic 4 Investigate Bivariate Data   📶 Go Online | PearsonRealize.com

Lesson 4-1

Construct and Interpret Scatter Plots

Video Activity

Lesson Overview

FOCUS

Objective

Students will be able to:

✔ construct a scatter plot to model paired data.

✔ utilize a scatter plot to identify and interpret the relationship between paired data.

Essential Understanding

A scatter plot is a graph on a coordinate plane that uses points to show the relationship between paired data. These points visually display any clusters, gaps, or outliers.

COHERENCE

In Topic 2 and Topic 3, students:

• were introduced to linear equations.

• learned to sketch and analyze the graphs of functions.

In this lesson, students:

• model data by constructing scatter plots.

• interpret scatter plots and identify clusters, gaps, and outliers on the scatter plot.

Later in this topic, students will:

• learn to draw a trend line that represents the relationship between paired data to make predictions.

• learn how to determine whether paired data have a linear association, a nonlinear association, or no association.

RIGOR

This lesson emphasizes a blend of **conceptual understanding** and **application**.

• Students realize that they can transform given paired data into a visual tool by constructing a scatter plot.

• Students identify and interpret clusters, gaps, and outliers on a scatter plot.

Math Anytime

Today's Challenge

Use the Topic 4 problems any time during this topic.

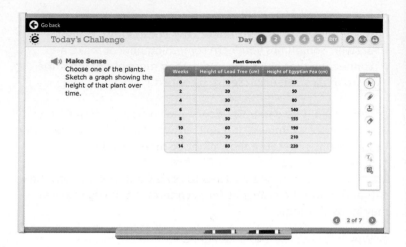

Watch the **Listen and Look For Video** for strategies and habits of mind to look for as students complete work on this lesson.

Mathematics Overview

In this lesson, students will construct and interpret scatter plots that show the relationship between two sets of data. Scatter plots give a visual representation of the relationship between the two quantities. Students will decide whether the data have a positive or negative association, or no association at all.

Applying Math Practices

Model with Math

Students will use paired data to construct scatter plots.

Look for and Make Use of Structure

Students will look for structure in scatter plots by identifying clusters, gaps, and outliers and using them to interpret the meaning of the data.

Generalize

Students will determine a relationship between given paired data and can state generalized rules about the paired data in a scatter plot as well as identify patterns in the data.

STEP 1 | Develop: Problem-Based Learning

15-20 min

Activity

Solve & Discuss It!

Look for Relationships As students work through the *Solve & Discuss It*, listen and look for students who base their recommendation for Luciana's strategy on relationships between the number of media posts per day and the number of new subscribers.

Before [WHOLE CLASS]

ETP

1 Implement Tasks that Promote Reasoning and Problem Solving

Q: What information does the table show you? [Sample answer: The number of social media posts per day and the corresponding number of new subscribers]

2 Build Understanding

Q: How will this information help Luciana attract new subscribers to BlastOn? [Sample answer: The information tells Luciana what she did during that campaign that got the greatest and least number of new subscribers.]

During [SMALL GROUP]

ETP

3 Support Productive Struggle in Learning Mathematics

Q: Based on the given data from Luciana's last campaign, which number of daily posts produced the greatest number of new subscribers? [5 daily posts]

Q: What relationship is most important to Luciana in planning the new campaign? [Sample answer: There is only one number of daily posts, 5, that gives the greatest number of new subscribers.]

After [WHOLE CLASS]

ETP

4 Facilitate Meaningful Mathematical Discourse

Ask students to share their solutions. If needed, project Tim's and Sadie's work and ask:

Q: What noticeable difference exists between Tim's and Sadie's conclusions? [Sample answer: In addition to what Tim says, Sadie suggests there should also be 6 posts a day and Luciana should consider 11 posts.]

5 Transition to Visual Learning

Q: How could you create a visual model to represent the data from Luciana's last campaign? [Sample answer: Create a graph that uses the *x*-axis to represent the *Number of Social Media Posts per Day* and the *y*-axis to represent the *Number of New Subscribers*. Then plot the paired coordinates.]

6 Extension for Early Finishers

Q: Based on Luciana's data, how many new subscribers could she reasonably expect to gain during the two-week campaign using the 5 daily posts strategy? Explain. [1,540 to 1,680; Sample answer: The data shows that when Luciana submitted 5 daily posts, she gained 110 and 120 new subscribers. Multiply these two numbers by 14, which represents the two-week period, to gain 1,540 to 1,680 new subscribers.]

Analyze Student Work

Available Online

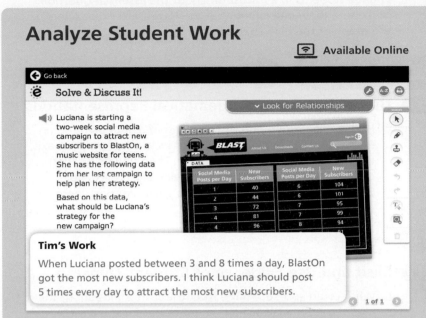

Tim's Work

When Luciana posted between 3 and 8 times a day, BlastOn got the most new subscribers. I think Luciana should post 5 times every day to attract the most new subscribers.

Tim's solution shows that he used the data to determine which number of daily posts resulted in gaining the most new subscribers.

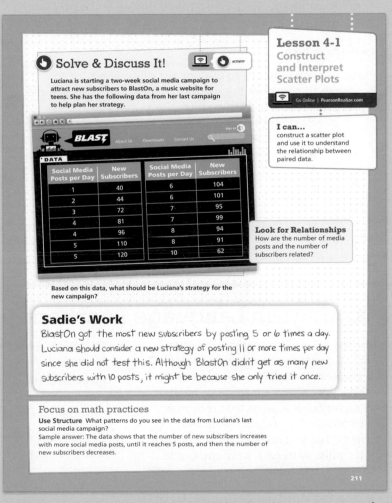

Sadie's Work

BlastOn got the most new subscribers by posting 5 or 6 times a day. Luciana should consider a new strategy of posting 11 or more times per day since she did not test this. Although BlastOn didn't get as many new subscribers with 10 posts, it might be because she only tried it once.

Sadie's solution shows that she used the data in a more general way. She suggests submitting between 5 to 6 daily posts *and* considering a test of 11 daily posts or more since no numbers of posts beyond 10 were tested.

STEP 2 | Develop: Visual Learning

Visual Learning | Assess

ETP Establish Mathematics Goals to Focus Learning

Engage students in a discussion about the *Essential Question*. Make sure they understand that the term *scatter plot* refers to the graph of the given paired data.

EXAMPLE 1 ▶ 👁 Construct a Scatter Plot

ETP Use and Connect Mathematical Representations

Q: How do you determine the meaning of a data point on a scatter plot? [Sample answer: Find its location on the *x*-axis, the number of hours after posting. Then find its location on the *y*-axis, the number of new viewers. For example, (3, 200) means that 3 hours after a particular post there were 200 new views.]

☑ Try It!

ETP Elicit and Use Evidence of Student Thinking

Q: What could you determine from the scatter plot about the age of subscribers Luciana should target for the BlastOn's concert giveaways? [Sample answer: About the same number of people from ages 10 to 15 entered the BlastOn's concert giveaways, so Luciana should equally target people from ages 10 to 15.]

Convince Me!

Q: Is Luciana required to use one set of numbers for the *x*-axis to construct the scatter plot? Explain. [No; Sample answer: The numbers used for the *x*- and *y*-axes are dependent on the axes labels.]

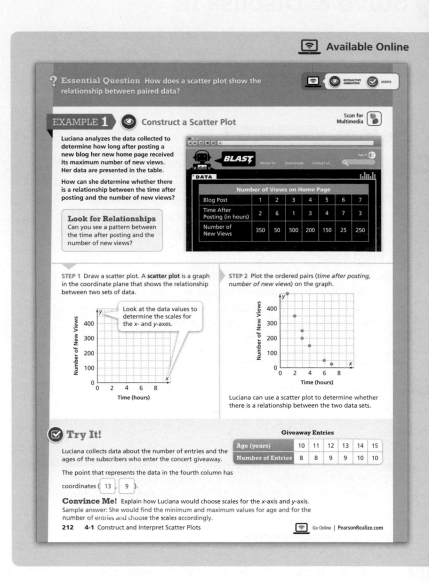

👁 Available Online

? Essential Question How does a scatter plot show the relationship between paired data?

EXAMPLE 1 👁 Construct a Scatter Plot   Scan for Multimedia

Luciana analyzes the data collected to determine how long after posting a new blog her new home page received its maximum number of new views. Her data are presented in the table.

How can she determine whether there is a relationship between the time after posting and the number of new views?

Look for Relationships
Can you see a pattern between the time after posting and the number of new views?

Number of Views on Home Page

Blog Post	1	2	3	4	5	6	7
Time After Posting (in hours)	2	6	1	3	4	7	3
Number of New Views	350	50	500	200	150	25	250

STEP 1 Draw a scatter plot. A **scatter plot** is a graph in the coordinate plane that shows the relationship between two sets of data.

Look at the data values to determine the scales for the *x*- and *y*-axes.

STEP 2 Plot the ordered pairs (*time after posting, number of new views*) on the graph.

Luciana can use a scatter plot to determine whether there is a relationship between the two data sets.

☑ **Try It!**

Luciana collects data about the number of entries and the ages of the subscribers who enter the concert giveaway.

Giveaway Entries

Age (years)	10	11	12	13	14	15
Number of Entries	8	8	9	9	10	10

The point that represents the data in the fourth column has coordinates (13 , 9).

Convince Me! Explain how Luciana would choose scales for the *x*-axis and *y*-axis. Sample answer: She would find the minimum and maximum values for age and for the number of entries and choose the scales accordingly.

212   4-1 Construct and Interpret Scatter Plots   📶 Go Online | PearsonRealize.com

 Students can access the *Visual Learning Animation Plus* by using the **BouncePages app** to scan this page. Students can download the app for free in their mobile devices' app store.

ⒺⓁⓁ English Language Learners

BEGINNING Before reading Example 2, direct students to the graph in Example 2. Tell students that a *cluster* is a group or collection, a *gap* is a space or hole, and an *outlier* is a point that is by itself. An *association* is a relationship. Tell students that you have an association, or relationship, with each of them. Guide students to use these new terms in simple sentences.

INTERMEDIATE Ask students to review Example 1.

Q: What is the meaning of the word *scatter*? [Sample answer: To throw in different directions]

Explain that synonyms are different words that have about the same meaning.

Q: What are synonyms for the word *scatter*? [Sample answer: Throw, toss]

Q: Work with a partner to identify some synonyms. [Sample answers: Relationship and connection, association and group, plot and place, word and term, error and mistake]

ADVANCED Ask students to review Example 3.

Q: What is the meaning of the word *scatter*? [Sample answer: To throw in different directions]

Q: Do you think scatter plot is a good name for this type of graph? Explain. [Yes; Sample answer: A scatter plot is a good name for this type of graph because the data points may be located anywhere on the graph. The data points may be scattered in a tight group (positive association) or in a loose group (no association).]

EXAMPLE 2 Interpret a Scatter Plot

ETP **Pose Purposeful Questions**

Q: Do you think a scatter plot is a good way to show this data set? Explain. [Yes; Sample answer: The data points may scatter throughout the coordinate plane. A scatter plot will present a good visual to see if there is a relationship between the data.]

Q: How does the graph show a positive association between the amount of sleep and the score a student gets on the math test? [Sample answer: The points cluster together and they tend to increase as a person gets more sleep.]

Q: What would the scatter plot have looked like if there were a negative association between the amount of sleep and the test scores? [Sample answer: The highest scores would have been associated with the people who slept the least, and the more a person slept, the worse his or her score would have been.]

Q: According to the scatterplot, which point is the outlier? Explain. [(10, 40); Sample answer: A person who slept 10 hours, got a score of 40. The scatter plot does not include reasons for the data.]

EXAMPLE 3 Construct and Interpret a Scatter Plot

ETP **Pose Purposeful Questions**

Q: How do you know that the scatter plot does not show an association between the number of minutes played and the number of fouls committed? [Sample answer: There is no clustering, patterns, or trend in the data. The points are spread all over the grid.]

☑ Try It!

ETP **Elicit and Use Evidence of Student Thinking**

Q: What is different about the scatter plot for points scored and minutes played and the scatter plot for fouls made? [Sample answer: In this scatter plot the data clusters and has a positive association. The more minutes a player plays, the more likely he or she is to score more points.]

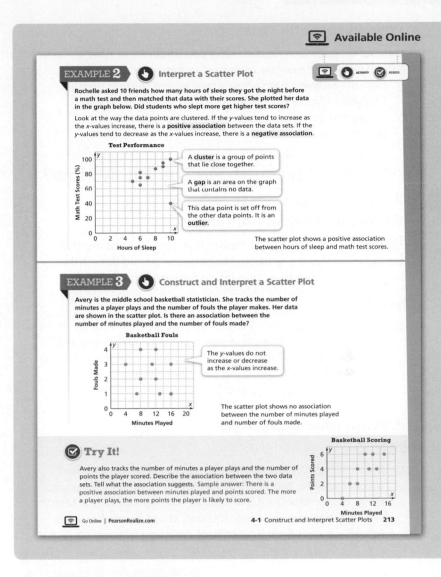

 ADDITIONAL EXAMPLES

For additional examples go to PearsonRealize.com.

Response to Intervention

USE WITH EXAMPLE 2 Some students may have trouble understanding the information a scatter plot provides. The following will provide extra opportunities for students to comprehend the material.

• Have students answer the following:

Q: How much sleep did the person who got the highest score on the test get? Explain. [10 hours; Sample answer: First find the point for the best test score, then find the amount of sleep this person got.]

Q: What was the score of the person who got 5 hours of sleep? [70%]

🏆 Enrichment

USE WITH EXAMPLE 3 Challenge advanced students to recognize that it is possible for paired data to produce a scatter plot that does not contain any clusters, gaps, or outliers.

• Have students answer the following:

Q: When a scatter plot does not contain any clusters, gaps, or outliers, do the paired data have a relationship or an association? [No; Sample answer: When paired data are spread out on the scatter plot, there appears to be no relationship or association.]

Q: Describe or draw a scatter plot for basketball scoring and time played that has 3 clusters but shows no relationship or association. [Sample answer: The players could have played for about 4, 8, or 12 minutes with each cluster scoring 8 points.]

KEY CONCEPT

ETP Pose Purposeful Questions

Q: How do gaps and clusters help you understand how a scatter plot shows the relationship between paired data? [Sample answer: Gaps show areas where there is no data. Clusters indicate where you are most likely to be able to show the relationship or association between the paired data.]

Do You Understand/Do You Know How?

ETP Build Procedural Fluency from Conceptual Understanding

? Essential Question Students should understand that scatter plots show a relationship between paired data if there is a positive or negative association between the data sets.

ITEM 4

Q: How can you determine where to plot a given data point on the scatter plot? [Sample answer: Let the *x*-axis represent the *Shoe Size* data and the *y*-axis represent the *Height* data. Then plot the corresponding pairs listed in the table.]

RTI Prevent Misconceptions

ITEM 5

Q: Why is Month 11 but not Month 12 considered an outlier? [Sample answer: Month 12 is within the range of the number of visitors for Months 1 through 10. The data point for Month 11 is not in the same range. It shows about three thousand visitors, which is far below that of the other data points.]

 Available Online

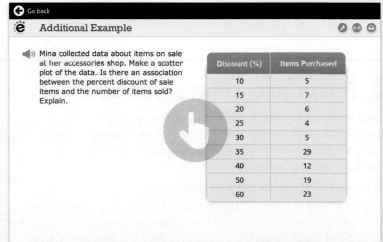

ADDITIONAL EXAMPLE **2**

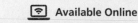 Available Online

Help students understand how to interpret a scatter plot and identify any clusters, gaps, and outliers.

Q: Is there an association between the paired data sets? Explain. [Positive association; Sample answer: As the sales discount increases (*x*-values), the number of items sold increases (*y*-values).]

Q: What are some possible reasons that a 35% discount may have such a high number of items sold compared to the other discounts? Explain. [Sample answer: There could have been a special sale where the store advertised more and reached out to more customers.]

Go back

Additional Example

Mina collected data about items on sale at her accessories shop. Make a scatter plot of the data. Is there an association between the percent discount of sale items and the number of items sold? Explain.

Discount (%)	Items Purchased
10	5
15	7
20	6
25	4
30	5
35	29
40	12
50	19
60	23

Answer: For discounts of 10% to 30%, sales are similar. For discounts of 25% to 60%, there is a positive association between the percent discount and the number of items sold. There is an outlier at (35, 29). It represents the greatest number of items sold, 29, and their discount, 35%.

Practice & Problem Solving

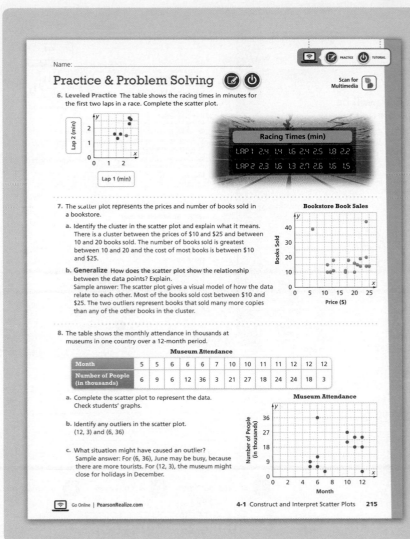

Available Online

Name: _____

Practice & Problem Solving

Scan for Multimedia

6. Leveled Practice The table shows the racing times in minutes for the first two laps in a race. Complete the scatter plot.

Racing Times (min)

| LAP 1 | 2.4 | 1.4 | 1.6 | 2.4 | 2.5 | 1.8 | 2.2 |
| LAP 2 | 2.3 | 1.6 | 1.3 | 2.9 | 2.6 | 1.6 | 1.5 |

7. The scatter plot represents the prices and number of books sold in a bookstore.

   Bookstore Book Sales

   a. Identify the cluster in the scatter plot and explain what it means.
   There is a cluster between the prices of $10 and $25 and between 10 and 20 books sold. The number of books sold is greatest between 10 and 20 and the cost of most books is between $10 and $25.

   b. **Generalize** How does the scatter plot show the relationship between the data points? Explain.
   Sample answer: The scatter plot gives a visual model of how the data relate to each other. Most of the books sold cost between $10 and $25. The two outliers represent books that sold many more copies than any of the other books in the cluster.

8. The table shows the monthly attendance in thousands at museums in one country over a 12-month period.

   Museum Attendance

   | Month | 5 | 5 | 6 | 6 | 6 | 7 | 10 | 10 | 11 | 11 | 12 | 12 | 12 |
   | Number of People (in thousands) | 6 | 9 | 6 | 12 | 36 | 3 | 21 | 27 | 18 | 24 | 24 | 18 | 3 |

   a. Complete the scatter plot to represent the data.
   Check students' graphs.

   b. Identify any outliers in the scatter plot.
   (12, 3) and (6, 36)

   c. What situation might have caused an outlier?
   Sample answer: For (6, 36), June may be busy, because there are more tourists. For (12, 3), the museum might close for holidays in December.

   Museum Attendance

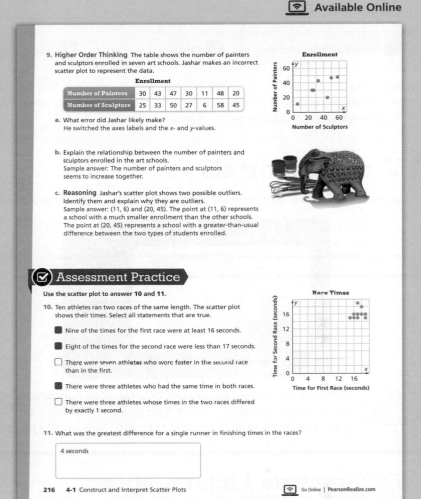

9. **Higher Order Thinking** The table shows the number of painters and sculptors enrolled in seven art schools. Jashar makes an incorrect scatter plot to represent the data.

   Enrollment

   | Number of Painters | 30 | 43 | 47 | 30 | 11 | 48 | 20 |
   | Number of Sculptors | 25 | 33 | 50 | 27 | 6 | 58 | 45 |

   a. What error did Jashar likely make?
   He switched the axes labels and the x- and y-values.

   b. Explain the relationship between the number of painters and sculptors enrolled in the art schools.
   Sample answer: The number of painters and sculptors seems to increase together.

   c. **Reasoning** Jashar's scatter plot shows two possible outliers. Identify them and explain why they are outliers.
   Sample answer: (11, 6) and (20, 45). The point at (11, 6) represents a school with a much smaller enrollment than the other schools. The point at (20, 45) represents a school with a greater-than-usual difference between the two types of students enrolled.

Assessment Practice

Use the scatter plot to answer 10 and 11.

10. Ten athletes ran two races of the same length. The scatter plot shows their times. Select all statements that are true.

   ☑ Nine of the times for the first race were at least 16 seconds.

   ☑ Eight of the times for the second race were less than 17 seconds.

   ☐ There were seven athletes who were faster in the second race than in the first.

   ☑ There were three athletes who had the same time in both races.

   ☐ There were three athletes whose times in the two races differed by exactly 1 second.

   Race Times

11. What was the greatest difference for a single runner in finishing times in the races?

   | 4 seconds |

English Language Learners

ITEM 7 You can use this item's scatter plot to confirm students' understanding of the cluster, gap, and outlier concepts.

Q: Write a paragraph that describes the scatter plot in your own words. Make sure you describe any gaps, outliers, or clusters. [Sample answer: The scatter plot shows that there are 2 outliers. The outliers do not fit in with the other data points. There is also 1 cluster from about $11 to $25 and 1 gap from about $13 to $17 in the scatter plot.]

Error Intervention

ITEM 9 Higher Order Thinking Point out that an outlier may indicate an error in data collection or in graphing the data in a scatter plot. Encourage students to check their work when they encounter an outlier in a data set.

You may opt to have students complete the automatically scored Practice & Problem Solving items online.

Item Analysis

Example	Items	DOK
1	6	1
2	7, 10, 11	2
	9	3
3	8	2

STEP 3 | Assess & Differentiate

Lesson Quiz

Use the student scores on the Lesson Quiz to prescribe differentiated assignments.

I Intervention 0–3 Points   **O** On-Level 4 Points   **A** Advanced 5 Points

You may opt to have students take the Lesson Quiz online. The Lesson Quiz will be automatically scored and appropriate remediation, practice, or enrichment will be assigned based on student performance.

Video Tutorials

Students can access instructional tutorials using the **Virtual Nerd app**.

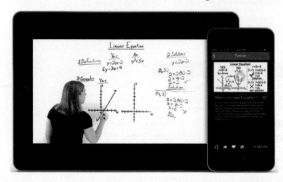

Students can also access the videos using the **BouncePages app** to scan exercise pages marked with this icon. Students can download both apps for free in their mobile devices' app store.

Available Online

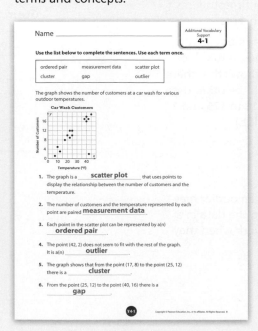

Name _____

Lesson Quiz 4-1

1. The scatter plot shows the number of visitors at an art show in relation to admission price. What does Point A on the graph represent?
   Sample answer: When the ticket price was $15, 120 visitors attended the art show.

2. What is a scatter plot?
   Ⓐ A table of measurement data used to construct a graph
   ● A display of points that shows the relationship between two sets of data
   Ⓒ A graph that has several different lines scattered on a coordinate plane
   Ⓓ A graph that is nonlinear

3. The following table shows the measurements of sharks at an aquarium. Complete the scatter plot below to represent the data.

Mass (kg)	0.07	68	70	82	85	90	100	105
Length (cm)	18	165	210	210	220	300	320	320

4. Refer to the scatter plot. Circle the clusters. Identify any gaps, and list any outliers in the scatter plot. What might the outlier represent?
   (0.07, 18); Sample answer: The outlier might represent a newborn shark.

5. For a–d, choose Yes or No to tell whether the following statements are true.
   a. The scatter plot in Question 1 shows a positive association.   ○ Yes   ● No
   b. The scatter plot in Question 4 shows a positive association.   ● Yes   ○ No
   c. No association means the y-values increase as the x-values decrease.   ○ Yes   ● No
   d. Scatter plots show the association between paired data.   ● Yes   ○ No

---

Differentiated Intervention

I = Intervention   **O** = On-Level   **A** = Advanced

Reteach to Build Understanding **I**

Provides scaffolded reteaching for the key lesson concepts.

Name _____

Reteach to Build Understanding 4-1

A scatter plot is a graph in the coordinate plane that shows the relationship between two sets of data.

The data in the table below can be written as ordered pairs: (8, 0), (12, 12), (14, 20), and (16, 28). The scatter plot shows the ordered pairs on the graph.

Text Messages Sent Today

Age (years)	8	12	14	16
Number of Text Messages	0	12	20	28

There is a positive association between the data sets.

Paul recorded several of his friends' scores on the latest science test and the number of minutes they spent reading the previous weekend. How can Paul construct a scatter plot of his data?

Time Spent Reading and Test Scores

Minutes Spent Reading	63	62	64	66	65
Test Score	65	75	65	70	90

1. A scatter plot has been started at the right. Add a title for the scatter plot and a label for the x-axis.
   See graph.

2. Write the data in the table as ordered pairs.
   (62, 75), (63, 65), (64, 65), (65, 90), (66, 70)

3. Complete the scatter plot by graphing your ordered pairs from Exercise 2.
   See graph.

4. Is there a relationship between the time students spent reading and their science test scores?
   The scatter plot shows no association between the time spent reading and science test scores.

On the Back!

5. After 5 minutes, Pablo jumped 14.6 feet. After 10 minutes, he jumped 14.1 feet. What are the two ordered pairs?
   (5, 14.6), (10, 14.1)

Additional Vocabulary Support **I** **O**

Helps students develop and reinforce understanding of key terms and concepts.

Name _____

Additional Vocabulary Support 4-1

Use the list below to complete the sentences. Use each term once.

ordered pair	measurement data	scatter plot
cluster	gap	outlier

The graph shows the number of customers at a car wash for various outdoor temperatures.

1. The graph is a **scatter plot** that uses points to display the relationship between the number of customers and the temperature.

2. The number of customers and the temperature represented by each point are paired **measurement data**.

3. Each point in the scatter plot can be represented by a(n) **ordered pair**.

4. The point (42, 2) does not seem to fit with the rest of the graph. It is a(n) **outlier**.

5. The graph shows that from the point (17, 8) to the point (25, 12) there is a **cluster**.

6. From the point (25, 12) to the point (40, 16) there is a **gap**.

Build Mathematical Literacy **I**

Provides support for struggling readers to build mathematical literacy.

Name _____

Build Mathematical Literacy 4-1

Read the problem and connect it to the graph.

The scatter plot shows the relationship between the age of the students in a club and the number of hours they participated in a dance-a-thon to raise money for their club during one month. Identify the cluster in the scatter plot and tell what it means. Then identify any gaps or outliers.

1. Underline the words in the problem that describe what a correct answer will contain.
   Check students' work.

2. On the scatter plot, underline the words that describe the quantity represented by the x-values of each data point. Circle the words that describe the quantity represented by the y-values.
   Check students' work.

3. Choose any point from the scatter plot and write its coordinates. Describe the meaning of this point.
   Sample answer: (16, 8); A 16-year-old club member spent 8 hours at the dance-a-thon to raise money for the club.

4. What is a cluster on a scatter plot? What is a gap?
   A cluster is a group of points that lie close together. A gap is an area on the graph that contains no data.

5. What is an outlier? How can you use a scatter plot to identify an outlier?
   An outlier is a data point that is set off from the rest of the data set. To find an outlier, look for any data point that is far from the other data points.

6. Circle the outlier on the scatter plot.
   Check students' work. The outlier is at (32,18).

Additional Practice

You may opt to have students complete the automatically scored Additional Practice items online.

Item Analysis

Example	Items	DOK
1	1	2
2	3, 6	2
	4	3
3	2, 5	2

PearsonRealize.com

Practice   Worksheets   Math Tools   Math Games

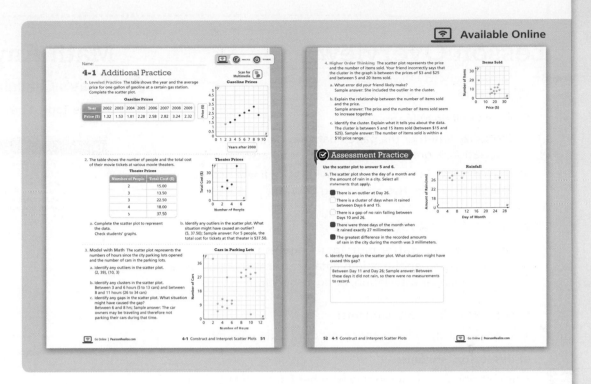

Available Online

Differentiated Intervention

I = Intervention   **O** = On-Level   **A** = Advanced

Enrichment O A

Presents engaging problems and activities that extend the lesson concepts.

Math Tools and Games I O A

Offers additional activities and games to build understanding and fluency.

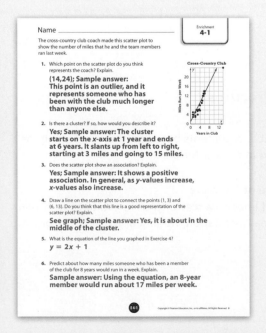

Lesson 4-2

Analyze Linear Associations

Lesson Overview

Objective

Students will be able to:

✔ recognize whether the paired data have a linear association, a nonlinear association, or no association.

✔ draw a trend line to determine whether a linear association is positive or negative and strong or weak.

Essential Understanding

A trend line on a scatter plot approximates the linear association between the paired data. Scatter plots can show a linear or nonlinear association, or no association.

Previously in this topic, students:

• created and analyzed scatter plots displaying paired data.

In this lesson, students:

• use a trend line to determine whether paired data have a linear association, a nonlinear association, or no association.

• determine whether linear associations are positive or negative, and whether they are strong or weak.

Later in this topic, students will:

• use the equation of a line to solve problems and make predictions in the context of bivariate measurement data.

This lesson emphasizes a blend of **conceptual understanding** and **application**.

• Students understand how to draw a trend line on a scatter plot that represents the relationship between paired data.

• Students classify the type of association that exists as linear, nonlinear, or no association.

FOCUS

COHERENCE

RIGOR

Math Anytime

Today's Challenge

Use the Topic 4 problems any time during this topic.

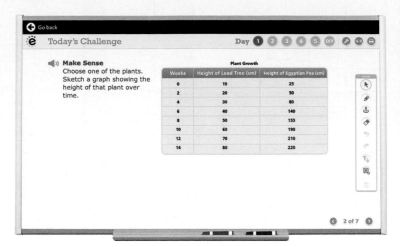

Mathematics Overview

In this lesson, students will extend their work with scatter plots to begin drawing trend lines to represent the relationship that exists between the quantities. The students will use trend lines to decide whether the paired data show a linear association, a nonlinear association, or no association. In addition, students will recognize when a linear association is positive or negative, and characterize it as being strong or weak.

Applying Math Practices

Construct Arguments

Students will make viable arguments based on the relationship or association determined in the scatter plot.

Look for and Make Use of Structure

Students will use trend lines on a scatter plot to evaluate whether paired data have a linear association, nonlinear association, or no association.

STEP 1 | Develop: Problem-Based Learning

15-20 min

Activity

Solve & Discuss It!

Look for Relationships As students work through the *Solve & Discuss It*, listen and look for students who make a general recommendation based on an analysis of the given information.

Before [WHOLE CLASS]

ETP **1 Implement Tasks that Promote Reasoning and Problem Solving**

Q: What is the decision that Angus needs to make? [Sample answer: He needs to decide whether he should stay up and study more or go to bed early and get lots of sleep before the test.]

2 Build Understanding

Q: What information does Angus have that can help him? [Sample answer: He has his last 6 test scores and the time he went to sleep before each test.]

During [SMALL GROUP]

ETP **3 Support Productive Struggle in Learning Mathematics**

Q: Is there any association between going to sleep early and the test scores? Explain. [No; Sample answer: Angus got similar scores on his tests when he went to sleep early and when he stayed up late to study.]

After [WHOLE CLASS]

ETP **4 Facilitate Meaningful Mathematical Discourse**

Ask students to share their solutions. If needed, project Luis' and Maria's work and ask:

Q: Did Luis and Maria reach the same conclusion? Whose method do you think is better? Explain. [Yes; Maria's; Sample answer: Maria uses all the data, and it's easier to analyze the data in a graph than in a list.]

5 Transition to Visual Learning

Q: How would you describe the graph that Maria made? [Sample answer: Maria's graph appears to have two sections, one where Angus went to sleep early and one where he stayed up late. There is no relationship among the data points.]

6 Extension for Early Finishers

Q: What conclusion might you make about a student who studied the longest but did not earn the highest score? Do you know if your conclusion is valid? [Sample answer: The student might not be very good at taking tests. Since the data is presented but not explained, any conclusion about why a student did poorly (or well) is speculation.]

Analyze Student Work

Available Online

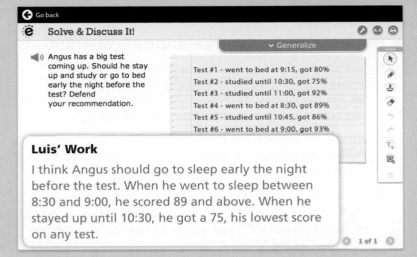

Go back

Solve & Discuss It!

∨ Generalize

Angus has a big test coming up. Should he stay up and study or go to bed early the night before the test? Defend your recommendation.

Test #1 - went to bed at 9:15, got 80%
Test #2 - studied until 10:30, got 75%
Test #3 - studied until 11:00, got 92%
Test #4 - went to bed at 8:30, got 89%
Test #5 - studied until 10:45, got 86%
Test #6 - went to bed at 9:00, got 93%

Luis' Work

I think Angus should go to sleep early the night before the test. When he went to sleep between 8:30 and 9:00, he scored 89 and above. When he stayed up until 10:30, he got a 75, his lowest score on any test.

1 of 1

Luis bases his answer on the data points that support his conclusion, not all the data points.

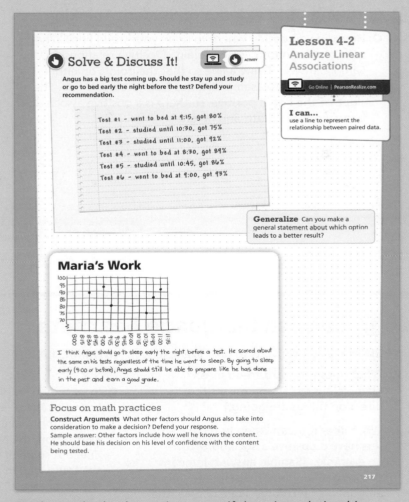

Solve & Discuss It!   ACTIVITY

Angus has a big test coming up. Should he stay up and study or go to bed early the night before the test? Defend your recommendation.

Test #1 - went to bed at 9:15, got 80%
Test #2 - studied until 10:30, got 75%
Test #3 - studied until 11:00, got 92%
Test #4 - went to bed at 8:30, got 89%
Test #5 - studied until 10:45, got 86%
Test #6 - went to bed at 9:00, got 93%

Lesson 4-2
Analyze Linear Associations

Go Online | PearsonRealize.com

I can...
use a line to represent the relationship between paired data.

Generalize Can you make a general statement about which option leads to a better result?

Maria's Work

I think Angus should go to sleep early the night before a test. He scored about the same on his tests regardless of the time he went to sleep. By going to sleep early (9:00 or before), Angus should still be able to prepare like he has done in the past and earn a good grade.

Focus on math practices

Construct Arguments What other factors should Angus also take into consideration to make a decision? Defend your response.
Sample answer: Other factors include how well he knows the content. He should base his decision on his level of confidence with the content being tested.

217

Maria graphs the data points to see if there is a relationship. Since there is no relationship, she decides that Angus should get a good night's sleep before a test.

ETP **Establish Mathematics Goals to Focus Learning**

Engage students in a discussion about the *Essential Question*. Make sure they understand that their line should show the trend between paired data.

 EXAMPLE **1** Linear Associations

ETP **Use and Connect Mathematical Representations**

Q: How can this line be called a good trend line if it passes through only one point? Explain. [Sample answer: Even though the line passes through just one point, many of the points are the same distance from the trend line.]

Q: What is the relationship between the paired data? Explain. [Positive relationship; Sample answer: The taller a person is, the longer the person's arm span is.]

Q: Which data point is farthest from the trend line? Would you call it an outlier? Explain. [(58, 62); Sample answer: It is not an outlier. This point is just a little bit farther from the line than most of the others.]

 Try It!

ETP **Elicit and Use Evidence of Student Thinking**

Q: How did you decide where to draw your trend line? What type of relationship is it? Explain. [Positive relationship; Sample answer: Draw a line so that the points on either side are about the same distance from the trend line. The slope of the line is positive, so there is a positive association between foot length and height.]

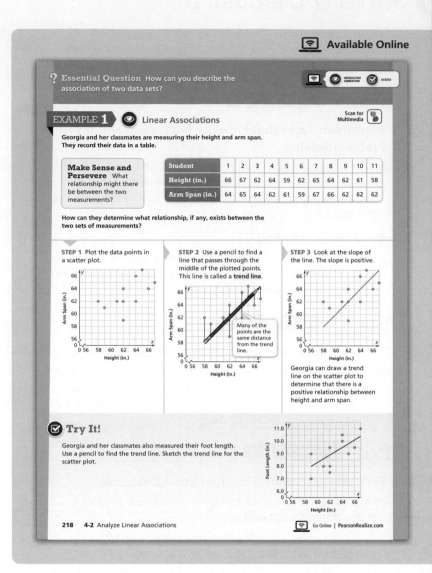

Students can access the *Visual Learning Animation Plus* by using the **BouncePages app** to scan this page. Students can download the app for free in their mobile devices' app store.

ELL **English Language Learners**

BEGINNING Ask students to read Example 1.

Q: What does the word *trend* mean? [Sample answer: Trend means the direction things are going.]

Q: What does it mean when two data sets have a positive association? Give an example. [Sample answer: It means that as one amount increases, the other amount also increases. For example, the more students enrolled in a school, the more teachers the school has in place.]

INTERMEDIATE Ask students to read Example 2.

Q: In your own words, tell the difference between a weak association and a strong association. [Sample answer: In a weak association, the points follow a trend line, but some of the points are far from the trend line. In a strong association, the points are all much closer to a trend line.]

ADVANCED Ask students to read Example 3.

Have students write a short description of the scatter plot so that a reader could visualize what the scatter plot would look like. [Sample description: The scatter plot is nonlinear and shows both a positive association and a negative association.]

Incorporate the students' descriptions into a classroom discussion.

EXAMPLE 2 Strength of Linear Associations

ETP Pose Purposeful Questions

Q: How do you know that these associations are linear? [Sample answer: The data points line up on the scatter plot so that a trend line can be drawn.]

Q: How can the Beach Visitors plot have a strong association and yet have an outlier? [Sample answer: The outlier is just one point that does not fit into the pattern. Most of the points are close to the trend line.]

EXAMPLE 3 Recognize Nonlinear Associations

ETP Pose Purposeful Questions

Q: What does it mean when an association is nonlinear? [Sample answer: A nonlinear association means that the data points in a scatter plot do not cluster in a way that would allow you to accurately draw a straight trend line.]

Q: Why does this scatter plot have an association even though it is not linear? [Sample answer: Even though the data points are not in a straight line, they still produce a clear shape instead of a random order.]

Try It!

ETP Elicit and Use Evidence of Student Thinking

Q: Look at part c. If you drew a line on this scatter plot through points (1, 1) and (6, 6) and extended the line to the edge of the graph, how would you explain that there is still no association? [Sample answer: Even though the line would have about the same number of data points above and below it, most of the data points are far away from the line, so there is no association.]

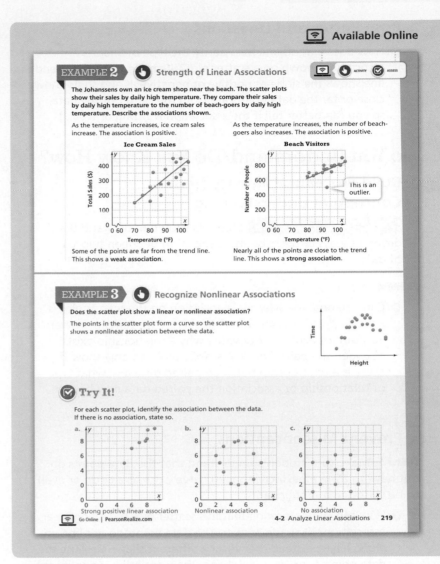

ADDITIONAL EXAMPLES

For additional examples go to PearsonRealize.com.

Response to Intervention

USE WITH EXAMPLE 2 Some students may have trouble correctly classifying scatter plots with positive or negative associations. They may need to be reminded of the difference between a line with a positive slope and a line with a negative slope.

• Have students answer these questions.

Q: How do you know that a scatter plot with data points rising from left to right has a positive association? [Sample answer: In a positive association, as the *x*-values increase, the *y*-values also increase. A trend line would slope upward from left to right.]

Q: How do you know that a scatter plot with data points falling from left to right has a negative association? [Sample answer: In a negative association, as the *x*-values increase, the *y*-values decrease. A trend line would slope downward from left to right.]

Enrichment

USE WITH EXAMPLE 3 Challenge advanced students to display their understanding of nonlinear associations by having them answer the following questions.

Q: How can you tell if a scatter plot has a nonlinear association or if it has no association? [Sample answer: In a scatter plot with a nonlinear association, many of the data points would show a pattern of some type. If the data points are random on a scatter plot, then they would show no pattern and there is no association.]

Q: Some nonlinear associations have data points that curve. What are some other shapes that could represent a nonlinear association? [Sample answer: A nonlinear association could also form circles, ovals, or u-shapes.]

STEP **2** | Develop: Visual Learning *continued*

 Key Concept   Activity

KEY CONCEPT

ETP Pose Purposeful Questions

Q: How does a trend line help clarify the type of linear association shown on a scatter plot? [Sample answer: A trend line shows the slope as positive or negative. It also shows how close or far the data points are from the center of the data, so you can better tell if the association is strong or weak.]

Do You Understand/Do You Know How?

ETP Build Procedural Fluency from Conceptual Understanding

? Essential Question Students should understand the different ways to describe the association between two sets of data.

ITEM 4

Q: Can you describe why the association on the scatter plot is a weak, positive association? Explain. [No; Sample answer: You cannot explain or describe why a relationship exists between the paired data. A scatter plot can only show if there is a relationship between paired data and what type of relationship or association the paired data may have.]

RtI Prevent Misconceptions

ITEM 5 Make sure students understand that the data points do not have to form a perfectly shaped curve (such as a circle or oval) to be classified as nonlinear.

Q: How can you determine that this scatter plot has a nonlinear association? [Sample answer: The data points do not line up along a line; instead they form a different shape. Because the data points form a curved shape, the association is nonlinear.]

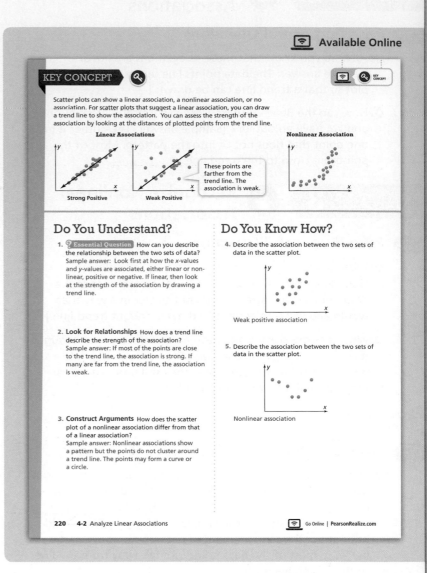

ADDITIONAL EXAMPLE **2**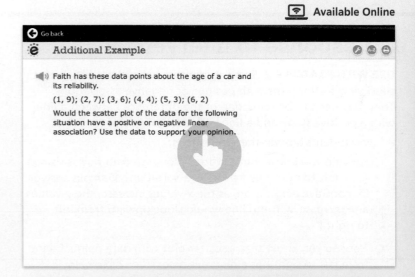

Help students understand the value of creating a scatter plot to visualize the situation in this additional example.

Make sure students understand how to interpret the data in the scatter plot.

Q: Could you answer the question without creating a graph? [Yes]

Q: Why is it helpful to create a scatter plot of the data? [Sample answer: The scatter plot shows the relationship or association between the age of the car and its reliability more clearly than the list of points do.]

Q: What would the slope of the trend line tell you about the type of association? Explain. [Sample answer: Since the slope would be negative, there is a negative association between the age of the car and its reliability.]

Answer: The age of the car and the reliability of the car would have a negative linear association because as the age of a car, *x*, increases, its reliability, *y*, decreases.

Practice & Problem Solving

Available Online

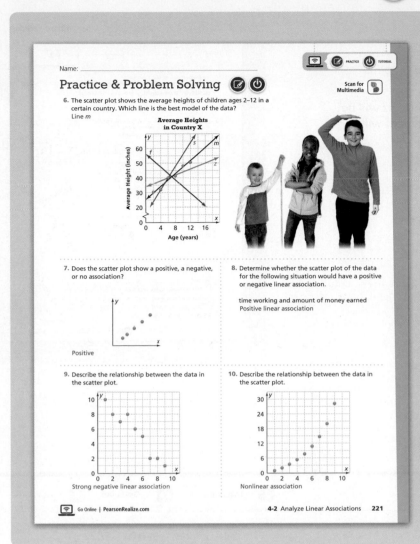

Name: _____

Practice & Problem Solving

Scan for Multimedia

6. The scatter plot shows the average heights of children ages 2–12 in a certain country. Which line is the best model of the data?
Line *m*

Average Heights in Country X

7. Does the scatter plot show a positive, a negative, or no association?

Positive

8. Determine whether the scatter plot of the data for the following situation would have a positive or negative linear association.

time working and amount of money earned
Positive linear association

9. Describe the relationship between the data in the scatter plot.

Strong negative linear association

10. Describe the relationship between the data in the scatter plot.

Nonlinear association

Go Online | PearsonRealize.com   4-2 Analyze Linear Associations   221

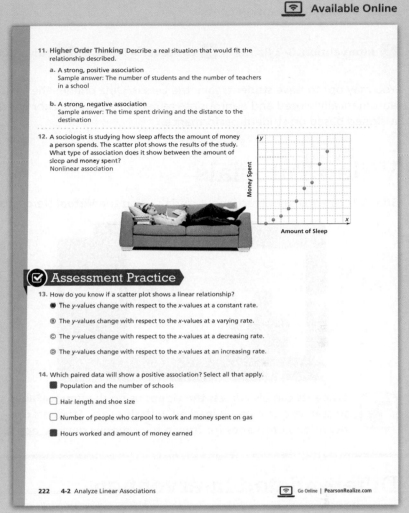

11. **Higher Order Thinking** Describe a real situation that would fit the relationship described.

a. A strong, positive association
Sample answer: The number of students and the number of teachers in a school

b. A strong, negative association
Sample answer: The time spent driving and the distance to the destination

12. A sociologist is studying how sleep affects the amount of money a person spends. The scatter plot shows the results of the study. What type of association does it show between the amount of sleep and money spent?
Nonlinear association

✓ Assessment Practice

13. How do you know if a scatter plot shows a linear relationship?
- Ⓐ The *y*-values change with respect to the *x*-values at a constant rate.
- Ⓑ The *y*-values change with respect to the *x*-values at a varying rate.
- Ⓒ The *y*-values change with respect to the *x*-values at a decreasing rate.
- Ⓓ The *y*-values change with respect to the *x*-values at an increasing rate.

14. Which paired data will show a positive association? Select all that apply.
- ■ Population and the number of schools
- ☐ Hair length and shoe size
- ☐ Number of people who carpool to work and money spent on gas
- ■ Hours worked and amount of money earned

222   4-2 Analyze Linear Associations   Go Online | PearsonRealize.com

---

⚠ Error Intervention

ITEM 8 Students may think that they need an image of a scatter plot to classify its association. Use this problem to show them they can determine an association without an image by using their reasoning skills. Have students answer the following question:

Q: How can you determine the association without a scatter plot? [Sample answer: Many people are paid on an hourly basis. Therefore, when a person works more hours, the amount of money he or she earns increases. A trend line would point upward from left to right.]

ⒺⓁⓁ English Language Learners

ITEM 12 Students might be unsure of what a sociologist is.

Q: In the context of the problem, what kind of work do you think a sociologist might do? [Sample answer: A sociologist is someone who studies the behavior of groups of people.]

You may opt to have students complete the automatically scored Practice & Problem Solving items online.

Item Analysis

Example	Items	DOK
1	6, 13	1
2	7, 8, 9, 14	1
	11	3
3	10, 12	1

STEP 3 | Assess & Differentiate

☑ Lesson Quiz

RtI Use the student scores on the Lesson Quiz to prescribe differentiated assignments.

I Intervention 0–3 Points   **O** On-Level 4 Points   **A** Advanced 5 Points

You may opt to have students take the Lesson Quiz online. The Lesson Quiz will be automatically scored and appropriate remediation, practice, or enrichment will be assigned based on student performance.

⏻ Video Tutorials

Students can access instructional tutorials using the **Virtual Nerd app**.

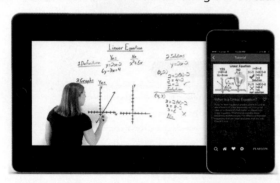

Students can also access the videos using the **BouncePages app** to scan exercise pages marked with this icon. Students can download both apps for free in their mobile devices' app store.

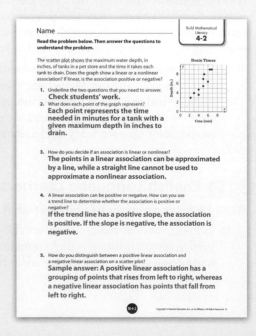

🛜 Available Online

Differentiated Intervention

I = Intervention   **O** = On-Level   **A** = Advanced

Reteach to Build Understanding **I**

Provides scaffolded reteaching for the key lesson concepts.

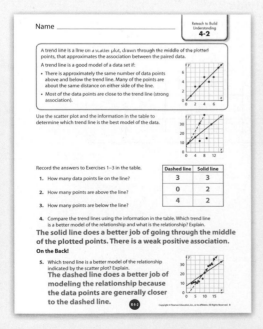

Additional Vocabulary Support **I O**

Helps students develop and reinforce understanding of key terms and concepts.

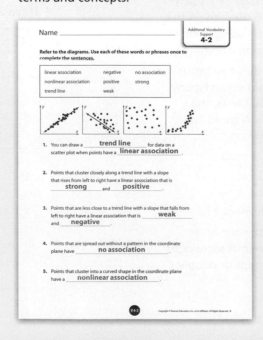

Build Mathematical Literacy **I**

Provides support for struggling readers to build mathematical literacy.

Practice   Worksheets   Math Tools   Math Games

Additional Practice

You may opt to have students complete the automatically scored Additional Practice items online.

Item Analysis

Example	Items	DOK
1	1, 2, 3, 4, 7, 8	2
2	5	2
2	7	3
3	6, 9, 10	2

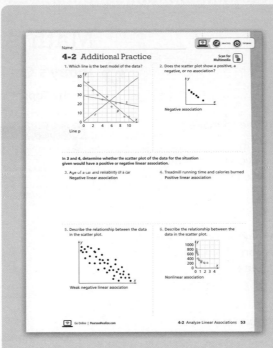

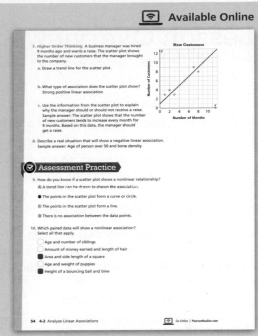

Differentiated Intervention

I = Intervention   **O** = On-Level   **A** = Advanced

Enrichment O A

Presents engaging problems and activities that extend the lesson concepts.

Math Tools and Games I O A

Offers additional activities and games to build understanding and fluency.

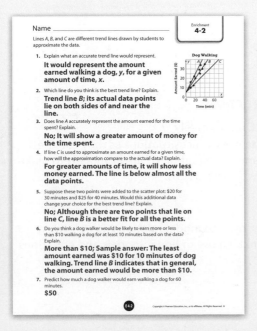

Activity

Lesson 4-3
Use Linear Models to Make Predictions

Lesson Overview

FOCUS

Objective

Students will be able to:

✔ use the slope and *y*-intercept of a trend line to make a prediction.

✔ make a prediction when no equation is given by drawing trend lines and writing the equation of the linear model.

Essential Understanding

Trend lines in linear models can help with making predictions about a data set. By determining the equation of a linear model, predictions of an outcome can be made.

COHERENCE

Previously in this topic, students:

• learned to interpret and construct scatter plots.

In this lesson, students:

• use linear models to make predictions from data given in scatter plots.

• learn how to make predictions when there is no equation given for the trend in a scatter plot.

In Topic 5, students will:

• solve systems of linear equations by graphing, using substitution, and using elimination.

RIGOR

This lesson emphasizes a blend of **conceptual understanding** and **procedural skill**.

• Students use trend lines in scatter plots to make predictions about a data set and predict outcomes not given in the scatter plot.

Math Anytime

Today's Challenge

Use the Topic 4 problems any time during this topic.

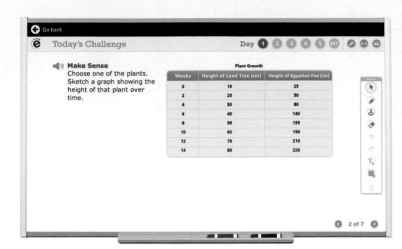

Mathematics Overview

In this lesson, students will continue their work with scatter plots and trend lines. When the data appear to have a linear association, students will sketch trend lines and write equations for them. Students will also learn how to make predictions about current or future trends for the data, using the equation of a trend line as a linear model of the relationship between the paired data.

Applying Math Practices

Reason Abstractly and Quantitatively

Students will make sense of abstract situations as they use the slope, the *y*-intercept, and the equation of linear models to make predictions about real-world situations.

Model with Math

Students will use scatter plots to model relationships between real-world quantities, making use of linear models and equations to solve problems.

STEP 1 | Develop: Problem-Based Learning

15-20 min

Activity

Solve & Discuss It!

Model with Mathematics As students work through the *Solve & Discuss It*, listen and look for students who understand the problem and apply what they know about scatter plots and the slope of a line to make reference to the data represented in the graph.

Before [WHOLE CLASS]

ETP **1 Implement Tasks that Promote Reasoning and Problem Solving**

Q: What are the two sets of data in the scatter plot? [Time (in minutes) and the Calories burned.]

2 Build Understanding

Q: Do you think that the paired data have a linear association, nonlinear association, or no association? Explain. [Linear association; Sample answer: Because the paired data resemble a line, and you could draw a trend line.]

During [SMALL GROUP]

ETP **3 Support Productive Struggle in Learning Mathematics**

Q: How can you decide where to draw the trend line? [Sample answer: Attempt to draw a line that keeps the points in a cluster close to the trend line.]

Q: How can you use the trend line to find out how many minutes Bao will need to exercise to burn 5,000 Calories? [Sample answer: Find a number of Calories that can be multiplied to get 5,000, for example 500. Since 500 × 10 = 5,000, multiply the time by 10 to find out how long Bao needs to exercise.]

After [WHOLE CLASS]

ETP **4 Facilitate Meaningful Mathematical Discourse**

Ask students to share their solutions. If needed, project Tracey's and Chris's work and ask:

Q: Is it possible that there is more than one trend line that is a good approximation of the relationship of the paired data? [Yes; Sample answer: The trend lines may be slightly different, but they should give an accurate picture of the cluster.]

Q: Would you expect all answers for how long it takes Bao to burn 5,000 Calories to be the same? Explain. [No; Sample answer: Each person's trend line may be slightly different. This would result in answers that are similar but not exactly the same.]

5 Transition to Visual Learning

Q: What does the trend line tell about the relationship between Calories burned and minutes exercised? [Sample answer: The trend line shows that there is a positive relationship.]

6 Extension for Early Finishers

Q: Do you think this trend line could continue indefinitely? Explain. [No; Sample answer: There is a limit to the number of minutes Bao can exercise.]

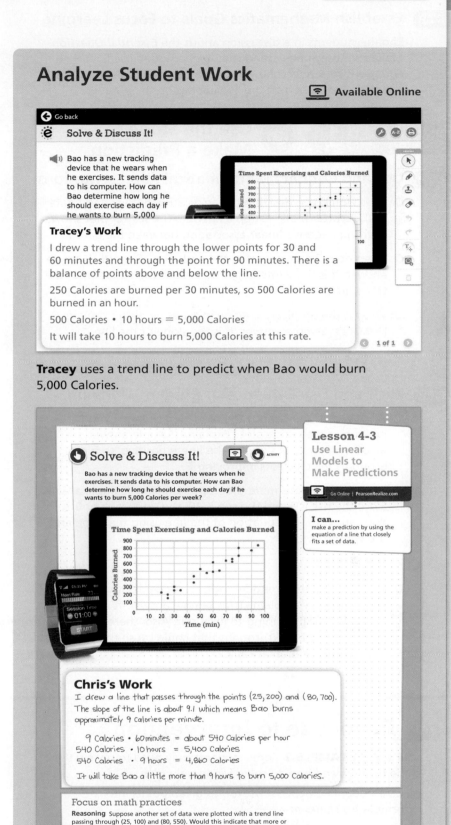

Analyze Student Work

Available Online

Tracey's Work

I drew a trend line through the lower points for 30 and 60 minutes and through the point for 90 minutes. There is a balance of points above and below the line.

250 Calories are burned per 30 minutes, so 500 Calories are burned in an hour.

500 Calories • 10 hours = 5,000 Calories

It will take 10 hours to burn 5,000 Calories at this rate.

Tracey uses a trend line to predict when Bao would burn 5,000 Calories.

Chris's Work

I drew a line that passes through the points (25, 200) and (80, 700). The slope of the line is about 9.1 which means Bao burns approximately 9 calories per minute.

9 Calories • 60 minutes = about 540 Calories per hour
540 Calories • 10 hours = 5,400 Calories
540 Calories • 9 hours = 4,860 Calories

It will take Bao a little more than 9 hours to burn 5,000 Calories.

Chris finds the slope of a trend line and uses it to estimate the time it would take Bao to burn 5,000 Calories.

ETP Establish Mathematics Goals to Focus Learning

Engage students in a discussion about the *Essential Question*. Make sure they understand that linear models use linear equations to connect the variables and that the slope of the line describes the effect the *x*-value has on the *y*-value.

EXAMPLE 1 Use the Slope to Make a Prediction

ETP Use and Connect Mathematical Representations

Q: How would you describe the association between the data in the scatter plot? [Sample answer: The scatter plot shows a strong negative linear association between the data.]

Q: What does 2.4 represent in the equation? Explain. [Sample answer: It is the *y*-intercept and part of the equation of the trend line.]

Q: What is the predicted change in times per year? Explain. [−0.0133; Sample answer: It is the slope of the line.]

☑ Try It!

ETP Elicit and Use Evidence of Student Thinking

Q: What can you tell about the predicted change by just looking at the scatterplot? Explain. [Sample answer: By observation the slope of the line is positive, so fuel economy in vehicles is improving.]

Q: How can you determine the slope? Explain. [Sample answer: Since the rise is 3 and the run is 10, the slope is $\frac{3}{10}$ or 0.3. You can write the equation of the line using the slope and the *y*-intercept.]

Convince Me!

Q: Do you think this trend line will continue like this for the next 100 years? Explain. [No; Sample answer: It already looks like it is beginning to level out. Also, there may be new scientific breakthroughs that could cause the scatter plot to change dramatically.]

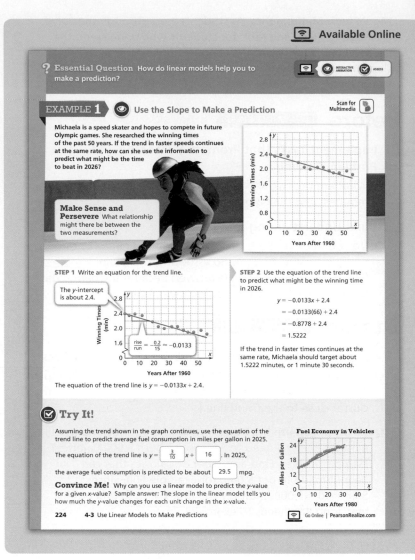

Students can access the *Visual Learning Animation Plus* by using the **BouncePages** app to scan this page. Students can download the app for free in their mobile devices' app store.

△ Response to Intervention

USE WITH EXAMPLE 2 Some students may need to review the slope formula and how to solve for an unknown.

• Have students practice substituting given points into the formula for slope, $m = \frac{y_2 - y_1}{x_2 - x_1}$.

Q: What is the slope of a line passing through (70, 500) and (90, 815)? [$\frac{(815 - 500)}{(90 - 70)} = \frac{315}{20} = \frac{63}{4}$]

• Have students review solving for the unknown variable, *b*.

Q: What is the *y*-intercept of a line if it has a slope of −2 and passes through the point (3, 4)? Explain. [10; Sample answer: $4 = -2(3) + b$, $4 = -6 + b$, $10 = b$]

🏆 Enrichment

USE WITH EXAMPLE 1 Challenge advanced students to make a prediction using the trend line and explain if their answer is reasonable.

Q: In the year 2100, predict the winning time in seconds. Does this answer seem plausible? Explain. [0.524 minutes or 31.44 seconds; Sample answer: Using the equation, $y = -0.0134x + 2.4$, this record does not seem possible. The trend line will probably start to flatten out.]

Activity Assess

EXAMPLE 2 Use a Scatter Plot to Make a Prediction

ETP **Pose Purposeful Questions**

Q: What can you tell about the relationship between the temperature and the number of people riding water rides by looking at the graph? [Sample answer: There is a positive relationship—the warmer the temperature, the more people visit the park.]

Q: For every 5 degrees the temperature increases, about how many more people attend the park? Explain.
[About 80 more people; Sample answer: From 70 to 90 degrees, about 315 more people attended the park. This is 4 groups of 5, so 315 divided by 4 = 78.75, which is about 80 people.]

Q: Why do you think the graph only goes from 70 to 100 degrees. [Sample answer: These are the realistic temperatures for when the park is open.]

EXAMPLE 3 Interpret the Slope and *y*-intercept

ETP **Pose Purposeful Questions**

Q: If you used the points (0, 8) and (80, 54) to find the slope, how would the equation of the trend line change? Explain.
[Same *y*-intercept, but a smaller slope; Sample answer: *y*-intercept: 8; slope: $\frac{(54-8)}{(80-0)} = \frac{46}{80} = \frac{23}{40}$. $\frac{23}{40} < \frac{3}{5}$ or $\frac{24}{40}$; $y = \frac{23}{40}x + 8$]

Q: What does a positive slope tell you about the sales of smoothies? [Sample answer: It tells you that as the temperature rises more smoothies are sold.]

Try It!

ETP **Elicit and Use Evidence of Student Thinking**

Q: According to the scatter plot, how many smoothies should employees expect to make on a 90-degree day?
[About 62,000]

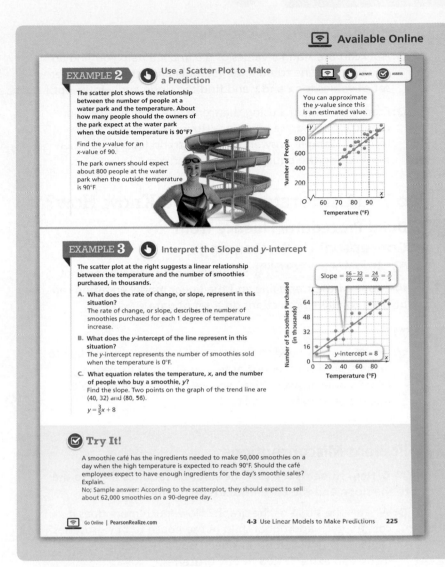

EXAMPLE 2 Use a Scatter Plot to Make a Prediction

The scatter plot shows the relationship between the number of people at a water park and the temperature. About how many people should the owners of the park expect at the water park when the outside temperature is 90°F?

Find the *y*-value for an *x*-value of 90.

The park owners should expect about 800 people at the water park when the outside temperature is 90°F

You can approximate the *y*-value since this is an estimated value.

EXAMPLE 3 Interpret the Slope and *y*-intercept

The scatter plot at the right suggests a linear relationship between the temperature and the number of smoothies purchased, in thousands.

A. What does the rate of change, or slope, represent in this situation?
The rate of change, or slope, describes the number of smoothies purchased for each 1 degree of temperature increase.

B. What does the *y*-intercept of the line represent in this situation?
The *y*-intercept represents the number of smoothies sold when the temperature is 0°F.

C. What equation relates the temperature, *x*, and the number of people who buy a smoothie, *y*?
Find the slope. Two points on the graph of the trend line are (40, 32) and (80, 56).

$y = \frac{3}{5}x + 8$

Slope $= \frac{56-32}{80-40} = \frac{24}{40} = \frac{3}{5}$

y-intercept = 8

Try It!

A smoothie café has the ingredients needed to make 50,000 smoothies on a day when the high temperature is expected to reach 90°F. Should the café employees expect to have enough ingredients for the day's smoothie sales? Explain.
No; Sample answer: According to the scatterplot, they should expect to sell about 62,000 smoothies on a 90-degree day.

Go Online | PearsonRealize.com   4-3 Use Linear Models to Make Predictions   225

ADDITIONAL EXAMPLES

For additional examples go to PearsonRealize.com.

ⒺⓁⓁ English Language Learners

BEGINNING Ask students to review Example 3.

Make sure students understand important concepts needed to make accurate predictions.

Q: In your own words, define *slope*.
[Sample answer: Slope refers to the steepness of a line or the rise over the run.]

Q: In your own words, define the *y*-intercept.
[Sample answer: The starting value when *x* = 0]

INTERMEDIATE Ask students to review Example 3.

Q: Have students tell what the terms *rate of change* and *starting value* mean. Then have them tell what it means in the context of the problem. [Sample answer: Rate of change means how fast something changes and the starting value is the *y*-intercept. In this problem, rate of change means how the number of people who buy smoothies changes as the temperature increases, and the starting value is 8 smoothies sold when the temperature is 0°F.]

ADVANCED Ask students to review Example 3.

Have students work in pairs to evaluate the statement: More smoothies are sold in warm weather than in cold weather. Display a list of math terms used in the explanations, such as trend line, graph, scatter plot, *x*-axis, *y*-axis, slope, *y*-intercept, and data points.

STEP **2** | Develop: Visual Learning *continued*

Key Concept   Activity

KEY CONCEPT

ETP ## Pose Purposeful Questions

Q: How can the *x* and *y*-values of 5.5 and 4.5 help you find an equation for the trend line? [Sample answer: Find another set of values for *x* and *y* and find the slope and *y*-intercept.]

Q: Predict a value of *x* using the trend line. Then check your prediction using the equation. How close were the two results? [Sample answer: Using the trend line, $y = 9$ when $x = 4$. Using the equation, $y = 9$ when $x = 4$.]

Do You Understand/Do You Know How?

ETP ## Build Procedural Fluency from Conceptual Understanding

❓ Essential Question Students should understand that the slope of the trend line and the linear model equation can be used to make predictions on a set of data.

ITEM 2

Q: Do you always need to find the equation for a trend line to make a prediction about other data points? Explain. [No; Sample answer: Often you can use the trend line to make a reasonable prediction.]

RtI ## Prevent Misconceptions

ITEM 4 Help students see that the solution requires them to use both the slope and the difference in the number of children.

Q: What is the slope of the graph? How much more does it cost for each additional child in the house to buy groceries? Explain. [21.08; Sample answer: For every additional child, it costs an extra $21.08 to buy groceries.]

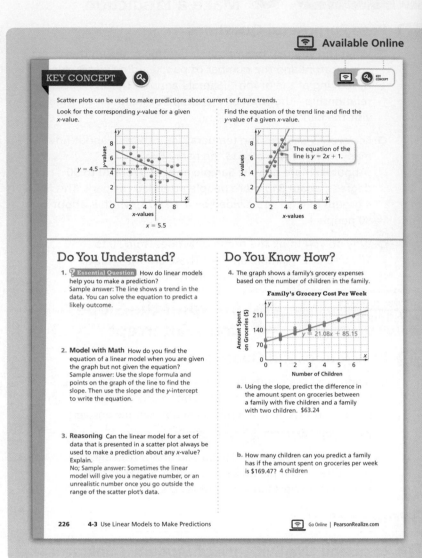

ADDITIONAL EXAMPLE **2**

Available Online

Help students transition from using linear equations to determine if there is an association to using an association to determine if a given value matches that association.

Q: Where could you look on the graph to find the point that represents a height of 57 inches? [Sample answer: Draw a horizontal line across at $y = 57$ and find where that intersects the trend line.]

Q: Does this graph show a strong association or a weak association? Explain. [Strong association; Sample answer: Most of the points are close to the trend line.]

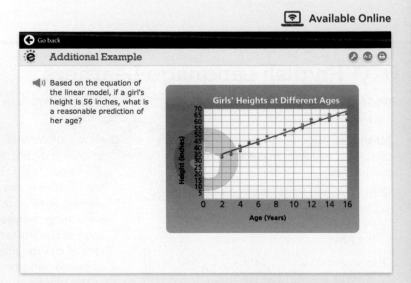

Answer: Lisa's height is in the range expected for a 12-year-old girl.

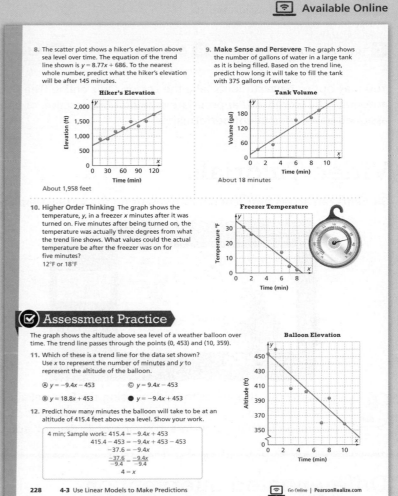

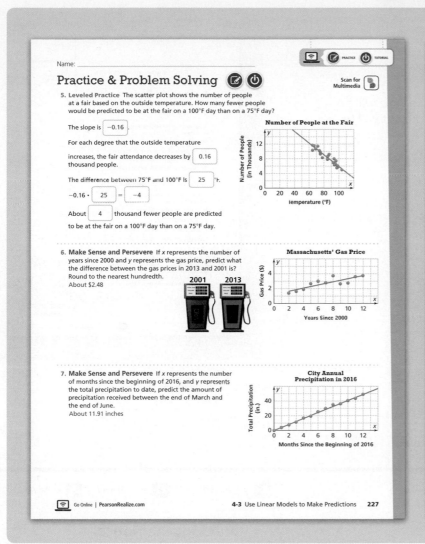

Practice & Problem Solving

Name: _____

Practice & Problem Solving

Scan for Multimedia

5. Leveled Practice The scatter plot shows the number of people at a fair based on the outside temperature. How many fewer people would be predicted to be at the fair on a 100°F day than on a 75°F day?

The slope is -0.16.

For each degree that the outside temperature increases, the fair attendance decreases by 0.16 thousand people.

The difference between 75°F and 100°F is 25 °F.

$-0.16 \cdot 25 = -4$

About 4 thousand fewer people are predicted to be at the fair on a 100°F day than on a 75°F day.

Number of People at the Fair

6. Make Sense and Persevere If x represents the number of years since 2000 and y represents the gas price, predict what the difference between the gas prices in 2013 and 2001 is? Round to the nearest hundredth.
About $2.48

Massachusetts' Gas Price
2001 2013

7. Make Sense and Persevere If x represents the number of months since the beginning of 2016, and y represents the total precipitation to date, predict the amount of precipitation received between the end of March and the end of June.
About 11.91 inches

City Annual Precipitation in 2016

Go Online | PearsonRealize.com   4-3 Use Linear Models to Make Predictions   227

8. The scatter plot shows a hiker's elevation above sea level over time. The equation of the trend line shown is $y = 8.77x + 686$. To the nearest whole number, predict what the hiker's elevation will be after 145 minutes.

Hiker's Elevation

About 1,958 feet

9. Make Sense and Persevere The graph shows the number of gallons of water in a large tank as it is being filled. Based on the trend line, predict how long it will take to fill the tank with 375 gallons of water.

Tank Volume

About 18 minutes

10. Higher Order Thinking The graph shows the temperature, y, in a freezer x minutes after it was turned on. Five minutes after being turned on, the temperature was actually three degrees from what the trend line shows. What values could the actual temperature be after the freezer was on for five minutes?
12°F or 18°F

Freezer Temperature

Assessment Practice

The graph shows the altitude above sea level of a weather balloon over time. The trend line passes through the points (0, 453) and (10, 359).

11. Which of these is a trend line for the data set shown? Use x to represent the number of minutes and y to represent the altitude of the balloon.

ⓐ $y = -9.4x - 453$
Ⓑ $y = 18.8x + 453$
ⓒ $y = 9.4x - 453$
● $y = -9.4x + 453$

Balloon Elevation

12. Predict how many minutes the balloon will take to be at an altitude of 415.4 feet above sea level. Show your work.

4 min; Sample work: $415.4 = -9.4x + 453$
$415.4 - 453 = -9.4x + 453 - 453$
$-37.6 = -9.4x$
$\dfrac{-37.6}{-9.4} = \dfrac{-9.4x}{-9.4}$
$4 = x$

228   4-3 Use Linear Models to Make Predictions   Go Online | PearsonRealize.com

---

🏆 Challenge

ITEM 10 Use this exercise to extend students' understanding of making predictions using the slope of the trend line.

Q: What is the equation that best represents the data in the graph? [Sample answer: $y = -4x + 35$]

Q: Using the equation for the trend line, how cold will the temperature be after 30 minutes? Do you think that will happen? Explain. [Between −82 degrees and −88 degrees; No; Sample answer: It is probably programmed to stop decreasing at a certain temperature.]

🔴 Error Intervention

ITEM 9 Students may be confused because the number 375 is not on the y-axis.

Q: Is there a number on the y-axis that is about half as large as 375? How can you use that point to make a prediction? [Sample answer: The number 180 is about half of 375. So it should take a little more than twice that long to fill the tank, or a little more than 16 minutes.]

You may opt to have students complete the automatically scored Practice & Problem Solving items online.

Item Analysis

Example	Items	DOK
1	5, 6, 7	1
2	8, 9, 12	1
2	10	2
3	11	1

Lesson Quiz

Use the student scores on the Lesson Quiz to prescribe differentiated assignments.

I Intervention 0–3 Points   **O** On-Level 4 Points   **A** Advanced 5 Points

You may opt to have students take the Lesson Quiz online. The Lesson Quiz will be automatically scored and appropriate remediation, practice, or enrichment will be assigned based on student performance.

 Video Tutorials

Students can access instructional tutorials using the **Virtual Nerd app**.

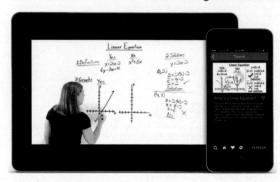

Students can also access the videos using the **BouncePages app** to scan exercise pages marked with this icon. Students can download both apps for free in their mobile devices' app store.

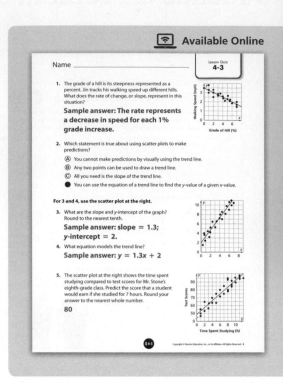

📶 Available Online

Name _____   Lesson Quiz **4-3**

1. The grade of a hill is its steepness represented as a percent. Jin tracks his walking speed up different hills. What does the rate of change, or slope, represent in this situation?
Sample answer: The rate represents a decrease in speed for each 1% grade increase.

2. Which statement is true about using scatter plots to make predictions?
Ⓐ You cannot make predictions by visually using the trend line.
Ⓑ Any two points can be used to draw a trend line.
Ⓒ All you need is the slope of the trend line.
● You can use the equation of a trend line to find the y-value of a given x-value.

For 3 and 4, use the scatter plot at the right.

3. What are the slope and y-intercept of the graph? Round to the nearest tenth.
Sample answer: slope = 1.3; y-intercept = 2.

4. What equation models the trend line?
Sample answer: y = 1.3x + 2

5. The scatter plot at the right shows the time spent studying compared to test scores for Mr. Stone's eighth-grade class. Predict the score that a student would earn if she studied for 7 hours. Round your answer to the nearest whole number.
80

Differentiated Intervention

I = Intervention   **O** = On-Level   **A** = Advanced

Reteach to Build Understanding **I**

Provides scaffolded reteaching for the key lesson concepts.

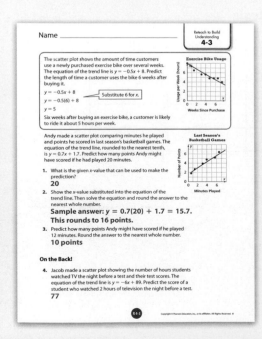

Name _____   Reteach to Build Understanding **4-3**

The scatter plot shows the amount of time customers use a newly purchased exercise bike over several weeks. The equation of the trend line is y = −0.5x + 8. Predict the length of time a customer uses the bike 6 weeks after buying it.

y = −0.5x + 8
y = −0.5(6) + 8   ⟵ Substitute 6 for x.
y = 5

Six weeks after buying an exercise bike, a customer is likely to ride it about 5 hours per week.

Andy made a scatter plot comparing minutes he played and points he scored in last season's basketball games. The equation of the trend line, rounded to the nearest tenth, is y = 0.7x + 1.7. Predict how many points Andy might have scored if he had played 20 minutes.

1. What is the given x-value that can be used to make the prediction?
20

2. Show the x-value substituted into the equation of the trend line. Then solve the equation and round the answer to the nearest whole number.
Sample answer: y = 0.7(20) + 1.7 = 15.7. This rounds to 16 points.

3. Predict how many points Andy might have scored if he played 12 minutes. Round the answer to the nearest whole number.
10 points

On the Back!

4. Jacob made a scatter plot showing the number of hours students watched TV the night before a test and their test scores. The equation of the trend line is y = −6x + 89. Predict the score of a student who watched 2 hours of television the night before a test.
77

Additional Vocabulary Support **I** **O**

Helps students develop and reinforce understanding of key terms and concepts.

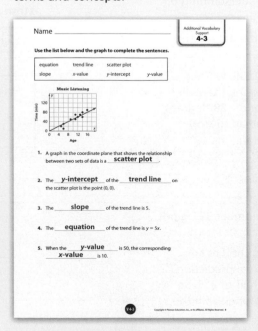

Name _____   Additional Vocabulary Support **4-3**

Use the list below and the graph to complete the sentences.

equation	trend line	scatter plot
slope	x-value	y-intercept	y-value

1. A graph in the coordinate plane that shows the relationship between two sets of data is a ____ **scatter plot** ____.

2. The ____ **y-intercept** ____ of the ____ **trend line** ____ on the scatter plot is the point (0, 0).

3. The ____ **slope** ____ of the trend line is 5.

4. The ____ **equation** ____ of the trend line is y = 5x.

5. When the ____ **y-value** ____ is 50, the corresponding ____ **x-value** ____ is 10.

Build Mathematical Literacy **I**

Provides support for struggling readers to build mathematical literacy.

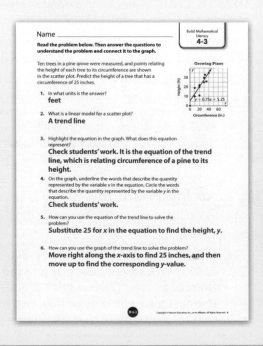

Name _____   Build Mathematical Literacy **4-3**

Read the problem below. Then answer the questions to understand the problem and connect it to the graph.

Ten trees in a pine grove were measured, and points relating the height of each tree to its circumference are shown in the scatter plot. Predict the height of a tree that has a circumference of 25 inches.

1. In what units is the answer?
feet

2. What is a linear model for a scatter plot?
A trend line

3. Highlight the equation in the graph. What does this equation represent?
Check students' work. It is the equation of the trend line, which is relating circumference of a pine to its height.

4. On the graph, underline the words that describe the quantity represented by the variable x in the equation. Circle the words that describe the quantity represented by the variable y in the equation.
Check students' work.

5. How can you use the equation of the trend line to solve the problem?
Substitute 25 for x in the equation to find the height, y.

6. How can you use the graph of the trend line to solve the problem?
Move right along the x-axis to find 25 inches, and then move up to find the corresponding y-value.

Practice Worksheets Math Tools Math Games

Additional Practice

You may opt to have students complete the automatically scored Additional Practice items online.

 Available Online

Item Analysis

Example	Items	DOK
1	1, 2	2
	5	3
2	4, 6	2
3	3	2

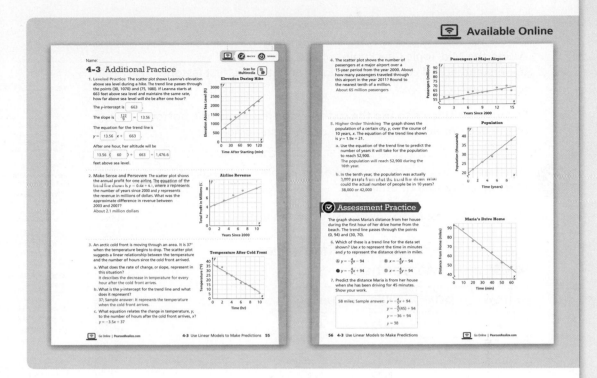

Differentiated Intervention

 = Intervention    = On-Level    = Advanced

Enrichment **O A**

Presents engaging problems and activities that extend the lesson concepts.

Math Tools and Games **I O A**

Offers additional activities and games to build understanding and fluency.

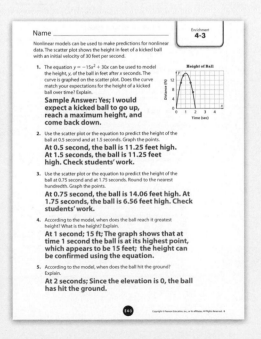

TOPIC 4
MID-TOPIC CHECKPOINT

Assess

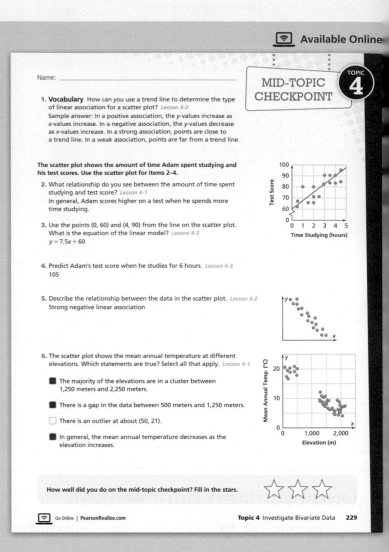

Assign the Mid-Topic Checkpoint to monitor students' understandings of concepts and skills taught in the first lessons in this topic.

Encourage students to use the self-assessment form at the bottom of the page to describe their level of understanding.

 You may opt to have students take the automatically-scored Mid-Topic Assessment online.

Use students' results to adjust instruction as needed.

 ## Item Analysis for Diagnosis and Intervention

Item	DOK	MDIS	Lesson
1	2	N72	4-2
2	1	N72	4-1
3	2	N72	4-3
4	3	N72	4-3
5	2	N72	4-2
6	2	N72	4-1

Mid-Topic Assessment Master

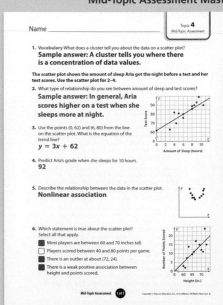

MID-TOPIC PERFORMANCE TASK

Assess

Assess students' ability to apply the concepts and skills in the first part of the topic using the Mid-Topic Performance Task, found in the Student's Edition or at PearsonRealize.com.

 ## Item Analysis for Diagnosis and Intervention

Part	DOK	MDIS	Lesson
A	1	N72	4-1
B	2	N72	4-1, 4-2
C	3	N72	4-2, 4-3

Scoring Guide

Part	Points	Mid-Topic Performance Task
A	2	Correct scatter plot of the data set
	1	Partially correct scatter plot graph of the data set
B	2	Correct linear association and the correct explanation of the relationship between the data set
	1	Correct linear association or the correct explanation of the relationship between the data set
C	2	Correct equation of the linear model and correct prediction
	1	Correct equation of the linear model or correct prediction

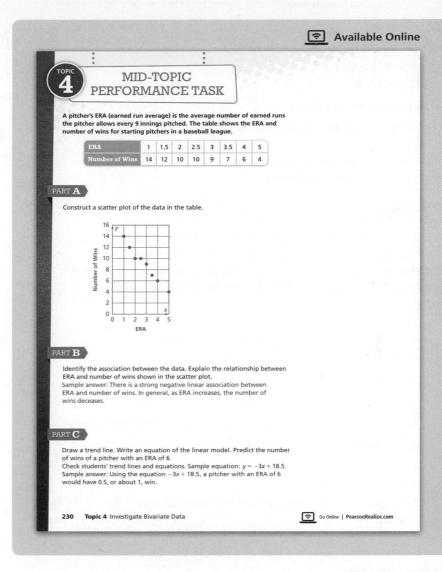

Available Online

TOPIC

4

MID-TOPIC PERFORMANCE TASK

A pitcher's ERA (earned run average) is the average number of earned runs the pitcher allows every 9 innings pitched. The table shows the ERA and number of wins for starting pitchers in a baseball league.

ERA	1	1.5	2	2.5	3	3.5	4	5
Number of Wins	14	12	10	10	9	7	6	4

PART A

Construct a scatter plot of the data in the table.

PART B

Identify the association between the data. Explain the relationship between ERA and number of wins shown in the scatter plot.
Sample answer: There is a strong negative linear association between ERA and number of wins. In general, as ERA increases, the number of wins deceases.

PART C

Draw a trend line. Write an equation of the linear model. Predict the number of wins of a pitcher with an ERA of 6.
Check students' trend lines and equations. Sample equation: $y = -3x + 18.5$.
Sample answer: Using the equation $-3x + 18.5$, a pitcher with an ERA of 6 would have 0.5, or about 1, win.

230 **Topic 4** Investigate Bivariate Data

Go Online | PearsonRealize.com

Lesson 4-4
Interpret Two-Way Frequency Tables

Lesson Overview

FOCUS

Objective

Students will be able to:

✔ organize paired categorical data into a two-way frequency table.

✔ compare and make conjectures about data displayed in a two-way frequency table.

Essential Understanding

Data can be displayed in a two-way frequency table, making it easier to analyze data. Individual data categories can be compared to all the data. Individual data can also be compared to sub-categories to make evidence-based conjectures.

COHERENCE

In Grade 6, students:

• reported the number of observations of data.

• described the type of observations of data.

In this lesson, students:

• create two-way frequency tables to display data.

• find and compare relationships between sub-categories of data.

Later in this topic, students will:

• create two-way frequency tables to display relative frequencies.

• find and compare relationships between relative frequencies.

RIGOR

This lesson emphasizes a blend of **conceptual understanding** and **application**.

• Students will apply their interpretation of data in two-way frequency tables to real-world applications to make conjectures.

Math Anytime

Today's Challenge

Use the Topic 4 problems any time during this topic.

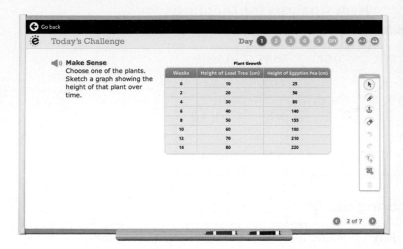

Watch the **Listen and Look For Video** for strategies and habits of mind to look for as students complete work on this lesson.

Mathematics Overview

In this lesson, students will organize data into a two-way frequency table. The table will allow them to make comparisons against total data points and other sub-categories that will allow them to make informed conjectures. Students will use their understanding to make conjectures about real-world situations.

Applying Math Practices

Model with Math

Students will construct two-way frequency tables to represent relationships in real-world situations and interpret two-way frequency tables to solve problems.

Look for and Make Use of Structure

Students will use the structure of the data in a two-way frequency table to fill in missing data and to separate given information into smaller relationships that can be compared easily.

STEP 1 | Develop: Problem-Based Learning

15-20 min

Activity

Explore It!

Use Structure As students work through the *Explore It*, listen and look for students to make data-based interpretations of the ski resort's poll.

Before 📱 WHOLE CLASS

STEP 1 Implement Tasks that Promote Reasoning and Problem Solving

Q: What is a poll? [Sample answer: A poll is a record of responses for a given question.]

2 Build Understanding

Q: Why should you use a table to display data? [Sample answer: A table organizes data so it is easier to understand.]

During 👥 SMALL GROUP

STEP 3 Support Productive Struggle in Learning Mathematics

Q: Why does the number of people polled add to 100 in both the column and row? [Sample answer: All the people either chose skiing or snow boarding and their ages were either over 35 or up to 35.]

Q: What information does the chart present? [Sample answer: The type of activity that people prefer based on their age.]

After 📱 WHOLE CLASS

STEP 4 Facilitate Meaningful Mathematical Discourse

Ask students to share their solutions. If needed, project Jake's and Mandy's work and ask:

Q: Jake made a broad description of the data, and Mandy made a more specific description of the data. Is one response better than the other? Explain. [No; Sample answer: Jake and Mandy both made accurate interpretations of the data.]

5 Transition to Visual Learning

Q: How is the data organized in the table? [Sample answer: It is separated into the responses to two questions by the age of the responders.]

6 Extension for Early Finishers

Q: What are two statements you can use to summarize the data shown in the table? [Sample answer: Younger people tend to like snowboarding more than skiing. The resort had more people older than 35 respond to the survey than people 35 and younger.]

Analyze Student Work

🛜 **Available Online**

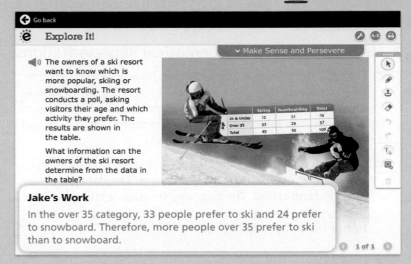

Jake's Work

In the over 35 category, 33 people prefer to ski and 24 prefer to snowboard. Therefore, more people over 35 prefer to ski than to snowboard.

Jake compares the preferred activity of people over 35 years old.

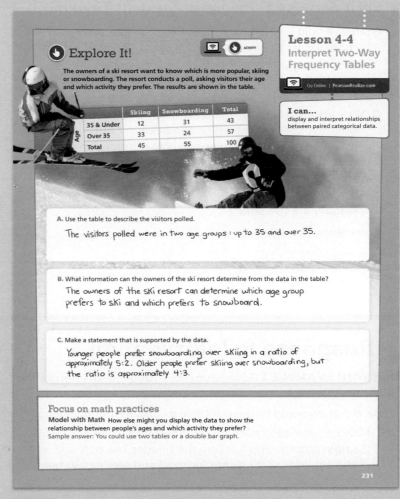

Explore It!

The owners of a ski resort want to know which is more popular, skiing or snowboarding. The resort conducts a poll, asking visitors their age and which activity they prefer. The results are shown in the table.

		Skiing	Snowboarding	Total
Age	35 & Under	12	31	43
	Over 35	33	24	57
	Total	45	55	100

Lesson 4-4
Interpret Two-Way Frequency Tables

🛜 Go Online | PearsonRealize.com

I can... display and interpret relationships between paired categorical data.

A. Use the table to describe the visitors polled.

The visitors polled were in two age groups: up to 35 and over 35.

B. What information can the owners of the ski resort determine from the data in the table?

The owners of the ski resort can determine which age group prefers to ski and which prefers to snowboard.

C. Make a statement that is supported by the data.

Younger people prefer snowboarding over skiing in a ratio of approximately 5:2. Older people prefer skiing over snowboarding, but the ratio is approximately 4:3.

Focus on math practices

Model with Math How else might you display the data to show the relationship between people's ages and which activity they prefer?
Sample answer: You could use two tables or a double bar graph.

231

Mandy compares each of the sub-categories by age.

STEP 2 | Develop: Visual Learning

ETP **Establish Mathematics Goals to Focus Learning**

Engage students in a discussion about the *Essential Question*. Make sure they understand how to interpret and construct a two-way frequency table.

EXAMPLE 1 ▸ 👁 Construct a Two-Way Frequency Table

ETP **Use and Connect Mathematical Representations**

Q: For both two-way frequency tables, how do you determine the quantities in the cells labeled "Total"? Explain. [Sample answer: Find the sum of the numbers in each column and in each row. The table total is on the bottom right. It is always the total number of people surveyed.]

Q: Does one of the tables do a better job of communicating the data? Explain. [Yes; Sample answer: The data is the same in both tables. The two-way frequency table that displays the types of books in the column category may be better for this situation.]

☑ Try It!

ETP **Elicit and Use Evidence of Student Thinking**

Q: How would you describe the data? [Sample answer: In City A almost twice as many people do not own boots. It is about the opposite in City B.]

Convince Me!

Q: Why are the totals for the columns and rows different, but both have the sum shown on the bottom right? [Sample answer: Because the columns display information about rain boots and the rows display information about cities, the values for the given cells are different. However, because 75 people were polled, the number of responses for each category are the same.]

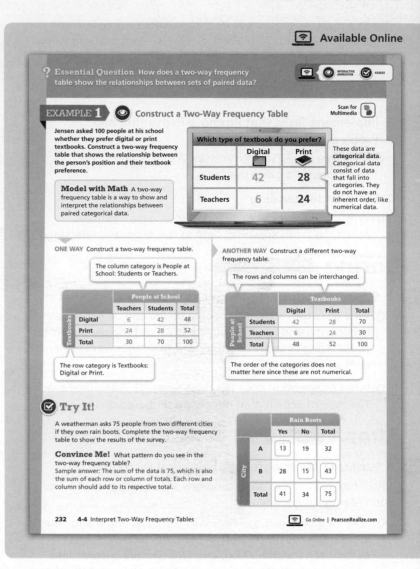

? Essential Question How does a two-way frequency table show the relationships between sets of paired data?

EXAMPLE 1 👁 Construct a Two-Way Frequency Table

Jensen asked 100 people at his school whether they prefer digital or print textbooks. Construct a two-way frequency table that shows the relationship between the person's position and their textbook preference.

Model with Math A two-way frequency table is a way to show and interpret the relationships between paired categorical data.

Which type of textbook do you prefer?

	Digital	Print
Students	42	28
Teachers	6	24

These data are **categorical data**. Categorical data consist of data that fall into categories. They do not have an inherent order, like numerical data.

ONE WAY Construct a two-way frequency table.

The column category is People at School: Students or Teachers.

People at School

		Teachers	Students	Total
Textbooks	Digital	6	42	48
	Print	24	28	52
	Total	30	70	100

The row category is Textbooks: Digital or Print.

ANOTHER WAY Construct a different two-way frequency table.

The rows and columns can be interchanged.

Textbooks

		Digital	Print	Total
People at School	Students	42	28	70
	Teachers	6	24	30
	Total	48	52	100

The order of the categories does not matter here since these are not numerical.

☑ Try It!

A weatherman asks 75 people from two different cities if they own rain boots. Complete the two-way frequency table to show the results of the survey.

Convince Me! What pattern do you see in the two-way frequency table?
Sample answer: The sum of the data is 75, which is also the sum of each row or column of totals. Each row and column should add to its respective total.

Rain Boots

		Yes	No	Total
City	A	13	19	32
	B	28	15	43
	Total	41	34	75

232 4-4 Interpret Two-Way Frequency Tables   Go Online | PearsonRealize.com

Students can access the *Visual Learning Animation Plus* by using the **BouncePages app** to scan this page. Students can download the app for free in their mobile devices' app store.

🔺 Response to Intervention

USE WITH EXAMPLE 1 Some students struggle with interpreting tables.

- Use either two-way frequency table to answer the following.

Q: How can you determine the number of teachers surveyed? [Sample answer: You can find the header Teachers and look at the total for that column (or row) and see that 30 teachers were polled.]

Q: How many teachers preferred print textbooks? Explain. [24; Sample answer: Look at the Teacher column and at the Print row in the table on the left. The cell where they intersect says 24, so 24 teachers preferred print textbooks.]

🏆 Enrichment

USE WITH EXAMPLE 3 Challenge students to interpret some of the data in the two-way frequency table.

Q: For which hair color is it more common to find green eyes? Explain. [Sample answer: It is more common in people with red hair. Even though only two people had green eyes and red hair, there were far fewer people with red hair.]

EXAMPLE 2 Interpret a Two-Way Frequency Table

ETP **Pose Purposeful Questions**

Q: Did women spend more time watching the winter or summer Olympics? Explain. [Summer Olympics; Sample answer: The row for Women shows that 27 spent more time watching the winter Olympics while 44 spent more time watching the summer Olympics.]

Q: Did more men or women report spending more time watching the winter Olympics? Explain. [Men; Sample answer: There were 45 men and 27 women who reported spending more time watching the winter Olympics.]

Q: Did people spend more time watching the winter or summer Olympics? Explain. [Summer Olympics; Sample answer: Since 78 people watched the summer Olympics and 72 people watched the winter Olympics, slightly more people preferred the summer Olympics.]

EXAMPLE 3 Construct and Interpret a Two-Way Frequency Table

ETP **Pose Purposeful Questions**

Q: How is this table different from the tables in Examples 1 and 2? Is it still a two-way frequency table? Explain. [Yes; Sample answer: This table shows three categories under Hair Color but it is still a two-way relative frequency table because it compares two types of related data—Eye Color and Hair Color.]

Try It!

ETP **Elicit and Use Evidence of Student Thinking**

Q: Suppose 8 boys and 11 girls walk to school. How could you include this data in the table? Explain. [Sample answer: You would need to add a column for Walk, add the number of boys and girls who walk, and the total number of students would change to 119.]

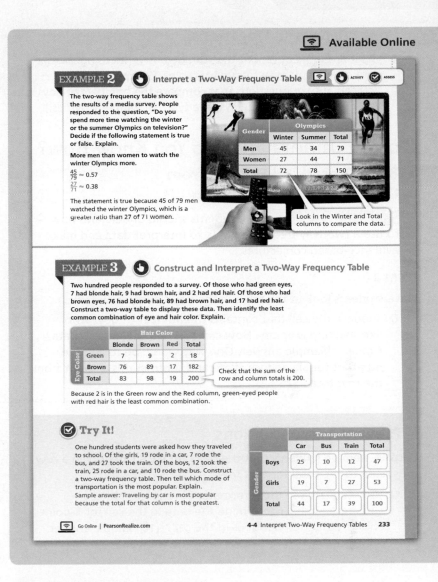

EXAMPLE 2 — Interpret a Two-Way Frequency Table

Available Online

The two-way frequency table shows the results of a media survey. People responded to the question, "Do you spend more time watching the winter or the summer Olympics on television?" Decide if the following statement is true or false. Explain.

More men than women to watch the winter Olympics more.

$\frac{45}{79} \approx 0.57$

$\frac{27}{71} \approx 0.38$

The statement is true because 45 of 79 men watched the winter Olympics, which is a greater ratio than 27 of 71 women.

Gender	Olympics		
	Winter	Summer	Total
Men	45	34	79
Women	27	44	71
Total	72	78	150

Look in the Winter and Total columns to compare the data.

EXAMPLE 3 — Construct and Interpret a Two-Way Frequency Table

Two hundred people responded to a survey. Of those who had green eyes, 7 had blonde hair, 9 had brown hair, and 2 had red hair. Of those who had brown eyes, 76 had blonde hair, 89 had brown hair, and 17 had red hair. Construct a two-way table to display these data. Then identify the least common combination of eye and hair color. Explain.

		Hair Color			
		Blonde	Brown	Red	Total
Eye Color	Green	7	9	2	18
	Brown	76	89	17	182
	Total	83	98	19	200

Check that the sum of the row and column totals is 200.

Because 2 is in the Green row and the Red column, green-eyed people with red hair is the least common combination.

Try It!

One hundred students were asked how they traveled to school. Of the girls, 19 rode in a car, 7 rode the bus, and 27 took the train. Of the boys, 12 took the train, 25 rode in a car, and 10 rode the bus. Construct a two-way frequency table. Then tell which mode of transportation is the most popular. Explain.
Sample answer: Traveling by car is most popular because the total for that column is the greatest.

		Transportation			
		Car	Bus	Train	Total
Gender	Boys	25	10	12	47
	Girls	19	7	27	53
	Total	44	17	39	100

Go Online | PearsonRealize.com

4-4 Interpret Two-Way Frequency Tables **233**

ADDITIONAL EXAMPLES

For additional examples go to PearsonRealize.com.

ELL English Language Learners

BEGINNING Read Example 2.

Q: How are the winter and summer Olympics different? [Sample answer: The winter Olympics includes sports that may require cold weather, such as ice hockey and skiing. The summer Olympics include sports such as track and swimming.]

Q: What do you think *prefer* means? [Sample answer: To *prefer* is to like one thing better than another thing.]

INTERMEDIATE Read Example 3.

Q: What does *respond* mean to you? [Sample answer: *Respond* means to reply or answer a question.]

Q: How does knowing the meaning of *respond* help you determine the number of people surveyed? [Sample answer: Since *respond* means to reply, the number of people surveyed, 200, is the same as the total number of people who replied.]

Q: Does a *response* need to be verbal or written? Explain. [Sample answer: A *response* can be spoken or written.]

ADVANCED Read Example 1.

Have students read Example 1. As a group, discuss how the placement of the title of the rows and columns and the placement of the values in the cells changes in the two tables. Then group students into pairs. Have them find a cell from each table that shows the same data, and then read or write the pairing it represents. Focus on having students see the information is the same but the wording is reversed. For example for 28 they might say, *28 students prefer print textbooks* and *Print textbooks were preferred by 28 students.*

KEY CONCEPT

ETP Pose Purposeful Questions

Q: What are some questions that can be answered using the data on this two-way frequency table? [Sample answer: You can answer questions that compare the numbers of boys and girls who participate in three types of winter activities.]

Do You Understand/Do You Know How?

ETP Build Procedural Fluency from Conceptual Understanding

? Essential Question Students should understand how to use a two-way frequency table to interpret data and make evidence-based conjectures.

ITEM 3

Have students look at the table in the Key Concepts and ask:

Q: Suppose the cell that contains the number of boys who like sledding is empty. How can you find the missing data? Explain. [Sample answer: One way would be to add the numbers for Ski and Ice Skate and subtract this amount from the row total, 52.]

🔴 Prevent Misconceptions

ITEM 4 Remind students that the pairs for each category in a row must sum to the total for that row.

Q: How can you use the information in the row titled Underclassmen to determine the data in the cell for 3-point Shots? What number goes in the cell? [10; Sample answer: Subtract the 18 free throws from the total 28.]

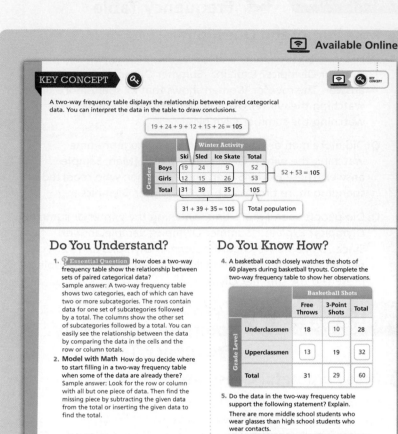

ADDITIONAL EXAMPLE **3**

📶 Available Online

Help students think about how they can use the two-way frequency table to answer the question.

Q: Which value will answer the question? Explain. [The greatest value; Sample answer: The greatest value is asking for the shot that resulted in the greatest number of points for the other team.]

Q: Why is the answer not low and to the right of the goalie, since there are more shots made to the right of the goalie and more low shots that result in a score? Explain. [Sample answer: There are more shots that result in scores that are to the left of the goalie and low than any of the other three possibilities.]

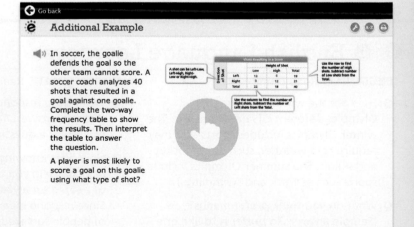

Answer: A shot that is to the left of the goalie and low

Practice & Problem Solving

Available Online

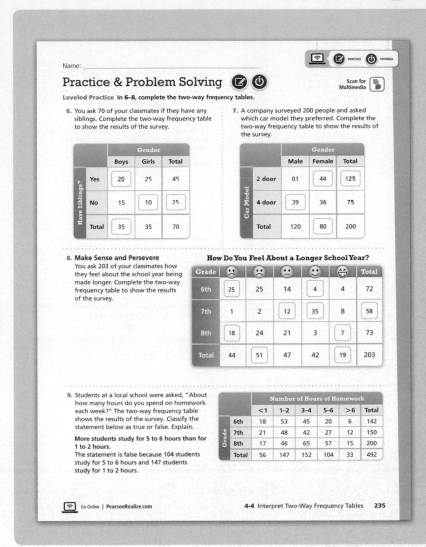

Name: _____

Practice & Problem Solving

Scan for Multimedia

Leveled Practice In 6–8, complete the two-way frequency tables.

6. You ask 70 of your classmates if they have any siblings. Complete the two-way frequency table to show the results of the survey.

		Gender		
		Boys	Girls	Total
Have siblings?	Yes	20	25	45
	No	15	10	25
	Total	35	35	70

7. A company surveyed 200 people and asked which car model they preferred. Complete the two-way frequency table to show the results of the survey.

		Gender		
		Male	Female	Total
Car Model	2 door	81	44	125
	4 door	39	36	75
	Total	120	80	200

8. Make Sense and Persevere You ask 203 of your classmates how they feel about the school year being made longer. Complete the two-way frequency table to show the results of the survey.

How Do You Feel About a Longer School Year?

Grade	😠	🙁	😐	🙂	😄	Total
6th	25	25	14	4	4	72
7th	1	2	12	35	8	58
8th	18	24	21	3	7	73
Total	44	51	47	42	19	203

9. Students at a local school were asked, "About how many hours do you spend on homework each week?" The two-way frequency table shows the results of the survey. Classify the statement below as true or false. Explain.

More students study for 5 to 6 hours than for 1 to 2 hours.
The statement is false because 104 students study for 5 to 6 hours and 147 students study for 1 to 2 hours.

		Number of Hours of Homework					
		<1	1–2	3–4	5–6	>6	Total
Grade	6th	18	53	45	20	6	142
	7th	21	48	42	27	12	150
	8th	17	46	65	57	15	200
	Total	56	147	152	104	33	492

Go Online | PearsonRealize.com

4-4 Interpret Two-Way Frequency Tables   235

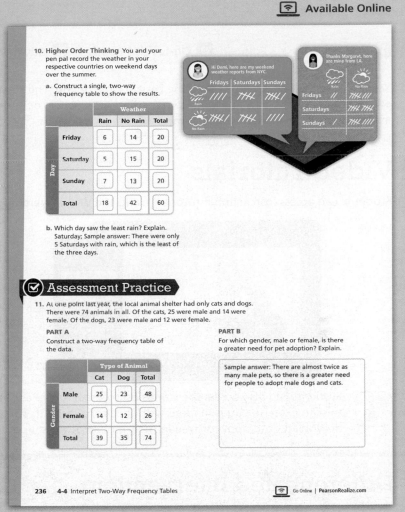

10. Higher Order Thinking You and your pen pal record the weather in your respective countries on weekend days over the summer.

a. Construct a single, two-way frequency table to show the results.

		Weather		
		Rain	No Rain	Total
Day	Friday	6	14	20
	Saturday	5	15	20
	Sunday	7	13	20
	Total	18	42	60

b. Which day saw the least rain? Explain.
Saturday; Sample answer: There were only 5 Saturdays with rain, which is the least of the three days.

✅ Assessment Practice

11. At one point last year, the local animal shelter had only cats and dogs. There were 74 animals in all. Of the cats, 25 were male and 14 were female. Of the dogs, 23 were male and 12 were female.

PART A
Construct a two-way frequency table of the data.

		Type of Animal		
		Cat	Dog	Total
Gender	Male	25	23	48
	Female	14	12	26
	Total	39	35	74

PART B
For which gender, male or female, is there a greater need for pet adoption? Explain.

Sample answer: There are almost twice as many male pets, so there is a greater need for people to adopt male dogs and cats.

236   4-4 Interpret Two-Way Frequency Tables

Go Online | PearsonRealize.com

⚠ Error Intervention

ITEM 6 Students may struggle completing a partially filled frequency table.

Q: How can you find out how many girls said No? [Sample answer: Subtract the number of Yes responses in the Girls column from the Total number of responses in the Girls column.]

🏆 Challenge

ITEM 10 Challenge students to correct a student's reasoning pertaining to the data in the charts.

Q: Suppose your pen pal said there were 42 sunny days. Would the statement be valid? Explain. [No; Sample answer: The two-way frequency table gives data for rain or no rain. You cannot assume that a day with no rain is sunny.]

You may opt to have students complete the automatically scored Practice & Problem Solving items online.

Item Analysis

Example	Items	DOK
1	6, 7, 8	1
2	9	2
3	10, 11	2

STEP 3 | Assess & Differentiate

PearsonRealize.com

Assess Tutorials Worksheets

✓ Lesson Quiz

 Use the student scores on the Lesson Quiz to prescribe differentiated assignments.

I Intervention 0–3 Points **O On-Level** 4 Points **A Advanced** 5 Points

You may opt to have students take the Lesson Quiz online. The Lesson Quiz will be automatically scored and appropriate remediation, practice, or enrichment will be assigned based on student performance.

⏻ Video Tutorials

Students can access instructional tutorials using the **Virtual Nerd** app.

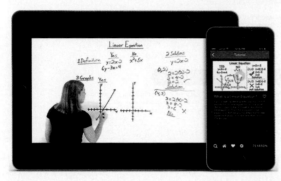

Students can also access the videos using the **BouncePages app** to scan exercise pages marked with this icon. Students can download both apps for free in their mobile devices' app store.

📶 Available Online

Differentiated Intervention

I = Intervention **O** = On-Level **A** = Advanced

Reteach to Build Understanding **I**

Provides scaffolded reteaching for the key lesson concepts.

Additional Vocabulary Support **I O**

Helps students develop and reinforce understanding of key terms and concepts.

Build Mathematical Literacy **I**

Provides support for struggling readers to build mathematical literacy.

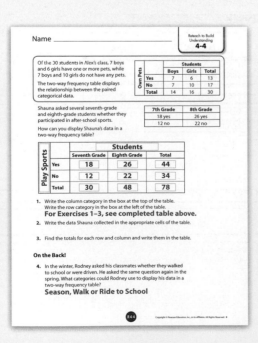

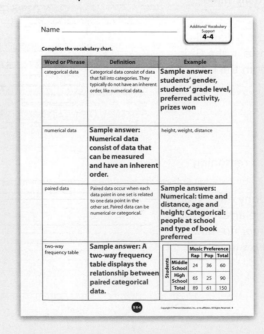

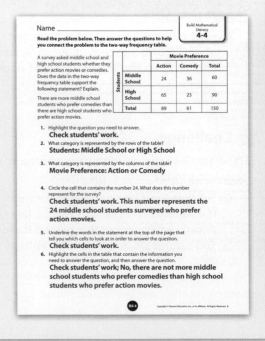

| Practice | Worksheets | Math Tools | Math Games |

Additional Practice

You may opt to have students complete the automatically scored Additional Practice items online.

Item Analysis

Example	Items	DOK
1	1, 5	2
2	2, 3	2
3	4	3

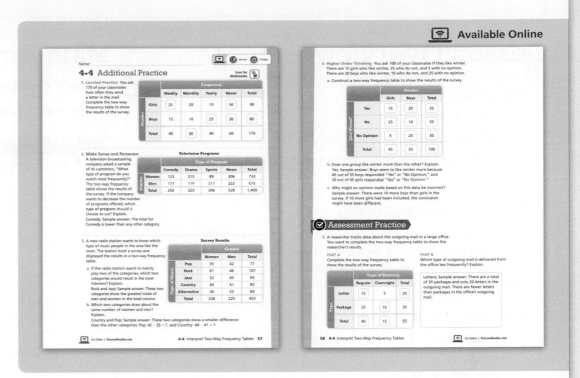

Differentiated Intervention

I = Intervention   **O** = On-Level   **A** = Advanced

Enrichment **O** **A**

Presents engaging problems and activities that extend the lesson concepts.

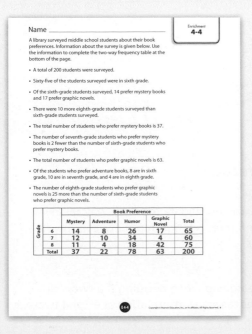

Math Tools and Games **I** **O** **A**

Offers additional activities and games to build understanding and fluency.

Lesson 4-5

Interpret Two-Way Relative Frequency Tables

Lesson Overview

FOCUS

Objective

Students will be able to:

✔ construct two-way relative frequency tables.

✔ compare and make conjectures about data displayed in a two-way relative frequency table.

Essential Understanding

Data can be organized in a two-way frequency table, and then used to construct a two-way relative frequency table. Relative frequency can be determined for the rows and the columns as well as for the whole table.

COHERENCE

Previously in this topic, students:

• constructed two-way frequency tables to display and interpret relationships between paired categorical data.

In this lesson, students:

• organize data into a two-way frequency table to construct a two-way relative frequency table.

• find and compare relationships between ratios of data in sub-categories to the row total, column total, or data set total.

In Grade 9, students will:

• summarize data in joint, relative conditional, and marginal two-way frequency tables.

RIGOR

This lesson emphasizes a blend of **procedural skill and fluency** and **application**.

• Students convert two-way frequency tables into two-way relative frequency tables. They determine the relative frequency as a ratio of a data value to the total of a row, a column, or the entire data set as a percent.

• Students interpret data in two-way relative frequency tables to answer questions about survey responses and to solve real-world problems.

Math Anytime

Today's Challenge

Use the Topic 4 problems any time during this topic.

Mathematics Overview

In this lesson, students will extend their work with two-way frequency tables to create two-way relative frequency tables that assist them with making comparisons and conjectures about the data in question. Students will reinforce their skills working with ratios and apply their understanding to analyze data from real-world situations such as survey responses.

Applying Math Practices

Make Sense and Persevere

Students will organize categorical data into two-way relative frequency tables, and interpret relationships between the data using rows and columns.

Critique Reasoning

Students will critique reasoning when deciding if a two-way frequency table provides the same information as a total two-way relative frequency table.

STEP 1 | Develop: Problem-Based Learning

15-20 min

Activity

Solve & Discuss It!

Make Sense and Persevere As students work through the *Solve and Discuss It*, listen and look for students to explain how the percentages of categorical data are calculated.

Before [WHOLE CLASS]

1 Implement Tasks that Promote Reasoning and Problem Solving

Q: What does it mean *to compare the percent of students to the percent of adults*? [Sample answer: It means to determine which percent represents the greater number.]

2 Build Understanding

Q: How is a percent calculated? [Sample answer: Divide the part by the whole. Then multiply by 100 to find the percent. Include a percent symbol in your answer.]

During [SMALL GROUP]

3 Support Productive Struggle in Learning Mathematics

Q: How many students out of the total number of students surveyed chose the small screen? [48 students out of 100 chose the small screen.]

Q: What percent of students chose a small screen? Explain. [48%; Sample answer: Divide 48 students by 100 students to get 0.48. Then multiply by 100 and include a percent symbol to get 48%.]

After [WHOLE CLASS]

4 Facilitate Meaningful Mathematical Discourse

Ask students to share their solutions. If needed, project Zack's and Joey's work and ask:

Q: Why are Zack's and Joey's percents different? [Sample answer: Zack used row data and Joey used column data.]

Q: Can both of the students be correct? Explain. [Yes; Sample answer: They compared different quantities. Zack's answer compares the percent of all the students vs. percent of all the adults, which is calculated by rows. Joey used the data in the "Small" column, and compares the number of students vs. adults who prefer small screens.]

5 Transition to Visual Learning

Q: Does using a percentage make it easier to compare the data in the table? Explain. [Yes; Sample answer: A percentage permits you to compare the frequencies relative to column total: 73% of the people who prefer small screens are students, while 27% are adults.]

6 Extension for Early Finishers

Q: What two statements can you write to summarize the data? [Sample answer: Large screen size matters more to adults than students. About two-thirds of all people surveyed prefer the larger screen size.]

Analyze Student Work

Available Online

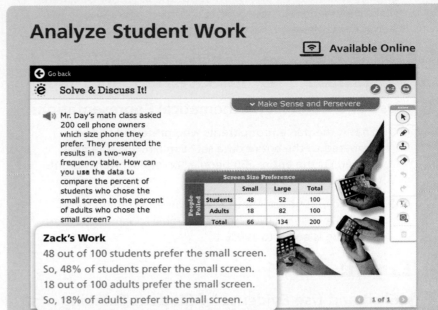

Zack's Work

48 out of 100 students prefer the small screen.

So, 48% of students prefer the small screen.

18 out of 100 adults prefer the small screen.

So, 18% of adults prefer the small screen.

Zack calculates the relative frequencies using the row data.

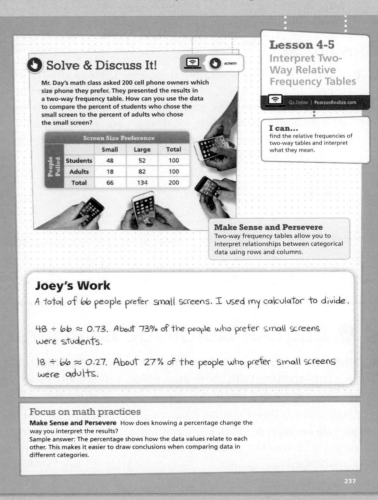

Joey calculates the relative frequencies using the column data.

ETP **Establish Mathematics Goals to Focus Learning**

Engage students in a discussion about the *Essential Question*. Make sure students know how to construct a two-way frequency table and how to calculate a percent.

 EXAMPLE **1** — Construct a Two-Way Relative Frequency Table

ETP **Use and Connect Mathematical Representations**

Q: What is the percent of parents who preferred to text compared to the entire data set? Explain. [8%; Sample answer: Of the entire 150 people, 12, or 8%, were parents who preferred to text.]

Q: What do you notice about row totals and column totals in the two-way relative frequency table? [Sample answer: Their sum is equal to 100%.]

 Try It!

ETP **Elicit and Use Evidence of Student Thinking**

Q: What is each number divided by to find the relative frequency? Explain. [82; Sample answer: There are 82 people in the survey.]

Convince Me!

Q: How is the two-way relative frequency table in the Try It! similar to the two-way frequency table? Explain. [Sample answer: The sum of the row percentage totals and the sum of the column percentage totals must equal 100%, just as the totals in the frequency table must equal 82. This is because 82 is 100% of the data set.]

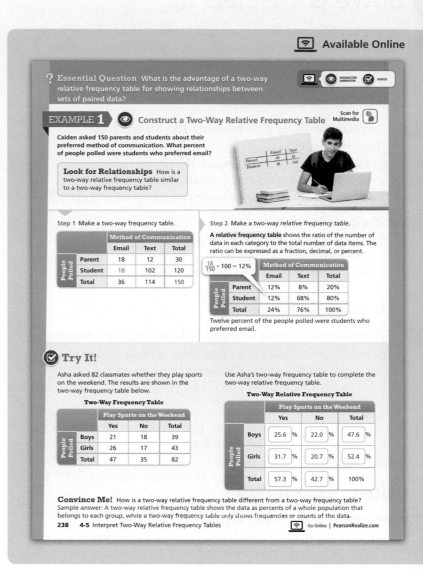

Students can access the *Visual Learning Animation Plus* by using the **BouncePages app** to scan this page. Students can download the app for free in their mobile devices' app store.

ELL English Language Learners

BEGINNING Read Example 1 to students. Begin a conversation with them about the meanings of the word *relative*.

Q: What does the word *relative* mean to you? [Sample answer: A *relative* is someone a person is connected to usually by blood or marriage.]

Give students an example of *relative* meaning *compared to*: A middle-school student is small relative to a professional football player.

Q: What does *relative* mean in this situation? [Sample answer: Compared to]

INTERMEDIATE Read Example 1. Help students clarify some terms used in the problem.

Q: How does the table help you understand the phrase "method of communication"? Explain. [Sample answer: The columns say "Email" and "Text." These are ways that people share information or communicate.]

Q: What does it mean to "prefer" something? [Sample answer: When given two or more choices, the one you like best is the "preferred" choice.]

ADVANCED Read Example 1.

Have students work in pairs. One student says the steps taken to answer the question using terms in the lesson, while the other student writes the terms. Have students come up with a list of words they might use, such as relative, frequency, percent, column, and row, to clearly explain how they solve the problem.

EXAMPLE 2 Compare Relative Frequency by Rows

ETP Pose Purposeful Questions

Q: In this situation, why are the faculty data divided by 27 and the student data divided by 68? [Sample answer: In this table, the required percentages are the percentages of each group. So the percentage of faculty who attended is the number of faculty who attended divided by all the faculty. For the students, it is the percentage of all the students.]

Q: The value in the total row is not the sum of the column. Explain. [Sample answer: The total row shows the relative frequency of each response compared to the total number of respondents. For example, there were a total of 95 faculty and students polled. Of these, 42 students and 15 faculty attended the last home game. This is a total of 57 people, which is 60% of 95.]

EXAMPLE 3 Compare Relative Frequency by Columns

ETP Pose Purposeful Questions

Q: Why is the number of 7th graders that check out E-books divided by the number 207? [Sample answer: There are 207 seventh graders.]

Q: If about 41.1% of 7th graders and about 63.5% of 8th graders check out E-books, why is the total for that row 52%? Explain. [Sample answer: 52% represents the total percentage of 7th and 8th graders who check out E-books. Of the 404 students who checked out either an E-book or an audio book, 210 students checked out an E-book, which rounds to 52% of the total.]

Try It!

ETP Elicit and Use Evidence of Student Thinking

Q: Could you answer the question in part (b) without finding a percentage? Explain. [Yes; Sample answer: More than half the 7th graders checked out audio books.]

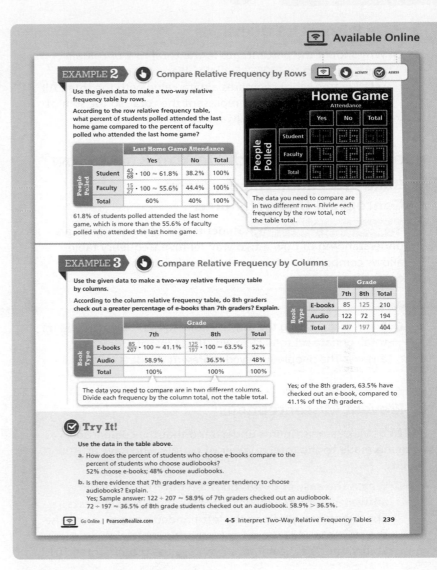

According to the row relative frequency table, what percent of students polled attended the last home game compared to the percent of faculty polled who attended the last home game?

	Last Home Game Attendance		
People Polled		Yes	No	Total
Student	$\frac{42}{68} \cdot 100 \approx 61.8\%$	38.2%	100%
Faculty	$\frac{15}{27} \cdot 100 \approx 55.6\%$	44.4%	100%
Total	60%	40%	100%

61.8% of students polled attended the last home game, which is more than the 55.6% of faculty polled who attended the last home game.

The data you need to compare are in two different rows. Divide each frequency by the row total, not the table total.

EXAMPLE 3 Compare Relative Frequency by Columns

Use the given data to make a two-way relative frequency table by columns.

According to the column relative frequency table, do 8th graders check out a greater percentage of e-books than 7th graders? Explain.

Book Type		7th	8th	Total
E-books	85	125	210
Audio	122	72	194
Total	207	197	404

	Grade		
Book Type		7th	8th	Total
E-books	$\frac{85}{207} \cdot 100 \approx 41.1\%$	$\frac{125}{197} \cdot 100 \approx 63.5\%$	52%
Audio	58.9%	36.5%	48%
Total	100%	100%	100%

The data you need to compare are in two different columns. Divide each frequency by the column total, not the table total.

Yes; of the 8th graders, 63.5% have checked out an e-book, compared to 41.1% of the 7th graders.

Try It!

Use the data in the table above.

a. How does the percent of students who choose e-books compare to the percent of students who choose audiobooks?
52% choose e-books; 48% choose audiobooks.

b. Is there evidence that 7th graders have a greater tendency to choose audiobooks? Explain.
Yes; Sample answer: 122 ÷ 207 ≈ 58.9% of 7th graders checked out an audiobook. 72 ÷ 197 ≈ 36.5% of 8th grade students checked out an audiobook. 58.9% > 36.5%.

 ADDITIONAL EXAMPLES

For additional examples go to PearsonRealize.com.

Response to Intervention

USE WITH EXAMPLE 2 Some students may need help deciding whether to find the ratio of the data to the entire data set or to a row or column total.

• Ask the following questions.

Q: What does the question ask you to compare? [Percent of students polled who attended the last home game to the percent of faculty polled who attended the last home game]

Q: What word or words help you determine whether you need to find the ratio of students who attended the last home game to all people polled or to all students polled? Explain. [Sample answer: The words *percent of students polled* indicates that the ratio is going to involve only students polled, not all people polled.]

Enrichment

USE WITH EXAMPLE 3 Challenge students to interpret a two-way relative frequency table by comparing marginal relative frequencies.

The data in the "Total" row and column are called *marginal frequencies* because they are along the margin of the table.

Q: Identify the marginal frequencies in the two-way frequency table. [210, 194, 207, 197]

Q: If you looked only at the marginal relative frequencies in the row totals, what might you conclude about what type of book 7th and 8th graders prefer? Explain. [Sample answer: About 52% of the students prefer E-books while 48% prefer audiobooks, so you might conclude that the preferences are about the same.]

Key Concept   Activity

STEP **2** | Develop: Visual Learning *continued*

KEY CONCEPT

ETP **Pose Purposeful Questions**

Q: Why should the percentages in the total row or column always add up to 100%? Explain. [Sample answer: The relative frequency compares a data value with the total. All the data values together represent the total, so the sum of the percentages should always be 100%.]

Do You Understand/Do You Know How?

ETP **Build Procedural Fluency from Conceptual Understanding**

? Essential Question Students should demonstrate an understanding of how a two-way relative frequency table allows comparisons of percentages rather than comparing data values.

ITEM 4

Q: Are you comparing the artistic ability to the row total, column total, or data set total? Explain. [Data set total; Sample answer: The people surveyed represent the data set total.]

Prevent Misconceptions

ITEM 6 Make sure students understand that the comparison is being made to the total number of people who have artistic ability.

Q: Why is the answer to this question different from the answer to item 5? Explain. [Sample answer: Item 5 asks about one group of people, left-handed people, so you use the row total, 131. Item 6 asks about people with artistic ability, the "Yes" column, so you use the column total, 101.]

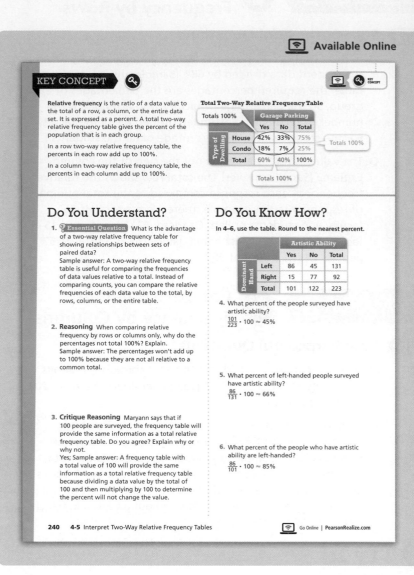

KEY CONCEPT

Relative frequency is the ratio of a data value to the total of a row, a column, or the entire data set. It is expressed as a percent. A total two-way relative frequency table gives the percent of the population that is in each group.

In a row two-way relative frequency table, the percents in each row add up to 100%.

In a column two-way relative frequency table, the percents in each column add up to 100%.

Total Two-Way Relative Frequency Table

Totals 100%

Type of Dwelling	Garage Parking		
	Yes	No	Total
House	42%	33%	75%
Condo	18%	7%	25%
Total	60%	40%	100%

Totals 100%   Totals 100%

Do You Understand?

1. **? Essential Question** What is the advantage of a two-way relative frequency table for showing relationships between sets of paired data?
Sample answer: A two-way relative frequency table is useful for comparing the frequencies of data values relative to a total. Instead of comparing counts, you can compare the relative frequencies of each data value to the total, by rows, columns, or the entire table.

2. **Reasoning** When comparing relative frequency by rows or columns only, why do the percentages not total 100%? Explain.
Sample answer: The percentages won't add up to 100% because they are not all relative to a common total.

3. **Critique Reasoning** Maryann says that if 100 people are surveyed, the frequency table will provide the same information as a total relative frequency table. Do you agree? Explain why or why not.
Yes; Sample answer: A frequency table with a total value of 100 will provide the same information as a total relative frequency table because dividing a data value by the total of 100 and then multiplying by 100 to determine the percent will not change the value.

Do You Know How?

In 4–6, use the table. Round to the nearest percent.

Dominant Hand	Artistic Ability		
	Yes	No	Total
Left	86	45	131
Right	15	77	92
Total	101	122	223

4. What percent of the people surveyed have artistic ability?
$\frac{101}{223} \cdot 100 \approx 45\%$

5. What percent of left-handed people surveyed have artistic ability?
$\frac{86}{131} \cdot 100 \approx 66\%$

6. What percent of the people who have artistic ability are left-handed?
$\frac{86}{101} \cdot 100 \approx 85\%$

240 **4-5** Interpret Two-Way Relative Frequency Tables   Go Online | PearsonRealize.com

ADDITIONAL EXAMPLE **1**

Help students make the transition from finding a certain percentage to finding and then comparing percentages.

Q: Why do you need to add a row and a column for the totals in the two-way frequency table? [Sample answer: The first table shows the parts. In order to find the percentage for each choice, you need to find the total number of responses.]

Q: How is this table different from the table in Example 1? [Sample answer: This table has three methods of communication. It has an extra column for this choice.]

Q: Is there a limit to the number of rows or columns a two-way relative frequency table can have? Explain. [No; Sample answer: The table needs enough rows and columns to display all of the necessary data.]

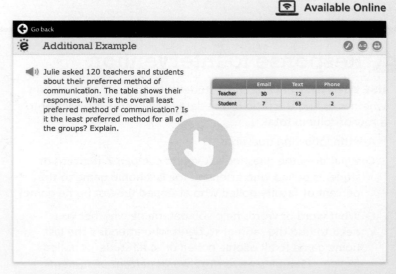

Go back

Additional Example

Julie asked 120 teachers and students about their preferred method of communication. The table shows their responses. What is the overall least preferred method of communication? Is it the least preferred method for all of the groups? Explain.

	Email	Text	Phone
Teacher	30	12	6
Student	7	63	2

Answer: The overall least preferred method of communication is Phone at 7%.

Practice & Problem Solving

Name: _____

Practice & Problem Solving

Scan for Multimedia

Leveled Practice In 7–8, complete the two-way relative frequency tables.

7. In a group of 120 people, each person has a dog, a cat, or a bird. The two-way frequency table shows how many people have each kind of pet. Complete the two-way relative frequency table to show the distribution of the data with respect to all 120 people. Round to the nearest tenth of a percent.

Two-Way Frequency Table

		Gender		
		Men	Women	Total
Pets	Dog	25	33	58
	Cat	20	15	35
	Bird	12	15	27
	Total	57	63	120

Total Two-Way Relative Frequency Table

		Gender		
		Men	Women	Total
Pets	Dog	20.8 %	27.5 %	48.3 %
	Cat	16.7 %	12.5 %	29.2 %
	Bird	10.0 %	12.5 %	22.5 %
	Total	47.5 %	52.5 %	100%

8. There are 55 vehicles in a parking lot. The two-way frequency table shows data about the types and colors of the vehicles. Complete the two-way relative frequency table to show the distribution of the data with respect to color. Round to the nearest tenth of a percent.

Two-Way Frequency Table

		Type of Vehicle		
		Car	Truck	Total
Color	Blue	15	10	25
	Red	13	17	30
	Total	28	27	55

Row Two-Way Relative Frequency Table

		Type of Vehicle		
		Car	Truck	Total
Color	Blue	60.0 %	40.0 %	100%
	Red	43.3 %	56.7 %	100%
	Total	50.9 %	49.1 %	100%

9. Men and women are asked what type of car they own. The table shows the relative frequencies with respect to the total population asked. Which type of car is more popular?
4-door

Total Two-Way Relative Frequency Table

		Type of Car		
		2-Door	4-Door	Total
Gender	Men	32%	18%	50%
	Women	15%	35%	50%
	Total	47%	53%	100%

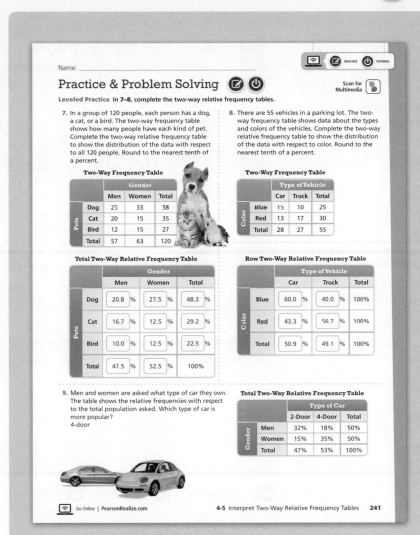

---

10. Make Sense and Persevere Students were asked if they like raspberries. The two-way relative frequency table shows the relative frequencies with respect to the response.

a. What percent of students who do not like raspberries are girls? 48%

b. Is there evidence of an association between the response and the gender? Explain.
No; Sample answer: The relative frequencies are all very close in value.

Column Two-Way Relative Frequency Table

		Like Raspberries?		
		Yes	No	Total
Gender	Boys	49%	52%	50.5%
	Girls	51%	48%	49.5%
	Total	100%	100%	100%

11. Higher Order Thinking All the workers in a company were asked a survey question. The two-way frequency table shows the responses from the workers in the day shift and night shift.

a. Construct a two-way relative frequency table to show the relative frequencies with respect to the shift.

Two-Way Frequency Table

		Response		
		Yes	No	Total
Shift	Day	68	32	100
	Night	22	78	100
	Total	90	110	200

		Response				
		Yes		No		Total
Shift	Day	68 %		32 %		100 %
	Night	22 %		78 %		100 %
	Total	45 %		55 %		100 %

b. Is there evidence of an association between the response and the shift? Explain.
Yes; Sample answer: 68% of workers in the day shift answered "Yes," but only 22% of workers in the night shift answered "Yes."

✓ Assessment Practice

12. Patients were given either Medicine A or Medicine B. The table shows the relative frequencies with respect to improvement.

PART A
Complete the sentence. A greater percent of people given [Medicine B] saw an improvement.

PART B
Is there evidence that improvement was related to the type of medicine? Explain.

Column Two-Way Relative Frequency Table

		Improvement?		
		Yes	No	Total
Type	Medicine A	26%	64%	50%
	Medicine B	74%	36%	50%
	Total	100%	100%	100%

Yes; Sample answer: The same number of people took each medicine, but the percent of people who reported improvement after taking Medicine B was significantly greater than the percent for Medicine A.

You may opt to have students complete the automatically scored Practice & Problem Solving items online.

Error Intervention

ITEM 8 Students may need help completing a row two-way relative frequency table.

Q: Will you divide each color and type of vehicle by the total for the whole table, the total for the columns, or the total for the rows? Explain. [Row total; Sample answer: The row total for the "Blue" row is 25, so divide 15 by 25 to find the relative frequency of blue cars.]

Challenge

ITEM 11 Challenge students to continue to interpret the data.

Q: Twenty-seven of the day workers are female. Of these, 17 responded yes. Twenty-two males responded no. Construct a two-way relative frequency table to show the relative frequencies with respect to gender on the day shift. [Male: 70% replied yes and 30% replied no; Female: 63% replied yes and 37% replied no]

Item Analysis

Example	Items	DOK
1	7, 8	2
2	11	3
3	9, 10	2
	12	3

Lesson Quiz

 Use the student scores on the Lesson Quiz to prescribe differentiated assignments.

I Intervention 0–3 Points   **O** On-Level 4 Points   **A** Advanced 5 Points

You may opt to have students take the Lesson Quiz online. The Lesson Quiz will be automatically scored and appropriate remediation, practice, or enrichment will be assigned based on student performance.

Video Tutorials

Students can access instructional tutorials using the **Virtual Nerd app**.

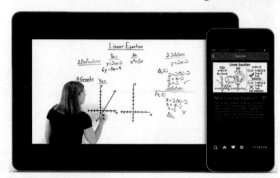

Students can also access the videos using the **BouncePages app** to scan exercise pages marked with this icon. Students can download both apps for free in their mobile devices' app store.

📶 Available Online

Name _____   Lesson Quiz 4-5

Use the two-way frequency table below for Exercises 1–4. Round your answers to the nearest percent.

		Lunch Order		
		Sandwich	Pasta	Total
Sport	Volleyball	19	15	34
	Swimming	26	10	36
	Total	45	25	70

1. Use the two-way frequency table to complete the relative frequency table to the right.

		Lunch Order		
		Sandwich	Pasta	Total
Sport	Volleyball	27%	21%	49%
	Swimming	37%	14%	51%
	Total	64%	36%	100%

2. Out of all the lunch orders, what percent are sandwiches?
64%

3. Use the two-way frequency table to complete the row relative frequency table.

		Lunch Order		
		Sandwich	Pasta	Total
Sport	Volleyball	56%	44%	100%
	Swimming	72%	28%	100%
	Total	64%	36%	100%

4. Did a greater percentage of volleyball players or swimmers order a sandwich?
Swimmers

5. Which of the following statements is true? Select all that apply.
- ☑ You can use a relative frequency table to examine how data sets are related by comparing percentages.
- ☐ Row and column relative frequency tables tell you the same information as total relative frequency tables.
- ☐ A column relative frequency table helps compare data in two different rows.
- ☑ In a column two-way relative frequency table, each column totals 100%.

Differentiated Intervention

I = Intervention   **O** = On-Level   **A** = Advanced

Reteach to Build Understanding **I**

Provides scaffolded reteaching for the key lesson concepts.

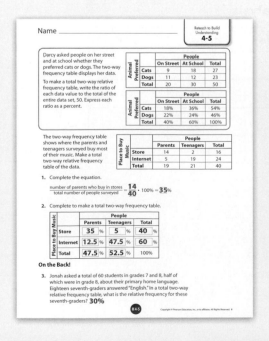

Additional Vocabulary Support **I** **O**

Helps students develop and reinforce understanding of key terms and concepts.

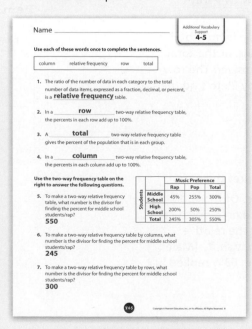

Build Mathematical Literacy **I**

Provides support for struggling readers to build mathematical literacy.

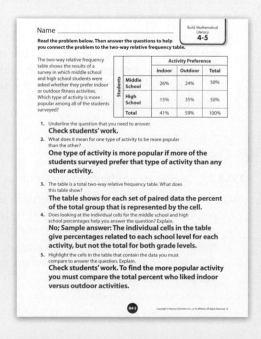

Practice | Worksheets | Math Tools | Math Games

Additional Practice

You may opt to have students complete the automatically scored Additional Practice items online.

Item Analysis

Example	Items	DOK
1	1, 2	2
2	3, 4	2
3	6	2
	5	3

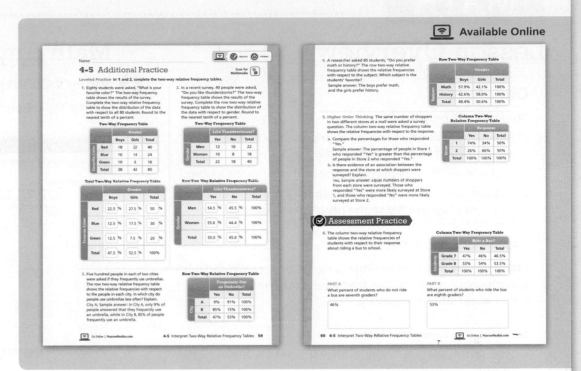

Differentiated Intervention

I = Intervention   O = On-Level   A = Advanced

Enrichment O A

Presents engaging problems and activities that extend the lesson concepts.

Math Tools and Games I O A

Offers additional activities and games to build understanding and fluency.

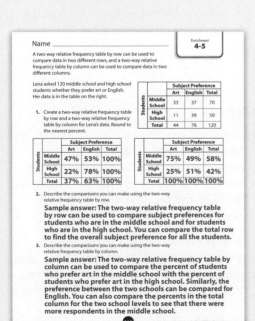

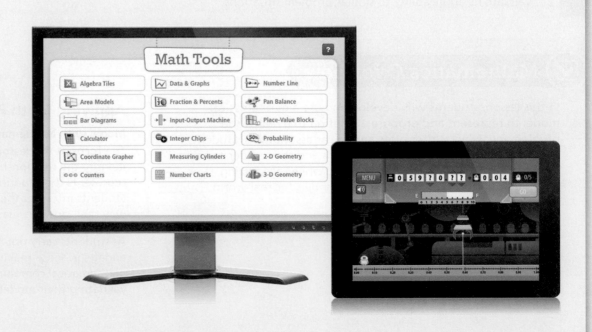

3-Act MATH

3-Act Mathematical Modeling: Reach Out

Lesson Overview

Objectives

Students will be able to:

✔ use mathematical modeling to represent a problem situation and to propose a solution.

✔ test and verify the appropriateness of their math models.

✔ explain why the results from their mathematical models may not align exactly to the problem situation.

Essential Understanding

Many real-world problem situations can be represented with a mathematical model, but that model may not represent a real-world situation exactly.

COHERENCE

Earlier in this topic, students:

• used scatter plots to analyze bivariate data and investigate patterns of association.

In this lesson, students:

• develop a mathematical model to represent and propose a solution to a problem situation involving scatter plots and linear associations.

Later in this course, students will:

• refine their mathematical modeling skills.

RIGOR

This mathematical modeling lesson focuses on **application** of both **math content** and **math practices and processes**.

• Students draw on their understanding of patterns and bivariate data concepts to develop a representative model.

• Students apply their mathematical model to test and validate its applicability to similar problem situations.

Math Anytime

Today's Challenge

Use the Topic 4 problems any time during this topic.

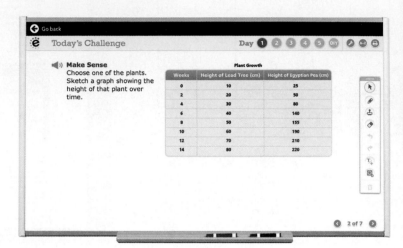

Mathematics Overview

In this lesson, students will develop and use a mathematical model to represent and propose a solution to a real-world problem involving scatter plots and linear associations. Students will reinforce both their procedural skills and their understanding of patterns and bivariate data concepts, while recognizing the limitations of some mathematical models for real-world situations.

Applying Math Practices

Model with Mathematics

The focus of this lesson is on mathematical modeling. Students identify the relationship among variables, develop a model that represents the situation, and use the model to propose a solution. Students interpret their solutions and propose explanations for why their answers may not match the real-world answer.

As students carry out mathematical modeling, they will also engage in sense-making, abstract and quantitative reasoning, and mathematical communication and argumentation. In testing and validating their models, students look for patterns and structure.

3-Act Mathematical Modeling

Video

ACT 1 ▸ **The Hook** ▸

Students will be tasked with determining the wingspan of a very tall person.

Play the Video and Brainstorm Questions

Have students complete **Question 1**. Encourage them to consider the situation and ask any questions that arise. Listen for interesting mathematical and non-mathematical questions. Ask students what makes each question interesting.

> **Q:** What questions do you have? [Sample questions: What do all these people have in common? Why is the last person tallest?]

Pose the Main Question

After the question brainstorming, pose the Main Question students will be tasked with answering. Have students complete **Question 2**.

Main Question

> **Q:** What is the wingspan of the last person?

Ask about Predictions

Have students complete **Questions 3–5**. You can survey the class for the range of predictions.

> **Q:** Why do you think your prediction is the answer to the Main Question?

> **Q:** Who had a similar prediction?

> **Q:** How many of you agree with that prediction?

> **Q:** Who has a different prediction?

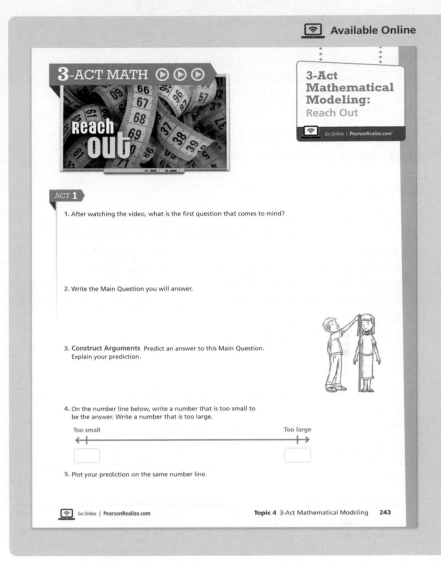

3-Act Mathematical Modeling *continued*

Activity

ACT 2 The Model

Identify Important Info

Have students complete **Question 6**.

> **Q:** What information would be helpful to solve the problem? [Sample answers: How tall each person is; how tall the final person is; what the average wingspan is; what the relationship between height and wingspan is]

> **Q:** How could you get that information?

> **Q:** Why do you need that information?

Reveal the information

Reveal the information provided below using the online interactivity. Have students record information in **Question 7**.

Sample measurements	Final person
Height: 5'9" Wingspan 68 in.	Height: 6'11"
Height: 5'3" Wingspan 66 in.	
Height: 5'7" Wingspan 64 in.	
Height: 5'7" Wingspan 68 in.	
Height: 5'10" Wingspan 72 in.	

Develop a Model

As students answer **Questions 8 and 9,** look for them to use a data display to organize the data. Guide students using a table or list to consider other ways to interpret the data.

Students may ask for additional data to analyze. You could have students collect data for the class to increase the number of data points on the scatter plot.

> **Q:** Why would it be useful to convert the measurements to inches? [Sample answer: You can display the data using feet and inches, though it's necessary to convert either to feet or inches to write an equation for the trend line.]

Use the Model to Propose a Solution

After students answer **Questions 8 and 9,** facilitate a discussion about solution methods. If needed, project the possible student solutions (shown below).

📶 Available Online

ACT 2

6. What information in this situation would be helpful to know? How would you use that information?

7. **Use Appropriate Tools** What tools can you use to get the information you need? Record the information as you find it.

8. **Model with Math** Represent the situation using the mathematical content, concepts, and skills from this topic. Use your representation to answer the Main Question.

9. What is your answer to the Main Question? Is it higher or lower than your initial prediction? Explain why.

244   **Topic 4** 3-Act Mathematical Modeling   📶 Go Online | PearsonRealize.com

---

Possible Student Solutions

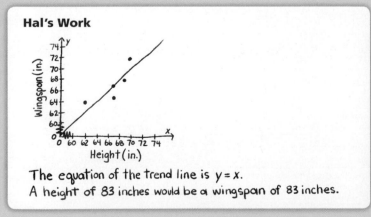

Hal's Work

The equation of the trend line is y = x.
A height of 83 inches would be a wingspan of 83 inches.

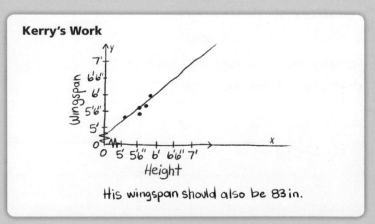

Kerry's Work

His wingspan should also be 83 in.

Hal converts all measurements to inches and makes a scatter plot. He finds the equation of a trend line and uses the equation to extrapolate an answer.

Kerry converts all measurements to inches and feet and also makes a scatter plot. She uses the trend line to extrapolate but does not write an equation for the line.

ACT 3 — The Solution and Sequel

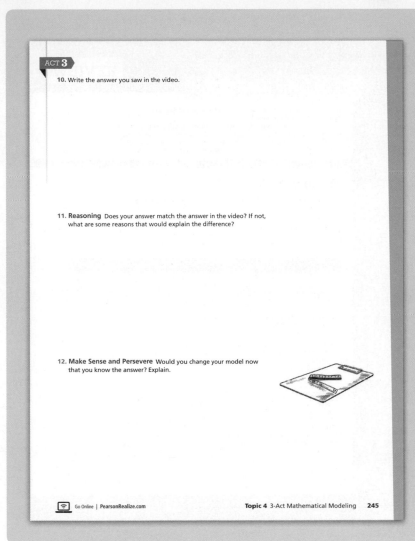

ACT 3

10. Write the answer you saw in the video.

11. Reasoning Does your answer match the answer in the video? If not, what are some reasons that would explain the difference?

12. Make Sense and Persevere Would you change your model now that you know the answer? Explain.

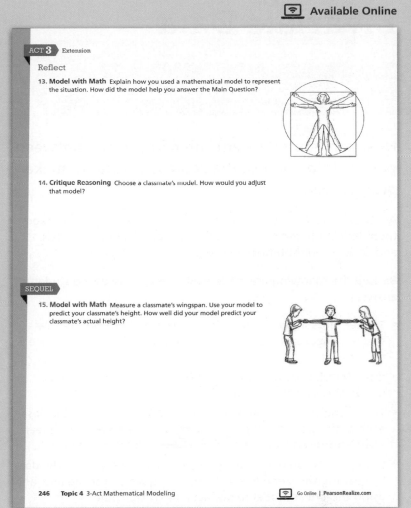

ACT 3 Extension

Reflect

13. Model with Math Explain how you used a mathematical model to represent the situation. How did the model help you answer the Main Question?

14. Critique Reasoning Choose a classmate's model. How would you adjust that model?

SEQUEL

15. Model with Math Measure a classmate's wingspan. Use your model to predict your classmate's height. How well did your model predict your classmate's actual height?

Use the Video to Reveal the Answer

The final part of the video shows the wingspan of the final person. Have students complete **Question 10**. Congratulate the students who were closest to the actual answer.

Main Question Answer

7'5" or 89 in.

Validate Conclusions

After students complete **Questions 11 and 12,** encourage them to discuss possible sources of error inherent in using math to model real-world situations. Look for students to point out that their models are still useful even though they are not perfect.

Q: Why does your answer not match the answer in the video? [Sample answer: This person is an outlier whose data point is not as close to the trend line.]

Q: How useful was your model at predicting the answer?

Q: How could your model better represent the situation?

Reflect on Thinking

Critique Reasoning If time allows, have students complete **Questions 13 and 14** as an extension. Use this opportunity to discuss how students incorporate mathematical processes during the task.

Pose the Sequel

Reasoning Use **Question 15** to present a similar problem situation involving trend lines. You can assign to early finishers or as homework so students can test the usefulness of their models.

Q: Measure a classmate's wingspan. Use your model to predict your classmate's height. How well did your model predict your classmate's actual height?

Using their models and the answer in the video, look for students to predict a height approximately equal to the wingspan, though the classmate's height may be slightly greater or less.

Q: Why might it be an advantage for a basketball player to have a wingspan significantly greater than their height? [Sample answer: A longer wingspan can make it easier to shoot, rebound, and block shots.]

Investigate Bivariate Data

? Topic Essential Question

How can you represent the relationship between paired data and use the representation to make predictions?

As students answer the Essential Question in writing, encourage them to include definitions, examples, non-examples, models, and other representations that support their answers.

Be sure the following are made explicit while discussing students' answers.

- Scatter plots show whether the association between two data sets is a linear association, a non-linear association, or if there is no association.

- If scatter plots show a linear association, a trend line can be drawn through the data points.

- The strength of a linear association is determined by how close each of the points in the scatterplot is to the trend line. Linear associations can be positive or negative, and strong or weak.

- Scatter plots can help make predictions about trends in the data by plotting the trend line, solving the equation for the line, and using this linear model to predict a likely outcome.

- Two-way frequency tables show the relationship between paired categorical data.

- The relationship between categories in a two-way frequency table can easily be seen by comparing the data inside each cell relative to either the row or column totals.

- Two-way relative-frequency tables have an advantage in showing the relationships between paired data. They allow for the comparison of the ratio of a data value relative to a total of a row, a column, or the entire data set. It is expressed as a percent.

Vocabulary Review

ORAL LANGUAGE Before students complete the page, reinforce oral language by using one or more of the following activities.

- Students can work in teams at the board, playing fill-in the blanks and taking turns spelling out the vocabulary terms. The winning team must also correctly define the term before being awarded a point.

- Students can also draw scatter plots with trend lines on the board. Have students describe their scatter plots using proper vocabulary terms such as linear association, nonlinear association, no association, strong or weak, positive or negative.

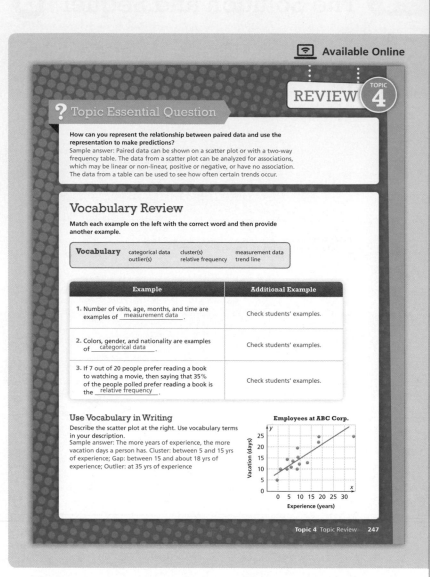

WRITING IN MATH After students complete the page, you can further reinforce writing in math by doing the following activity.

- Have students write a riddle using three of the vocabulary terms. Then, have them work with a partner and try to guess each other's riddles.

Concepts and Skills Review

Concepts and Skills Review

LESSON 4-1 Construct and Interpret Scatter Plots

Quick Review

A scatter plot shows the relationship between paired measurement data. Scatter plots can be used to interpret data by looking for clusters, gaps, and outliers.

Example

The table shows the temperature and number of tickets sold at a movie theater. Construct a scatter plot of the data. Is there a relationship between temperature and the number of tickets sold?

Temperature (°F)	Tickets Sold
40	120
45	100
50	125
55	105
60	90
65	105
80	60
85	55
90	60
95	50

Determine the scales and plot the points.

There are clusters between 40°F and 65°F, and between 80°F and 95°F. The scatter plot shows that when temperatures are 80°F or above, there are fewer tickets sold.

Practice

The table shows the distance in miles and price of airfare in dollars.

Distance (mi)	Airfare ($)
200	250
250	300
300	275
350	150
400	400
450	425
500	350
550	250
600	475
700	325
750	200

1. Construct a scatter plot.

2. Is there a relationship between distance and airfare? Explain.
   Sample answer: There do not appear to be any clusters, gaps, or outliers. There does not appear to be any pattern in the data, so there is not a relationship between the distance and airfare.

Go Online | PearsonRealize.com

LESSON 4-2 Analyze Linear Associations

Quick Review

The association between the data in a scatter plot can be linear or nonlinear. A trend line is a line on a scatter plot, drawn near the points, which approximates the association between paired data. If the data are linear, the association can be positive or negative, and strong or weak.

Example

Identify the association between the data.

Points are close to a trend line, so the association is linear and strong. The y-values increase as x-values increase, so the association is positive.

Practice

Identify the association between the data on each scatter plot.

1.

Weak negative linear association

2.

Nonlinear association

LESSON 4-3 Use Linear Models to Make Predictions

Quick Review

To make predictions, substitute known values into the equation of a linear model to solve for an unknown.

Example

Predict the volume of a tank after 24 minutes.

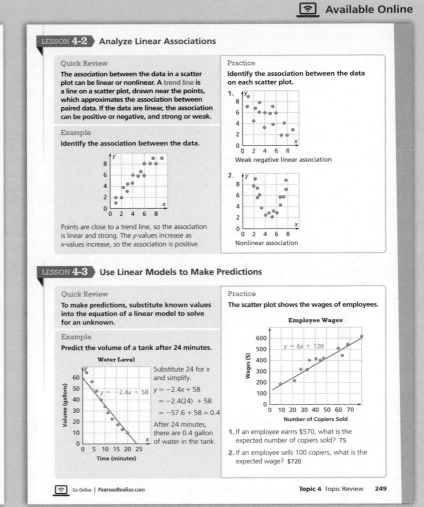

Substitute 24 for x and simplify.

$$y = -2.4x + 58$$
$$= -2.4(24) + 58$$
$$= -57.6 + 58 = 0.4$$

After 24 minutes, there are 0.4 gallon of water in the tank.

Practice

The scatter plot shows the wages of employees.

1. If an employee earns $570, what is the expected number of copiers sold? 75

2. If an employee sells 100 copiers, what is the expected wage? $720

Available Online

Concepts and Skills Review

LESSON 4-4 Interpret Two-Way Frequency Tables

Quick Review

A two-way frequency table displays the relationship between paired categorical data.

Example

The two-way frequency table shows the results of a random survey about the favorite drink of boys and girls. Mr. Marcum said that boys are more likely than girls to prefer milk. Is the statement true or false? Explain.

	Milk	Water	Juice	Total
Boys	10	8	12	30
Girls	7	3	10	20
Total	17	11	22	50

The statement is not true because 10 out of 30 boys prefer milk, which is less than 7 out of 20.

Practice

1. The two-way frequency table shows the results of a random survey of movies watched by 100 students. Mrs. Leary said that according to the data, girls are more likely than boys to watch movie A. Is the statement true or false? Explain.

	A	B	C	Total
Boys	14	12	19	45
Girls	16	22	17	55
Total	30	34	36	100

The statement is false because the ratio of boys who chose movie A, 14 out of 45, is greater than the ratio of girls who chose movie A, 16 out of 55.

LESSON 4-5 Interpret Two-Way Relative Frequency Tables

Quick Review

Relative frequency is the ratio of a data value to the total of a row, a column, or the entire data set. It is expressed as a percent.

Example

Make a two-way relative frequency table to show the distribution of the data with respect to all 150 students polled. What percent of students take Spanish?

	Spanish	French	German	Total
Boys	21	36	15	72
Girls	33	15	30	78
Total	54	51	45	150

	Spanish	French	German	Total
Boys	14%	24%	10%	48%
Girls	22%	10%	20%	52%
Total	36%	34%	30%	100%

$$\frac{54}{150} \cdot 100 = 36\%$$

Thirty-six percent of students take Spanish.

Practice

The two-way table shows the eye color of 200 cats participating in a cat show.

	Green	Blue	Yellow	Total
Male	40	24	16	80
Female	30	60	30	120
Total	70	84	46	200

1. Make a two-way relative frequency table to show the distribution of the data with respect to gender. Round to the nearest tenth of a percent, as needed. Check students' tables.

2. What percent of cats that are female have blue eyes? 50%

Fluency Practice

Hidden Clue

Students practice fluently grouping like terms to solve for a variable in multistep equations during a partner activity that reinforces mathematical practices.

Getting Started Students may work independently or with a partner. Go over the instructions. Point out that one of the coordinates of the ordered pair is given and the other needs to be determined by solving the equation.

Students should solve each problem and complete their own graph. Encourage students to record their work on a separate sheet of paper.

As Students Do the Activity Remind students that even though one of the coordinates is given, ignore it while solving for the variable to determine the unknown coordinate.

Some students may prefer to find all the ordered pairs first, then graph them. Allow this strategy as it provides the same fluency practice.

Another Activity Have students work together to write more equations that result in the same ordered pairs. Have them imagine how they might rewrite the riddle, but have the same graph.

Extra Challenge Create your own Hidden Clue. Draw a new graph on grid paper, and then write new equations to solve. Trade with a partner to solve their Hidden Clue.

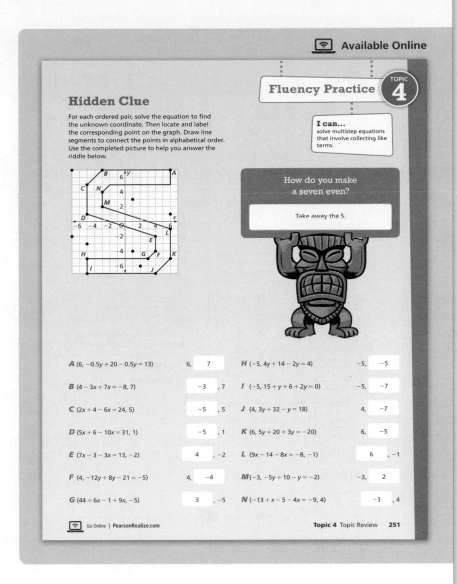

Available Online

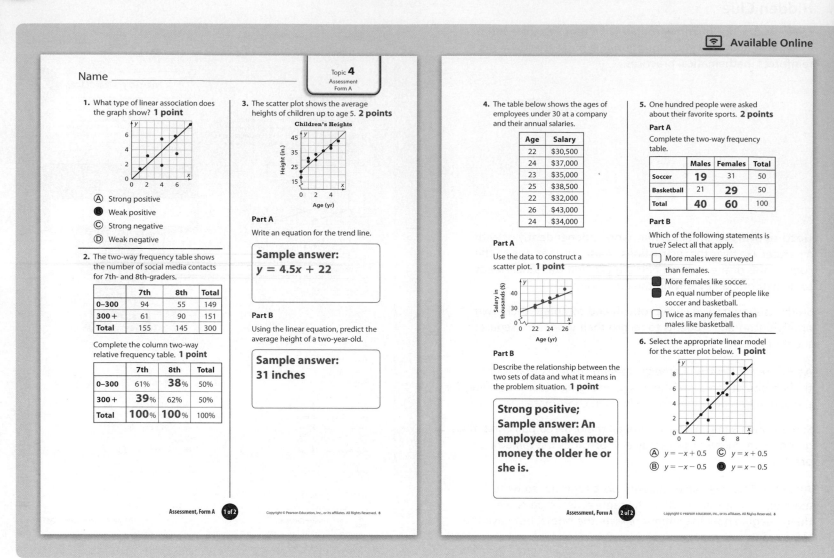

1. What type of linear association does the graph show? **1 point**

Ⓐ Strong positive
● Weak positive
Ⓒ Strong negative
Ⓓ Weak negative

2. The two-way frequency table shows the number of social media contacts for 7th- and 8th-graders.

	7th	8th	Total
0–300	94	55	149
300+	61	90	151
Total	155	145	300

Complete the column two-way relative frequency table. **1 point**

	7th	8th	Total
0–300	61%	**38**%	50%
300+	**39**%	62%	50%
Total	**100**%	**100**%	100%

3. The scatter plot shows the average heights of children up to age 5. **2 points**

Children's Heights

Part A

Write an equation for the trend line.

> **Sample answer:**
> $y = 4.5x + 22$

Part B

Using the linear equation, predict the average height of a two-year-old.

> **Sample answer:**
> **31 inches**

4. The table below shows the ages of employees under 30 at a company and their annual salaries.

Age	Salary
22	$30,500
24	$37,000
23	$35,000
25	$38,500
22	$32,000
26	$43,000
24	$34,000

Part A

Use the data to construct a scatter plot. **1 point**

Part B

Describe the relationship between the two sets of data and what it means in the problem situation. **1 point**

> **Strong positive; Sample answer: An employee makes more money the older he or she is.**

5. One hundred people were asked about their favorite sports. **2 points**

Part A

Complete the two-way frequency table.

	Males	Females	Total
Soccer	**19**	31	50
Basketball	21	**29**	50
Total	**40**	**60**	100

Part B

Which of the following statements is true? Select all that apply.

☐ More males were surveyed than females.
■ More females like soccer.
■ An equal number of people like soccer and basketball.
☐ Twice as many females than males like basketball.

6. Select the appropriate linear model for the scatter plot below. **1 point**

Ⓐ $y = -x + 0.5$ Ⓒ $y = x + 0.5$
Ⓑ $y = -x - 0.5$ Ⓓ $y = x - 0.5$

Assessment, Form A 1 of 2   Copyright © Pearson Education, Inc., or its affiliates. All Rights Reserved. 8
Assessment, Form A 2 of 2   Copyright © Pearson Education, Inc., or its affiliates. All Rights Reserved. 8

Assess students' understanding of the topic concepts and skills using the Topic Assessments found at PearsonRealize.com.

Use the Item Analysis Chart on the facing page to assign intervention to students based on their scores on the paper and pencil version of the Topic Assessments.

You may opt to have students take the Topic Assessment online at PearsonRealize.com. The online assessment is auto-scored, with differentiated intervention automatically assigned to students based on their scores.

You can use ExamView to generate additional Topic Assessments.

There are two versions of the Topic Assessment, Form A and Form B. These parallel versions assess the same content item for item. The Item Analysis chart on the next page can be used with both versions.

🛜 Available Online

Name _____

1. What type of linear association does the scatter plot show? **1 point**

Ⓐ Strong positive
Ⓑ Weak positive
● Strong negative
Ⓓ Weak negative

2. The two-way frequency table shows the number of stores in two different cities.

	City A	City B	Total
Restaurants	94	75	169
Retail	123	108	231
Total	217	183	400

Complete the column two-way relative frequency table. **1 point**

	City A	City B	Total
Restaurants	43%	**41**%	42%
Retail	**57**%	59%	58%
Total	**100**%	**100**%	100%

3. The scatter plot shows the average weights of children at a pediatrics clinic. **2 points**

Children's Weights

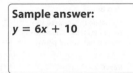

Part A

Write an equation for the trend line.

Sample answer:
$y = 6x + 10$

Part B

Using the linear equation, predict the average weight of a seven-year-old.

Sample answer:
52 pounds

4. The table below shows the ages of employees over 50 at a company and the amount of money they have in their retirement accounts.

Age	Amount in Account
52	$73,000
54	$81,000
53	$110,000
55	$122,000
58	$92,000

Part A

Use the data to construct a scatter plot. **1 point**

Employees and Retirement Accounts

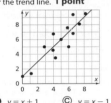

Part B

Describe the relationship between the two sets of data and what it means in the problem situation. **1 point**

Sample answer: There is no association between age and amount of money in a retirement account.

5. In a survey, 135 adults were asked where they prefer to live. **2 points**

Part A

Complete the two-way frequency table.

	Males	Females	Total
Country	**50**	23	73
City	42	**20**	62
Total	**92**	**43**	135

Part B

Which statement is true? Select all that apply.

■ More males than females were surveyed.
☐ More males want to live in the city than in the country.
■ More females want to live in the country than in the city.
☐ More males want to live in the country than the total for city.

6. Select the appropriate linear equation for the trend line. **1 point**

Ⓐ $y = x + 1$ Ⓒ $y = x - 1$
Ⓑ $y = -x - 1$ Ⓓ $y = -x + 1$

Assessment, Form B **1 of 2**   Copyright © Pearson Education, Inc., or its affiliates. All Rights Reserved. 8

Assessment, Form B **2 of 2**   Copyright © Pearson Education, Inc., or its affiliates. All Rights Reserved. 8

 Item Analysis for Diagnosis and Intervention

Item	DOK	MDIS
1	1	N88
2	2	N90
3A	2	N88
3B	1	N88
4A	2	N72

Item	DOK	MDIS
4B	1	N72
5A	1	N89
5B	1	N89
6	1	N88

TOPIC 4

Performance Assessment

PearsonRealize.com

Assess

📡 **Available Online**

Name _____

Topic **4**
Performance Assessment
Form A

The basketball team at Mountain Middle School is getting ready for the first tournament of the year.

1. The table shows the number of minutes Romy practices on her own and the number of baskets she makes the following day in team practice.

Week 1	Solo practice time (min)	23	62	100	98	62
	Number of baskets	15	25	33	29	30
Week 2	Solo practice time (min)	0	18	75	120	23
	Number of baskets	11	15	38	35	12

Part A

Use the data to construct a scatter plot in the space at the right, comparing the time Romy practices on her own to the number of baskets she makes in team practice the following day. **3 points**

Sample answer:

Baskets Per Practice Time

Number of Baskets (y-axis: 0, 10, 20, 30)
Solo Practice Time (min) (x-axis: 0, 20, 40, 60, 80, 100, 120)

Part B

What association is there between the data, if any? **1 point**

> Strong positive linear association

Part C

Draw a trend line for the data. About how many baskets should Romy expect to make the next day if she practices for 45 minutes on her own? **2 points**

> Check students' work; Sample answer: about 22 baskets

Part D

Find the equation for the trend line through the points (0, 11) and (100, 33). Then use it to predict the number of baskets Romy would make after practicing for 80 minutes. **2 points**

> $y = 0.22x + 11$; about 29 baskets

Performance Assessment, Form A **1 of 2**   Copyright © Pearson Education, Inc., or its affiliates. All Rights Reserved. 8

---

2. Romy's basketball coach wants to encourage her players to practice more.

Part A

Complete the two-way frequency table with the following information:

- Of the 5 starting players, 4 spend extra time practicing
- Two of the five 2nd-string players practice extra time
- Two of the eight 3rd-string players practice extra

1 point

	Extra Practice Time		
Players		Yes	No	Total
Starting	4	1	5
2nd String	2	3	5
3rd String	2	6	8
Total	8	10	18

Part B

Complete the total relative frequency table. Round to the nearest percent. **2 points**

	Extra Practice Time		
Players		Yes	No	Total
Starting	22%	6%	28%
2nd String	11%	17%	28%
3rd String	11%	33%	44%
Total	44%	56%	100%

Part C

What does the total relative frequency table tell you about the players who practice the most? **1 point**

> Sample answer: The players who practice the most are the starters at 22%.

Part D

Is there an association between extra practice time and being a starting player? Explain. **2 points**

> Yes; Sample answer: 22% of the starting players practice, but only 11% of the 2nd-string or 3rd-string players practice. Also, the greatest percent of players who do not practice are on the 3rd-string.

Performance Assessment, Form A **2 of 2**   Copyright © Pearson Education, Inc., or its affiliates. All Rights Reserved. 8

Assess students' ability to apply the topic concepts and skills using the Topic Performance Assessments found at PearsonRealize.com.

Item Analysis for Diagnosis and Intervention

Item	DOK	MDIS
1A	2	N72
1B	2	N72
1C	3	N88
1D	1	N88
2A	2	N89
2B	3	N90
2C	3	N90
2D	4	N90

Scoring Guide		
Item	**Points**	**Topic Performance Assessment (Form A)**
1A	3	Completed and correct scatter plot
	2	Mostly correct scatter plot with a missing title, missing labels, or incorrect plotted points
	1	Partially correct scatter plot, with incorrect title, missing labels, and incorrect or missing plotted points
1B, 2C	1	Correct answer
1C	2	Correct trend line and prediction
	1	Correct trend line or prediction
1D	2	Correct equation and prediction
	1	Correct equation or prediction
2A, 2B	2	Complete and correct table
	1	Incomplete table
2D	2	Correct answer and valid explanation
	1	Correct answer or valid explanation

Available Online

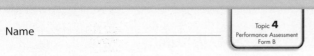

Name _____

Topic **4**
Performance Assessment
Form B

Imani predicts that students who spend more time playing video games have lower grades.

1. Imani took a survey of her classmates and organized the data in the table below.

Video Game Playing Time (hours per day)	0	1	2	2.5	1	5	6	3	4	3.5	2	5
Grade Point Average (GPA)	4	2.9	3.1	2.2	2.9	2.2	1.2	2.6	2.9	1.8	3.8	1.8

Part A

Use the data to construct a scatter plot in the space provided. **2 points**

Sample answer:

Part B

Draw a trend line and determine the association between the two sets of data. Is Imani's prediction correct? Explain. **3 points**

> **Weak negative linear association; Sample answer: Imani's prediction is somewhat correct because students' GPAs tend to decrease as the time spent playing video games increases. Since the association is weak, there may be no relationship.**

Part C

Write an equation for the trend line. **1 point**

> **Sample answer:** $y = -0.06x + 3.5$

2. Imani's math teacher wants to encourage his students to spend less time playing video games and more time studying. He conducts his own study of students, their grades, and whether or not they play video games.

Part A

Complete the two-way frequency table with the following information:

- 1 out of 8 A-average students plays video games
- Half of the 8 B-average students play video games
- 2 of the 15 C-average students do **NOT** play video games **1 point**

		Play Video Games		
		No	Yes	Total
Grade Average	A	7	1	8
	B	4	4	8
	C	2	13	15
	Total	13	18	31

Part B

Complete the two-way relative frequency table. Round to the nearest percent. **2 points**

		Play Video Games		
		No	Yes	Total
Grade Average	A	23%	3%	26%
	B	13%	13%	26%
	C	6%	42%	48%
	Total	42%	58%	100%

Part C

What does the total relative frequency table tell you about the students who play video games the most? **1 point**

> **Sample answer: The students who play video games the most have a C average in math class.**

Part D

Is there evidence of an association between playing video games on a regular basis and having a lower GPA? Explain. **2 points**

> **Yes; Sample answer: Most of the A-average students do not play video games, while most of the C-average students do play video games on a regular basis.**

Assess students' ability to apply the topic concepts and skills using the Topic Performance Assessments found at PearsonRealize.com.

 Item Analysis for Diagnosis and Intervention

Item	DOK	MDIS
1A	2	N72
1B	3	N88
1C	2	N88
2A	2	N89
2B	3	N90
2C	4	N90
2D	4	N90

Scoring Guide		
Item	**Points**	**Topic Performance Assessment (Form B)**
1A	3	Completed and correct scatter plot
	2	Mostly correct scatter plot
	1	Partially correct scatter plot
1B	3	Correct trend line drawn, identification of association, and valid explanation
	2	Correct trend line drawn and correct identification of association, but incorrect explanation
	1	Incorrect trend line drawn, incorrect or no identification of association, and/or incorrect explanation
1C, 2C	1	Correct answer
2A, 2B	2	Complete and correct table
	1	Incomplete table
2D	2	Correct answer and valid explanation
	1	Correct answer or valid explanation

CUMULATIVE/BENCHMARK ASSESSMENT

PearsonRealize.com

Assess

📶 Available Online

Topics 1-4 Cumulative/Benchmark Assessment

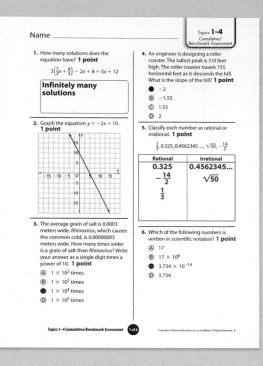

Name _____

Topics 1-4 Cumulative/Benchmark Assessment

1. How many solutions does the equation have? **1 point**

$$3\left(\tfrac{2}{3}x + \tfrac{4}{3}\right) - 2x + 8 = 5x + 12$$

Infinitely many solutions

2. Graph the equation $y = -2x + 10$. **1 point**

3. The average grain of salt is 0.0003 meters wide. *Rhinovirus*, which causes the common cold, is 0.00000003 meters wide. How many times wider is a grain of salt than *Rhinovirus*? Write your answer as a single digit times a power of 10. **1 point**
Ⓐ 1×10^2 times
Ⓑ 1×10^3 times
● 1×10^4 times
Ⓓ 1×10^5 times

4. An engineer is designing a roller coaster. The tallest peak is 310 feet high. The roller coaster travels 155 horizontal feet as it descends the hill. What is the slope of the hill? **1 point**
● −2
Ⓑ −1.55
Ⓒ 1.55
Ⓓ 2

5. Classify each number as rational or irrational. **1 point**
$\frac{1}{3}, 0.325, 0.4562345..., \sqrt{50}, -\frac{14}{2}$

Rational	Irrational
0.325	0.4562345...
$-\frac{14}{2}$	$\sqrt{50}$
$\frac{1}{3}$	

6. Which of the following numbers is written in scientific notation? **1 point**
Ⓐ 17
Ⓑ 17×10^6
● 3.734×10^{-14}
Ⓓ 3.734

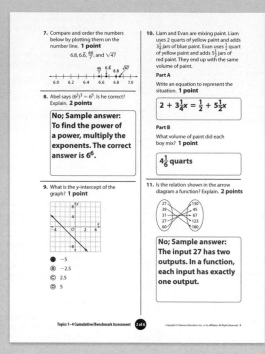

7. Compare and order the numbers below by plotting them on the number line. **1 point**
$6.8, 6.\overline{6}, \frac{46}{7},$ and $\sqrt{47}$

8. Abel says $(6^2)^3 = 6^5$. Is he correct? Explain. **2 points**
No; Sample answer: To find the power of a power, multiply the exponents. The correct answer is 6^6.

9. What is the y-intercept of the graph? **1 point**
● −5
Ⓑ −2.5
Ⓒ 2.5
Ⓓ 5

10. Liam and Evan are mixing paint. Liam uses 2 quarts of yellow paint and adds $3\frac{1}{4}$ jars of blue paint. Evan uses $\frac{1}{2}$ quart of yellow paint and adds $5\frac{1}{2}$ jars of red paint. They end up with the same volume of paint.
Part A
Write an equation to represent the situation. **1 point**
$2 + 3\frac{1}{4}x = \frac{1}{2} + 5\frac{1}{2}x$
Part B
What volume of paint did each boy mix? **1 point**
$4\frac{1}{6}$ quarts

11. Is the relation shown in the arrow diagram a function? Explain. **2 points**
No; Sample answer: The input 27 has two outputs. In a function, each input has exactly one output.

12. Jason surveyed 90 people on their preference of fruits or vegetables. Complete the two-way frequency table. **1 point**

Type of Food	Child	Adult (18+)	Total
Fruit	26	26	52
Vegetable	14	24	38
Total	40	50	90

13. Use the table in Exercise 12. Which statement is true? Select all that apply. **1 point**
☐ More children than adults were surveyed.
■ The same number of adults and children prefer fruit.
☐ More people prefer vegetables.
■ More people prefer fruit.
■ More adults than children prefer vegetables.

14. Complete the two-way relative frequency table using the information from Exercise 12. **1 point**

Type of Food	Child	Adult (18+)	Total
Fruit	28.9%	28.9%	57.8%
Vegetable	15.5%	26.7%	42.2%
Total	44.4%	55.6%	100%

15. Students at a community college were asked a survey question. The two-way frequency table shows the responses from full-time students and part-time students.

Two-Way Frequency Table
	Yes	No	Total
Full-time	67	33	100
Part-time	27	73	100
Total	94	106	200

Is there evidence that responding yes was related to attending the college full-time or part-time? Explain. **2 points**
Yes; Sample answer: The same number of full-time students and part-time students responded to the survey, but the percent of full-time students who responded yes was significantly greater than the percent of part-time students who responded yes.

16. The state fair charges $14 for admission. Each ride costs $6. What is the function, S, that relates the amount spent, S, to the number of rides, r? **1 point**
Ⓐ $S = 6r - 14$
Ⓑ $S = 14r - 6$
● $S = 6r + 14$
Ⓓ $S = 14r + 6$

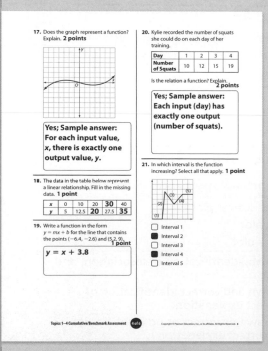

17. Does the graph represent a function? Explain. **2 points**
Yes; Sample answer: For each input value, x, there is exactly one output value, y.

18. The data in the table below represent a linear relationship. Fill in the missing data. **1 point**

x	0	10	20	30	40
y	5	12.5	20	27.5	35

19. Write a function in the form $y = mx + b$ for the line that contains the points $(-6.4, -2.6)$ and $(5.2, 9)$. **1 point**
$y = x + 3.8$

20. Kylie recorded the number of squats she could do on each day of her training.

Day	1	2	3	4
Number of Squats	10	12	15	19

Is the relation a function? Explain. **2 points**
Yes; Sample answer: Each input (day) has exactly one output (number of squats).

21. In which interval is the function increasing? Select all that apply. **1 point**
☐ Interval 1
■ Interval 2
☐ Interval 3
■ Interval 4
☐ Interval 5

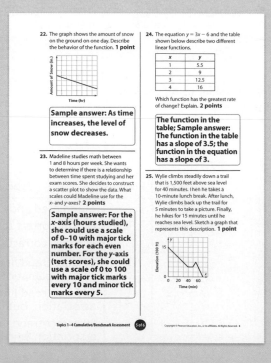

22. The graph shows the amount of snow on the ground on one day. Describe the behavior of the function. **1 point**
Sample answer: As time increases, the level of snow decreases.

23. Madeline studies math between 1 and 8 hours per week. She wants to determine if there is a relationship between time spent studying and her exam scores. She decides to construct a scatter plot to show the data. What scales could Madeline use for the x- and y-axes? **2 points**
Sample answer: For the x-axis (hours studied), she could use a scale of 0–10 with major tick marks for each even number. For the y-axis (test scores), she could use a scale of 0 to 100 with major tick marks every 10 and minor tick marks every 5.

24. The equation $y = 3x - 6$ and the table shown below describe two different linear functions.

x	y
1	5.5
2	9
3	12.5
4	16

Which function has the greatest rate of change? Explain. **2 points**
The function in the table; Sample answer: The function in the table has a slope of 3.5; the function in the equation has a slope of 3.

25. Wylie climbs steadily down a trail that is 1,500 feet above sea level for 40 minutes. Then he takes a 10-minute lunch break. After lunch, Wylie climbs back up the trail for 5 minutes to take a picture. Finally, he hikes for 15 minutes until he reaches sea level. Sketch a graph that represents this description. **1 point**

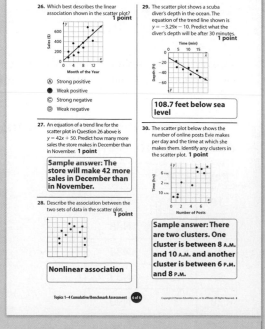

26. Which best describes the linear association shown in the scatter plot? **1 point**
Ⓐ Strong positive
● Weak positive
Ⓒ Strong negative
Ⓓ Weak negative

27. An equation of a trend line for the scatter plot in Question 26 above is $y = 42x + 50$. Predict how many more sales the store makes in December than in November. **1 point**
Sample answer: The store will make 42 more sales in December than in November.

28. Describe the association between the two sets of data in the scatter plot. **1 point**
Nonlinear association

29. The scatter plot shows a scuba diver's depth in the ocean. The equation of the trend line shown is $y = -3.29x - 10$. Predict what the diver's depth will be after 30 minutes. **1 point**
108.7 feet below sea level

30. The scatter plot below shows the number of online posts Evie makes per day and the time at which she makes them. Identify any clusters in the scatter plot. **1 point**
Sample answer: There are two clusters. One cluster is between 8 A.M. and 10 A.M. and another cluster is between 6 P.M. and 8 P.M.

Items 3 and 5–8 assess content taught in Topic 1. Items 1, 2, 4, and 9–10 assess content taught in Topic 2. Items 11, 16–22, 24, and 25 assess content taught in Topic 3. Items 12–15, 23, and 26–30 assess content taught in Topic 4.

Item Analysis Topics 1–4 Cumulative/Benchmark Assessment

Item	DOK	MDIS
1	1	K33–K36
2	1	K49
3	1	L84
4	1	K50
5	1	L80
6	1	L84
7	1	L73
8	2	L83
9	1	K49, K52
10A	3	K27, K28
10B	1	K29
11	1	K51
12	1	N89
13	2	N69, N89
14	2	N89, N90
15	3	N69, N89

Item	DOK	MDIS
16	1	K52
17	1	K51, K52
18	1	K52
19	1	K50, K52
20	1	K51
21	1	K53
22	1	K52
23	1	N72
24	2	K52
25	2	K53
26	1	N69, N72
27	2	N69, N72
28	1	N69, N72
29	1	N69, N72
30	1	N69, N72

You may opt to have students take the Cumulative/Benchmark Assessment online at PearsonRealize.com. The online assessment is auto-scored, with differentiated intervention automatically assigned to students based on their scores.

Scoring Guide

Item	Points	Cumulative/Benchmark Assessment
8	2 1	Correct answer and explanation Correct answer or explanation
11	2 1	Correct answer and explanation Correct answer or explanation
15	2 1	Correct answer and explanation Correct answer or explanation
17	2 1	Correct answer and explanation Correct answer or explanation
20	2 1	Correct answer and explanation Correct answer or explanation
23	2 1	Both axes labeled correctly One axis labeled correctly
24	2 1	Correct answer and explanation Correct answer or explanation

TOPICS 1-4 | **251F** | Cumulative/Benchmark Assessment

ACKNOWLEDGEMENTS

Photographs

Photo locators denoted as follows: Top (T), Center (C), Bottom (B), Left (L), Right (R), Background (Bkgd)

Cover klagyivik/Fotolia.

F16 (CL) Aurielaki/Fotolia, (TR) Taras Livyy/Fotolia; **F17** piai/Fotolia; **F18** kues1/Fotolia; **F19** FedotovAnatoly/Fotolia; **F20** (Bkgrd) totallypic/Fotolia, (CL, CR) abert84/Fotolia; **F21** (CL) Eyematrix/Fotolia, (CR) totallypic/Fotolia; **F22** darnell_vfx/Fotolia; **F23** blueringmedia/Fotolia; **003** hywards/Fotolia; **004** (tablet) yossarian6/Fotolia, (tree) Givaga/Fotolia, (solar panel) lily/Fotolia, (girl) Maridav/Fotolia, (mineral) marcel/Fotolia, (faucet) Ilya Akinshin/Fotolia, (bulb) robertovich/Fotolia, (wood) Kletr/Fotolia, (pump) phive2015/Fotolia, (globe) Somchai Som/Shutterstock, (tree rings) oscar0/Fotolia, (water) 31moonlight31/Fotolia, (oil) ptasha/Fotolia; **007** (L) Photka/Fotolia, (CL) yurakp/Fotolia, (TC) Jane Kelly/Fotolia, (C) Yuri Bizgaimer/Fotolia; **010** Castleski/Shutterstock; **011** Injenerker/Fotolia; **013** (TL) Xalanx/Fotolia, (TC) Alex Stokes/Fotolia, (C) Pongmoji/Fotolia, (CR) Sunnysky69/Fotolia; **018** Doko/Shutterstock; **019** (TL) Richard Laschon/123RF, (TC) Aelita2/123RF, (TR) Pavel Losevsky/Fotolia; **022** Sakdam/Fotolia; **023** (BR) Dred2010/Fotolia, (BCR) Giuseppe Porzani/Fotolia; **025** (CL) Leah-Anne Thompson/Fotolia, (TC) andreusK/Fotolia, (C) hrerickson/Fotolia, **029** Perytskyy/Fotolia; **032** (CL) Monkey Business Images/Shutterstock, (TL) Warut Prathaksithorn/123RF; **033** (TCR) Wildarun/Fotolia, (TR) Dirk Ercken/Shutterstock; **039** (L) Edyta Pawlowska/Fotolia, (TCL) Iarygin Andrii/Fotolia, (C) michaeljung/Fotolia, (CL) Jeka84/Fotolia; **040** Dmitry Chulov/Fotolia; **045** (TL) Voyagerix/Fotolia, (TR) mimagephotos/Fotolia; **051** hywards/Fotolia; **055** Lev/Fotolia; **058** Tarik GOK/Fotolia; **060** Frender/Fotolia; **061** (C) Jeanne McRight/Fotolia, (TC) Stillfx/Fotolia; **063** Royaltystockphoto/Fotolia; **066** PRinMD68/Fotolia; **067** (CL) Brocreative/Fotolia, (C) neirfy/Fotolia, (CR) Kletr/Fotolia; **070** GRIN/NASA; **079** iStockphoto/Getty Images; **081** Mihai Simonia/Shutterstock; **082** (TC) Gelpi/Fotolia, (TCR) iagodina/Fotolia, (TR) yongtick/Fotolia, (CL) eranda/Fotolia, (C) Sergiy Serdyuk/Fotolia, (CR) eranda/Fotolia, (BCR) Photobank/Fotolia, (BR) yossarian6/Fotolia; **085** (CL) annexs2/Fotolia, (C) Pack/Fotolia, (TC) opka/Fotolia; **087** vladimirs/Fotolia; **091** (T) Kurhan/Fotolia, (CL) Claireliz/Fotolia, (C) chones/Fotolia; **102** freeskyline/Fotolia; **103** TAlex/Fotolia; **113** Mihai Simonia/Shutterstock; **117** (T) Petrov Vadim/Fotolia, (CL) Carolyn Franks/Fotolia, (CR) Carolyn Franks/Fotolia; **123** WavebreakMediaMicro/Fotolia; **129** Minicel73/Fotolia; **132** Ljupco Smokovski/Fotolia; **135** (CL) Razoomanetu/Fotolia, (CR) zuzule/Fotolia, (TC) Vladvm50/Fotolia; **139** kraska/Fotolia; **141** RobertoC/Fotolia; **155** Gemenacom/Shutterstock; **156** yossarian6/Fotolia; **159** (CL) WavebreakmediaMicro/Fotolia, (C) maxximmm/Fotolia; **163** (C) begiz/Fotolia, (CR) SkyLine/Fotolia, (BR) photology1971/Fotolia, (BCR) Anatolii/Fotolia; **165** ALCE/Fotolia; **168** Hugo Félix/Fotolia; **170** Alekss/Fotolia; **172** (CL) Dmitry Vereshchagin/Fotolia, (C) markobe/Fotolia; **179** Gemenacom/Shutterstock; **188** (TR) Giuseppe Porzani/Fotolia, (TCR) paleka/Fotolia; **189** (C) Aleksei Kurguzov/123RF, (CR) Francesco Italia/Fotlia, (BCR) lilu13/Fotolia; **190** cherezoff/Shutterstock; **191** (TC) ryanking999/Fotolia, (TCR) Alekss/Fotolia, (TR) efks/Fotolia; **194** Stefano Cavoretto/Shutterstock; **195** (C) airdone/Fotolia, (TC) cherezoff/Shutterstock; **196** (Bkgrd) Lonely/Fotolia, (L) photosvac/Fotolia, (R) photosvac/Fotolia; **197** Sergey Novikov/Shutterstock; **198** (CL) Fotofermer/Fotolia, (CR) Evgeny Skidanov/Fotolia; **207** StepanPopov/Shutterstock; **208** (Bkgrd) adimas/Fotolia, (CL) Daniel Thornberg/Fotolia, (C) deepspacedave/Fotolia, Daniel Thornberg/Fotolia, (CR) Lucky Dragon/Fotolia, jfunk/Fotolia, (T) sergiy1975/Fotolia, (TL) vlorzor/Fotolia, (TC) GVS/Fotolia, (TCR) brm1949/Fotolia, (TR) Luis Louro/Fotolia, (B) pkproject/Fotolia, (BL) StepStock/Fotolia, (BCL) Jürgen Fälchle/Fotolia, (BR) yossarian6/Fotolia, (BCR) leonardogonzalez/Fotolia; **215** Uwimages/Fotolia; **221** (C) Sandra Gligorijevic/Fotolia, (R) carballo/Fotolia, (CR) Maron/Fotolia; **222** Ljupco Smokovski/Fotolia; **223** Lucadp/Fotolia; **224** Shock/Fotolia; **225** (C) Comstock Images/Stockbyte/Getty Images, (TC) Denyshutter/Fotolia; **231** (TL) Camerawithlegs/Fotolia, (CR) Silvano Rebai/Fotolia; **233** (T) Jayzynism/Fotolia, (TL) Kadmy/Fotolia, (TC) Jovannig/Fotolia, (TR) Echo/Cultura/Getty Images, (C) Fantasticrabbit/Fotolia, (BL) Samott/Fotolia, (BR) Frinz/Fotolia; **235** DigiClack/Fotolia; **237** WavebreakMediaMicro/Fotolia; **238** (TC) dallasprice_120/Fotolia, (TCR, TR) vadymvdrobot/Fotolia; **241** Ermolaev Alexandr/Fotolia; **243** StepanPopov/Shutterstock; **251** Ryan Burke/Getty Images.